EVOLUTION
The Modern Synthesis

JULIAN HUXLEY

M.A., D.Sc., F.R.S.

EVOLUTION

THE MODERN SYNTHESIS

Third Edition
with a new Introduction edited by
John R. Baker, D.Sc., F.R.S.

Contributors
John R. Baker, D.Sc., F.R.S.
E. B. Ford, F.R.S.
Alister Hardy, M.A., D.Sc., F.R.S.
Bernard Kettlewell, M.A., M.B., B.Chir., M.R.C.S., L.R.C.P.
P. L. Pearson, Ph.D.
Vernon Reynolds, B.A., Ph.D., M.A.
Mark Richmond, B.A., Ph.D., Sc.D.
H. N. Southern, M.A., D.Sc.
T. Stanley Westoll, D.Sc., F.R.S.E., F.R.S.

London
GEORGE ALLEN & UNWIN LTD
RUSKIN HOUSE   MUSEUM STREET

First published in 1942
Second impression 1943
Third impression 1944
Fourth impression 1945
Fifth impression 1948
Sixth impression 1955
Second edition 1963
Third Edition 1974

© *George Allen & Unwin Ltd*, 1963, 1974

ISBN 0 04 5750181

Printed in Great Britain
in 12 pt Bembo type
by Alden & Mowbray Ltd
at the Alden Press, Oxford

Dedicated to T. H. Morgan
many-sided leader in biology's advance

CONTENTS

PREFACE TO THE FIRST EDITION

In 1936, I had to find a subject for the presidential address to the Zoology Section of the British Association. After some hesitation, I chose "Natural Selection and Evolutionary Progress", since it seemed to me that these were two interrelated topics of fundamental biological importance, yet on which much misapprehension existed. Even among professional zoologists the modern conception of natural selection and its mode of operation is quite different from that of Darwin's day, but much of the research on which the changed outlook is based is so recent that the new ideas have not spread far. The idea of evolutionary progress, on the other hand, has been undeservedly neglected. Thus it seemed to me valuable to attempt to give a broad account of the two concepts and their relation to each other.

The result exceeded my expectations. So many of my colleagues expressed interest and the wish that the address might be available in more extended and more permanent form, that I decided to essay expanding it into a book.

The result is the present volume. I am fully conscious of its limitations and imperfections, but I believe that it will serve a useful purpose. The writing of it has so much clarified my own thinking, and the discussion of the problems that arose with colleagues has resulted in so many ideas and points of view which were novel both to them and to myself, that I am encouraged to believe it will be of general service. I also feel sure that a classification and analysis of evolutionary trends and processes as observed or deduced in nature, and the attempted relation of them to the findings of genetics and systematics, is of first-class importance for any unified biological outlook; and since others better equipped than I seem reluctant to attempt the task, I have tried my hand at it.

I owe a great deal to J. B. S. Haldane's *The Causes of Evolution*; but though our books overlap, they differ considerably in scope and treatment. Dobzhansky's, Waddington's, and Goldschmidt's valuable and distinctive books did not appear until much of the present volume was already in proof; but I have tried to take advantage of them where possible. My debt to R. A. Fisher's work is obvious. Fisher has radically transformed our outlook on the subject, notably by pointing out how the effect of a mutation can be altered by new combinations and mutations of other genes. Any originality which this book may possess lies partly in its attempting to generalize this idea still further, by stressing the fact that a study of the effects of genes during development is as essential for an understanding of evolution as are the study of mutation and that of selection. I may also claim that taxonomic data have not previously been analysed on so large a scale in the light of modern genetic and evolutionary views. Equally obvious is my debt to the Morgan school and to Goldschmidt; but clearly this would apply to any modern book dealing with evolution.

I have taken for granted in my reader an acquaintance with the basic principles of Mendelian heredity and the major groups of the animal kingdom. With this equipment, the layman interested in biology will, I hope, find the book suited to his needs, though I hope that it will appeal mainly to professional biologists interested in the more general aspects of their subjects.

I would like to record my special gratitude to Mr. E. B. Ford, of Oxford, who has read the book in typescript, and with whom I have discussed all the genetic problems involved: he has been fertile in suggestion and prodigal of assistance. To Professor L. T. Hogben, F.R.S., I owe several valuable suggestions on the evolution of species. I should also like to thank Professor R. A. Fisher, F.R.S., Professor H. J. Muller, Dr. C. D. Darlington, F.R.S., Professor Hale Carpenter, Dr. W. B. Turrill, and Mr. Moy Thomas for help and advice; and particularly Mr. James Fisher for valuable assistance in revising the book for press.

The time is ripe for a rapid advance in our understanding of evolution. Genetics, developmental physiology, ecology, systematics, paleontology, cytology, mathematical analysis, have all provided new facts or new tools of research: the need to-day is for concerted attack and synthesis. If this book contributes to such a synthetic point of view, I shall be well content.

THE ZOOLOGICAL SOCIETY, LONDON
March 1942

INTRODUCTION TO THE THIRD EDITION

This Introduction has been written by my old pupils and colleagues at the Oxford Department of Zoology and others
invited to contribute by Dr. John Baker. I wish to express my
deep gratitude to them all.

JULIAN S. HUXLEY

Editor's foreword. When the stock of the second edition of this
book was exhausted, Sir Julian Huxley asked some of his former
pupils to help in the preparation of a third. As a result, five
zoologists met Mr. Rayner Unwin to discuss what should be done.
It was agreed that new matter should not be inserted in a book
that had gained for itself a special place in biological literature. It
seemed better to do what Sir Julian had himself done in preparing
the second edition, namely, to leave the work intact and bring
it up to date by adding a new Introduction. This suggestion
received Sir Julian's approval. The zoologists present at the
meeting agreed to contribute to the new Introduction and one
of them was appointed Editor.

It was recognized that if an Introduction worthy to stand
between the covers of Sir Julian's book were to be produced, it
would be necessary to call in others to deal with those branches
of the subject in which none of the original group had special
knowledge. The team was therefore expanded by the inclusion
of authorities on various topics that would otherwise have had
to be left untouched. The nine contributors were not asked,
however, to perform the task—impossible within the imposed
limit of space—of dealing with every important advance within
their own fields; on the contrary, they were encouraged to follow
their own bents as they wished, provided that they made references to papers or books that would supply wider information.

This Introduction is not just a set of independent review-
articles. It is intended to be read as a whole, divided only by
sub-titles. Many readers, however, will want to know who was
the author of each contribution, and this information is therefore
given here.

Emeritus Professor E. B. Ford, Department of Zoology, Oxford University: "*The mechanism of evolution*" (p. xiv)

Professor Mark Richmond, Department of Bacteriology, Bristol University: "*Microbial genetics and its relevance to evolution*" (p. xxvi)

Dr. H. N. Southern, Department of Zoology, Oxford University: "*Evolutionary ecology*" (p. xxxii)

Dr. Bernard Kettlewell, Department of Zoology, Oxford University: "*The evolution of industrial melanism in Lepidoptera*" (p. xl)

Emeritus Professor Sir Alister Hardy, Department of Zoology, Oxford University: "*Behaviour as a selective agent in evolution*" (p. xliv)

Professor T. Stanley Westoll, Department of Geology, University of Newcastle upon Tyne: "*Evidence from palaeontology*" (p. xlviii)

Dr. John R. Baker, Department of Zoology, Oxford University: "*The fossil Hominidae of East Africa*" (p. lvii)

Dr. P. L. Pearson, Instituut voor Anthropogentica, Rijksuniversiteit te Leiden: "*Man and pongids: evidence from chromosomes, bearing on their relationship*" (p. lxiii)

Dr. Vernon Reynolds, Anthropology Laboratory, Department of Human Anatomy, Oxford University: "*The evolution of hominid social behaviour*" (p. lxx)

An integrated bibliography of all the papers and books quoted by the nine contributors is printed on pp. 661-74, separately from St. Julian's lists on pp. 618-52 and 653-60

See review in Times

It was thought that those who took up this book for the first time in its third edition would not wish to be faced at the outset with two long Introductions. Sir Julian's Introduction to the second edition, which retains its full value today, is therefore placed after the main body of the text, on pp. 579-617

The mechanism of evolution. There are a number of situations which tend to promote rapid evolution. One of these results from adaptations to a new and distinct habitat in which, if a species can survive, powerful selection will be operating to promote appropriate adaptations to its novel environment. Such colonization can arise as a result of very exceptional acts of migration, but clearer instances of it have been due to accidental or planned introductions by man.

The house sparrow, *Passer domesticus*, was brought to North America from England and Germany in 1852. It proved highly successful there and is now become one of the commonest birds in the United States and southern Canada. Spreading in all directions over a vast area, it has given rise to a number of local races. These are the subject of an authoritative study by Johnston and Selander (1964). The birds are dark in the Vancouver district, which they reached in 1900, and pale from south-west California to Texas. On the other hand, they are remarkably dark also, and possess other distinctive features, round Mexico City, though they did not arrive there until 1933.

These distinct populations are not to be identified merely by their average appearance but are true geographical races, distinguishable even when single specimens are examined, owing to differences in colour, shape of the beak, and other features. We can here compare the results of evolutionary speculation with what can occur in nature. In 1930 R. E. Moreau, a considerable authority on the subject, decided that the *minimum* number of years required for the evolution of a geographical race in birds was about 5,000. The number of years taken to achieve that result round Mexico City was thirty.

The work of Johnston and Selander on the sparrow is an outstanding example of the results that can accrue from careful observation, and the analysis of data, when applied to evolution in progress. Yet it must be admitted that birds have nearly always been studied by the techniques of ecology and animal behaviour; rarely by those of ecological genetics, to the great detriment of ornithology. To mention a single example only; when we consider how large an amount of work has been carried out on the ringing of birds, it is disappointing to find that it has hardly ever been applied to establish population-numbers and death-rates in nature, using species which maintain localized populations. Yet when the marking, release and recapture of birds was directed to obtain such information (Blackwell and Dowdeswell, 1951), it proved quite practicable.

In contrast with the sparrow, species which successfully establish themselves in a region new to them do not always display visible indications of the adaptations to it which they must surely evolve. For example, the European butterfly *Thymelicus lineola* (Hesperiidae), imported accidentally, reached London, Ontario, about 1910. It has spread thence widely in the north-eastern United States and in New Brunswick. The caterpillar feeds upon coarse grasses, and the insect has become common enough in some places to constitute a minor agricultural pest. Yet the imago has altered not at all in appearance in the New World, except that a pale variety is rather commoner there than in the Old.

One may presume that its colour-pattern is palaeogenic (p. xxv) and that it has adjusted to its new habitat by means of "cryptic" physiological changes. There is a fair probability that these will be detectable by a study of its protein variation carried out by means of electrophoresis (Burns, 1966), a technique that has already proved successful in the Lepidoptera, and indeed widely in animals and plants (Ford, 1971).

Though the evolution which takes place when a species establishes itself in a new habitat is likely to be rapid and profound, it is on the whole exploiting a rare event. On the other hand, polygenic variation provides a very frequent basis for promoting useful adaptations. It is one often accelerated by isolation or by response to an unusual environment.

There are several reasons for this. It is partly due to the large amount of continuous yet genetic variation to which polygenic segregation gives rise; and to the fact that the substitutions at each locus have individually only a small effect, likely to disturb the balanced gene-complex but little. Moreover, since their cumulative result is attained gradually, the situation allows genetic repair and adjustment to take place meanwhile. There is a further point here; that with the wide ambit of such variation, genes potentially valuable in diverse types of environment are liable to be held in the population and to provide a basis from which special adaptations can be built up. We may consider a few examples to illustrate the evolutionary aspect of polygenic variation.

One of great interest is due to the work of Bradshaw and his colleagues on plants adapted to grow on poisoned soil (Bradshaw et al., 1965). Old workings where ores of zinc, copper, lead and other metals have been mined are found in North Wales; their spoil-tips remain bare of vegetation, looking like the landscape of the moon, since plants cannot in general grow on ground contaminated in this way. Yet here and there at such sites Bradshaw noticed that a few clumps of grass were established. These proved to be genetically tolerant of the metallic ores to which they were exposed. In most species, including the grass *Agrostis tenuis*, such tolerance is polygenic, though in *Festuca ovina* one gene seems to play a more decisive part than the others. Since the non-tolerant and tolerant individuals take up the metal to an equal degree, this must be rendered innocuous within the tissues of the plants able to withstand it. These are not restricted to grasses, and may indeed belong to very different groups (e.g. *Silene inflata*); but some species, even those which grow at the edge of the mines (e.g. *Dactylis glomerata*) have never been known to acquire tolerance.

Bradshaw (1971) gives an excellent general survey of this type of adaptation. An instructive instance of it is to be found on a small copper mine at Drws y Coed, North Wales. Owing to the shape of the valley in which this is situated, the wind is principally channelled from its prevailing quarter, the west, and in that direction *Agrostis tenuis* passes in one metre from the completely non-tolerant to the completely copper-tolerant conditions, exactly at the edge of the mine. Downwind, tolerance fades out over 150 metres beyond the contaminated soil (McNeilly, 1968). These facts indicate not only the influence of wind-blown pollen but show that there is powerful selection against non-tolerant plants on polluted ground and against the copper-adapted ones in normal conditions. Yet it seems likely that owing to the polygenic nature of this character, a few slightly tolerant specimens exist in the general population and that it is from these that the adaptations to toxic soil have been built up.

Plants that have acquired the ability to grow on the spoil-tips are developing genetic isolating mechanisms there. These involve flowering-time, for grasses flower a week earlier than on the surrounding uncontaminated ground (McNeilly and Antinovics, 1968); also a tendency to increased self-fertilization (Antinovics, 1968).

Turning now to an example of another kind, the butterfly *Maniola jurtina* (Satyridae) has provided valuable material for research on evolution and adaptation. The number of spots on the underside of each hind wing has principally been used for that purpose. Its frequency can take values from 0 to 5 and the genetic component of the variation is polygenic. Its heritability at 15°C. is 0·14 in the males and 0·65 ± 0·14 in the females. At about 22°C. this rises to 0·47 ± 0·20 in the males and to 0·78 ± 0·16 in the females (McWhirter, 1969). Here we will consider the latter sex only, in which the variation is much the greater. There is one generation of the insect in the year, and the caterpillar feeds upon various species of grass.

This butterfly has been studied in a wide variety of localities, including the Isles of Scilly where it has been possible to analyse its adjustment to the large and small islands respectively, to calculate population-sizes by the technique of marking, release and recapture and, repeatedly, to estimate the selection-pressures to which the early stages and the imago are exposed in nature. The opportunity has also been taken to examine the responses of *M. jurtina* to changes in its habitat. One aspect of that work was incomplete and unpublished when the second edition of this book appeared, and brief mention of it must be made now.

White Island is, in all, about half a mile long, but it consists of two parts of about equal extent, each with a maximum height of approximately forty metres. They have different micro-climates since they are bent at right angles, while the southern has high ground running along its eastern side but the north-western has a central hill. They are separated by an isthmus rising very little above high water and about fifty metres wide.

M. jurtina had been collected there during the period 1953–7. Female spotting was similar over the whole island, having a single high mode at 0 spots, and was homogeneous for all years. During a great gale in the winter of 1957–8 the sea washed across the isthmus, leaving a belt of sand and shingle separating into two parts what had been a continuous land-mass. This barren strip of ground constituted a barrier to the butterflies which, as had previously been found, even ten metres of unsuitable terrain will do; after about that distance they are seen to turn back, as is their habit when they fly out over the sea (Ford, 1971, p. 65). As a result, M. jurtina immediately (in 1958) evolved a new spotting type on the southern part of the island, with approximately equal values at 0, 1, and 2 spots; while on the north-western half, spotting persisted as before. Thus the two populations became strikingly distinct. Since they continued unaltered season by season for eleven years, the captures may respectively be summed over that time, giving a value of $\chi^2_{(3)} = 68 \cdot 20$ for the difference between them.

By 1969, plants had colonized the shingle washed up by the great storm, so that M. jurtina was crossing the isthmus freely, and on the southern part of the island it had returned to its pre-1958 condition; on the north-western it remained as it was.* Evidently the insect was able to adapt itself to the special habitat of southern White Island when provided with the isolation needed to make that possible, but not otherwise. Having regard to the suddenness of the transition, its permanence (maintained, necessarily, by selection) and its eventual equally sudden reversal, it is clear that the selective forces involved must have been great. They amounted to a disadvantage of the non-spotted individuals in the southern area, throughout the time it was isolated, of 58% compared with the north-western one.

Much interest has centred upon the "boundary phenomenon" in M. jurtina; but as the first published account of this appeared in

---

* Lack of space in an article of prescribed length makes it impossible to quote the spot-frequencies in detail. They can be obtained from Ford (1972).

1959, a general description of it is not appropriate here. More recent work, greatly extending our knowledge on the subject must, however, be mentioned now.

The "boundary" region extends from Hawkchurch, in the extreme west of Devon, to Lanivet in east Cornwall. It became apparent in the females, within that range only, as an area of genetic instability in the transition from the Southern English spot-distribution, unimodal at 0, to the East Cornish one, bimodel at 0 and 2 spots. Thus it was detected by an analysis of spot-*numbers*. It may manifest itself, in different years, at distinct sites and as an extremely sudden change, within a few yards, or one observable over many miles.

The unusual nature of the boundary region receives confirmation from the researches of McWhirter and Creed (1971), who studied the *position* of the spots. For that purpose, they employ a "costality index": being in any one locality the proportion of the spots at the two costal positions expressed as a percentage of total spotting in the two costal plus the two anal positions on the hind-wings. As with spot number, the males show no marked disturbance at the boundary, the costality index rising steadily from east to west; the boundary region (48·9–49·0) being intermediate between southern England (47·6) and west Cornwall (49·4). In the females, on the other hand, the boundary region is not intermediate between southern England and the extreme south-west; there is a decrease in the costality index from 74·5 in southern England to 66·2 in east Cornwall, and then a rise to 71·2 in west Cornwall and to 86·6 in Scilly. Thus, in spot placing, as well as in spot number, the boundary region shows a departure from regular east to west changes in the females, though not in the males.

In studying the protein variation of *Maniola jurtina* by means of electrophoresis, P. T. Handford (1973, two papers) has obtained completely independent corroboration of the boundary phenomenon, and also of the general results of work on that butterfly in the Isles of Scilly.

The impact of selection upon this insect has been strikingly demonstrated in another of its aspects by V. Scali (1971), working in Tuscany. Above 700 metres, these butterflies behave in that part of Italy very much as in England, but at lower altitudes their imaginal ecology is different. They emerge from the pupa earlier, from late May to mid-June, and pairing takes place at once. The males then die and the females survive the heat of the summer by aestivating in bushes. Thus they disappear from view until early September, when they become active again. This cycle produces an almost completely unisexual population whose members fertilize their eggs with sperm received two and a half months before.

Scali has found that the average spot-frequency of the females is quite different at their two periods of flight. It is approximately flat-topped, at 0, 1 and 2 spots at emergence and is decisively unimodal at 0 in September. That change involves selection of about 64% operating in favour of the lower-spotted specimens during aestivation.

This cycle of spotting recurs regularly each year, showing that the genes for the higher spotted type are at an advantage in the earlier stages of the life-history but at a disadvantage in the imago, while those for lower spot numbers are the reverse. This is *endocyclic* variation taking place, that is to say, within the life-history of each individual. It contrasts with the *cyclic* type, in which selective advantages and disadvantages are regularly reversed after one or more generations (for an excellent example of this in the ST and CH inversions of *Drosophila pseudoobscura*, see Dobzhansky, 1951). Scali's observations in Tuscany provide an instance of remarkably powerful endocyclic selection.

When we come to consider evolution and adaptations controlled by major genes, we are faced with the concept of *polymorphism*. This was defined in 1940, and its attributes are described widely in the literature (see Ford, 1971, for a survey of them). However, one of these, the *super-gene*, has been analysed much more fully in the last ten years and therefore needs some discussion here.

Most adaptations require the co-operation of several major

genes. When these are needed for the development of some basic character, the heart for instance, they must be kept mainly homozygous by selection, and consequently they can be scattered among the chromosomes. Not so for polymorphic adaptations, in which the co-adapted genes must be so clustered as to segregate together. This is achieved by bringing them into a closely linked group which can act as a single unit. Of course occasional crossing-over will separate them, producing an ill-adapted association which, however, can be eliminated by selection in the same way as a disadvantageous mutant. Super-genes, then, oppose Mendel's law of "independent assortment". If their components chance initially to be on the same chromosome, they can be maintained in association by decreasing progressively crossing-over between them or, more effectively, by including them within an inversion, whether "long" or "short". Should they start on different chromosomes, they must first be brought on to the same one by structural interchanges. These are not extremely rare. Thus Jacobs et al. (1971) found four instances of them among 2538 men, inmates of Scottish penal institutions, whose chromosomes they examined.

The super-gene may be strikingly exemplified from butterfly mimicry. That subject suffered in earlier years from two publications, each of which constituted a potential menace to its analysis: those of Punnett (1915) and of Goldschmidt (1945). Both propounded for it explanations of obvious improbability, sustained by mis-statements of fact. However, their conclusions have been disproved in almost every particular by the penetrating researches on *Papilio dardanus* conducted with outstanding success by C. A. Clarke and P. M. Sheppard. That work, which they concluded in 1961, they have now extended, with similar results, to the S.E. Asiatic *P. polytes* and *P. memnon*.

In the latter species, Clarke et al. (1968), and Clarke and Sheppard (1971), studied a number of female mimics. All but two have tailless models and are themselves tailless, the normal state in *P. memnon*. The exception is provided by the two *achates* forms copying, respectively, *Atrophaneura coon* and *A. aristolochiae*. Both these species are tailed; so also are their mimics, due to a gene sex-controlled to the female. It has been brought into the super-gene determining the colour and pattern so that it segregates appropriately with those characters. On the Island of Palawan, however, *P. memnon* is exceptional since both sexes are always tailed, a condition controlled by a major gene different from the one occurring elsewhere and producing the *achates* forms. Since in Palawan wing-shape does not take part in the mimicry involving colour and pattern, the distinct gene for tails occurring there has, unlike the other, not been brought into the super-gene: a remarkably satisfying example of evolutionary genetics.

Though polymorphism is normally maintained by a balance of selective agencies (Ford, 1971), Kimura (1968), followed by King and Jukes (1969), have argued that in protein variation it is mainly due to random genetic drift acting upon a number of selectively neutral isoalleles. That concept is suspect in view of the improbability that a change can often take place in a gene without affecting its selective advantage. Not only had the opinions of Kimura on this matter been open to criticism prior to 1971 (Ford, loc. cit.), but further studies have also tended to contradict them.

Space prevents more than a brief reference to these. Prakash et al. (1969) had shown that there is little or no diversity of allele frequencies when controlling protein polymorphism in distinct sub-populations of *Drosophila pseudoobscura*, though this would be expected with random drift. Their result was, however, challenged by Kimura and Ohta (1971) on the ground that only a small amount of migration between the sub-populations would turn them into a panmictic unit in which much differentiation of allele-frequency under "neutral" mutation would not be expected However, Bulmer (1971) points out that this work of Prakash et al. contains further information undetected by Kimura and Ohta, and opposed to their conclusions. Bulmer gives the order of the alleles in that of electrophoretic mobility. When classified as rare (under 10%) or common (over 10%), there is a marked tendency for rare alleles to be at the beginning or end of a series, not in the middle. With a chance to the contrary of 1/12150, the results obtained by Bulmer are not equally likely: a situation incompatible with random drift.

Moreover, Bullini and Coluzzi (1972), working on *Aedea aegypti*, studied a phosphoglucomutase locus in populations established in different parts of the world. They found that the allele with intermediate electrophoretic mobility was always at the highest frequency. They obtained also comparable results in *A. mariae*. These findings are quite opposed to the theory of Kimura. So are the results of detailed experiments by Powell (1971). He kept populations of *Drosophila willistoni* for 45 weeks in cages some of which were maintained in constant and others in varying environments. The average heterozygosity per individual, and the average number of alleles per locus, proved to be higher in the populations exposed to the heterogeneous environments. Thus it may be said that we have no solid foundation for the view that protein polymorphism is often selectively neutral: quite the reverse seems true.

In normal circumstances, when we encounter polymorphic variation, we can be confident that the phases must have selective advantages and disadvantages: a conclusion of great importance in the study of human blood groups once their polymorphic basis was recognized. The powerful differential elimination which may affect an incompatible foetus had already been widely appreciated, both in respect of the OAB and Rhesus groups, prior to the 1963 edition of this book; but the subject has been much developed subsequently (see Clarke, 1971).

Numerous further associations between the blood groups and disease have been reported in recent years (Ford, 1973), but one is of such outstanding importance that special reference must be made to it. That is to say, it is now established that those of blood groups A and AB are much more liable to develop smallpox, and in a more severe form, than are the O and B types. When first reported, this was denied on experimental grounds by Harris et al. (1963) and others. But the association is now fully established: by Vogel and Chakravartti (1966) in Western Bengal and Bihar and confirmed by Bernhard (1966) both in India and Pakistan. The correlation seems limited to severe epidemics in unvaccinated populations. Its anthropological significance is great indeed.

There is a proposition due to McWhirter (1957) which was generally neglected when first propounded but is now falling into place as a basic concept. That is to say, ancient genes strongly resist minor changes in their genetic environment. This is due to the fact that they must have evolved appropriate gene-complexes that will have become included as an adjusted component of the genotype. They will tend therefore to be persistent and carried over intact with those co-adapted to them during species formation. On the other hand, relatively new genes not working in such entrenched gene-complexes, will prove more easily dislodged by minor genetic changes. McWhirter has named these two types *palaeogenes* and *neogenes* respectively. Thus the gypsies, who retain their north Indian value of blood group B after centuries of life in Europe, demonstrate a palaeogenic situation. Sickle-cell anaemia is, on the other hand, neogenic. It is a reaction to what Darlington (1964) shows to be the relatively recent spread of *Plasmodium falciparum*, and rapidly falls in frequency when public health measures reduce malaria (Clarke, 1964, p. 74).

Turning now to speciation, Dobzhansky and Pavlovsky (1966) report a remarkable instance in which their stock of *Drosophila paulistorum* became male-sterile in crosses with its own, Orinocan, race. The F1 individuals had previously been fully fertile in both sexes when so mated, and the change took place between 1958 and 1963. It seems that the situation is exceptional, since the culture in question, from Llanos, can induce "infective" sterility owing, apparently, to the presence of some symbiont adjusted to it but causing partial sterility on outcrossing. There is evidence, however, that this process occurs also in nature.

Doubtless speciation usually results from the accumulation of adaptive, and of course interacting, genes operating in some degree of isolation. It has been quantified to a slight extent. Hubby and Throckmorton (1968), using protein variation, examined 18 loci in 27 *Drosophila* species and found that pairs of the sibling type differed in 50% of the genes in question, while a change affected 82% of them in those that were closely related but distinguishable morphologically. Also Selander et al. (1969), again using protein variation, but in *Mus musculus*, demonstrated that two subspecies in Jutland differed at 32% of the 41 loci employed in comparing them.

Recent advances in understanding the mechanism of evolution have been largely due to the technique of ecological genetics, which combines genetic studies in the laboratory with detailed observation and specially contrived experiments in the field. It has demonstrated that selection for advantageous qualities in nature is, in general (Ford, 1971, p. 360), twenty or thirty times greater, often more, than had been supposed in the 1930s, when 1% was deemed its normal maximum value (Fisher, 1930). That discovery, which alters profoundly our concept of micro-evolution, could not have been made merely by means of laboratory genetics or of population genetics, nor yet by mathematical analysis in the absence of the necessary field-work, without which the essential parameters involved cannot be known.

Microbial genetics and its relevance to evolution. Present-day readers of the Introductions to the two previous editions of this book must be struck by the relatively little emphasis then placed on micro-organisms in an evolutionary context. This view was not unjust: all our early understanding of this subject came from observations on multicellular forms, and it is only recently that substantial advances have been made in the microbial field. Two very distinct developments have conspired to bring this change about. First, the elucidation of the molecular basis of inheritance, much of it carried out with micro-organisms as experimental material, has given us the means to understand the origin and nature of variation (see, for example, Hayes, 1968; Stent, 1971): secondly, man's preoccupation with his health, and particularly with infectious disease and the resistance of the causative organisms to antibiotics, has led him to set up a mammoth system of surveillance which gazes on many of the activities of bacteria, particularly where they interact with man (Anderson,

1968). As a result we now have abundant epidemiological information which can be interpreted in molecular terms and through this combination of opportunities we have a wonderful chance to watch evolution—and it has not been wasted. We know much of what controls the ebb and flow of bacteria in an ecological niche (Jones and Sneath, 1970; Richmond, 1970). Furthermore, studies with bacteria are beginning to pose some pertinent questions about the molecular basis of evolution in higher forms, even to the extent of suggesting some fruitful experiments.

The discovery that the bacterial genome consists of double-stranded DNA and that every gene is normally present as only a single copy has enormous implications for the evolution of micro-organisms and contrasts this group with higher forms. Mutations in the bacterial genome, by and large, express themselves phenotypically and there is little of the protective effect afforded by a diploid state. As a springboard for evolution the haploid and highly mutable state of bacterial cultures is an advantage since it allows rapid variation within a population and consequent rapid adjustment as selection-pressure is applied. Moreover the potential disadvantages, which could be so disruptive to an organized multicellular organism, can largely be avoided by bacteria. Their relatively fast growth-rate allows them to replace members of the population killed by lethal mutations and consequently the bacteria *as a population* survive and evolve with great plasticity (Skehal and Carlile, 1974). It may be almost mischievous to think of a bacterial population as a whole as analogous to a single multicellular organism, yet by stressing this comparison one sees, perhaps more clearly, some of the advantages and disadvantages of the haploid state to the two types of biological unit. And as an extension of this approach one can describe with some accuracy the evolutionary changes in genetic organization that must have accompanied the successful appearance of muticellular forms. The emergence of diploidy is certainly one of them.

In exercising its role as the hereditary material in living systems, DNA is, in many ways, one of the most paradoxical of molecules. In one sense it must have the most monumental and unshakeable stability: man today is recognizable as the same organism that inhabited the earth centuries ago. But it must also have great reactivity and flexibility: not only must it replicate at each cell division (Mitchison, 1970), its potential for change is the source of all evolutionary possibilities for an organism. Clearly therefore stability must be balanced against change within very precise limits. Too much of one and the organism will be too inflexible to cope with shifts in environmental pressure: too much of the other and the survival of the population will be jeopardized.

One field of bacterial research that has recently been investigated extensively has much importance in understanding some of the influences that set this balance between stability and change. Ionizing radiations damage bacteria and produce mutations, yet many organisms are equipped with enzymes which scan the DNA for changes in its composition and correct them (Moseley, 1968). Such repair enzymes, as they are called, are normally nucleases and their biochemical study has been intense (Witkin, 1969; Clarke, 1971). Not only do these enzymes allow micro-organisms to penetrate exotic environmental niches— such as those with a high radiation flux like the tanks used for storing moderating rods from nuclear power stations (Setlow & Duggan, 1964); they also allow bacteria to contend with some of the more normal aspects of the environment such as high levels of ultra-violet irradiation from bright sunlight; and certainly they protect the organisms against some potential evolutionary changes (Moseley, 1968). So far as is yet known repair enzymes are present in all organisms and their presence stresses one important element underlying evolution. The evolutionary consequence of a change in DNA composition does not just depend on its survival for long enough to exert its effect. Moreover there are suggestions that some of these repair enzymes are functionally related to those that catalyse recombination; and one is left with the tantalizing possibility that recombination may have evolved as a specialized manifestation of "repair activity" There is certainly much scope here for further research.

In any highly evolved population most point-mutations are likely to be deleterious and indeed there has even been discussion as to whether evolution to more "advanced" forms can ever be expected to occur by simple changes of this kind (see, for example, Mayr, 1963). Unquestionably the most important contribution that the study of micro-organisms has made to our understanding of the molecular basis of evolution over the past few years has been to show, with Prokaryotes at least, that blocks of genetic information, often comprising tens or even hundreds of genes, can be transferred intact between bacteria. So evolution need not proceed by selection of point mutants or similar minor alterations: changes which involve the acquisition of blocks of information already refined by selection-pressure elsewhere are quite common.

The first experiments which showed gene-transfer to be possible were done before the Second World War and were already given prominence in the earlier editions of this book. They involved the demonstration by Avery and his colleagues of the transfer of naked DNA between bacteria—usually of a given species (Avery, Macleod & McCarty, 1944). Latterly two other routes of gene-transfer have been discovered. In *transduction* the DNA that passes from cell to cell is protected against destruction outside the cell by the coat of a bacterial virus particle, which acts as the transfer vehicle (Zinder, 1953), while during *conjugation* it seems likely that protection is afforded by sex-pili—hair-like structures that join the bacterial strains participating in the transfer process (Brinton, 1965).

Although the exact details of the transfer mechanism in each of these examples are very different, all share a common property. In every case a block of genetic material passes between bacteria to give rise to a number of new phenotypic characters in the recipient. With *transformation*—the transfer of naked DNA—and transduction the scope for fertile transfers seems to be restricted to a relatively small number of strains of the same or a closely related species, but with conjugation gene-exchange can occur across interspecific and even intergeneric boundaries at relatively high frequency. Thus antibiotic resistance genes may be transferred between Pseudomonads and members of the Enterobacteriaceae, even though there is good evidence that there can be relatively little similarity between the chromosomal DNA of these two groups of organisms.

As time goes on it becomes more and more likely that bacterial plasmids play an absolutely central part in gene-transfer—interstrain, interspecific and intergeneric—and thus in bacterial evolution (Richmond, 1970; Richmond & Wiedeman, 1974). Plasmids are self-replicating pieces of DNA that normally exist completely independently of the bacterial chromosome (Meynell, 1973). Indeed they may even survive in so-called "minicells"—mutant bacteria that completely lack chromosomal DNA (Inselberg, 1970). Many plasmids are therefore excellently adapted to effect gene-transfer. Not only are they commonly of about the right size to fit conveniently into the head of a bacterial virus particle (thus facilitating transfer by transduction if a virus is available); they also carry the genes to ensure their replication independently of the chromosome and also, in many cases, the necessary information to promote their *own transfer* to bacteria that lack them (Clowes, 1973). Many plasmids can therefore be thought of as infectious groups of genes which can survive adventitiously in bacterial cells but which may nevertheless profoundly affect phenotypic properties and hence the potential to survive.

The existence of these bacterial plasmids—and they are certainly present in many if not all bacterial strains—has vital importance for those interested in evolution. First, the genes on a plasmid are often related functionally (various antibiotic resistance genes closely linked on the same piece of DNA, for example) and this means that blocks of information that fit the recipient to survive in certain clear-cut ecological niches (in hospitals where the determinants are antibiotic resistance markers, for example) may be transferred as a single event (Anderson, 1968; Richmond, 1973). Another consequence is that one can no longer afford to study populations consisting of single species or strains. One must begin to consider all the organisms in a given niche regardless of their taxonomic relationship (Jones & Sneath, 1970). A practical example of this is the incidence and type of antibiotic resistant bacteria in the gut of man. It is no longer sufficient to consider only strains of *Escherichia coli*. Transfer between pseudomonads and other enteric bacteria requires that all examples of both these groups of organisms are to some extent part of the same gene-pool, and by analogy with the idea put forward earlier might be regarded as part of the same bacterial "organism".

The early days of classical bacteriology were bedevilled by those who wanted to apply the concepts of speciation to bacteria; but all that has been said about the genetic flexibility of these organisms argues that such a classification, as though they were lions and tigers, would be unsatisfactory if not impossible for bacteria. And even the early taxonomists had to admit the existence of "intermediates" (Bergey, 1957). For example, most Salmonellae typically cannot ferment lactose, but transfer of a plasmid carrying the *lac* genes leads to an "intermediate" Salmonella strain that can ferment this sugar—and such variants have certainly been detected in the wild (Easterling et al., 1969). Not that genetic exchange has reached the point at which there is a continuous range of characters across all bacterial "species" and "genera". Certain taxonomic groupings are detectable; but it is equally sure that genes may be transferred across these barriers, particularly if they are carried on a plasmid in one of the inter-acting "species" (Jones & Sneath, 1970).

To maintain its maximal evolutionary potential an organism must not isolate itself from genetic change to the extent that profitable additions and modifications to its DNA are excluded, yet it must moderate any effects to the point at which they are not merely destructive. This is the crux of evolution at a molecular level. In practice bacterial cultures seem to be very wary of the amount and type of DNA that they will accept as additions to their hereditary content; and DNA *restriction* systems—as the processes for limiting the permanent survival of exogenous DNA in the bacterial cell are called—have been studied extensively over the last few years (Arber, 1968; Boyer, 1971). In general it seems that any exogenous DNA reaching a bacterial cell is examined by various enzyme systems for the extent of its "foreign-ness", and if unacceptably different is immediately destroyed by nuclease action. Such restriction systems therefore reduce very significantly the range of exogenous DNA that can survive for any length of time in bacterial cells. At present it is uncertain just how foreign DNA is assessed for what it is and dealt with by the cell; and, as with the investigation of repair systems, much remains to be discovered about the detailed working of bacterial restriction mechanisms. In particular it is uncertain how frequently the restriction system fails and truly foreign DNA survives, a point of crucial importance for potential change. Furthermore the existence and properties of such systems in bacteria raise interesting questions about the presence of similar processes in higher forms, since they are also likely to be as vulnerable to challenge by exogenous genetic information as their prokaryotic counterparts.

In summary, therefore, studies with microbial systems have allowed us to make enormous strides in understanding the molecular processes that underlie the evolution of prokaryotic populations. In many respects the haploid nature of the bacteria makes them simpler to analyse than the equivalent eukaryotic systems, but we are now just reaching the point at which the study of the haploid state and its implications is beginning to suggest the areas for profitable study in more complex forms. In particular one must begin to wonder whether all evolution of multicellular organisms has been based on relatively simple genetic changes or whether the transfer of blocks of pre-refined genetic information has occurred in these forms at various stages of their phylogeny. In this context we know that virus particles infect the cells of these complex organisms frequently (preoccupation with our health again!), and these may be just the vehicles to transport this additional genetic information from cell to cell. This, at least, will allow "foreign" DNA a chance to challenge any restriction systems the recipient cells may have available to assess the potential of the new information, ultimately for the evolution of the whole biomass.

Evolutionary ecology.* Much attention has continued to be

* This term was introduced by Orians (1962) and defined by Lack (1965) as

focused, particularly by ornithologists, on species-formation and competition, though the earlier controversies between those who maintained that species could arise sympatrically and those who denied this have been damped by Mayr's (1963) extensively documented arguments in favour of speciation by geographical isolation. There has never been any difficulty in demonstrating the working and outcome of competition in the laboratory (cf. the life-work of Park in his papers of 1948 and later dates on the flour beetles *Tribolium confusum* and *T. castaneum*), but results have not been so convincing in the field.

Examination of what has become known as "the principle of competitive exclusion" (previously called Gause's hypothesis) has largely been confined to inference from present distribution. Lack, in many papers but especially in his book published in 1971, has maintained that closely related species apparently co-existing avoid competing by ecological divergence in food and/or habitat. The crux that divides evolutionary ecologists is whether this divergence is the result of past competition or whether it is maintained by present active competition. Hutchinson's (1957) distinction between an animal's fundamental niche (where it *can* live) and its realized niche (where it is allowed to live) has stimulated some interesting analyses. Miller (1964) found that four species of pocket gophers in Colorado were separated by occupying different types of soil; nevertheless they ranged from highly specialized species which could burrow in the harder soils to generalized species living in more friable soils; wherever a more specialized species was absent, a less specialized one occupied its habitat.

Even here active competition is not indubitably established. The most elegant demonstration comes from Connell's (1961) study of the barnacles *Chthamalus stellatus* and *Balanus balanoides*. The former occupies only the highest zone between tide lines, the latter all the rest. Connell showed that, if *Balanus* was removed, *Chthamalus* colonized the lower areas. This distribution is fought

concerning those features of a species or population that are evolutionary adaptations (i.e. have survival value) and are not merely the consequences of population dynamics.

out afresh after each spat-fall, since larvae of both species are
found over a broader zone than are adults.

An interesting area of advance has come from examining the
winter habitats of migrant birds; for example, Fretwell (1969) has
shown that variation in the tarsal length of some American
fringillines is adaptive to their winter habitats: similarly some
wading birds obey Bergman's Rule as to wing-length in their
winter and not in their summer quarters. Again, owing to the
immense labours of Moreau (1972), a fair picture is now available
of the African winter-quarters and habitats of Palaearctic migratory birds. Moreau estimates that some 5,000 million passerines
crowd into Africa each autumn, some species into notably
restricted areas; the majority occupy grassland and savannah
habitats in Africa, in contrast to their summer quarters in Eurasia
(largely woodland), and again the majority do not pass south of
the equator, thus choosing the less favourable dry season for
overwintering (south of the equator they would encounter a wet
season). In terms of species, about a fifth of the African non-forest
bird fauna at this time consists of immigrants. That competition
is severe and mortality high is therefore not surprising, and Lack
(1971) suggests that selection is more stringent on these species in
their winter than in their summer quarters. Moreau points out
also that much of this intricate migration system, with its associated adaptations (behavioural, e.g. for navigation, and physiological, e.g. accumulation of fat for immense journeys) must have
evolved during the last 10,000 years, with more and more birds
pouring into Africa as their breeding grounds expanded after the
last glaciation.

Another aspect of evolutionary ecology upon which much
research has been done is the determination of the size of the
clutch in birds. Lack has consistently argued (1947 and *passim*)
that birds lay that number of eggs which corresponds to the
brood-size which will contribute most surviving young to the
next generation. Many careful and detailed experiments, mainly
by supplying artificially larger than average clutches or broods
for the parents to raise, have been performed over many years to
test whether additions of this kind would lower rather than

increase the ultimate output, as the hypothesis would demand. In five species from three families (notably in the swift (*Apus apus*) (Perrins, 1964)) this hypothesis has been upheld. Others, however, have proved refractory; gannets (*Sula bassana*), studied by Nelson (1964) on the Bass Rock, proved quite capable of rearing two young instead of one. Lack explains these discrepancies by changes in the environment to which the species has not yet had time to adapt itself. Since the species is increasing in numbers rapidly, there has probably been a change for the better in its food supply.

Another view has been put forward (Cody, 1966), originating from the important work of MacArthur, set out fully in Mac-Arthur and Wilson (1967). This maintains that, in a relatively unstable environment, natural selection will favour the greatest output of viable young (in their terminology the intrinsic rate of increase, r, will be maximized; this they call r selection); and this accords with Lack's hypothesis. On the other hand, in stable environments, such as tropical rain forest, whose carrying capacity (K) is full to the brim, selection may favour a decrease in r and a diversion of energy to, for example, the avoidance of predators by raising fewer young faster or to the better use of resources by narrow specialization (K selection).

A striking instance of these contrasting strategies is seen in the African cichlid fishes which have long puzzled zoologists. Fryer and Iles have recently (1969, 1972) collated and interpreted the vast amount of data that exists about these fish. On one hand, the many species of the genus *Tilapia* are generalized, widespread, and adapted to habitats where drought and other catastrophes recur. Their productivity is high, some species resorting to what is called "stunting", i.e. producing vast quantities of young while remaining at a very small size. On the other hand, the well-known species swarms (mainly of the genus *Haplochromis*) are rigorously confined to the old African lakes and are highly specialized for very narrow ecological niches. Their productivity is low. Here, very clearly, is displayed the distinction between MacArthur and Wilson's r and K selection.

Mention should be made here also of the work of Wynne-

Edwards (1962). He put forward the view, based mainly on evidence from birds, that many adaptations that appear to lower the intrinsic rate of increase, such as reduced size of clutch, an extended pre-breeding period, intermittent breeding, and, in general, rigorous territorial systems, allow many populations to stay below the danger limit of eating out their food supply. Further, many forms of social display enable populations, as it were, to assess their numbers and react accordingly. A corollary of this idea is that populations that fail to achieve this kind of efficiency will be eliminated: selection, therefore, operates at the inter-group level within a species.

This view has been hotly contested, the last corollary in particular, mainly on the ground that natural selection can operate only at the individual level. Lack (1966) rejects the whole of this theory on the principle of Occam's razor, i.e. it is unnecessary since the adaptations cited can be explained equally well as the result of natural selection at the individual level.

Nevertheless, some very interesting results have come from intensive field work on territorial systems that appear to depress the intrinsic rate of natural increase. The results of Jenkins, Watson, Miller and others (summarized in Watson and Moss (1970)) with red grouse (*Lagopus lagopus*) in Scotland are particularly relevant. In the populations they studied, only those pairs that could maintain a territory were able to breed; not only were unsuccessful birds driven out to marginal habitats but their mortality from predation and disease was strikingly high.

Lack (1965) maintains that the situation is an artificial one in which unnaturally high densities are maintained in a habitat simplified by man. However, Southern (1970) has shown that a similar system operates with the tawny owl (*Strix aluco*) in a habitat of deciduous woodland that is as nearly natural as any that can be found in Great Britain.

If we now turn to an aspect of evolutionary ecology which is more nearly allied to population genetics, namely intraspecific variation, many new and interesting facts have come to light during the last decade or so. Much attention has been focused on what has been called covert variation, namely the existence of biochemical variants in species. These may be valuable in detecting reproductive isolation which would otherwise be unsuspected. A notably clear instance concerns the eider ducks (*Somateria mollissima*) near Aberdeen. In general, eider populations from Iceland to Holland are dimorphic for types of egg-white protein (Milne and Robertson, 1965), the alleles for fast and slow mobility, as determined by electrophoresis, being situated at a single locus and the *b* gene (for slow mobility) being constant at a rate of about 0·1. However, on the Sands of Forvie near Aberdeen two populations are distinguishable, one resident on the west side of Forvie and one migratory on the east side. Consistently over two years the frequency of *b* has been 0·14 in the residents and 0·27 in the migrants.

Using similar criteria (4 groups of blood proteins controlled at five loci by 14 alleles), Rasmussen (1970) examined 14 populations of deermice, *Peromyscus maniculatus*, in Arizona and found considerable divergence in gene frequencies between populations only two miles apart. These results indicate a mosaic of sub-populations (which Rasmussen calls "demes") more or less isolated reproductively by their organization into social units. On the other hand, two populations divided by the Grand Canyon of the Colorado river show the same frequencies of these genes.

Interesting information on the results of artificial selection on gene frequencies has come from the now widespread application of poisons and pesticides to the populations of economically harmful species. Resistance by insects (e.g. to DDT) has been established long ago but resistance by vertebrates was first reported (for *Rattus norvegicus*) in 1958. The blood anti-coagulant, warfarin, came into widespread use against rats in the late 1940s and there are now two areas of considerable extent in Great Britain (between Edinburgh and Glasgow and in central Wales), as well as other much smaller areas, where this poison fails to work (Drummond, 1970). The genes controlling this resistance are different in the two localities. The house mouse (*Mus musculus*) has reacted similarly to this kind of selection.

Probably the biggest experiment on selection ever performed

in the field has been the introduction of the pox virus of myxomatosis for reducing populations of wild rabbits (*Oryctolagus
cuniculus*) (Fenner and Ratcliffe, 1965). Australia and western
Europe are the main areas concerned and the initial savage impact
on the rabbits (1950–1955) is common knowledge. In Australia
and Great Britain the adaptation between host and pathogen has
been carefully followed, and an interesting divergence demonstrated. In Australia the main vectors were various mosquitoes,
and selection has caused the spread of virus strains with much
reduced lethality. Since the course of the sickness is lengthened,
mosquitoes can communicate these strains more frequently than
the more virulent ones. The result has been that the original highly
virulent strain has now been displaced in the Australian rabbit by
a number of strains which differ in virulence. Australia still has
rabbit trouble, but of much reduced proportions. In Great
Britain, on the other hand, the highly virulent strain still co-
exists with less virulent strains, possibly because of the different
vector situation (the rabbit flea is the main vector and remains
infective longer than mosquitoes). The result is that, except for
local increases, which may be transient, the rabbit is still a fairly
uncommon animal in Britain.

To move back to selection operating under natural conditions,
mention must be made of one or two among the many studies
that have been made recently on the chemical defences of plants
against herbivores. Feeny (1970) found that leaves of the oak
(*Quercus robur*) near Oxford had a high nitrogen content and
little tannin when they were freshly opened in May-June: later
in the summer the situation was reversed. Of Lepidoptera alone
110 species feed on oak leaves in the spring compared with some
70 species later in the summer. The strategy of the early feeders
is to grow fast and pupate early (in some years complete defolia-
tion may occur); that of the late feeders is to grow more slowly,
some of them overwintering as larvae, though others, which
mine the leaves, can grow faster by avoiding the tannin-loaded
palisade cells.

Janzen (1969), working in the forests of Central America, has
found that certain beetles of the family Brucidae are specialized

for feeding on the seeds of leguminous trees. Defensive adaptations by the trees have taken two directions, either to produce more and larger seeds to saturate the attacks or to produce fewer and smaller seeds, which are toxic.

In the same area of central America an ingenious strategy has been evolved by mammals (e.g. some squirrels and peccaries) (Janzen, 1973) for surviving the dry season with its acute shortage of food. What remains is mostly toxic, but each species contains a different poison. By eating a little of this and a little of that, these mammals avoid taking a lethal dose of any species.

Polymorphic variation in birds has also attracted attention. The pale-breasted morph of the Arctic skua (*Stercorarius parasiticus*) increases in proportion to the dark-breasted morph as one ascends the latitudes to the high north. Berry and Davis (1970) examined the proportion of matings on Fair Isle (where dark birds predominate) and found an excess of instances where a dark male had mated with a pale female owing to the fact that dark males mate earlier than pale ones. Their interpretation is that early breeding is advantageous in the more southerly seaboard colonies, where they feed by harrying the colonial sea-birds, whereas later breeding is favoured in more northern inland colonies that feed on lemmings and voles; hence pale birds preponderate there.

Another instance, which shows the importance of knowing the population dynamics of the species studied, is that of the common guillemot (*Uria aalge*) with its white eye-ring morph, the proportion of which was surveyed by Southern (1962, 1965) at ten-year intervals from 1938 to 1958. Some colonies showed changes during these periods in the proportion of this morph as high as 10%; other colonies remained remarkably stable. However, a study by means of colour-ringed birds at a Scottish colony revealed an annual survival rate of 0·87. At this rate a change of 10% in ten years would demand a selection-pressure in the realm of fantasy. Therefore, either the changeable colonies must have had a much higher rate of turnover, which is improbable, or else there must occasionally be mass movements between colonies.

The evolution of industrial melanism in Lepidoptera. The earlier editions of this book were written at a time when industrial melanism was a much discussed but little understood phenonemon. It was placed under the heading of "Special Cases", but only two-and-a-half pages were devoted to it in the first edition (1942). In the second (1963) one further paragraph was added. It is indeed a special case for several reasons. It was one of the first instances which, when analysed, demonstrated visual selective advantages greatly in excess of those previously recorded (Kettlewell, 1955, 1956, 1958; Clarke and Sheppard, 1963, 1966). Twenty years ago 1% was considered high. The spread of *Biston betularia* f. *carbonaria* was first analysed by J.B.S. Haldane (1924) on grounds of theory. He demonstrated that the selective advantage of the black form near Manchester between 1848 and 1898 must have been about 30% to 50%. This was an entirely new dimension in selective pressures, yet it has been proved to be correct experimentally in *Biston betularia* for both f. *carbonaria* in polluted and f. *typica* in unpolluted countryside. Furthermore it has been shown that cryptic advantage alone could account for the rapid spread of industrial melanism (Kettlewell, 1973). This species is one of over a hundred in this country in which melanic forms are spreading rapidly, though each of course behaves somewhat differently.

In the last few years several other species have been fully investigated, in particularly *Phigalia pilosaria* Schiff. (syn. *pedaria*) by Lees (1971) and *Gonodontis bidentata* L. by Askew, Cook, and Bishop (1971). The behaviour and distribution of their melanic forms is entirely different from that of *B. betularia*. Lees has developed a satisfactory method of assessing the various physical and biotic parameters which affect the forms of *pilosaria* when at rest on oak trunks. He has studied seventeen of these and found that the single variable, oak trunk reflectance, could account for 64%, though others contribute to a less degree.

Industrial melanism is widespread throughout the Palaearctic wherever air-pollution is taking place, in particular in Europe in the following places: the Netherlands (Lempke, 1960), Germany and the Rhine Valley (Warnecke, 1913), Czechoslovakia and

Poland (Drozda, 1970). It is found throughout most industrial areas of North America (Owen, 1961, 1962), where it merges into other types of melanism. So far it has not been recorded from equatorial regions and it has been suggested that this may be due to the disadvantages of heat absorption in the tropics.

The genetics of melanic forms. Previous editions have pointed out correctly that the method of inheritance of industrial melanic forms is usually a single gene difference with dominance of the melanic form. Less frequently, melanism is controlled multifactorially, but here again each contributing gene has dominance. Other interesting information has been provided on the presence of allelomorphism in both *B. betularia* (Clarke and Sheppard, 1964) and also *P. pilosaria* (Lees, 1968, 1971), in which a blacker form is dominant to a lighter one: f. *typica* is recessive to both.

Only recently has an industrial melanic polymorphism with recessive inheritance been investigated: such situations are rare. The species *Lasiocampa quercus* ssp. *quercus* in Lancashire and *L. quercus* ssp. *callunae* in Yorkshire have an identical form ("*olivacea*") which is also found at a phenotype frequency of up to 70% in Caithness, Scotland, a completely pollution-free area. This form in each of the three localities is genetically distinct. In two of the three localities it has been shown that gulls are responsible for intensive selective predation (Kettlewell, Cadbury, and Lees, 1971; Kettlewell, 1959). The homozygous recessive melanic form appears on the other hand to be physiologically inferior, for example on comparing larval and imaginal samples and in the assembling capability of the females. A further point is that in the Lancashire population, all "*olivacea*" arise from black larvae, while in Yorkshire only a proportion do. Lees has shown that this is due to crossing-over (Kettlewell, Cadbury, and Lees, 1971); in one brood this was 8·9% and in another, 25·6%.

Wright and Smith (1956) investigated the genetics of the melanic form of the normally aposematic insect *Arctia caja* L., in which the heterozygote is variable. The homozygote melanic, f. *fumosa*, is distinct; all of these arise from black larvae.

Cadbury (1969) and Kettlewell (1973) worked on the recessive melanic form of *Lycia hirtaria* Clerck and released many hundreds of melanic individuals into London parks and squares where f. *typica* abounds (f. *nigra* occurs here rarely, but it is getting more common (de Worms, 1961)). The selective predation rate was high in favour of f. *nigra* ($\chi^2_{(1)} = 10\cdot08$. $0\cdot01 > P > 0\cdot001$; n = 198).

Other recessive polymorphisms occur in *Antitype chi* L. in northern England and in *Meristis trigrammica* Hufn., which occurs throughout Britain.

Physiological advantages and disadvantages. Further evidence of hardiness and increased vigour among dominant melanic forms has been recorded. Thus when larvae of backcross broods of industrial origin of *Biston betularia* were fed on foliage heavily contaminated by pollution fallout, a higher proportion of the *carbonaria* melanic form survives (Kettlewell, 1963). Clarke and Sheppard (1963, 1964), however, failed to substantiate this; nevertheless they have shown (1966) by other means that homozygous *carbonaria* are physiologically inferior to the heterozygote, and many other species show this even to a point of lethality as in homozygous *Biston strataria* Hufn. f. *robiniaria* (Robinson, 1971).

Choice of background. The importance of knowing whether the various colour forms of cryptic Lepidoptera are individually capable of choosing their correct background has been somewhat overlooked, though if the various forms of *B. betularia*, for example, took up random positions on available trunks and boughs, such a polymorphism would have to await a time when a high proportion of available sites offered advantages to melanic forms in order to spread. A minimum amount of investigation has so far been undertaken. Kettlewell (1955) first worked on background choice, using melanic and typical sibs of the peppered moth; both chose correct positioning ($\chi^2_{(1)} = 10\cdot9$, $P = 0\cdot001$). Sargent (1966, 1968, 1969a and b) and Sargent and Keiper (1969) demonstrated that Macrolepidoptera were able to choose optimal backgrounds. Conn has recently shown that correct background choice occurs in female *B. betularia* ($\chi^2_{(1)} = 35\cdot89$, $P < 0\cdot001$ in one set of experiments (n = 67) and $\chi^2_{(1)} = 4\cdot30$, $P < 0\cdot05$, in another (n = 126)), and also in both sexes of *Phigalia pilosaria* (females: $\chi^2_{(1)} = 13\cdot47$, $P < 0\cdot001$, (n = 211); males: $\chi^2_{(1)} = 15\cdot05$, $P < 0\cdot001$ (n = 322)).

Smokeless zones. Since the Beaver report on air pollution of 1954, certain specified areas in Britain have been designated as "smokeless zones". In these, fuel burnt for domestic purposes has to be monitored before being used. The results have been encouraging. Since 1962, *B. betularia* f. *typica* has increased in several areas in the Liverpool district where Clarke and Sheppard (1966) have carried out extensive investigations. They did this first by sampling and secondly by release experiments with dead deep-frozen specimens. The *carbonaria* frequency dropped from 93·3% in 1959 to 90·2% in 1963 ($P > 0·01$, $n = 4229$). The release experiments show that whereas previously f. *typica* had a 50% disadvantage, the figure had dropped since 1962 to 20%. They account for this by the fact that the cryptic disadvantage of 20% was counter-balanced by the physiological disadvantages of the homozygous *carbonaria*. Wild sampling since 1962 has shown a similar change in several other areas: Brentwood, Essex; Bishop's Stortford and Tring, Hertfordshire; and Totteridge in North London (Kettlewell, 1973). More recently (1973) similar and highly significant frequency changes have been recorded from East Anglia and north London.

The origins of industrial melanism. It is now recognized that many cryptic species maintain balanced polymorphisms of their melanic forms in completely rural countryside; also that these melanic forms may be similar to their industrial counterparts. In the majority of such polymorphisms the black forms are dominant. Thus up to 20% of *Cleora repandata* L. in ancient Caledonian pine forests in Perthshire are the melanic f. *nigricata;* the comparable industrial f. *nigra* contributes over 90% in parts of the Midlands (Kettlewell, 1957). Usually in Britain there is no direct contact nor spread between the two biotopes, and species have had to await a mutation. In North America, however, there are often pockets of rural melanism near industrial centres. This is in part due to the common occurrence of fire-resistant trees which have black trunks (for example the New Jersey Pine Barrens (Kettlewell, 1973)). These have served as reservoirs of melanism throughout the past. The question posed therefore is how could nearly full dominance of a melanic form be maintained in

Britain at each mutation after its absence as a polymorphism for thousands of years.

Modifications of dominance. Kettlewell (1965) crossed British *Biston betularia* f. *carbonaria* with North American *Biston cognataria* Gn. from a district in Canada where its melanic form (f. *swettaria*) does not occur. After three generations of outcrossing f. *carbonaria* to Canadian f. *typica*, dominance was broken down and a graded series from black to light occurred. He decided to attempt to reconstitute dominance by crossing the hybrid melanics to British f. *typica*, anticipating several years of such crosses. It came as a surprise that in the first generation, clear-cut disruptive selection took place.

From these results it appears that there are present in the British gene-complex modifiers which affect the expression of dominance and that these are themselves dominant. The antiquity of melanism throughout living creatures suggests that these may be considered as palaeogenes (Kettlewell, 1973).

The natural history of industrial melanism. Present-day industrial melanism has arisen from two sources: local migration from areas of non-industrial origin as is common in North America, and fresh mutations as is usually the case (but not always) in Britain. Their dominance has been achieved under entirely different, but nevertheless advantageous conditions in the distant past.

It is likely that one melanic form has been superseded by another and darker one, the whole forming an allelomorphic series, the darker having dominance over the lighter. The maintenance of the degree of melanism in each form is controlled by palaeogenes which ensure nearly full expression of each form at mutation. This is due to the recurring need for melanism, and its antiquity.

The blackest industrial melanic forms occurring today are therefore the product of two separate mechanisms, substitution of one allele by another and the local selection of modifiers enhancing melanism. Both have been brought about by natural selection, in particular by intensive visual selective predation.

Behaviour as a selective agent in evolution. In the last twenty years there has been a growing realization that changes in the behaviour of members of an animal species can bring about an evolutionary change by their new behaviour-pattern acting as a selective agent within the Darwinian system. The concept is a development of the idea first put forward independently in the same year (1896) by J. Mark Baldwin, C. Lloyd Morgan, and H. F. Osborn; a statement of the principle, which they called Organic Selection, was drawn up by Baldwin in consultation with the other two and published in *Nature* (1897). Later on it was sometimes referred to as the "Baldwin effect" and had usually been thought to be of only minor significance. Julian Huxley in the first edition of this book refers to it twice (pp. 304 and 523) and recognizes that "the principle is an important one which would appear to have been unduly neglected by recent evolutionists". G. G. Simpson (1952) put his finger on the reason for this neglect; these ideas were put forward, he says, "shortly before the rediscovery of Mendelism gave a radically different turn to biological thought."

Whilst the effect had hitherto been associated mainly with small evolutionary changes such as the fixation of habitat or feeding preferences, Huxley showed its importance in bringing about *structural change* in the following concise statement (his p. 524): ". . . an organism may in the first instance become adapted to an ecological niche merely by behaviour (whether genetic or purely habitual) and any consequent non-heritable modifications, after which mutations for the kind of structural change suitable to the particular mode of life will have a better chance of being selected. Where the modifications are extensive, the process of their replacement by mutations may closely simulate Lamarckism."

Subsequently A. C. Hardy (1949, 1957) stressed the importance of Organic Selection in bringing about the "selection of structural variations by habit as opposed to selection of other variations by the environment." Independently R. F. Ewer (1952, 1960) emphasized the same effect and in the latter paper gave good examples from her studies of the feeding habits of the African Suidae; she sums up her views by saying, "Thus behaviour will tend to be always one jump ahead of structure, and so to play a decisive role in the evolutionary process." In his book *The Living Stream*, Hardy (1965) deals with these issues at greater length, firstly from the strictly biological position in chapters on "Behaviour as a selective force" and "Habit in relation to bodily structure"; here he discusses the importance of the spread of new habits through the populations of a species and the consequent part played by behavioural selection in both adaptive radiation and convergent evolution. Later in the book he develops the more philosophical implications of such selection which would follow if one were to consider the higher animals as conscious, inquisitive, exploring individuals; he argues that such a view, linked with the philosophical ideas of Michael Polanyi (1958, 1959), would enable one to regard a strictly Neo-Darwinian system of evolution as not entirely the materialistic process it has often been held to be.

In the meantime other writers on evolution have stressed the importance of behaviour in the process. C. H. Waddington (1959) points out that "An animal by its behaviour contributes in a most important way to determining the nature and intensity of the selective pressures which will be exerted on it." Ernst Mayr (1960) in discussing the emergence of evolutionary novelties writes as follows:

It is very often the new habit which sets up the selection pressure that shifts the mean of the curve of structural variation. Let us assume, for instance, that a population of fish acquires the habit of eating small snails. In such a population any mutation or gene combination would be advantageous that would make the teeth stronger and flatter, facilitating the crushing of snail shells. In view of the ever present genetic variation, it is virtually a foregone conclusion that the new selection pressures (owing to the changed habit) would soon have an effect on the facilitating structure.

Ten years later in an abstract of a paper on evolution and behaviour Mayr (1970) sums up his views thus:

Changes in behaviour, such as a preference for a new

habitat, food, or mode of locomotion, may set up new selection pressures. Much evidence indicates that most major evolutionary shifts (the origin of higher taxa) began with a behavioural shift. Anything that reinforces an advantageous shift genetically, will be selected for.

Jacques Monod in his *Le hasard et la nécessité* (1970) made just the same point (the quotation is from p. 121 of the English translation (1972)):

It is also evident that the initial choice of this or that kind of behaviour can often have very long-range consequences, not only for the species in which it first appears in rudimentary form, but for all its descendants, even if these constitute an entire evolutionary subgroup.

He summarizes his views under the heading "Behaviour orients the pressures of selection".

R. D. Martin has recently (1972) published an extensive and detailed study of the adaptive radiation and behaviour of the Malagasy lemurs; while not actually dealing with the role of selection in the process he provides a wealth of material for the discussion of the part played by behaviour in evolution.

Since it is now being recognized that changes in behaviour can be so vital a factor in evolution, it should not be forgotten that historically this was also a most prominent part of the theory of Lamarck. While part of the mechanism of his system of evolution, that regarding the supposed direct inheritance of the effects of use and disuse, has been shown to be wrong, he should perhaps be given more credit for having been the first to insist that changes in habit would form an important element in the process. He never supposed that the environment influenced animal evolution directly. While he asserted that it influenced the form of animals, he went on to say, in the following significant passage, that he should not be taken literally, for the environment can effect no direct changes upon the organization of animals. As it has been so often overlooked, the quotation is given here in full; it occurs in Chapter 7 of his *Philosophie zoologique* (1809, Vol. 1, p. 221):

*Ici, il devient nécessaire de m'expliquer sur le sens que j'attache
à ces expressions:* Les circonstances influent sur la forme et
l'organisation des animaux, *c'est-à-dire qu'en devenant très-
differentes, elles changent, avec le temps, et cette forme et l'organisation elle-même par des modifications proportionnées.*
*Assurément, si l'on prenait ces expressions à la lettre, on
m'attribuerait une erreur; car quelles que puissent être les circonstances, elles n'opèrent directement sur la forme et sur l'organisation des animaux aucune modification quelconque.*

Again and again Lamarck made the point that changes in the
environment can bring about changes in the habits of animals
and that it is these *changes of habit* which can be so important in
bringing about evolutionary change.

Evidence from palaeontology. Many recent developments in
geological science have given new data, and in some cases
almost new dimensions, concerning the evolution of life on earth.
First of these is the far greater certainty in the time-scale, which
now allows data from far back in the Pre-Cambrian to be
evaluated. For a convenient summary of methods and their
application to the fossil record, see Harland et al. (1964).

It is now widely accepted that the earth has existed as a planet
for about 4500 million years (m.y.), and actual rocks of the crust
have been found with an age of 3800 m.y. The first identifiable
fossil cellular structures, e.g. from the Fig Tree Shales of South
Africa, date from about 3,100 m.y.; the fossil structure known
as stromatolites, almost certainly of algal origin, from rather
more than 2,500 m.y.; the first identifiable blue-green algae
(eukaryotes!) from about 1,000 m.y.; and Metazoa, mainly in
the form of trace-fossils and impressions, occur in the late Pre-
Cambrian, perhaps up to 700 m.y. ago; the base of the Cambrian
is taken to be about 570 m.y. ago. In the more recent parts of the
record a new tool is available, since there have been frequent
reversals in the polarity of the earth's magnetic field, which
leave an impressed magnetic vector in some of the rocks deposited
during each phase; and there is emerging a useful palaeomagnetic

correlation, tied up with radiometric age-determinations on sequences of lavas and sediments, that is most useful over the last few million years of earth history, and therefore important to the record of the evolution of man. Some other consequences of these aspects of the time-scale will be noted later.

Another important geological development has been the great swing-over of opinion, now overwhelmingly in favour of continental drift. But this is now subsumed under a more embracing theory of plate-tectonics, which carries the important corollary that the ocean floor material is being continuously formed along great mid-oceanic ridges with median rifts, and consumed by subduction elsewhere, particularly around the present Pacific, where ocean crust disappears under "continental" materials. Over aeons of time such great changes have provided endless opportunities for deployment of the biota into new areas. They also make increasing sense of the past distribution of land-faunas, and two examples recently recorded may be noted: (a) the existence in India and Antarctica of Permo-Triassic terrestrial reptiles apparently specifically identical with some from the South African Karroo deposits, already known to have much in common with South American faunas, and providing excellent evidence of subsequent drift; and (b) the data considering the degree of endemism or external communication of land-faunas of various ages from different continents or plates has become far more significant. A good insight into some of the exciting new possibilities is given, for example, in *Organisms and Continents through Time* (Palaeontological Association, London, Special Paper 12, 1973). New possibilities also arise from this recent work for studying the physical background to faunal provinces deduced from marine organisms of various ages.

A very valuable treatment of systematics and of distribution through time has been provided in recent years by the *Treatise on Invertebrate Paleontology* (Moore, 1953 et seq.), in which each group has been handled by experts in such a way as to provide a very balanced picture of taxonomic diversity. This has been followed up by *The Fossil Record* (Harland et al., 1967), in which plants and vertebrates are also considered, and in which a number of important developments have been indicated, particularly in relation to times of unusually rapid diversification and deployment in various phyla, and to the nature and distribution through time of major reductions in numbers and diversity and of extinctions. Increasing accuracy of stratigraphical correlation and the rapid increase in knowledge of fossil floras and faunas have shown that some of the long-discussed major extinctions, such as the large overturn at about the end of the Permian, and the extinction of ammonites and of dinosaurs at the end of the Cretaceous, are rather less completely clear-cut and sudden than has often been assumed. The problem is therefore not so much to search for a truly catastrophic cause as to explain rapid dwindling of major stocks over periods of perhaps 10 million years—still a very remarkable change.

One particular aspect deserves mention. Magnetic reversals of the earth's field, as noted above, have a very long history, and are sufficiently clearly defined over the last 5 m.y. to serve as an additional time-scale. They can be applied even to cores of ocean-floor sediments, which yield particularly abundant microfossils. The present "normal" period (apart from a brief and not yet fully accepted event) has lasted about 700,000 years, and no one has therefore observed the reversal process; we do not know whether it was sudden, or involved weakening of the field to zero and its growth to a maximum, or whether the change took some other course. But either a very weak field or virtual absence of magnetic field would result in disappearance of the Van Allen belt and increase of penetrating extra-terrestrial radiation. Whether this would greatly increase mutation rates has been much debated. It has been suggested that extinction of certain planktonic species present in submarine cores may be linked with such short periods of more intensive radiation, but this matter is at best regarded as *sub judice*. Nevertheless some fluctuation in the intensity of extra-terrestrial penetrating radiation may have to be taken into consideration in evolutionary thought; nor should the almost certain far greater intensity of terrestrial radioactivity during the earliest parts of earth-history be forgotten as a factor affecting the earliest life on our planet.

There is now a vast literature on the geochemical evolution of the hydrosphere and atmosphere. It is at least a very probable hypothesis that the primary atmosphere was largely devoid of free oxygen, and that photosynthesizing plants of generally algal character were responsible for production of an increase in atmospheric oxygen. By late Pre-Cambrian times, about 600 m.y. ago or probably earlier, the Pasteur concentration of oxygen (about 1% of the present level) had been comfortably passed, and traces of metazoan life—often only as impressions of rather problematic organisms—are found in several places below Cambrian strata. (It should be noted that the base of the Cambrian is rather arbitrarily defined by the appearance of such trilobites as *Fallotaspis* in the Atlas Mountains and elsewhere by *Olenellus* and other forms.) Far and away the most significant of these late Pre-Cambrian or "Eo-Cambrian" faunas is the Ediacara fauna from South Australia, so beautifully described by Glaessner (e.g. 1962); some of these "problematica" seem to be represented by relatives in similar stratigraphical positions in other continents.

Animals with hard skeletons are of course characteristic of Phanerozoic time, i.e. the Cambrian and later geological periods. Though the appearance of such skeletons in several groups is often said to be "sudden", in fact it cannot be shown that it was simultaneous, and it may well have spread over a few tens of million years. Nevertheless this remains the most significant aspect of the fossil record of animals and continues to pose great problems.

Turning now to a few of the classical case-studies of evolutionary sequences in fossils, many of which have been re-studied, the most significant recent feature has been the improvement in methodology from the original *description* of sequential change (often with reasonable statistical handling) to *functional analysis* of the change, especially in relation to far better knowledge of the sedimentary environment. Thus the evolution of the Cretaceous echinoid *Micraster* has been reconsidered by Nichols (1959) as showing divergent specializations in relation to depth of burrowing in a soft limy mud. Another celebrated study, initiated by H. H. Swinnerton (1940) and continued by A. E. Trueman (1940), concerned the evolution of the Lower Jurassic thick-shelled curved *Gryphaea* from an *Ostraea* ancestor. This case has been further discussed by Westoll (1950), who considered the change in coiling angle and maximum size, and especially by Hallam and by Joysey (Joysey, 1959, gives good references). There is little doubt that we are dealing, not with an "orthogenesis", but with rapid adaptation to life on a soft sea-floor of animals initially adapted to a hard substratum to which one valve became cemented. Similar changes seem to have led to gryphaeoid forms from oysters at other geological times—one of the most frequently quoted examples of iterative evolution. Indeed the case of *Gryphaea* has provided a graveyard of disputed ideas, from which resurrection will be selective rather than general. And of course it hardly needs saying that the evolution of the horses is now known to be far from the simple "orthogenetic" picture once widely accepted, and involves a number of stages of adaptation to one environment and habit of life after another.

Ever since G. G. Simpson's "Tempo and Mode in Evolution" was published (1944—see also Simpson, 1953), the speed of evolutionary change and the mode of origin of larger taxa have provoked a considerable literature. Rensch (1960) is another major contributor to this field. True quantitative studies based throughout on measured parameters are almost impossible to achieve in such problems. Westoll (1949) applied a specified but subjective "scoring-system" to characters shown by the Dipnoi, and showed an accelerated offset from a parental stock, then a slowing down to practically zero change (see also Simpson, 1953). Subsequent studies indicate that some modifications to the scheme need to be made, but the overall picture is fully confirmed, while the description of the Lower Devonian lungfish *Uranolophus* (Denison, 1968 *a*, *b*) greatly strengthens the early stages of the proposed evolution. Unpublished work on coelacanths indicates a very similar but still more rapid early offset and accelerated change, followed by rapid decline to remarkable stability of form and structure. Such an evolutionary pattern can clearly be discerned at somewhat lower taxonomic levels, for example in the case of the horses, in which a conservative, browsing, forest-glade-dwelling, functionally 3-toed group gave rise rapidly to grazing savannah-dwelling horses with reduced lateral toes, and this again (by further development of the "sprung" joints in the limbs and functional loss of the lateral toes) to *Equus;* in each case conservative types continued for some time (Simpson, 1951, etc.). This kind of interpretation differs markedly from the ancestral lines slowly converging backwards into remote times, as postulated for example by Jarvik (e.g. 1960) for the major groups of fishes.

The fossil history of fishes has lately received very much attention; a convenient source of information on the earlier members is the revision by R. S. Miles of Moy-Thomas's *Palaeozoic Fishes* (1971). Out of such richness one remarkable investigation worth notice is that of C. Patterson (1964) on the emergence of certain acanthopterygian teleosts, in which acquisition of "new" characters has been traced through several closely related lineages—an excellent contribution to the "grade v. clade" argument with which Julian Huxley's name is associated.

Another Huxleyan field is that associated with relative growth. Newell (1949) and Westoll (1950) discussed growth-studies in fossils and made much use of Huxley's work on allometry, and other examples are noted in Gould (1966), Macurday (1968), and in Raup and Stanley's stimulating *Principles of Palaeontology* (1971). Some instances of evolutionary lines involving remarkable changes in proportions with time (lineage allomorphosis in the sense of Westoll, 1950) will be noted below. We may here note that ontogenetic anisometric growth (heterauxesis) and allomorphosis should be sharply distinguished, and that where an evolutionary lineage involved increase in maximum size there is a tendency, in such forms as molluscs which show incremental skeletal growth, to produce classical cases of palaeontological "recapitulation". Newell (1949) determined the length of the external suture (i.e. the complex line where the edge of a septum meets the external shell of the conch) at several growth-stages of five closely related genera of late Carboniferous and Permian ammonoids, which are at least a close approximation to a phyletic series. In each genus a heterauxesis curve closely satisfies Huxley's equation of allometry ($Y = aX^b$, where in this case $Y =$ half-length of external suture and $X =$ shell diameter); the five straight lines on a log/log plot are nearly parallel, but from the earliest to latest the factor a increases apparently steadily from 0·11 to 1·30, and b varies somewhat on either side of 1·26, apparently rather randomly. Raup and Stanley (1971) discuss this case from a functional standpoint; their book gives references to other interesting cases, and also to the extremely elegant study in the morphology of the coiled shells of molluscs, of which Raup and his collaborators have produced remarkable simulations using analogue-computing.

The species-concept in palaeontology has been the subject of several symposia, notably that edited by Sylvester-Bradley (1956), wherein most of the difficulties of terminology and those arising from the nature of the fossil record are discussed.

It is now abundantly clear that at least the great majority of tetrapods (with the possible exception, according to the thesis so strongly maintained by E. Jarvik, of the Urodela) are descended from a group of crossopterygian fishes (cousins at one or two removes of early coelacanths) of which *Eusthenopteron* is extremely well known. Jarvik, in numerous papers (see good list of references in Moy-Thomas and Miles, 1971) has made the most exhaustive investigation of the head and visceral skeleton of this form, and Andrews and Westoll (1970) have dealt with the post-cranial skeleton. From a creature morphologically closely similar to *Eusthenopteron* it is possible to derive the skull-structure of primitive tetrapods in the most convincing detail, and (*pace* Jarvik) the process involves the most radical changes in proportions of the cranium and its associated dermal bones, while the structure of the cheek, palate, and mandible show only the minimal change necessary to maintain the basal articulation with the cranium (first noted by Westoll, see e.g. 1943). At the same time the transverse intra-cranial "joint", typically present in both endocranium and dermal skull-roof in crossopterygians, is closed and buttressed by a variety of modifications of dermal bones. The posterior moiety of the cranium is drastically shortened, a process carried further in the evolutionary lines leading to reptiles (Romer, 1941). The functional explanation has probably to do with development of the neck-joint and maintenance of head-posture when aquatic bouyancy was lost. This proportional change is one of the most drastic of those encountered in the line "fish to man", and it seems to have been a fairly rapid one. So far as the post-cranial skeleton is concerned, it is now known that the vertebral column of *Eusthenopteron* and its close allies provides a perfect starting-point for the evolution of the vertebral column of the vast majority of tetrapods. Furthermore the pectoral limb is developed as a load-bearing member, whose structure can convincingly be related to that of the tetrapod limb less the manus, and there is even indication of a cartilaginous sacral rib (Andrews and Westoll, 1970). Thus many of the basic requirements for tetrapods were already present in these fishes. It seems now pretty clear that the early evolution of tetrapods was rapid; no doubt this was possible because a variety of new ecological niches were not only available but largely unoccupied by possible competitors. Only a tantalizingly fragmentary skull-roof (*Elpistostege*) seems to record this offset; but by about the end of the Devonian the earliest tetrapods so far known (*Ichthyostega*, etc.) were fully developed, though *Ichthyostega* retains obvious traces of its fish ancestry (Jarvik, 1952).

New discoveries are rapidly adding to our knowledge of Carboniferous tetrapods, with the not unexpected result that classifications and interrelationships are under almost constant revision. It will suffice here to indicate that several groups of "primitive reptiles" now have their first records pushed back deeper into the Carboniferous, while the "amphibian" groups that seem to be most closely related to them (the Anthracosauria in Romer's (1966) usage (see also Romer, 1968)) appear, in our present state of knowledge, about as early in the records as other taxa regarded as the direct ancestors of most labyrinthodonts. Once again a fairly rapid differentiation and structural modification seems to be indicated, even though the basic morphological differences between these earliest known forms may be so apparently trivial as to cause much debate concerning interrelationships, before the end of the Carboniferous differentiation is clear.

The great complex of mammal-like reptiles is also receiving much attention, and new discoveries have greatly clarified some important evolutionary problems. Here it is only intended to draw attention to one problem—the remarkable change in shape and proportions of the skull in the transition from an advanced cynodont towards the Theria. The general background for this transition is now fairly well documented, though the Mesozoic record is largely based on jaw-fragments and teeth. The discovery of such forms as *Probainognathus* (Romer, 1970), in which the dentalo-squamosal articulation has just been achieved, the remarkable similarities between cheek-teeth patterns in galesaurid cynodonts and such teeth as those of *Eozostrodon* (*Morganucodon*) and *Kuenotherium* (cf. Crompton and Jenkins, 1968; Parrington, 1971; and papers by Kermack et al. and others quoted therein) which seem to represent stocks from which diverse later mammalian groups can be derived, indicate some of the very many reasons for focusing attention on cynodonts, and especially galesaurid cynodonts, as truly mammalian ancestors. Nevertheless other members of the Cynodontia parallel this development to some extent, as witness *Diarthrognathus*, which has also acquired a dentalo-squamosal articulation but is almost certainly not ancestral to Theria (though possibly related to the problematical haramyids—Romer, 1968), and the Tritilodontidae, which show a remarkable convergence to the multituberculates. So much of mammalian palaeontology is concerned with precise study of dentitions and their occlusion-relationships that minutiae are now fiercely argued. But a case has been made out (though it has also been attacked) for the proposition that apparently tiny differences in the angulation of the main row of cusps on the cheek-teeth can lead rapidly and inexorably to strongly divergent patterns. The most important governing factors may well have been the "new" jaw-joint, more strictly prescribing mandibular movements, and the great reduction in replacement of cheek-teeth in true mammals; the old reptilian multiple and often apparently alternate replacement, for which Edmund (1960) was the first of many to suggest a recognizable pattern, cannot give rise to precise occlusion. The dentalo-squamosal junction is associated with the lesser size and failing original function of the "post-dentary" bones of the lower jaw, which makes them free to be partly converted to ear-ossicles. But there is one remarkable change of proportions in the skull, to which Parrington and Westoll (1940) drew attention, and which was briefly analysed by Westoll (1962). It involves the change in attitude of the occipital plate and the forward swing of the basi-occipital and sphenoid parts of the cranium, so that the cynodont pterygoid girder is telescoped. This can be related to change of posture of the head and neck and of neuromuscular control of a new stance, on legs drawn more nearly into the vertical plane of movement, and in consequence could lead rapidly to the necessity of a better brain (Westoll, 1962).

A similar principle to that just enunciated can be applied to the truly remarkable distortion of the occipital and basal regions of the human skull compared with that typical of a quadrupedal mammal, which goes together with the bipedal habit and the erect gait (Westoll, 1962). It is even possible to rationalize much of the improvement in man's brain on this basis, since the development of the generalized mammalian gait and posture, and even more so that of man, is related to progressive changes to control inherently less stable stances and movements (resulting in necessary improvements in neuromuscular co-ordination), while at the same time more "information" from the outside world must be processed more quickly.

The fossil Hominidae of East Africa. Very diverse opinions have been expressed on this subject as a result of discoveries made since the publication of the second edition of this book. In the field of taxonomy the extremes are reached in one direction by an author (Brace, 1967) who suggests that all the australopithecines should properly be included in the genus *Homo*, and in the other by an article in which their resemblances to the pongids are strongly stressed (Zuckerman, 1970). Most students of the subject agree, however, in dividing the Hominidae into the subfamilies

Australopithecinae and Homininae, each represented by a single genus, *Australopithecus* and *Homo* respectively.

The recent work of Maglio (1972) and Partridge (1973) on the dating of East African *and South African* hominids has made it necessary to revise opinions previously held on the subject discussed here (cf. Tobias, 1973).

The Australopithecinae. The great majority of the australopithecines of East Africa belong to the "robust" form, characterized in particular by large stature, sagittal and nuchal crests on the skull, low cranial vault, and highly developed brow-ridges. The first East African specimen, discovered in 1959 in Bed I of the Olduvai Gorge, Tanzania, was named *Zinjanthropus boisei* by L. S. B. Leakey (Leakey, L. and Howell, 1960), but nowadays it is referred to the genus *Australopithecus*. *A. boisei* is without doubt closely related to *A. (Paranthropus) robustus* of South Africa. Many australopithecines from the East Rudolf region of northern Kenya are very similar to *A. boisei*, but R. E. F. Leakey (1970, 1971) does not assign them definitely to the same species. One of his crania, KNM-ER 406, is a particularly fine specimen (Leakey, R. et al., 1971). It was taken from a deposit at a lower level than a tuff dated 2.61 m.y. BP. It is suggested that those East Rudolf specimens that are more "gracile" (less robust) than the rest may be females of the same species (Leakey, R., 1971).

It is not supposed that either *A. boisei* or its northern representative is on the direct line of human ancestry.

It is uncertain whether the range of the gracile species, *A. africanus*,* extended to East Africa. Part of a mandible discovered at Lothagam Hill, west of Lake Rudolf, has received the provisional name of *Australopithecus* cf. *africanus* (Patterson et al., 1970; Howell, 1972). It has been suggested, however, that it

---

* Throughout the present article the name *A. africanus* is used provisionally for the gracile species found at Sterkfontein and Makapansgat in the Transvaal. The type to which the specific name *africanus* relates is the incomplete and immature skull found long ago at Taung in what was then British Bechuanaland. There is reason, however, to suppose that this specimen should properly be assigned to the species now known as *A. robustus* (cf. Tobias, 1973). If so, the name for the gracile species found at Sterkfontein and Makapansgat will perhaps have to be changed back to *A. transvaalensis* Broom.

should be referred to the genus *Ramapithecus* (Leakey, R., 1973*a*). The site is extremely ancient. It lies below a basalt sill dated 3.71 m.y. by K-Ar analysis, and the age of the specimen itself is put tentatively at 5.0–5.5 m.y. If it is actually an *Australopithecus*, it is the earliest known member of the Hominidae (unless *Ramapithecus* be included in that family). Isolated teeth assigned to *A.* cf. *africanus* have been found in the Omo region of southern Ethiopia. (On the possible existence of *A. africanus* in East Africa, see also p. lx.)

A primitive stone chopper industry had long been known in the rocks of the Olduvai Gorge, and it was natural that when *A. boisei* was discovered, L. S. B. Leakey should conclude that this species was the toolmaker (Leakey, L. and Howell, 1960). This possibility was still entertained in later years (Leakey, L. 1961*b*; Tobias, 1967), but R. E. F. Leakey (1970) considers that *A. boisei* did not make stone tools. There is evidence that *A. africanus* ('*A. prometheus*') used the bones, teeth, and horns of animals as weapons and for other purposes in the Transvaal (Dart, 1949, 1957; Wolberg, 1970); and if this species existed in East Africa, it may have done so there also.

The Homininae. The discovery of a mandible and parts of two parietal bones at Olduvai Gorge on 2 November 1960 has probably caused more interest than any other single event connected with the evolution of the Hominidae in East Africa. The bones were found in the lowest Bed (Bed I) (Leakey, L. 1961*b*). The discovery of many further remains of the same species at higher levels in the gorge made much fuller description possible, and the name *Homo habilis* was formally assigned to them, with "Olduvia Hominid 7" from site *F.L.K.N.N.*I as the type specimen (Leakey, L. et al., 1964). The age is estimated at about 1.8 m.y.

Homo habilis was characterized by L. S. B. Leakey and his colleagues by the following features (among many others). The cranial capacity is greater than that of the Australopithecinae, but less than that of *Homo erectus*. The cranial bones are thin, and indeed the tendency of the skeleton as a whole is towards the gracile condition; for instance, there is no sagittal crest. The greatest width of the brain-case is not near the base of the cranium, but high up, on the parietals. The lambdoid suture, viewed from behind, appears as a *low*, wide arch (as in *H. erectus*). The body of the mandible is rather massive. There is a tendency for the tooth-crowns to be lengthened in the mesio-distal direction and narrowed buccolingually; this is particularly evident in the premolars and lower molars. The clavicle and hand-bones show some resemblances to those of *H. sapiens*; the terminal phalanges of the fingers and thumb are broad. The hallux is stout and adducted.

Robinson (1965, 1966) has argued that the supposed *H. habilis* material from Bed I at Olduvai may represent an "advanced" form of *A. africanus*, and the Bed II specimens an early *Homo erectus*; he has even gone further and suggested that there should be two and only two species of the genus *Homo*, namely *H. transvaalensis* (*A. africanus*) and *H. sapiens* (enlarged to include *H. erectus*). It may be remarked that whenever a species has evolved adastogenetically (i.e. without cladogenesis (Baker, 1974)) and a fairly complete series of intermediate fossils is available, the point at which a new specific name should be given cannot generally be decided on objective grounds. This may account for the fact that some students of the subject regard all specimens usually called *H. habilis* as members of the species *A. africanus*.

Excavations carried out in 1968 and 1969 in the Plio-Pleistocene formations of East Rudolf revealed the presence of hominids possessing characters suggesting that they might be very early representatives of the genus *Homo* (Leakey, R., 1970); and further specimens of a similar kind, found in the same area in the next year, were provisionally referred to that genus without the attachment of a specific name (Leakey, R., 1971). A cranium of particular interest, obtained in the same locality, was discovered in 1972. This cranium, identified as KNM-ER 1470, was briefly mentioned by R. E. F. Leakey in a preliminary paper (1973a), and described more fully, with accompanying photographs, in a later communication (Leakey, R., 1973b). A particularly clear photograph, in oblique frontal view, has been published elsewhere (Calder, 1973). This cranium is chiefly remarkable for its great capacity and the age of the rock in which it lay. "1470" was unfortunately much fragmented, but a careful reconstruction suggests that its capacity may have amounted to 810 ml. Still more remarkable is its extreme age. The horizon at which it lay was below a deposit of tuff that had been dated at $2.61 \pm < 0.26$ m.y. by ^{40}Ar/^{39}Ar spectrum analysis (Fitch and Miller, 1970).

In his 1973b paper R. E. F. Leakey defers reference of this specimen to a particular species, preferring to call it simply "an advanced Plio-Pleistocene hominid". Tobias (1973) accepts it as a member of the genus *Homo* and remarks that ". . . as a provisional judgment, it may even extend our concept of the range, in time and morphology, of *H. habilis*." This, indeed, appears the most likely solution of the taxonomic problem, though certainty is not likely to be reached until similar, more complete specimens are found. The facial skeleton and the base of the cranium are incomplete, and it is unfortunate that the molars and premolar crowns are not preserved. In general, however, one has the impression of an advanced, gracile form. It is clearly distinct from *H. erectus*.

A bone "lissoir" presumably for smoothing skins, was found at the site (*F.L.K.N.N.*I) where the first specimen of *H. habilis* was afterwards unearthed (Leakey, L., 1960), and stone implements of the Oldowan industry were revealed at the same level by later excavations (Leakey, L., 1961a; cf. Leakey, M., 1970). These included choppers, polyhedrons, discoids, scrapers, and gravers, all found at a lower level than a tuff dated 1.75 m.y. The idea naturally suggested itself that the newly discovered hominine might be the makers of the tools previously attributed to *A.* (*Zinjanthropus*) *boisei*. L. S. B. Leakey and his collaborators eventually gave the specific name *habilis* (handy) to indicate their belief that the new species was a maker of stone tools, but they did not rule out the possibility that *A. boisei* might have made some of them (Leaky, L. et al., 1964). The latter opinion is not held today by all students of the subject (see p. lix).

Five stone flakes, confirmed as having been struck off artificially, were found in an East Rudolf deposit dated 2.61 m.y. These flakes seem to set back the earliest period of definitely recognized human artifacts in East Africa from about 1.8 m.y. at Olduvai Gorge to 2.61 m.y. in the East Rudolf area (Leakey, R., 1970; Leakey, M., 1970). R. E. F. Leakey ascribes them to the unspecified *Homo* discovered in this region by members of his expeditions (Leakey, R., 1970).

Skeletal remains attributed to *H. erectus*, though not very typical of this species, have been found from time to time in the rocks of East Africa (Leakey, L., 1966; Day, 1971), and, as has been mentioned, Robinson regards some of the fossils that others call *H. habilis* as early representatives of this species. Attempts have understandably been made to fit the various hominids of East Africa into an evolutionary sequence. *H. habilis* certainly shows resemblances to *A. africanus*, and the following series has been suggested: *A. africanus*→*H. habilis*→*H. erectus*→*H. sapiens* (Tobias, 1973). This view, however, is not accepted by all who have studied the subject. There is support for the hypothesis that *H. habilis* was the direct ancestor of *H. sapiens*, and that *H. erectus* represents a side-branch in hominine evolution (Leakey, L. and Goodall, 1970). There are some crania that seem to link *H. habilis* with *H. sapiens*, others with *H. erectus* (cf. Leakey, M. et al., 1971). It may, indeed, be true that *H. erectus* is not on the direct line from *habilis* to *sapiens*; but if so, it is not easy to account for the resemblances that exist between *H. erectus* and the Australids (Australian aborigines) (Baker, 1974).*

Three incomplete crania attributed to *H. sapiens* have been found in Omo deposits dated not later than middle Upper Pleistocene (Butzer, 1969). The best specimen, Omo II, shows resemblances to the Solo skulls of Java and other early representatives of *sapiens*; Omo I has a more modern appearance and is compared with the Swanscombe remains (Day, 1969). Omo III is too fragmentary to allow useful comparisons to be made.

* The tentative suggestion may be made that the Australids may have evolved from *H. erectus*, while most other races of modern man have *H. habilis* as their direct ancestor. This would not exclude the possibility of some degree of miscegenation in the ancestry of the Australids.

Human leg-bones have recently been found in northern Ethiopia in deposits said to be more than 3 m.y. old (Meredith, 1974). They are being examined at Case Western Reserve University, Ohio. No precise information is available at the time of writing.

Man and pongids: evidence from chromosomes, bearing on their relationship. The introduction of techniques in the late 1950s and early 1960s, which permitted the preparation and examination of chromosomes derived from a wide range of animal species, quickly led to comparisons being made between the karyotypes of man and his primate cousins (Hamerton et al., 1963; Chu and Bender, 1961; Chiarelli, 1962). These established that the chromosome number in the chimpanzee, gorilla, and orang-utan was 48, not 46 as in man, and, on the basis of sizes and shapes, made possible the comparison of individual chromosomes with their supposed human counterparts. The general conclusion was that the chimpanzee karyotype most closely resembled that of man, and that the orang-utan, although possessing the same chromosome number as the chimpanzee and gorilla, had a very different karyotype. Despite the limitations of analysis based entirely on sizes and shapes, attempts have been made to assess how the human 46-chromosome karyotype has been derived from an ancestral line with 48 chromosomes (Chiarelli, 1972). Deductions were made which went far beyond reasonable levels permitted by morphological criteria alone.

The discovery that the human Y-chromosome has an intensely fluorescent region (Zech, 1969) and that characteristic banding patterns produced either by quinacrine fluorescence (Caspersson et al., 1971) or Giemsa staining (Pearson, 1972) permitted the unequivocal identification of individual human chromosomes, now enables the fine karyotypic features of man and the hominoid apes to be re-evaluated on a firmer basis than previously. The present account is concerned with identifying those features of the human karyotype which appear to be unique and those which have apparently remained unchanged over a long period in the evolution of the hominoid apes.

Distribution of intensely fluorescent chromatin. In man the chromatin comprising the distal end of the human Y-chromosome has a unique intensity of fluorescence when stained with quinacrine hydrochloride or mustard. This property is variably shared by restricted paracentric regions in chromosomes 3 and 4 and the acrocentrics (Pearson, 1972).

In the chimpanzee the Y-chromosome does not fluoresce intensely but the satellites and/or the short arms of the acro-centrics do. In a small sample of chimpanzees (*Pan troglodytes*, ten animals studied to date), five to seven acrocentric chromo-somes had intensely fluorescent regions. It seems that the fre-quency of apparently polymorphic regions is stabilized at a higher figure in the chimpanzee than in man (Pearson, 1973). The lack of intensely fluorescent chromatin on the Y-chromo-some is not surprising in view of its small size and the fact that in man, where the Y-chromosome is variably larger, all the differences can be accounted for by changes in the length of the intensely fluorescent portion. In *Pan paniscus*, which was reported to differ from *Pan troglodytes* by having a larger Y and a pair of small acrocentrics replaced by a pair of small metacentrics (Hamerton et al., 1963), the Y does not fluoresce, but the extra metacentrics appear to be formed by the addition of intensely fluorescent short arms to the pair of chimpanzee acrocentrics, which are homologous in banding criteria with the human chromosome 22.

In the lowland gorilla (*Gorilla gorilla*) the Y-chromosome is large and has an intensely fluorescent region similar to that of man. In addition, intensely fluorescent paracentric bands are present on acrocentric chromosomes and also on one pair of submetacentric chromosomes. The latter band in some cases exhibits extreme size differences between homologues. Despite the presence of a large Y-chromosome in the orang-utan (*Pongo pygmaeus*), intensely fluorescent chromatin is not found in that species or elsewhere in the Primates, or indeed among mammals. This indicates that it must have had a rather recent origin, that man, chimpanzee, and gorilla form a natural group, and that they have had a recent common ancestor (Pearson et al., 1971).

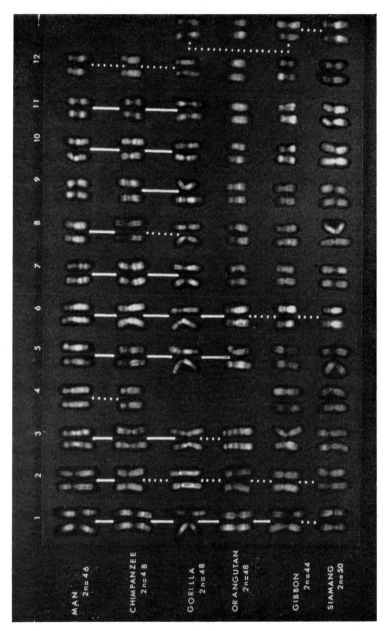

1a. Karyotypes of the Hominoidea. Continuous white lines have been drawn between those chromosomes that show some evidence of banding homology, and dotted white lines between those where the evidence for homology is tentative.

1b. Continuation of 1a.

The nature of the intensely fluorescent chromatin is obscure. Its renaturation kinetics suggest that it consists of repetitive nucleotide sequences, and the failure to extract out a light DNA satellite from human chromatin (Corneo, 1973) corresponding to it makes unlikely the proposal that it is made up of sequences rich in adenine-thymine (Weisblum and Haseth, 1972). Functionally it seems to be associated with the nucleolus in the interphase nucleus (Bobrow et al., 1971), and the suggestion has been made that such heterochromatic chromatin serves the purpose of a genetic buffer by isolating and preventing crossing over between regions known to be ultra-conservative in evolution, such as the 5S RNA cistrons and other parts of the chromosome (Yunis and Yasmineh, 1971).

While the significance of this chromatin is still in the realms of speculation, its unique character as an indicator of the direction of evolution cannot be doubted.

Secondary constrictions. A comparative fluorescent karyotype of the hominoid apes and man is shown in Plates 1a and 1b. White lines have been drawn connecting those chromosomes believed to show some evidence of homology on the basis of banding patterns. The human chromosomes 1, 9, and 16 have an obvious paracentric secondary constriction in their long arms which manifests itself as an extended quinacrine-negative region. Similar regions are lacking in the great apes in chromosomes 1 and 16, and in these animals even the identity of chromosome 9 is in some doubt. It may be concluded that the chromatin comprising the secondary constrictions of Nos. 1 and 16 has either had a unique development in man or has increased in quantity above that found in comparable positions in the karyotypes of the great apes. This is verified by C banding techniques which fail to demonstrate in the ape chromosomes any blocks of repetitive chromatin comparable to those found in the human 1 and 16.

The discovery that the secondary constriction region of the human chromosome 9 had a unique differential staining behaviour with alkaline Giemsa (Bobrow et al., 1971) prompted a search for comparable chromatin in the karyotypes of the great apes.

Surprisingly, there appears to be much more chromatin of this type in the chimpanzee than in man, but it is more widely distributed in the karyotype. This observation has been verified by using the *in situ* hybridization technique (Jones, 1973). It demonstrates that the No. 9 chromatin consists of DNA sequences of human satellite 3 (Corneo, 1973), which appears to be homologous with chimpanzee satellite A. (Jones, 1973). The pattern of variation in the gorilla is astonishing, since large blocks of chromatin appear to be stained. These correspond in part to the short arms of at least one pair of C group chromosomes and probably include the X-chromosome, but this observation, made on only one specimen, requires to be verified on others.

At present, then, it seems that the secondary constriction chromatin of the human Nos 1 and 16 is unique. This has been verified by the inability of human satellite 2 to bind locally to chimpanzee chromosomes with *in situ* hybridization (Jones, personal communication), while it does so to chromosomes 1 and 16 in man (Jones and Corneo, 1971). On the other hand the chromatin comprising the secondary constriction of the human 9 is distributed widely throughout the karyotypes of both the chimpanzee and the gorilla. This observation requires further confirmation, however, in a wider range of specimens of both animals and other members of the Hominoidea.

Change and conservatism in the hominid karyotype. Certain facts can be deduced from the overall pattern of variation present in the karyotypes shown in Plate 1.

(i) The gibbon and siamang have few autosomal karyotype features common to other members of the Hominoidea, and, more surprisingly, to each other. We may conclude that these genera split off, both from each other and from other members of the Hominoidea, at a very early stage in the evolution of the taxon.

(ii) The X-chromosome is identical in all members and this fits well with Ohno's theories on the conservation of the X (Ohno, 1969).

(iii) With minor banding variations, chromosomes 1, 5, 6, 13, 14, 15, 19, 20, 21, 22, and X are found in man, chimpanzee, gorilla, and orang-utan, and chromosomes 3, 7, 8, 10, and 11 in man, chimpanzee, and gorilla.

(iv) In chromosomes 3 and 5 there seems to be a pericentric inversion difference between some species. The fluorescent pattern does not at present permit the postulation of widespread pericentric inversion differences between species as suggested by Turleau and de Grouchy (1972).

(v) Certain human chromosomes appear to have had a more recent origin, since they are present only in man or in man and chimpanzee. These include chromosomes 2, 4, 9, 17, and 18.

(vi) It may be concluded that different chromosomes have evolved at different rates. Some, including 1, 21, and X, have remained unchanged for a major portion of the evolutionary time-scale of the Hominoidea, while others have apparently evolved rapidly. It seems unlikely that differential mutation rates would account for these discrepancies. Retention of favour-

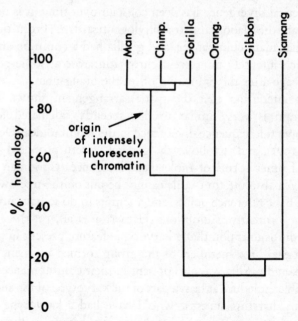

Figure 1. A cladogram showing the genetical relationships of the Hominoidea.

able gene linkages on particular chromosomes is the most probable explanation for the conservation of particular chromosomes.

Phylogenetical considerations. It is possible, by calculating the proportion of homologous chromosome bands present in the karyotypes of pairs of species, to construct a comparison matrix for all species combinations. The values that represent the percentage homology between species will give a crude assessment of the genetical divergence between species. The relationships present in the matrix can be represented in two-dimensional form to give a cladogram of the type shown in figure 1, by use of a simple unweighted cluster analysis technique (Sokal and Sneath, 1963). From the figure it can be seen that man, chimpanzee, and gorilla are closely grouped and that the orang-utan has a much lower percentage homology. The gibbon and the siamang appear to have little homology with each other or with other members of the Hominoidea. On the assumption that the rate of genetical divergence has been constant over time, it is possible to equate the cladogram to a phylogentical tree. From this it is clear that man, chimpanzee, and gorilla had a common ancestor in which intensely fluorescent chromatin arose at some point in the lineage after the branching off of the orang-utan.

It is interesting that the spatial arrangement shown in the cladogram is very similar to that recently calculated for the fibrinopeptide sequence divergence in the Hominoidea (Doolittle et al., 1971), and it follows the general pattern proposed on the basis of other forms of molecular divergence (Goodman et al., 1971). An absolute time-scale cannot be put on the tree owing to lack of basic reference points, and attempts to do so have involved making too many assumptions (Hamerton et al., 1963).

On the assumption that a karyotypic feature present in at least two of the three members of the group formed by man, chimpanzee, and gorilla was also present in their common ancestor, it is possible to deduce at least a part of the karyotype of the ancestor. It seems that this ancestor would have had a karyotype rather similar to that of the chimpanzee, but having a fluorescent Y-chromosome.

In the argument given above it is assumed that the common ancestor had 48 chromosomes and therefore that ancestral man must have lost two chromosomes. It was pointed out some time ago that this might have occurred by centric fusion of the acrocentric chromosomes (Hamerton et al., 1963; Chiarelli, 1962). This has recently been supported by the suggestion that the human chromosome 2 has originated *de novo* from centric fusion of the two non-homologous acrocentrics (Turleau and de Grouchy, 1972). Although the idea seems attractive at first sight, certain difficulties are involved in it. The banding patterns of at least one of the pairs of acrocentrics suggested does not fit the pattern required to constitute a chromosome 2 in man.

One of the dangers involved in comparative cytogenetics is that of oversimplifying the parameters involved. Thus, in the present context, a reasonable approach is to match up all those chromosomes in which banding patterns show homology between species-pairs, and then to see to what extent the remainder can be fitted into the pattern. What is not permissible is to make comparisons and create "homologies" where neither the morphology nor banding criteria give firm support for this course of action.

In the present study several areas of such uncertainty exist, including the precise origin of the 46-chromosome karyotype from an ancestral 48-chromosome line.

The present observations will have to be confirmed in different laboratories by the use of a variety of differential staining techniques and larger samples of the animals concerned. In particular, however, the *in situ* hybridization technique should be used for localizing those DNA sequences that are complementary to various types of human and primate satellite DNA, to establish which bands are homologous. The localization of the human ribosomal cistrons (Henderson et al., 1972) must be repeated in the hominoid apes and use made of the apparent localization of the 9S RNA cistrons to the long arm of chromosome 2 in man (Price et al., 1972), to test whether or not the human 2 has been produced from centric fusion of the two long acrocentric chromosomes present in the great ape karyotypes.

The evolution of hominid social behaviour. The study of hominid social behaviour must necessarily be speculative: therein lies both its fascination and its great weakness. The scientist who will not go beyond the evidence has nothing positive to say about it (though he will probably be critical of the theories of others). Yet the study of human behaviour as an end-product of evolution has not been without its exponents. Darwin (1872) devoted a book to an evolutionary examination of facial expressions and other emotional signals in animals and man. His ideas were not followed up until recently, with studies by Blurton Jones (1967), Grant (1969), Ekman (1969), Eibl-Eibesfeldt (1970), and others. The basic procedure followed by these authors is to isolate a number of postures, gestures, and facial expressions that have communicative significance and to draw conclusions about their social meaning and underlying motivations based on the contexts in which the behavioural acts occur and their effects on other individuals. This method, familiar in ethology since the pioneering work of Huxley (1923) and others on non-human species, is not without its critics when the subject is *human* social behaviour. The relative size of the human cortex, the relatively long period of human infancy and youth, the uniquely human transmission of culture through the intermediary of language—what Huxley (1962) called psychosocial evolution—these and other features of man are widely thought to be sufficient to make human socialization categorically different from that of other species (e.g. Montagu, 1968). Certainly in many respects man is unique and it is probably unwise to explain a human activity in evolutionary terms if a clear explanation can be found in terms of cultural acquisition. Thus playing football is not an evolved behaviour pattern. But immediately the problem arises: is *play* perhaps an evolved behaviour pattern, football being merely a cultural variant? Do we in fact learn the *rules of football*, but not how to play in the general sense?

This brings us on to one line of enquiry: the comparative

approach. In the first place we can look at other human societies. A survey of the literature from social anthropology indicates that there are games in many societies. Children, in particular, play in all parts of the world, usually in ways involving physical activity, whereas adult games are sometimes physical (as in lacrosse, originally a North American Indian game) and sometimes involve mental gymnastics, as in the ancient game of chess, or the even more ancient games with board and beads played in ancient Egypt. The argument here is the argument from universals—that universality of cultural acts implies a "natural" or evolutionary origin for them. This argument has been used by Levi-Strauss (1970) and other writers on human behaviour, e.g. Tiger and Fox (1971). Universality, however, is not in itself an argument for evolutionary origins. As has been stated before now (e.g. Makarius, 1968), circumstances that are universal in human society imply no more than that they are concomitant with such society and perhaps are even a precondition of it.

The comparative approach can however be extended further to include non-human animals. In the case of play, this is found to be a very widespread and perhaps even universal characteristic of mammalian behaviour (see e.g. Jewell, 1966). In most species it is confined to the young. Young predatory mammals such as polecats and cats play in ways resembling prey-catching behaviour. Young ungulates such as lambs and foals play in ways involving rapid locomotion. The play of young primates involves complex gymnastics and much social interaction with peers. If human children are regarded as a mammalian species and studied as such their play patterns involve gymnastics, rough-and-tumble, hitting, crying, and a number of other behaviour patterns as well as a relatively large obsession with objects by comparison with other species (Blurton-Jones, 1967; McGrew, 1971). Few studies of this kind have been made on children in other cultures, but one such study has now indicated that some of the characteristic behaviour patterns seen in English children are also seen in the Kalahari Bushmen (Konner, 1972). There do seem therefore to be species-typical facial expressions and types of interaction in human children, even though it is equally clear from psychological and anthropological studies that childhood is the period during which human beings are learning and being absorbed into the language, concepts, customs, institutions, and attitudes of their particular society or social group (e.g. Whiting, 1953; Mead, 1935; Klineberg, 1951; Malinowski, 1922 and Berger and Luckmann, 1967, for a variety of culture-orientated approaches to the topic of human socialization).

The age of children studied ethologically has been remarkably uniform. Most studies to date have been on pre-school children, aged 3 to 5 years (Blurton-Jones, 1967, 1972; Grant, 1969; Clark Wyon and Richards, 1969; Brannigan and Humphries, 1969). The reason is probably that such children are, in our culture, easy to observe in their nursery schools, and also not yet in a formal educational setting. Other studies have moved into younger age groups (e.g. Richards & Bernal, 1972; Wolff, 1969), starting as soon after birth as practicable. Such work will doubtless help to clarify the extent of species uniformity and of non-cultural individual differences during infancy and the methods by which behavioural development is conditioned by cultural parameters (such as parental attitudes and language during growth.

Other studies have focused on adult social behaviour. Lorenz (1966), Morris (1967, 1971), and others have been concerned with the behaviour of adults and have used an evolutionary framework for their explanations. Lorenz, deriving his ideas largely from the studies of birds and fish conducted by ethologists in Germany and elsewhere from the 1930s onwards, concludes that man has a fundamental aggressive drive, and that in modern circumstances this is extremely dangerous and needs to be discharged in safe ways. Morris does not favour a hierarchy of instincts with aggression at the top but sees human behaviour as a product of many motivations, one or other of which is in the ascendant depending on sex and age and circumstances. Our sexual, maternal, playful, and exploratory behaviours are seen as the outcome of evolutionary processes and are just as powerful as our aggressive feelings. Both these authors have been and continue to be accused of biological positivism, of directing undue attention to biological processes and laying insufficient stress on the extent to which adult human actions are the outcome of the emphases of particular cultures and particular civilizations. Against this criticism it can be held that culture is a part of nature and that therefore biology has to be the framework for explanation of culture and civilization. Fox (1970) has called man the "cultural animal" as have others, e.g. Loffler (1968). But the distinction between the events of the human mind and those of the natural world is not easily overcome. The cognitive side of human development and the extent to which even physiological, let alone behavioural and social, processes can be subject to cognitive control presents particularly difficult problems for ethological analysis.

There is much in Morris's books, however, that is of value. In particular the analysis of face-to-face behaviour, while in many cases unsupported by adequate empirical evidence, calls for further research in cross-cultural ethology. Some such work has now been accomplished by Eibl-Eibesfeldt (1970, 1971). His observations of human facial expressions and gestures in a variety of cultures in Europe, North and South America, Asia, the Pacific, and Australia, including some of the least and some of the most technologically advanced, has thrown up a lot of new information about the extent of cross-cultural similarity in human social behaviour, and his explanation of this is straightforwardly evolutionary.

For instance, Eibl-Eibesfeldt has drawn attention to the "eyebrow flash", used everywhere in greeting a fellow human. Flirting behaviour everywhere involves brief direct glances alternating with gaze-aversion and accompanied by smiling. Submission involves gaze-aversion and lowering of the body relative to the superior person, while dominance is expressed by raising the body, emphasizing the shoulders by padding or other decorations, and staring. Greeting a fellow tends to involve smiling and touching the partner, while intense greeting involves embracing and kissing or rubbing the mouth on the partner's cheek.

These and other behaviour-patterns are seen by Eibl-Eibesfeldt as products of evolution, just like the social signals of any other species. He even makes an effort to explain their form by reference to the process of ritualization—the evolution of a social signal with a specific function from more fundamental body movements. For example, kissing on the mouth is considered to be ritualized mouth-to-mouth feeding, while rubbing the mouth on the partner's cheek is considered to be a derivation from the neonate's "rooting response" i.e. the rhythmic side-to-side head movements of the baby searching for the nipple. Such arguments are, it would seem, impossible to prove but certainly provide suggestions for further study, either along comparative lines between cultures, or between species (there are for example some suggestive similarities between human greetings and those of chimpanzees), or along developmental lines. When, for instance, do we in our culture begin to shake hands with each other? How do we learn this? And what do we learn? It might be interesting to compare, say, England and France, for some French people take what is to an English person an inordinate amount of time whenever they meet and part, shaking hands and/or kissing twice, once on each cheek. In Uganda, shaking hands involves gripping the partner's thumb half way through the ritual. Such variations could be studied with a view to drawing up a taxonomy of greeting rituals and trying to isolate common elements. These common elements would then provide a firmer basis for comparisons with other species and for speculations about evolutionary origins and functions than we have at present.

From the details of face-to-face social behaviour let us now move on to consider the evolution of human society in the wider sense, that is with regard to the form and structure of social groups. This aspect has attracted a great deal of interest and many of the arguments used have been derived from studies of non-human primates. Such arguments have used morphological and ecological comparisons as sources of speculative ideas.

Washburn and DeVore (1961), after a field study of baboons in Kenya, compared baboon social organization and ecology with that of extant hunter-gatherers. They noted among other things that while human groups were smaller than baboon groups, human groups had much larger ranges than those of baboons. One of the biggest contrasts was thus in terms of density. DeVore and others subsequently developed the idea that the more arboreal forest-living primates tended to live in smaller groups and to be less hierarchical and less territorial than terrestrial, savannah-living groups, and also that population density was lower on the savannah than in forest. In terms of human evolution the idea that grew up during the late fifties and early sixties was that as our hominid ancestors left the arboreal way of life in forests for the terrestrial way of life on the savannahs, so their social groups became more baboon-like; i.e. more closed to outsiders, more hierarchically organized, and more territorial. Received opinion at that time concerning hunter-gatherers still extant was that they did live in closed territorial groups (the idea was developed and elaborated by Radcliffe Brown (1931)); so the postulated social system of "early man" (*Homo erectus?*) seemed reasonable enough.

By the mid-1960s, however, a greater number of primate species had been studied behaviourally in the field, including Hamadryas baboons, gorillas, chimpanzees, and patas monkeys. Chimpanzees in particular had a very different kind of social organization from that of baboons, with little or no evidence of ranges or territories and with "open" groups, i.e. groups that had no fixed membership but which were *ad hoc* assemblages of individuals for feeding, travelling, or other social purposes such as grooming and sex. Such at any rate was the picture of social life reported by Reynolds and Reynolds (1965) and by Goodall (1965). Reynolds (1966) developed the idea that the social life of "early" man and indeed of his hominid ancestors (*Australopithecus*) and perhaps even of his pongid ancestors (*Dryopithecus* —*Aegyptopithecus*) need not ever have consisted of baboon-like societies based on closed groups with permanent membership but might always have been of the "open", chimpanzee kind. Social groups based on aggressive dominance and territoriality were not, on this view, early hominid adaptations to life on the savannahs, but were seen as relatively recent developments of a cultural kind resulting from a much later adaptation—the adaptation to a settled way of life resulting from the agricultural revolution a mere 10–15,000 years ago. Recent studies and re-studies of modern hunter-gatherers such as the Australian aborigines, Pygmies, Bushmen and Eskimos have cast serious doubts on Radcliffe-Brown's notion of them as territorial and exclusive, and have shown them to be nomadic, exchanging members and sharing both land and resources in time of need (Lee and Devore, 1968). Thus modern evidence seems to lend support to the "chimpanzee model".

Others, however, e.g. Crook (1967) and Fox (1967) have maintained that ecological considerations should take precedence over the phylogenetic ones advocated by Reynolds. Open groups have been seen as a forest adaptation, not viable on the savannahs, and it has been argued that even with a pongid-hominid phylogeny, savannah adaptedness implies some closure of groups and some development of territoriality or exclusiveness of range use.

One question that has puzzled many students of hominid social evolution is the existence in all known human societies of the "nuclear family". In rather few primates has a one male plus one female plus young unit been reported, only in fact in gibbons, siamangs, night monkeys, *Callicebus* monkeys and marmosets. In these species, families are antagonistic to each other and do not form larger units, so they cannot be considered of the human type. The closest approximation to the human nuclear family found in other primate species is the "one-male-group" as found in Hamadryas baboons (Kummer, 1968) and geladas (Crook, 1968). In these two primate genera, *Papio* and *Theropithecus*, the basic unit of social organization consists of an adult male with one or more adult females and their young. Further, in each case this social unit, though it maintains social coherence in a number of ways, is but a sub-unit of a wider society, thus resembling the human nuclear family. The resemblance has led some anthropologists, e.g. Campbell (1966) and Jolly (1970), to conclude that we should use one or other of these species as models for hominid social evolution. A counter-argument, employed by Fox (1970) among others, is that the male is a subsequent grafting-on, for primarily economic reasons, to the basic biological family of mother and children.

Perhaps we should remember, in conclusion, the political implications of an over-enthusiastic embracing of any of the possible speculative arguments or positions. To make any statements about the biological infra-structure of society, or of human limitations with regard to the possibilities of social organization or reorganization based on supposedly evolved predispositions, is to talk not only a scientific but also a political language, that will be recognized as such by political thinkers and taken up by them even despite denials of political intent by the scientists themselves. This somewhat distasteful fact should perhaps make us careful to emphasize the speculative nature of all arguments in this field.

THE THEORY OF NATURAL SELECTION

I. THE THEORY OF NATURAL SELECTION

Evolution may lay claim to be considered the most central and the most important of the problems of biology. For an attack upon it we need facts and methods from every branch of the science—ecology, genetics, paleontology, geographical distribution, embryology, systematics, comparative anatomy—not to mention reinforcements from other disciplines such as geology, geography, and mathematics.

Biology at the present time is embarking upon a phase of synthesis after a period in which new disciplines were taken up in turn and worked out in comparative isolation. Nowhere is this movement towards unification more likely to be valuable than in this many-sided topic of evolution; and already we are seeing the first-fruits in the re-animation of Darwinism.

By Darwinism I imply that blend of induction and deduction which Darwin was the first to apply to the study of evolution. He was concerned both to establish the fact of evolution and to discover the mechanism by which it operated; and it was precisely because he attacked both aspects of the problem simultaneously, that he was so successful.* On the one hand he amassed enormous quantities of facts from which inductions concerning the evolutionary process could be drawn; and on the other, starting from a few general principles, he deduced the further principle of natural selection.

* This method is not, as has sometimes been asserted, a circular argument. See discussion in Huxley, 1938*b*.

It is as well to remember the strong deductive element in Darwinism. Darwin based his theory of natural selection on three observable facts of nature and two deductions from them. The first fact is the tendency of all organisms to increase in a geometrical ratio. The tendency of all organisms to increase is due to the fact that offspring, in the early stages of their existence, are always more numerous than their parents; this holds good whether reproduction is sexual or asexual, by fission or by budding, by means of seeds, spores, or eggs.* The second fact is that, in spite of this tendency to progressive increase, the numbers of a given species actually remain more or less constant.

The first deduction follows. From these two facts he deduced the struggle for existence. For since more young are produced than can survive, there must be competition for survival. In amplifying his theory, he extended the concept of the struggle for existence to cover reproduction. The struggle is in point of fact for survival of the stock; if its survival is aided by greater fertility, an earlier breeding season, or other reproductive function, these should be included under the same head.

Darwin's third fact of nature was variation: all organisms vary appreciably. And the second and final deduction, which he deduced from the first deduction and the third fact, was Natural Selection. Since there is a struggle for existence among individuals, and since these individuals are not all alike, some of the variations among them will be advantageous in the struggle for survival, others unfavourable. Consequently, a higher proportion of individuals with favourable variations will on the average survive, a higher proportion of those with unfavourable variations will die or fail to reproduce themselves. And since a great deal of variation is transmitted by heredity, these effects of differential survival will in large measure accumulate from generation to generation. Thus natural selection will act constantly to improve and to maintain the adjustment of animals and plants to their surroundings and their way of life.

A few comments on these points in the light of the historical

* The only exception, so far as I am aware, is to be found in certain human populations which fall far short of replacing themselves.

development of biology since Darwin's day will clarify both his statement of the theory and the modern position in regard to it.

His first fact has remained unquestioned. All organisms possess the potentiality of geometric increase. We had better perhaps say *increase of geometric type*, since the ratio of offspring to parents may vary considerably from place to place, and from season to season. In all cases, however, the tendency or potentiality is not merely to a progressive increase, but to a multiplicative and not to an additive increase.

Equally unquestioned is his second fact, the general constancy of numbers of any species. As he himself was careful to point out, the constancy is only approximate. At any one time, there will always be some species that are increasing in their numbers, others that are decreasing. But even when a species is increasing, the actual increase is never as great as the potential: some young will fail to survive. Again, with our much greater knowledge of ecology, we know to-day that many species undergo cyclical and often remarkably regular fluctuations, frequently of very large extent, in their numbers (see p. 110 Elton, 1927). But this fact, although it has certain interesting evolutionary consequences, does not invalidate the general principle.

The first two facts being accepted, the deduction from them also holds: a struggle for existence, or better, a struggle for survival, must occur.

The difficulties of the further bases of the theory are greater, and it is here that the major criticisms have fallen. In the first place, Darwin assumed that the bulk of variations were inheritable. He expressly stated that any which were not inheritable would be irrelevant to the discussion; but he continued in the assumption that those which are inheritable provide an adequate reservoir of potential improvement.*

As Haldane (1938, p. 107) has pointed out, the decreased interest in England in plant-breeding, caused by the repeal of the

---

* *Origin of Species* (6th ed., one vol. ed., p. 9): ". . . any variation which is not inherited is unimportant for us. But the number and diversity of inheritable deviations of structure, both those of slight and those of considerable physiological importance, are endless. No breeder doubts how strong is the tendency to inheritance: that like produces like is his fundamental belief." And so on.

Corn Laws, led Darwin to take most of his evidence from animal-breeders. This was much more obscure than what the plant-breeders in France had obtained: in fact Vilmorin, before Darwin wrote, had fully established the roles of heritable and non-heritable variation in wheat.

Thus in Darwin's time, and still more in England than in France, the subject of inheritance was still very obscure. In any case the basic laws of heredity, or, as we should now say, the principles of genetics, had not yet emerged. In a full formulation of the theory of Natural Selection, we should have to add a further fact and a further deduction. We should begin, as he did, with the fact of variation, and deduce from it and our previous deduction of the struggle for existence that there must be a *differential survival* of different types of offspring in each generation. We should then proceed to the fact of inheritance. Some variation is inherited: and that fraction will be available for transmission to later generations. Thus our final deduction is that the result will be a differential transmission of inherited variation. The term Natural Selection is thus seen to have two rather different meanings. In a broad sense it covers all cases of differential survival: but from the evolutionary point of view it covers only the differential transmission of inheritable variations.

Mendelian analysis has revealed the further fact, unsuspected by Darwin, that recombination of existing genetic units may both produce and modify new inheritable variations. And this, as we shall see later, has important evolutionary consequences.

Although both the principle of differential survival and that of its evolutionary accumulation by Natural Selection were for Darwin essentially deductions, it is important to realize that, if true, they are also facts of nature capable of verification by observation and experiment. And in point of fact differential mortality, differential survival, and differential multiplication among variants of the same species are now known in numerous cases.

The criticism, however, was early made that a great deal of the mortality found in nature appeared to be accidental and non-selective. This would hold for the destruction of the great majority of eggs and larvae of prolific marine animals, or the death of seeds which fell on stony ground or other unsuitable habitats. It remains true that we require many more quantitative experiments on the subject before we can know accurately the extent of non-selective elimination. Even a very large percentage of such elimination, however, in no way invalidates the selection principle from holding for the remaining fraction (see p. 467). The very fact that it is accidental and non-selective ensures that the residue shall be a random sample, and will therefore contain any variation of selective value in the same proportions as the whole population. It is, I think, fair to say that the fact of differential survival of different variations is generally accepted, although it still requires much clarification, especially on the quantitative side. In other words, natural selection within the bounds of the single generation is an active factor in biology.

2. THE NATURE OF VARIATION

The really important criticisms have fallen upon Natural Selection as an evolutionary principle, and have centred round the nature of inheritable variation.

Darwin, though his views on the subject did not remain constant, was always inclined to allow some weight to Lamarckian principles, according to which the effects of use and disuse and of environmental influences were supposed to be in some degree inherited. However, later work has steadily reduced the scope that can be allowed to such agencies: Weismann drew a sharp distinction between soma and germplasm, between the individual body which was not concerned in reproduction, and the hereditary constitution contained in the germ-cells, which alone was transmitted in heredity. Purely somatic effects, according to him, could not be passed on: the sole inheritable variations were variations in the hereditary constitution.

Although the distinction between soma and germplasm is not always so sharp as Weismann supposed, and although the principle of Baldwin and Lloyd Morgan, usually called Organic Selection, shows how Lamarckism may be simulated by the later replacement of adaptive modifications by adaptive mutations, Weismann's conceptions resulted in a great clarification of the position. It is owing to him that we to-day classify variations into two fundamentally distinct categories—modifications and mutations (together with new arrangements of mutations, or recombinations; see below, p. 20). Modifications are produced by alterations in the environment (including modifications of the internal environment such as are brought about by use and disuse), mutations by alterations in the substance of the hereditary constitution. The distinction may be put in a rather different but perhaps more illuminating way. Variation is a study of the differences between organisms. On analysis, these differences may turn out to be due to differences in environment (as with an etiolated plant growing in a cellar as against a green one in light; or a sun-tanned sailor as against a pale slum-dweller); or they may turn out to be due to differences in hereditary constitution (as between an albino and a green seedling in the same plot, or a negro and a white man in the same city); or of course to a simultaneous difference both in environment and in constitution (as with the difference in stature between an undernourished pigmy and a well-nourished negro). Furthermore, only the second are inherited. We speak of them as genetic differences: at their first origin they appear to be due to mutations in the hereditary constitution. The former we call modifications, and are not inheritable.

The important fact is that only experiment can decide between the two. Both in nature and in the laboratory, one of two indistinguishable variants may turn out to be due to environment, the other to genetic peculiarity. A particular shade of human complexion may be due to genetic constitution making for fair complexion plus considerable exposure to the sun, or to a genetically dark complexion plus very little tanning: and similarly for stature, intelligence, and many other characters.

This leads to a further important conclusion: characters as such are not and cannot be inherited. For a character is always the joint product of a particular genetic composition and a particular set of environmental circumstances. Some characters are much more stable in regard to the normal range of environmental variation than are others—for instance, human eye-colour or hair-form as against skin-colour or weight. But these too are in principle similar. Alter the environment of the embryo sufficiently, and eyeless monsters with markedly changed brain-development are produced.

In the early days of Mendelian research, phrases such as "in fowls, the character rose-comb is inherited as a Mendelian dominant" were current. So long as such phrases are recognized as mere convenient shorthand, they are harmless; but when they are taken to imply the actual genetic transmission of the characters, they are wholly incorrect.

Even as shorthand, they may mislead. To say that rose-comb is inherited as a dominant, even if we know that we mean the genetic factor for rose-comb, is likely to lead to what I may call the one-to-one or billiard-ball view of genetics. There are assumed to be a large number of characters in the organism, each one represented in a more or less invariable way by a particular factor or gene, or a combination of a few factors. This crude particulate view is a mere restatement of the preformation theory of development: granted the rose-comb factor, the rose-comb character, nice and clear-cut, will always appear. The rose-comb factor, it is true, is not regarded as a sub-microscopic replica of the actual rose-comb, but is taken to represent it by some form of unanalysed but inevitable correspondence. .

The fallacy in this view is again revealed by the use of the difference method. In asserting that rose-comb is a dominant character, we are merely stating in a too abbreviated form the results of experiments to determine what constitutes the difference between fowls with rose-combs and fowls with single combs. In reality, what is inherited as a Mendelian dominant is the gene in the rose-combed stock which differentiates it from the single-combed stock: we have no right to assert anything more as a result of our experiments than the existence of such a differential factor.

Actually, every character is dependent on a very large number (possibly all) of the genes in the hereditary constitution: but some of these genes exert marked differential effects upon the visible appearance. Both rose- and single-comb fowls contain all the genes needed to build up a full-sized comb: but "rose" genes build it up according to one growth-pattern, "single" genes according to another.

This principle is of great importance. For instance, up till very recently the chief data in human genetics have been pedigrees of abnormalities or diseases collected by medical men. And in collecting these data, medical men have usually been obsessed with the implications of the ideas of "character-inheritance". When the character has not appeared in orthodox and classical Mendelian fashion they have tended to dismiss it with some such phrase as "inheritance irregular", whereas further analysis might have shown a perfectly normal *inheritance* of the gene concerned, but an irregular *expression* of the character, dependent on the other genes with which it was associated and upon differences in environment (see discussion in Hogben, 1933).

This leads on to a further and very vital fact, namely, the existence of a type of genetic process undreamt of until the Mendelian epoch. In Darwin's day biological inheritance meant the reappearance of similar characters in offspring and parent, and implied the physical transmission of some material basis for the characters. What would Darwin or any nineteenth-century biologist say to facts such as the following, which now form part of any elementary course in genetics? A black and an albino mouse are mated. All their offspring are grey, like wild mice: but in the second generation greys, blacks, and albinos appear in the ratio 9 : 3 : 4. Or again, fowls with rose-comb and pea-comb mated together produce nothing but so-called walnut combs: but in the next generation, in addition to walnut, rose, and pea, some single combs are produced.

To the biologist of the Darwinian period the production of the grey mice would have been not inheritance, but "reversion" to the wild type, and the reappearance of the blacks and whites in the next generation would have been "atavism" or "skipping a generation". Similarly the appearance of single combs in the fowl cross would have been described as reversion, while the production of walnut combs would have been regarded as some form of "sport."

In reality, the results are in both cases immediately explicable on the assumption of two pairs of genes, each transmitted from parent to offspring by the same fundamental genetic mechanism. The "reversions", "atavisms", and "sports" are all due to new combinations of old genes. Thus, although all the facts are in one sense phenomena of inheritance, it is legitimate and in some ways desirable to distinguish those in which the same characters reappear generation after generation from those in which new characters are generated. As Haldane has put it, modern genetics deals not only with inheritance, but with recombination.

Thus the raw material available for evolution by natural selection falls into two categories—mutation and recombination. Mutation is the only begetter of intrinsic change in the separate units of the hereditary constitution: it alters the nature of genes.*

Recombination, on the other hand, though it may produce quite new combinations with quite new effects on characters, only juggles with existing genes. It is, however, almost as important for evolution. It cannot occur without sexual reproduction: and its importance in providing the possibility of speedily combining several favourable mutations doubtless accounts for the all-but-universal presence of the sexual process in the life-cycle or organisms. We shall in later chapters see its importance for adjusting mutations to the needs of the organism.

Darwinism to-day thus still contains an element of deduction, and is none the worse for that as a scientific theory. But the facts available in relation to it are both more precise and more numerous, with the result that we are able to check our deductions and to make quantitative prophecies with much greater fullness than was possible to Darwin. This has been especially notable as regards the mathematical treatment of the problem, which we owe to R. A. Fisher, J. B. S. Haldane, Sewall Wright, and others. We can now take mutation-rates and degrees of advantage of one

---

* Strictly speaking, this applies only to gene-mutation. Chromosome-mutation, whether it adds or subtracts chromosome-sets, whole chromosomes, or parts of chromosomes, or inverts sections of chromosomes, merely provides new quantitative or positional combinations of old genes. However, chromosome-mutation may alter the *effects* of genes. Thus we are covered if we say that mutation alters either the qualitative nature or the effective action (including the mode of transmission) of the hereditary constitution.

mutation or combination over another, which are within the limits actually found in genetic experiments, and can calculate the rates of evolution which will then occur.

If mutation had a rate that was very high it would neutralize or over-ride selective effects: if one that was very low, it would not provide sufficient raw material for change; if it were not more or less at random in many directions, evolution would run in orthogenetic grooves. But mutation being in point of fact chiefly at random, and the mutation-rate being always moderately low, we can deduce that the struggle for existence will be effective in producing differential survival and evolutionary change.

3. THE ECLIPSE OF DARWINISM

The death of Darwinism has been proclaimed not only from the pulpit, but from the biological laboratory; but, as in the case of Mark Twain, the reports seem to have been greatly exaggerated, since to-day Darwinism is very much alive.

The reaction against Darwinism set in during the nineties of last century. The younger zoologists of that time were discontented with the trends of their science. The major school still seemed to think that the sole aim of zoology was to elucidate the relationship of the larger groups. Had not Kovalevsky demonstrated the vertebrate affinities of the sea-squirts, and did not comparative embryology prove the common ancestry of groups so unlike as worms and molluscs? Intoxicated with such earlier successes of evolutionary phylogeny, they proceeded (like some Forestry Commission of science) to plant wildernesses of family trees over the beauty-spots of biology.

A related school, a little less prone to speculation, concentrated on the pursuit of comparative morphology within groups. This provides one of the most admirable of intellectual trainings for the student, and has yielded extremely important results for science. But if pursued too exclusively for its own sake, it leads, as Radl has pithily put it in his *History of Biological Theories*, to spending one's time comparing one thing with another without ever troubling about what either of them really is. In other words, zoology, becoming morphological, suffered divorce from physiology. And finally Darwinism itself grew more and more theoretical. The paper demonstration that such and such a character was or might be adaptive was regarded by many writers as sufficient proof that it must owe its origin to Natural Selection. Evolutionary studies became more and more merely case-books of real or supposed adaptations. Late nineteenth-century Darwinism came to resemble the early nineteenth-century school of Natural Theology. Paley *redivivus*, one might say, but philosophically upside down, with Natural Selection instead of a Divine Artificer as the *Deus ex machina*. There was little contact of evolutionary speculation with the concrete facts of cytology and heredity, or with actual experimentation.

A major symptom of revolt was the publication of William Bateson's *Materials for the Study of Variation* in 1894. Bateson had done valuable work on the embryology of *Balanoglossus*; but his sceptical and concrete mind found it distasteful to spend itself on speculations on the ancestry of the vertebrates, which was then regarded as the outstanding topic of evolution, and he turned to a task which, however different it might seem, he rightly regarded as piercing nearer to the heart of the evolutionary problems. Deliberately he gathered evidence of variation which was discontinuous, as opposed to the continuous variation postulated by Darwin and Weismann. The resultant volume of material, though its gathering might fairly be called biassed, was impressive in quantity and range, and deeply impressed the more active spirits in biology. It was the first symptom of what we may call the period of mutation theory, which postulated that large mutations, and not small "continuous variations", were the raw material of evolution, and actually determined most of its course, selection being relegated to a wholly subordinate position.

This was first formally promulgated by de Vries (1901, 1905) as a result of his work with the evening primroses, *Oenothera*, and was later adopted by various other workers, notably T. H. Morgan, in his first genetical phase. The views of the early twentieth-century geneticists, moreover, were coloured by the rediscovery of Mendel's laws by Correns, de Vries, and Tscher-mak in the spring of 1900, and the rapid generalization of them, notably by Bateson.

Naturally, the early Mendelians worked with clear-cut differences of large extent. As it became clearer that mendelian inheritance was universal, it was natural to suppose all mendelian factors produced large effects, that therefore mutation was sharp and discontinuous, and that the continuous variation which is obviously widespread in nature is not heritable.

Bateson did not hesitate to draw the most devastating conclusions from his reading of the mendelian facts. In his Presidential Address to the British Association in 1914, assuming first that change in the germplasm is always by large mutation and secondly that all mutation is loss, from a dominant something to a recessive nothing, he concluded that the whole of evolution is merely an unpacking. The hypothetical ancestral amoeba contained—actually and not just potentially—the entire complex of life's hereditary factors. The jettisoning of different portions of this complex released the potentialities of this, that, and the other group and form of life. Selection and adaptation were relegated to an unconsidered background.

Meanwhile the true-blue Darwinian stream, leaving Weismannism behind, had reached its biometric phase. Tracing its origin to Galton, biometry blossomed under the guidance of Karl Pearson and Weldon. Unfortunately this, the first thorough application of mathematics to evolution, though productive of many important results and leading to still more important advances in method, was for a considerable time rendered sterile by its refusal to acknowledge the genetic facts discovered by the Mendelians. Both sides, indeed, were to blame. The biometricians stuck to hypothetical modes of inheritance and genetic variation on which to exercise their mathematical skill; the Mendelians refused to acknowledge that continuous variation could be genetic, or at any rate dependent on genes, or that a mathematical theory of selection could be of any real service to the evolutionary biologist.

It was in this period, immediately prior to the war, that the legend of the death of Darwinism acquired currency. The facts of mendelism appeared to contradict the facts of paleontology, the theories of the mutationists would not square with the Weismannian views of adaptation, the discoveries of experimental embryology seemed to contradict the classical recapitulatory theories of development. Zoologists who clung to Darwinian views were looked down on by the devotees of the newer disciplines, whether cytology or genetics, *Entwicklungsmechanik* or comparative physiology, as old-fashioned theorizers; and the theological and philosophical antipathy to Darwin's great mechanistic generalization could once more raise its head without fearing too violent a knock.

But the old-fashioned selectionists were guided by a sound instinct. The opposing factions became reconciled as the younger branches of biology achieved a synthesis with each other and with the classical disciplines: and the reconciliation converged upon a Darwinian centre.

It speedily became apparent that mendelism applied to the heredity of all many-celled and many single-celled organisms, both animals and plants. The mendelian laws received a simple and general interpretation: they were due in the first place to inheritance being particulate, and in the second place to the particles being borne on the chromosomes, whose behaviour could be observed under the microscope Many apparent exceptions to mendelian rules turned out to be due to aberrations of chromosome-behaviour. Segregation and recombination, the fundamental mendelian facts, are all but universal, being co-extensive with sexual reproduction; and mutation, the further corollary of the particulate theory of heredity, was found to occur even more widely, in somatic tissues and in parthenogenetic and sexually-reproducing strains as well as in the germtrack of bisexual species. Blending inheritance as originally conceived was shown not to occur, and cytoplasmic inheritance to play an extremely subsidiary role.

The Mendelians also found that mutations could be of any extent, and accordingly that apparently continuous as well as obviously discontinuous variation had to be taken into account in discussing heredity and evolution. The mathematicians found that biometric methods could be applied to neo-mendelian postulates, and then become doubly fruitful. Cytology became intimately linked with genetics. Experimental embryology and the study of growth illuminated heredity, recapitulation, and paleontology. Ecology and systematics provided new data and new methods of approach to the evolutionary problem. Selection, both in nature and in the laboratory, was studied quantitatively and experimentally. Mathematical analysis showed that only particulate inheritance would permit evolutionary change: blending inheritance, as postulated by Darwin, was shown by R. A. Fisher (1930a) to demand mutation-rates enormously higher than those actually found to occur. Thus, though it may still be true in a formal sense that, as such an eminent geneticist as Miss E. R. Saunders said at the British Association meeting in 1920, "Mendelism is a theory of heredity: it is not a theory of evolution", yet the assertion is purely formal. Mendelism is now seen as an essential part of the theory of evolution. Mendelian analysis does not merely explain the distributive hereditary mechanism: it also, together with selection, explains the progressive mechanism of evolution.

Biology in the last twenty years, after a period in which new disciplines were taken up in turn and worked out in comparative isolation, has become a more unified science. It has embarked upon a period of synthesis, until to-day it no longer presents the spectacle of a number of semi-independent and largely contradictory sub-sciences, but is coming to rival the unity of older sciences like physics, in which advance in any one branch leads almost at once to advance in all other fields, and theory and experiment march hand-in-hand. As one chief result, there has been a rebirth of Darwinism. The historical facts concerning this trend are summarized by Shull in a recent book (1936). It is noteworthy that T. H. Morgan, after having been one of the most extreme critics of selectionist doctrine, has recently, as a result of modern work in genetics (to which he has himself so largely contributed), again become an upholder of the Darwinian point of view (T. H. Morgan, 1925, and later writings); while his younger colleagues, notably Muller and Sturtevant, are strongly selectionist in their evolutionary views.

The Darwinism thus reborn is a modified Darwinism, since it must operate with facts unknown to Darwin; but it is still Darwinism in the sense that it aims at giving a naturalistic interpretation of evolution, and that its upholders, while constantly striving for more facts and more experimental results, do not, like some cautious spirits, reject the method of deduction.

Hogben (1931, p. 145 seq.) disagrees with this conclusion. He accepts the findings of neo-Mendelism and the mathematical conclusions to be drawn from them; but, to use his own words, "the essential difference between the theory of natural selection expounded by such contemporary writers as J. B. S. Haldane, Sewall Wright, and R. A. Fisher, as contrasted with that of Darwin, resides in the fact that Darwin interpreted the process of artificial selection in terms of a theory of 'blending inheritance' universally accepted by his own generation, whereas the modern view is based on the Theory of Particulate Inheritance. The consequences of the two views are very different. According to the Darwinian doctrine, evolution is an essentially continuous process, and selection is essentially creative in the sense that no change would occur if selection were removed. According to the modern doctrine, evolution is discontinuous. The differentiation of varieties or species may suffer periods of stagnation. Selection is a destructive agency."

Accordingly, Hogben would entirely repudiate the title of Darwinism for the modern outlook, and would prefer to see the term Natural Selection replaced by another to mark the new connotations it has acquired, although on this latter point he is prepared to admit the convenience of retention.

These objections, coming from a biologist of Hogben's calibre, must carry weight. On the other hand we shall see reason in later chapters for finding them ungrounded. In the first place, evolution, as revealed in fossil trends, is "an essentially continuous process". The building-blocks of evolution, in the shape of mutations, are, to be sure, discrete quanta of change. But firstly, the majority of them (and the very great majority of those which survive to become incorporated in the genetic constitution of living things) appear to be of small extent; secondly, the effect of a given mutation will be different according to the combinations of modifying genes present (pp. 68 seq.); and thirdly, its effect may be masked or modified by environmental modification. The net result will be that, for all practical purposes, most of the variability of a species at any given moment will be continuous, however accurate are the measurements made; and that most evolutionary change will be gradual, to be detected by a progressive shifting of a mean value from generation to generation.

In the second place, the statement that selection is a destructive agency is not true, if it is meant to imply that it is *merely* destructive. It is also directive, and because it is directive, it has a share in evolutionary creation. Neither mutation nor selection alone is creative of anything important in evolution; but the two in conjunction are creative (p. 475).

Hogben is perfectly right in stressing the fact of the important differences in content and implication between the Darwinism of Darwin or Weismann and that of Fisher or Haldane. We may, however, reflect that the term *atom* is still in current use and the atomic theory not yet rejected by physicists, in spite of the supposedly indivisible units having been divided. This is because modern physicists still find that the particles called atoms by their predecessors do play an important role, even if they are compound and do occasionally lose or gain particles and even change their nature. If this is so, biologists may with a good heart continue to be Darwinians and to employ the term Natural Selection, even if Darwin knew nothing of mendelizing mutations, and if selection is by itself incapable of changing the constitution of a species or a line.*

It is with this reborn Darwinism, this mutated phoenix risen from the ashes of the pyre kindled by men so unlike as Bateson and Bergson, that I propose to deal in succeeding chapters.

---

* It should be added that Hogben was in 1931 concerned to stress mutation-pressure as an agency of change—than a new and not generally accepted conception. Since then he has allowed much more weight to the joint role of selection and mutation in producing adaptive change (see Hogben 1940).

CHAPTER 2

THE MULTIFORMITY OF EVOLUTION

I. THE HETEROGENEITY OF EVOLUTION

With the reorientation made possible by modern genetics, evolution is seen to be a joint product of mutation, recombination, and selection. Contrary to the views of the Weismann school, selection alone has been shown to be incapable of extending the upper limit of variation, and therefore incapable by itself of causing evolutionary change. Contrary to the views of the more extreme mutationists and the believers in orthogenesis, mutation alone has been shown to be incapable of producing directional change, or of overriding selective effects. The two processes are complementary. Their interplay is as indispensable to evolution as is that of hydrogen and oxygen to water. And, as we shall see in detail later, the third process, of recombination, is almost equally essential, not only for conferring plasticity on the species and allowing for a sufficient speed of evolutionary change, but also for adjusting the effects of mutations to the needs of the organism.

In this book I shall endeavour to analyse some of the main types of evolutionary change in terms of this dual responsibility, and then to disentangle the various main roles (for they are numerous and diverse) of selection. This analysis will lead finally to a discussion of the problem of evolutionary progress—whether any such process exists, whether it is explicable on selectionist terms, and whether there is any prospect of its future continuance.

In the first place, then, evolution is an alarmingly large and varied subject. The students of a particular aspect of evolution are prone to think that their conclusions are generally applicable, whereas in most cases they are not. The paleontologists unearth long evolutionary series and claim that evolution is always gradual and always along a straight course, which may be either adaptive or non-adaptive. However, as Haldane (1932a) has pointed out, their conclusions apply almost entirely to animals, and to animals which are mostly of marine type and all belonging to abundant species. In some land plants, on the contrary, we now have evidence of a wholly different method of evolution, namely, the discontinuous and abrupt formation of new species. And in rare forms, as Sewall Wright (1932) and Haldane (1932a) especially have stressed, the course of evolution, or at least of specific and generic evolution, will not run in the same way as in abundant and dominant types (see also p. 387).

Meanwhile the comparative physiologist and a certain type of naturalist will inevitably be struck by the adaptive characters of animals and plants: organisms are seen by them as bundles of adaptations, the problem of evolution becomes synonymous with the problem of the origin of adaptation, and natural selection is erected into an all-powerful and all-pervading agency. This was the orthodox post-Darwinian view up to the end of the nineteenth century, as represented by Darwin himself in such books as the *Fertilization of Orchids*, by Wallace in his *Darwinism*, by Weismann in *The Evolution Theory*, by Poulton in *The Colours of Animals*.

The systematist, on the other hand, and often the ecologically minded naturalist, struck by the apparent uselessness of the characters on which they determine species and genera, are apt to overlook other characters which are adaptive but happen to be of no use in systematics, and to neglect the broad and obviously adaptive characters seen in larger taxonomic groups and in paleontological trends. The result, as recorded for instance in Robson and Richards' book, *The Variation of Animals in Nature* (1936), and Robson's work on *The Species Problem* (1928), is an undue belittling of the role of selection in evolution, and an over-emphasis on the origin of species as the key problem of evolutionary biology.

The paleontologist, confronted with his continuous and long-range trends, is prone to misunderstand the implications of a discontinuous theory of change such as mutation, and to invoke orthogenesis or lamarckism as explanatory agencies. Since there are more rare than abundant species, the biogeographer will have to discount the fact that he is dealing mainly with processes irrelevant to the major trends of evolution regarded as a long-range process; while the ecologist and the pure physiologist, appalled by the complexity of the phenomena which they study, are apt to give up the quest for any evolutionary explanation at all.

2. THE PALEONTOLOGICAL DATA

We may perhaps take up these points a little more in detail. There is first the point of the unrepresentative nature of the material upon which the paleontologist relies. The chief groups which have yielded detailed results of past evolutionary change by means of fossils are the molluscs, the echinoderms, the brachiopods, the graptolites, and the trilobites. Among the vertebrates we have, of course, numerous important fossils which reveal the past history of the phylum; but for the most part they serve merely to show the general course of evolution and the broad relationship of the various groups: this is so with the famous *Archaeopteryx*, with the extinct orders of reptiles, with the reptilian forms ancestral to mammals, with the ostracoderms, whose primitive structure has been revealed by the work of Stensiö. Only in the placental mammals, however, and notably in the horses, the titanotheres, the elephants, and one or two other lines, do we meet with an abundance of fossil forms sufficient to give us what we may call (remembering the words of the psalmist, "a thousand years in thy sight are but as yesterday") the day-to-day progress of evolutionary change. And even here the abundance and the consequent detailed accuracy of the record are less than in the other groups mentioned.

All these others are aquatic and almost exclusively marine. The graptolites and trilobites endured only for a short period of the geological record. So, among the molluscs, did the ammonites and (so far as abundance and fossil preservation are concerned) the nautiloids. The lamellibranchs, on the other hand, and the sea-urchins and starfish among the echinoderms have remained abundant up to the present. This, however, does not appear to matter. In all cases where fossils are abundantly preserved over a considerable period, we find the same phenomena. The change of form is very gradual. It is often along similar lines in related types. And in general it appears that different characters vary independently: at any one horizon, for instance, the fossil sea-urchins of the genus *Micraster* include a few specimens showing characters reminiscent of the average of the horizon before, a few with the same characters anticipating the average of the horizon next deposited; but in general the average development of the various diagnostic characters will be nearly constant, though there is no rigid correlation and many specimens will show some characters in advance of and others behind the mean for the particular time (Hawkins, 1936). A similar state of affairs has been found in the history of the horses (Matthew, 1926).

As showing the restricted nature of the material on which the paleontologist relies, it may be mentioned that Professor Hawkins (1936), in his presidential address to the Geology Section of the British Association at Blackpool, drew very far-reaching conclusions as to the method and course of evolution on the basis of echinoderms, molluscs, and brachiopods alone. No trends in vertebrates and no trends in land animals were discussed by him.

3. EVOLUTION IN RARE AND ABUNDANT SPECIES

It is furthermore obvious that only abundant and widespread species will be of any service in tracing the detailed course of past evolution. Now there are various peculiarities distinguishing rare from abundant species. In the first place, abundant species will have a larger reservoir of inheritable variation, both actual and potential. This can be deduced on theoretical lines from what we know of mutation (Wright, 1932). In addition, it has been demonstrated as a fact in several cases. Darwin, on the basis of qualitative inspection, asserted that it was so. And R. A. Fisher, using all the apparatus of biometric and probability technique, has now demonstrated that it holds for such diverse characters as the colour of moths' wings and the dimensions of birds' eggs (Fisher and Ford, 1928; Fisher, 1937a). This will obviously confer upon abundant species a greater evolutionary plasticity, a higher potency of adaptive change.

Rare species, on the other hand, will not only possess less evolutionary adaptability, but will, as Sewall Wright (1932) has emphasized, be prone to have useless or even deleterious mutations become accidentally fixed in their constitution. When numbers are increasing after being abnormally low, a chance mutation may spread through a considerable proportion of the population (p. 61). Further, genes which are neutral or even deleterious have a chance of becoming incorporated in a small local population-unit. Such "accidental" divergence may continue to an indefinite extent. Furthermore, rare species will tend to become subdivided into discontinuous groups, and these, once isolated, will have a greater likelihood of differentiating into separate species, partly by the accidental accumulation of mutations, as we have just seen, and partly because selection can work on them unhampered by immigration from other areas inhabited by slightly different types. Haldane (1932a) draws attention to the fact that the rare fern *Nephrodium spinulosum* has no fewer than four well-marked local subspecies (or even species, according to some authorities) in isolated areas of Britain alone.

Many abundant species, on the other hand, will differentiate into subspecies in different parts of a continuous range; these will differ adaptively in accordance with the environment, but there will not be complete isolation between them (except as the result of climatic or geological change producing a barrier) and migration will keep distributing genes from one subspecies to its neighbours (Chap. 5, § 3)

When this is so, Sewall Wright (1931) points out that the

variability of a species will be at a maximum; for the agency of selection will have added partial local differentiation to the intrinsic variability of a large population, and migration will be ensuring new recombinations of the genes determining sub-specific characters.

In abundant plant species, the chief tendency appears to be to differentiate into numerous ecotypes, many of which will co-exist in the same geographical region (pp. 275 seq.). These too will be able to exchange genes, and thus to promote variability.

Furthermore, as Haldane (1932a) has stressed, competition and therefore selection in rare species will be more between the species as a whole and its environment, or between it and other related species, while in abundant species they will be more between individual members of the same species. And this *intra-specific* selection has various peculiar results in evolution, many of them in the long run being harmful to the stock (p. 478).

We must also mention the interesting work of Willis, summarized in his book, *Age and Area* (1922). In the first place, he points out that rare species are more numerous than abundant species. For instance, out of 809 species of flowering plants in Ceylon, 65 per cent are rare, including 37 per cent "extremely rare" (see p. 204). His figures apply chiefly to flowering plants, but even a casual acquaintance with systematics makes it clear that a situation of this type is general, and that the systematist and biogeographer are dealing with many more scarce than abundant species.

The discontinuous formation, *per saltum*, of new species in plants I shall treat of later in detail, in connection with the species problem in general. Suffice it to say here that the phenomenon is known in several groups of flowering plants, and may well prove to be considerably commoner than is now generally supposed, save by a few cytologists and geneticists.

4. ADAPTATIONS AND THEIR INTERPRETATION

On the subject of adaptation, also, I shall have more to say in a later chapter. But it is clear that, whatever value we allow to the deductive method and its implications as regards adaptation, it must not be allowed too free a rein. Speculation must be constantly checked by observation and experiment.

A striking example of this comes from recent work on sexual selection (see summaries in Huxley, 1938*a*, 1938*b*, 1938*c*). Under the impetus of Darwin's great work, *The Descent of Man*, what may be called the orthodox Darwinian view came to be generally held, namely, that all bright colours of higher animals which are restricted to the male sex, are, in the absence of definite evidence to the contrary, to be interpreted as owing their origin to sexual selection; the same was assumed for the songs of birds. When these bright colours were known to be conspicuously shown off in some special display attitude, the conclusion was regarded as incontrovertible; but even when this was not the case, as with most of the bright colours of male ducks, the presumption was regarded as sound. It was rather the opposite of the presumption of British law that a prisoner is to be regarded as innocent until definite proof of guilt is adduced. In reaction against this attitude, however, many biologists adopted an equally uncritical attitude of scepticism, and many even proclaimed that sexual selection had been "disproved" and that no masculine colour or other characters had any function in stimulating the female.

However, while this scepticism is wholly unjustified in face of the vast body of positive evidence, notably from field study, recent work, both observational and experimental, largely on birds but also on lizards (see Noble and Bradley, 1933), has shown that the Darwinian presumption in its sweeping form was erroneous. Only when the bright colour or other performance is solely or mainly used in display before the female can it hold. If so, however, the presumption is very strong that its origin is to be sought in sexual selection in the modern sense, which differs considerably from that in which it was originally employed by Darwin, and the burden of proof is on the other side.

Song, on the other hand, as a result of detailed observation, is now regarded as having its prime function as a "distance threat" to rival males and its secondary function as an advertisement, so long as the singer is unmated, to unmated females. The same is true of bright colours in the males of territorial species. Similarly bright colours have in many cases been proved to have the function of simple threat and not that of display. The most striking case is perhaps that of our common robin (*Erithacus rubecula*). It was known that the bright red colour of the breast is actually displayed very prominently in a special stiff erect pose during the breeding season, and it had been generally assumed that this was a display of the male towards the female. The observations of Burkitt (1924–5), however, and of Lack (1939), and experiments with stuffed birds have shown that this pose is one of threat and is used by members of either sex, but exclusively towards territorial rivals. It is noteworthy that in the robin, both sexes hold territories in autumn and early winter, so that the marked development of threat action and threat colouration in the female as well as the male has an obvious adaptive significance.

Observation again has shown that one and the same colour or structure may be employed in different ways as a threat to rivals or as a display to potential mates—this holds for blackcock and ruffs, for instance; while in other cases, as in the train of the peacock, the display function appears to be the only one. Thus deductive speculation, though legitimate in its place, must be closely checked.

Precisely similar considerations apply to all other cases of adaptation. For instance, elementary observation shows a correlation between the prevailing colour and pattern of animals and that of their environment. This provides a *prima facie* case for the relation being an adaptive one. But this deduction is a first approximation only. The next step is to make detailed ecological observations on particular cases; to see whether alternative explanations may not be preferable (such as the view that there is a direct effect of the colour of the environment on the organism, or an indirect effect via the prevailing climate; see Dice and Blossom, 1937, for a case where the climatic interpretation can be rejected); and, where possible, to check the adaptive value by experiment. We shall then be able to reject a certain number of suggestions (such as that of Thayer (1909) that the pink colour of flamingos enables them to escape detection against the sunset sky), and to retain a certain body of firmly established fact and a considerable residuum of high probability.

We need not be deterred by arguments of a negative nature, such as that which maintains that a particular arrangement cannot be adaptive, because related species do not show it; for these can be shown to rest on a lack of biological logic (p. 466).

On the basis of such a step-by-step analysis, we shall obtain strong support for the view that adaptation is all-pervading and of major importance, even if it does not apply to numerous details of the structure and function of organisms. And this will enable us to discount non-adaptive theories of evolution, such as orthogenesis, as being based either on incomplete data or on deliberate rejection of the adaptational point of view.

5. ADAPTATION AND SELECTION

Finally, another and even more important point of method must be mentioned. It concerns the types of conclusions which can be drawn from different types of data. I will begin with an example.

Various writers, naturally comprising a number of pale-ontologists, have advanced views on genetics and selection, which are based upon the data of paleontology. For instance, some have claimed that Lamarckian theories of inheritance and evolutionary change must be true, since paleontological change is in the majority of cases of a functional nature, suiting the stock pre-gressively to a particular mode of life. For instance, MacBride (1936), after reviewing certain evidence for the inheritance of habit, continues: "When fully documented evidence for evolution as displayed by a minute study of species and races of living forms or by the study of lineage series in fossils is carefully studied, this dependence of evolutionary change on change in habit and function becomes apparent." And he draws the further conclusion that the changed habit or function is the direct cause of the evolutionary change.

Others, while not going so far in a positive direction, insist that any selective theory based upon inheritable variation occur-ring at random, or at least in many directions, cannot be true.

The reason alleged is that the fossil record shows nothing of this randomness, but always advances along definite directions. Still others, more impressed by this fact of direction, and by the further fact that the directional change does not always seem to be functional, but may be of an apparently useless or even deleterious nature, assert not merely that selection cannot be responsible, but that the prime cause of evolution must be the inner momentum which in technical parlance is called orthogenesis (see e.g. Hawkins, 1936, and Chap. 9 of this book).

Quite bluntly and simply, all such assertions are unjustified. They are unjustified on the score of simple logic and scientific method. Paleontology is of such a nature that its data by themselves cannot throw any important light on genetics or selection. As admitted by various paleontologists (e.g. Swinnerton, 1940), a study of the *course* of evolution cannot be decisive in regard to the *method* of evolution. All that paleontology can do in this latter field is to assert that, as regards the type of organisms which it studies, the evolutionary methods suggested by the geneticists and evolutionists shall not contradict its data. For instance, in face of the gradualness of transformation revealed by paleontology in sea-urchins or horses it is no good suggesting that large mutations of the sort envisaged by de Vries shall have played a major part in providing the material for evolutionary change. Even here, however, let us be careful to note the restriction imposed by the phrase "as regards the type of organisms which it studies". The main lines of evolution in the more abundant forms of sea-urchins, horses, and the like may depend upon gradual change: but this is no reason for assuming that this holds for all organisms. And as a matter of fact, as we shall set forth more in detail later, abrupt changes of large extent do play a part in certain kinds of evolution in certain kinds of plants.

It may be worth while to see why and how the assertions, positive and negative, that we have just been commenting on, are methodologically unjustified. In the first place to state that the functional nature of evolutionary change presupposes a genetic mechanism like that postulated by Lamarckism, which involves the inheritance of modifications in the individual brought about by use and function, is a *non sequitur*. A functionally-guided course of evolution is consonant with a lamarckian method for evolution but it is also consonant with an anti-lamarckian Darwinism. For the natural selection of "spontaneous" variations which in their origin have nothing to do with the effect of use or disuse, provides a perfectly adequate formal explanation of the genesis of organisms adapted to their mode of life, and therefore of a functionally-guided course of evolution. The difference lies in the intermediary steps: in the one case the effect of use or function is supposed to be direct, in the other indirect, *via* the sifting mechanism of selection.

There is thus a *non sequitur* in the fundamental postulate of functionally-directed fossil lineages presupposing lamarckian evolution. MacBride (e.g. 1936), however, goes even further. He implies that *all* evolutionary change is functionally determined. But in the first place we shall later describe certain trends revealed by paleontology, notably in ammonites and lamellibranchs, for which no functional explanation has so far been suggested (p. 506). And, in the second place, the evidence on the differences between allied species, as collected by such authors as Robson and Richards (1936), indicates that many specific characters are non-adaptive. Even if we discount many of these as being in all probability useless consequences or correlates of useful characters, a residuum remains. Thus here again we find are brought out the multiformity of evolution and the impossibility of ascribing all kinds of evolutionary change to a single mechanism.

Similarly the argument that straight-line or directional evolution as revealed by paleontology rules out the natural selection of random variations is simply not true. On the postulate of natural selection, the overwhelming majority of the individuals which survive will clearly be of the adapted type. The likelihood of any obviously maladjusted types surviving to become fossilized is negligible. Further, at any one moment, if there is a constant pressure of selection, and if the raw material on which it acts is constituted by small mutations, as appears to be the case (pp. 51, 58 n.), the main alteration of the stock will be brought about by the slightly lower survival- and reproduction-rate of the types which, though already broadly adapted, are not so highly adapted as others. Thus for the most part the constitution of the stock, as revealed in the bulk of those individuals which reach maturity, will change by a gradual increase of more highly as against less highly adapted types, not by the selection of "the adapted" as against "the non-adapted".

Again, directional evolution does not necessitate orthogenesis, since, so long as it is functional and adaptive, natural selection will also provide a formal explanation of it. An orthogenetic theory will be necessary if studies on mutation show that mutation (a) is so frequent that it can override selective influences and (b) if it also tends to occur repeatedly in the same direction. It will also be necessary to account for directional evolution which is useless or deleterious, or is not correlated with adaptive function. These points we shall discuss later (pp. 504 seq.).

6. THE THREE ASPECTS OF BIOLOGICAL FACT

If we look at the matter in the most general light, we shall see that every biological fact can be considered under three rather distinct aspects. First, there is the mechanistic-physiological aspect: how is the organ constructed, how does the process take place? Secondly, there is the adaptive-functional aspect: what is the functional use of the organ or process, what is its biological meaning or value to the organism or the species? And in the third place, there is the historical aspect: what is the temporal history of the organ or process, what has been its evolutionary course? A couple of examples will illuminate the point. The auditory ossicles or small bones of our middle ear operate so as to transmit vibrations of the ear-drum to the fluid on the inner ear. Their functional significance is to enable us to hear. And historically they are derived from the inner portions of the upper jaw, the lower jaw, and the hyoid, which have changed their function in the course of evolution. Or again, the notochord, which appears transitionally in the development of all higher vertebrates, is historically a recapitulation of the stage when all ancestral vertebrates possessed no backbone but a notochord persistent through life. Mechanistically, it is developed by a process of self-determination from the central portion of the invaginated dorsal lip of the blaostsporc. Functionally, it appears to serve as a temporary scaffolding around which the true backbone may afterwards be most conveniently laid down.

Sometimes a character may possess no present functional value, and can only be understood in the light of its evolutionary past. This appears to be true for the hind-limb bones of whales or the vestigial hairs on our own bodies. But in all cases the three aspects are distinct; each must be investigated separately by appropriate methods, which may have no relevance to the other aspects; and discoveries concerning any one aspect can only be of limiting nature, and not decisive or essential, with regard to the other two aspects. They represent three separate fields of discourse, which may overlap, but are of fundamentally different natures.

These considerations apply to evolution as to all other biological phenomena. Paleontology deals with the historical course of evolution. The machinery for the transmission of hereditary factors, together with any differential survival or reproduction of individuals of different types, constitutes the mechanism of the process. The adaptations of species or evolutionary lines, and the reasons for their spread or their extinction, constitute the functional aspect.

We have seen the illegitimacy of using data on the course of evolution to make assertions as to its mechanism; but the converse is just as indefensible. For instance, as we have already said, the assumption of the de Vriesian mutationists that discontinuous variations of large extent are the main source of evolutionary change is not consonant with the facts revealed by paleontology. Again, the demonstration that small mutations occur and can serve as the raw material on which natural selection may act to effect gradual evolutionary change, does not mean that this is necessarily the only type of evolutionary change possible. We have already mentioned that species may be formed abruptly, and other large variations are known to occur and to serve, in some cases, as building-blocks of evolutionary change (Chap. 6, §§ 8, 9).

The consideration of evolution thus demands data from the following branches of biology. As regards its historical course, directly from paleontology and indirectly from systematics and biogeography. As regards mechanism, from genetics and cytology, and, since the expression of a gene is important, from studies of development and growth; in addition, systematics may throw light on the types of variation to be found in nature. And as regards biological meaning, from physiology and ecology for the study of adaptation; from mathematics, selection experiments, and, indirectly, from paleontology, for the study of survival and extinction. All these are necessary, but none of them alone is sufficient.

7. THE MAIN TYPES OF EVOLUTIONARY PROCESS

If we may anticipate some of the results of later chapters, we may summarize our conclusions briefly as follows. Evolution in biology is a loose and comprehensive term applied to cover any and every change occurring in the constitution of systematic units of animals and plants, from the formation of a new sub-species or variety to the trends, continued through hundreds of millions of years, to be observed in large groups.

The main processes covered by the term are as follows. (1) Long-continued trends, as revealed by indirect evidence and in some cases by the immediate data of fossils. These are for the most part towards specialization (p. 486), a number of them towards that peculiar form of specialization called degeneration (p. 558), and a few towards that all-round biological improvement which may be styled evolutionary progress (p. 559). All these are essentially adaptive, or, if you prefer it, functionally guided. In addition, certain trends occur which cannot be interpreted adaptively, at least in the light of present knowledge, such as that of various lines of ammonites to greater complexity followed by progressive unrolling of the spiral and by other simplifications (p. 506).

Indirect evidence for similar trends, at least for those of adaptive type, is provided by comparative anatomy and embryology. When a group is considered as a whole, it will be found in the early stages of its history to be radiating into a number of trends; in other words, its evolution is essentially divergent.

An important complication is provided by the fact that selection may have quite different effects according to the group of individuals on which it acts. Thus selection in social insects like bees and ants in which most individuals are neuters and reproduction is concentrated in a small special caste, can produce characters in the species of quite a different type from those possible to animals of the usual type, in which all individuals are capable of reproduction (p. 482). Again, in higher mammals, the fact that the mother nourishes a litter within her body will lead to a special type of selection acting upon the unborn young, and this will have repercussions on the evolution of the species (p. 525). Similarly, the competition between pollen-grains in higher plants leads to a type of selection which is absent in higher animals (p. 481), while the necessity for internal fertilization in higher animals has led to the type of selection, with characteristic effects, known as sexual or inter-male selection (pp. 425 seq.).

Again, the existence of growing-points and other regions of permanently embryonic tissue in higher plants gives them opportunities for asexual reproduction and for taking advantage of mutations that are denied to higher animals.

(2) Minor systematic changes, as revealed by detailed taxonomy, ecology, cytology, and genetics. When we come to minor systematic change, we find some very different processes at work. Some processes of species-differentiation will, of course, form part of a major trend, whether by the direct evolution of a species into an altered form or by its divergence into two lines of incipient specialization. But many processes involving the formation of species and subspecies will be of a different character. Plant species may be produced discontinuously so that no selection is involved in their formation, but only in their subsequent fate (p. 340). A large species may become broken up into slightly differentiated subspecies, each somewhat adapted to local conditions, but interbreeding to a certain degree with neighbouring species. If really small local groups are wholly isolated from

interbreeding with the rest of the species, their total variability will be insufficient to respond readily to selection, useless or even deleterious characters due to chance (pp. 199 seq.) may crop up in them, and they will be more prone than larger groups to become extinguished when conditions alter. The same is true of once numerous species which dwindle until they become small.

In certain conditions, as on the Galapagos archipelago, the few immigrants which have succeeded in reaching the place have blossomed out into an extraordinary array of species; it seems that local isolation, coupled with absence of biological competition, is involved (see Swarth, 1931, 1934, and Chap. 6, § 7 of this book).

It may be presumed, on somewhat indirect evidence, that "useless" non-adaptive differences due to isolation of small groups may be enlarged by the addition of further differences of the same sort to give generic distinction, though it seems probable that differences of family or higher rank are always or almost always essentially adaptive in nature.

As we shall discuss more fully later (p. 478), both competition and therefore selection in abundant species are mainly intraspecific, between individuals of the same species; while with rare species they are mainly interspecific, between the species as a whole and its rivals, or as a struggle of the species as a whole to survive in its changing local environment.

A species, besides becoming differentiated into local subspecies, may show polymorphism. In some cases, as with various mimetic butterflies, the different forms are highly adaptive and differ in many details, while in other cases, as with the existence of two or more colour-phases (e.g. in black and red squirrels, or pale and normal clouded yellow butterflies; pp. 96 seq.), the forms differ in some simple mendelian character and their adaptive significance is not at all obvious. In some such cases certain by-products of the mendelian mechanism of heredity and mutation seem to be responsible for permitting this sharp polymorphism to occur, though in others there is a selective balance, weighted differently in ecologically different parts of the organism's range (pp. 103 seq.).

Again, in higher animals, mutual recognition may be at a premium. The recognition may be of one member by all others, as with the recognition marks of gregarious birds and mammals; or it may be between members of opposite sex, as in colours, sounds, or scents promoting the approximation or stimulating the coition of the sexes; or between members of the same sex, as with threat-characters. In most of these cases it is biologically desirable to prevent confusion with similar characters of related species occupying the same area (pp. 288 seq.). Recognition-characters accordingly are in most cases not only striking but strikingly different from species to species. Selection in these conditions operates to produce distinctiveness—difference for the sake of difference (see Lorenz, 1935, Huxley, 1938c).

In still other cases, frequently in plants and rarely in animals, an interbreeding group (species or subspecies) has been produced by crossing between two or more incipient or fully differentiated species. The results differ according to the precise genetic and cytological mechanisms operative (Chap. 6, §§ 8, 9); in some cases, however, an abnormal degree of variability is generated.

All these different processes—the adaptive and the non-adaptive trends, and all the various types of specific, subspecific, and polymorphic divergences—are equally part of evolution. If the long-range trends are in the long view the more important, the minor changes probably concern a far larger number of species. It would seem clear that we cannot expect to find a single cause of evolution: rather we must look for several agencies which alone or in combination will account for the very various processes lumped together under that comprehensive term.

Looking at the matter from another angle, we are beginning to realize that different groups may be expected to show different kinds of evolution.

Only forms which are able to dispense entirely with bisexual reproduction will be able to establish new species by autopolyploidy; the establishment of new species by hybridization and allopolyploidy will in the main be confined to forms with unlimited growth of the type found in higher plants; purely apomictic forms will show a host of slightly different pure lines;

animal groups with wide powers of dispersal like birds will tend to develop characters for sex-recognition and discrimination to prevent intercrossing with other species; the type and amount of variation and differentiation will be different in cross-fertilizing as against self-fertilizing or non-sexual forms, in fertile polyploids as against diploids, in sedentary as against mobile forms (Chap. 4).

Just as there is no one method of the origin of species, so there is no one type of variation. Different evolutionary agencies differ in intensity and sometimes in kind in different sorts of organisms, partly owing to differences in the environment, partly to differences in way of life, partly to differences in genetic machinery. No single formula can be universally applicable; but the different aspects of evolution must be studied afresh in every group of animals and plants. We are approaching the time when evolution must be studied not only broadly and deductively, not only intensively and analytically, but as a comparative subject.

CHAPTER 3

MENDELISM AND EVOLUTION

I. MUTATION AND SELECTION

The essence of Mendelian heredity is that it is particulate. The genetic constitution is composed of discrete units. Each kind of unit can exist in a number of discrete forms. The hereditary transmission of any one kind of unit is more or less independent of that of other units, the restriction of independence being a partial one, concerned with the phenomenon of linkage. The units are the Mendelian factors or genes, while their different forms are called allelomorphs or alleles.

The particulate nature of inheritance enables calculations to be made as to the proportions of offspring of different types in different generations after a cross. Like the atomic theory in chemistry, it is the basis of quantitative treatment.

The hereditary particles or genes are located within the visible chromosomes, whose manœuvres distribute their contained genes equally to all cells of the body, and determine the quantitative details of Mendel's laws. Within a particular chromosome, each gene has its appointed place, which it keeps permanently (apart from rare rearrangements; pp. 89 seq.). Of recent years, the study of the giant chromosomes in the salivary glands has converted *Drosophila* from an unfavourable into an exceedingly favourable cytological object. It is now possible in this genus to check genetic prophecies cytologically and cytological prophecies genetically, in a remarkably complete and detailed way. (For the cytological basis of heredity see Darlington, 1937; briefer treatment in M. J. D. White, 1937.)

It used to be imagined that the precise·arrangement of the genes within the chromosomes was biologically irrelevant. To-day, however, we know that this is not so. Genes (all or many of them) have somewhat different actions according to what neighbours they possess. This is the so-called position effect (p. 85), which, only recently discovered, will probably turn out to be widespread, although in some organisms (such as maize) it does not seem to occur. Where it occurs, it is likely to be of fundamental importance as well, since the rearrangement of blocks of genes (sections of chromosomes) within the chromosome outfit (p. 89), though considerably rarer than gene-mutation, is not infrequent in the long perspective of evolution; and this, through the position effects which it frequently causes, provides a large and previously unsuspected source of variability and potential evolutionary change. Its contribution, however, must be much less varied and much less abundant than that of gene-mutation (Muller, 1940).*

This does not affect the basic conception of the gene as particulate. Genes are in many ways as unitary as atoms, although we cannot isolate single genes. They do not grade into each other: but they vary in their action in accordance with their mutual relations. In this they are again like atoms: the chemical behaviour of a compound will be altered when we transfer an atom from one position to another in the molecule, even though the substantive constitution of the molecule remains unchanged. Thus the whole is not merely the sum of its parts: it is also their relation.

The discreteness of the genes may prove to be nothing more

---

* A special case of position effect is the modification of variegation (mosaicism) of various sorts in *Drosophila*, exerted on various genes if translocated into proximity with heterochromatin ("inert" regions of the chromosomes). Schultz's summary (1941) makes it clear that this is caused by a change in the nucleic acid metabolism of the translocated regions, and that this exerts its effects in early stages of development, by causing a process akin to inactivation of the genes involved. The degree of this inactivation decreases with the distance from the point of breakage and re-union with the inert region.

than the presence of predetermined zones of breakage at small and more or less regular distances along the chromosomes. For the independent hereditary behaviour of genes, from which their discreteness is deduced, is due to two facts. When the genes to be tested are in different kinds of chromosomes, their independence is due merely to the independent behaviour of the two chromosomes. But when they are both in the same kind of chromosome, their independence depends on what is known as crossing-over. Prior to the formation of reproductive cells, the two homologous chromosomes of each kind pair together. Where they touch, they may break and exchange segments; in the daughter-chromosomes the kinds of genes and their order remain as before, but one or more blocks of genes from one chromosome will have exchanged places with precisely corresponding blocks of genes from the other. The breaks do not always occur in the same place. If there is more than one break in a chromosome-pair, the second break is at a considerable distance from the first; thus breaks can normally not occur on both sides of a single gene. What happens is thus that genes are separated from their erstwhile neighbours in a chromosome by these breaks; and it is the fact that breaks may occur at different places in the chromosome which makes it possible for any gene in a chromosome to be separated from its neighbours and thus to be inherited independently. Knowing this, we may put the matter the other way round, and say that the process of exchange of sections after breaking, and the fact that breakage only occurs at certain spots, determines what we call the gene (see discussion in Grüneberg, 1937); a gene-unit is thus a section of the chromosome between two adjacent sites of potential breakage at crossing-over.*

The chromosomes may thus be looked on as "super-molecules". built up out of a series of regions, each region marked off by zones of potential breakage. The portions of these regions which we can recognize by their effects in inheritance are what we

---

* It is possible, though not fully established, that the breaks underlying sectional rearrangements may not invariably coincide with the sites of potential breakage underlying crossing-over. If so, sectional chromosome-mutations may actually break genes in two (Muller, 1940; Raffel and Muller, 1940).

call genes. Rearrangement of the regions, as well as change within a single region, or the loss or duplication of a region or set of regions, can and normally will cause alterations in the action of the chromosome and its parts on the developing organism. Similarly the doubling of the whole chromosome-outfit, by producing a different relation between gene-outfit and cytoplasm, will also alter the characters of the organism.

The number of genes is much larger than was originally imagined. *Drosophila* is the only organism where adequate quantitative knowledge is available. Several recent estimates, based on different methods of approach (see summary in Gulick, 1938), vary from a minimum of over 2,000 to a maximum of well under 13,000, with a probable number of about 5,000, for this minute insect. The size of a *Drosophila* gene must be between 10^{-8} and 10^{-5} μ^3 and probably between 10^{-7} and 10^{-6} μ^3, equivalent to some 10 medium-sized protein molecules (see also Lea, 1940). In some other organisms (*Lilium*) the genes may be larger, and in others more numerous (e.g. in man, perhaps 4 to 6 times more so than in *Drosophila*). It will be seen what astronomical possibilities of recombination and mutual interaction are afforded by an assemblage of this magnitude.

A gene-mutation will then be any intrinsic change in substance or structure, affecting the mode of action of one of these unit-regions.

One of the notable biological discoveries of the last few years was that of Muller, on the effect of X-rays in producing gene-mutations. The ordinary rate of mutation can by this means be multiplied a hundred-and-fifty fold, and a certain number of wholly new mutations, in addition to many already known, are produced. It is, however, interesting, in view of our discussion, to note that X-rays also induce the rearrangement of chromosome-sections by translocation, inversion, etc. In view of the assertions of certain biologists that mutation is of its essence pathological, it should be mentioned that X-ray treatment can produce reverse mutation—i.e. cause a previously mutated gene to revert to normal (Patterson and Muller, 1930; Timoféeff-Ressovsky, 1934a, 1937), Comment is needless.

Timakov (1941) in wild *Drosophila* has detected a gene increasing mutation-rate at least 40 times, and possibly to a level higher than that induced by X-rays.

The fact that the genes and their arrangement normally remain constant, until altered by some kind of mutation (after which they again remain constant in their new form until a further mutation supervenes), accounts for the resemblance between parents and offspring, The fact of Mendelian recombination, by which new combinations of old genes are produced according to Mendel's second law (and to the rules of crossing-over), accounts for the great majority of the differences between parents and offspring, and between members of a family or population. But gene-mutation, though a rare event, appears to account for most that is truly new in evolution. Under the head of gene-mutation, position-effect due to very small sectional rearrangements can legitimately be included, since it involves a structural change and a novel effect; further, it cannot for practical reasons be excluded, since there is at present in many cases no possibility of distinguishing between it and true gene-mutation. Recombination also may in certain cases produce evolutionary novelty, for instance after a cross between two previously isolated types. Finally, as we shall see later, hybridization, with no subsequent recombination, may sometimes be responsible for evolutionary change (Chap. 6, § 9).

However, gene-mutations (including position-effects) appear to be the most important source of novelty in evolution, and we must now say a little more about them.

In the first place, no trace has been found in *Drosophila*, where analysis has been pushed to an extraordinary pitch of refinement, of any characters not dependent on chromosomal (and therefore mendelizing) differences (Muller, 1940). Secondly, although complete proof cannot be offered, the presumption, in the absence of evidence to the contrary, is that all mendelizing gene-differences owe their origin to mutation: up to the present we know of no other way by which they could have come into existence.

Finally, a number of mutations are known which are roughly

neutral, or actually or potentially useful (pp. 118, 449). In barley, Gustafsson (1941) induced by X-rays three mutations which increased yield, one of them markedly. Among those which are potentially useful a few cases may be mentioned here. Banta and Wood (1928) discovered a "thermal race" of the crustacean *Daphnia longispina*, which had its optimum 6°-8° C. higher and its thermal death-point 5° C. higher than the long-established parthenogenetic strain from which it originated. It was also immobilized more quickly by low temperatures. Thus it was potentially adapted to a warmer environment than its parent strain. Its origin from sexually inbred individuals showed that it depended upon a recessive mutation arising during the long preceding period of parthenogenetic reproduction. Other more immediately useful mutations arose in the same way, e.g. some causing greater fertility and others greater longevity (Davenport, 1928).

Very important results were obtained by Johannsen (1913) in following up his classical researches on pure lines for seed-weight in beans. As is well known (see Johannsen, 1926), he showed that the prime effect of selection in a mixed population was to isolate pure lines, and that further selection then had no further effect, in the absence of mutation. But he also showed that mutations might occur in pure lines, and might then be selected. During his experiments, two mutations, one for higher and one for lower seed-weight, were detected and "captured" by his selection for high and low seed-weight respectively.

Another interesting case is that of the variety of tobacco, originated apparently by mutation, described by Garner and Allard (1920). This did not flower at all in its place of origin (Washington); but when the daily period of light was reduced to twelve hours, it flowered and set seed better than the stock from which it had arisen. In other words, it was potentially better adapted than the parent stock to more tropical latitudes.

Still another case is the mutation described by McEwen (1937) in *Drosophila*, which abolishes the fly's phototropism. This would be adaptive in dark surroundings. It is noteworthy that this last effect is produced by the same recessive mutation that changes the body-colour to tan: thus here a useless visible effect is correlated with a potentially useful physiological effect (a "correlated character" in Darwin's usage).

Of mendelizing differences, alike in domestic and wild species, which are actually or potentially favourable, there is an abundance. We need only think of the genes producing small and large size in poultry (Punnett and Bailey, 1914); those producing the specific differences between the two species of snapdragon crossed by Baur (1923); the mimetic polymorphic forms of various butterflies (p. 101); the different forms of heterostyled flowers such as primrose (*Primula*) and loosestrife (*Lythrum*); the single-brooded and double-brooded condition in silkworms; and so on. An interesting case of a *Drosophila* mutant establishing itself in considerable numbers in the wild is the vermilion-eyed type of *D. hydei* (Spencer, 1932). This mutant must be very delicately balanced in its selective relations. The recent establishment of other marked mutant types, like the black hamster, the black Tasmanian opossum, the *simplex*-toothed field-vole, etc., are discussed later (pp. 103–6, 203). In our own species, the work of Blakeslee and his collaborators (see Blakeslee and Fox, 1932) has established the existence of remarkable differences, apparently mendelian, in sensitivity of taste and smell in regard to various chemical compounds and natural odours. These seem under present conditions to be, in themselves, somewhat selectively neutral. Later work (Fisher, Ford and Huxley, 1939) has shown that in chimpanzees not only are the same differences found, but tasters and non-tasters occur in about the same proportions as in man—close to $3:1$. This appears to indicate a stable balance between the two conditions, and one depending upon some advantage, of unknown nature, enjoyed by the heterozygotes. The different blood-group genes would seem to fall into a somewhat similar category, though here the proportions vary markedly in different populations: some of these genes occur also in various lower mammals.

Many differences between "good" species have also been shown to depend on mendelizing gene-differences (see Goldschmidt, 1928, Chap. 15; Haldane, 1932a, Chap. 3; Lamprecht, 1941).

Further, an increasing number of characters once held to be non-mendelian are being shown to depend on mendelian genes (e.g. the multiple factors influencing the hooded pattern in rats, p. 65; the distinctive characters of wild subspecies of the deer-mouse *Peromyscus*); and indeed wherever F2 shows greater variability than F1, inheritance must be particulate. Thus it may be legitimately argued that the majority of all inherited characters must rest on a mendelian basis. Even in the present incomplete state of our knowledge, there are strong presumptive grounds for this assertion, so that the onus of proof now lies on those who would maintain the contrary in any particular case.

In addition, initially deleterious factors can be rendered useful by genetic-evolutionary methods which we shall discuss in subsequent sections of this chapter.

Finally, mutations, while they seem to occur more readily in certain directions than in others (Chapter 9), can be legitimately said to be random with regard to evolution. That is to say, the directions of the changes produced by them appear to be unrelated either to the direction of the evolutionary change to be observed in the type, or to the adaptive or functional needs of the organism. Evolutionary direction has to be imposed on random mutation through the sifting and therefore guiding action of selection. It is, of course, possible that as the laborious technique of testing for mutation-rate is extended to more species, certain mutations may be discovered which show very much higher rates than others. However, the general agreement already found between organisms so different as a monocotyledonous angiosperm, an insect, and a mammal would indicate that in most species we may expect to find some mutations occurring at a rate of 1 in 10^5 individuals or even higher, and many genes with a mutation-frequency of about 1 in 10^6. Occasional genes with much higher mutation-rates occur (see summary in Dobzhansky, 1937, Chapter 2), and some genes promote increased mutation-frequency in other genes. In cotton, hybridization may increase the mutation-frequency of certain genes (Harland, 1936). Mutation-frequency must in some way be balanced against length of life; otherwise the chromosomes of long-lived species would become crowded with lethals before reproduction (Dobzhansky, 1937, p. 33). Again, the mutation-rate for haemophilia in man is on the same scale as that for most *Drosophila* genes if computed per life-cycle, but much lower on the basis of time (Haldane, 1935*b*). Certainly species vary in mutation-rate: thus the fern *Nephrolepis exaltata* has produced many more mutants than any other species of the genus (Benedict, 1931). Zuitin (1941) in *Drosophila* finds that mutation-rate is increased by sudden environmental changes (see p. 137).

With mutation-rates of this order of magnitude, evolution must always be a somewhat slow process, judged in terms of years, but its speed in relation to geological time will be quite adequate. R. A. Fisher (1930*a*, 1932) has discussed the matter in a general way. He clears the ground by pointing out that "blending inheritance," which was currently postulated in Darwin's day, would be constantly annulling variability: to be accurate, the variance (in the absence of selective mating) would be halved in each generation. As a result, new genetic variations (i.e. what we should to-day call mutations) would have to be exceedingly abundant—far in excess of anything observed in actual fact—to produce the variance actually observed; and any variability available for selection to act upon would have to be of very recent origin. It was largely for these reasons that Darwin ascribed so high an influence to "the direct effects of environment".

The discovery that inheritance is almost entirely particulate and non-blending removes these difficulties, so that in point of fact the rise of Mendelism, far from being antagonistic to Darwinian views (as was claimed, notably by the early Mendelians themselves, in the years immediately following its rediscovery), makes a selectionist interpretation of evolution far simpler. In mathematical language, it indefinitely conserves much genetic variance instead of rapidly dissipating it, and thus amasses material on which selection can work.* Further, if particulate inheritance

---

* A certain number of rare mutant genes will be lost to the species by accidental elimination. In addition, genetic variance will be reduced by the selective elimination of deleterious mutant genes.

and discontinuous mutation as they are known at the present time are the general basis of genetics and variation, selectionist views also gain support over those strictly to be called orthogenetic (Chapter 9), in which the direction of mutation itself is supposed to determine the course of evolution, and over those to be called Lamarckian, in which the effects of use and function are supposed to be inherited. For no rate of hereditary change hitherto observed in nature would have any evolutionary effect in the teeth of even the slightest degree of adverse selection. Either mutation-rates many times higher than any as yet detected must be sometimes operative, or else the observed results can be far better accounted for by selection. A mutation with partial dominance occurring once in 10^5 individuals will, if selectively neutral, take a period of somewhat over 10^5 generations to establish itself in half the individuals of the species. If there were the faintest adverse selection against it, it could never increase at all. But if it conferred an advantage of only 1 per cent—i.e. if an individual bearing one such mutant gene has an expectation of reproducing itself which is only 1 per cent higher than those without the mutant gene, then it would establish itself in half the individuals of the species in a period of only about 10^2 generations (R. A. Fisher, 1930a; Haldane, 1932a). Fisher (1937b) has also made interesting studies on the form of the wave by which advantageous genes advance.

Haldane (references and summary in appendix to Haldane, 1932a) has made a number of valuable theoretical studies on the rate of evolutionary change to be expected with various given degrees of selective advantage for autosomal dominants and recessives and other types of mutations. One important conclusion is that intense competition favours variable or plastic response to the environment rather than high average response. This presumably helps to explain the large variability to be found in many natural populations.

For ordinary natural selection involving a simple dominant with a selective advantage of 1 in 1,000 (i.e. where the ratio of dominant to recessive changes from 1 to 1·001 in each generation) it will take nearly 5,000 generations to increase the proportion of the dominant from 1 to 50 per cent, and nearly 12,000 more to raise it to 99 per cent. For an advantage of 1 in 100 the number of generations must be divided by 10. In the early stages of selection of a single mutation with constant effects, when the gene is still very rare, dominants can spread much more rapidly than pure recessives, unless a certain degree of inbreeding occurs.

These results may be actualized in certain cases: e.g. in dominant melanism (p. 93) when conditions alter so as to favour the melanic mutant, the rate of change in the constitution of the population is of the order deduced. However, Haldane's detailed conclusions are not likely to be so directly applicable to evolutionary problems as was thought at the time, since we now realize that dominance or recessivity are themselves in large measure a result of evolution, produced in response to the deleterious nature of most mutations (p. 75). The mutations that are of value for evolution will in most cases be of very small extent, of slight effect, and often at least of incomplete dominance or recessiveness. Further, we are now realizing that evolution will in general proceed, not by the selection of single mutations, but by the selection of mutations in relation to a favourable combination of existing small gene-differences, or in many cases by the selection of such new recombinations alone, to be followed later if occasion offers by appropriate new mutations (p. 124). According to R. A. Fisher, this process will be considerably quicker than that of the selection of single recessives, which are the commonest obvious mutations found, and accordingly were, when Haldane wrote, usually considered to be the main source of evolutionary variance.

It will be observed that the amount of variance provided by mutation will, with a constant mutation-rate, vary directly with the size of the population. In a given time, therefore, a rare species cannot lay hands on the same store of mutations as would be available to an abundant species. The problem of the relation of size of population to evolution is, however, much more complex than this (see p. 200; R. A. Fisher, 1930a, Chap. 4, and 1937a; SewallWright, 1931, 1932, 1940). We must consider how much variance a population can hold, as well as how much variance it is provided with by mutation.

Many rare mutations must be extinguished by mere random loss: the individuals or gametes containing them fail to reproduce. There must always be a tendency for "minority" genes, which are present in low frequencies, to be lost from the germ-plasm by such accidental extinction if of no selective advantage. Even with a definite selective advantage such as 1 per cent, which is of the order of magnitude for rapid evolutionary change, the chances are strongly against a lone mutation surviving in the species (see, e.g., Haldane, 1939b). Mutations with a deleterious effect will of course be lost through selection, the rate of loss depending on the intensity of the effect.

Thus repeated mutation (i.e. a definite mutation-rate) together with a considerable-sized population, are necessary for new mutations to have an evolutionary chance.* Such abundant species as have been analysed prove to be carrying a surprisingly large number of recessive mutations in their germ-plasm (see p. 75, and Dobzhansky, 1937, Chap. 3).

In addition, the probability of mere accident playing a part in the actual survival of particular genes or gene-combinations is enhanced in small populations. This has been especially emphasized by Wright, who points out that we should expect to see, in the case of small species or isolated subspecies, certain types of useless or even deleterious change, which would not occur in an abundant form, becoming incorporated in the constitution through chance recombination.

Already in 1912 Lloyd had discovered instances of this process of accidental multiplication and decline of mutant genes, but without realizing its full theoretical implications; and by 1918 Muller had drawn general attention to its importance. Sewall

---

* R. A. Fisher (1937a) points out that the *number* of the rare approximately neutral genes carried by a species increases roughly as the logarithm of its population-size. Such genes, however, will only cause observable variability of any magnitude if they can increase their *frequency*, as will occur if they are slightly favourable or if changed conditions cause them to become so. Thus, as Ford (1940c, p. 89) points out, increased variability ascribable to large population-size depends on genes actually engaged in causing evolutionary change, and the observed fact of such increased variability demonstrates the spread in nature of genes with small advantageous effects.

Wright later christened the process "drift", and worked out its consequences in full detail (see Wright, 1940).

What may be regarded as the converse of the Sewall Wright phenomenon of drift in small populations is the impossibility of securing good results in artificial selection when only small numbers are employed. This, the general experience of poultry-breeders, has been confirmed by Hays (1940) in definite experiments designed to test the point. Using a flock never exceeding 50 birds, and often much smaller, he was unable in the course of eight generations to raise egg-production, though marked progress can be obtained by using large flocks. Apparently the numerous genes needed for the requisite multiple gene-combinations are not available in such small populations. In some characters involved in fecundity, indeed, the effect was contrary to the direction of selection—a result comparable with the deleterious changes sometimes seen in small populations in nature (p. 201).

The smaller the size of a natural population and the more perfectly it is isolated the more likely is drift to proceed to its limit, resulting either in the complete loss of a mutation from the group, or its fixation in all the individuals of the group—accompanied, of course, by the complete loss of its normal allele.

In larger and less isolated populations, however, drift will normally proceed only within limits, causing the frequency of a gene to fluctuate round a position of equilibrium. This equilibrium-frequency will be determined by the balance between the two opposing processes of mutation-frequency on the one hand and adverse selection on the other, while, as we have seen, population-size will also have an effect. Thus in large populations, slightly deleterious mutations may be present with reasonable frequency, especially when recessive, and will then constitute a reservoir of potential evolutionary change, since their unfavourable effects can generally be neutralized by appropriate combinations of modifiers (pp. 68 seq.).

In some cases, as with haemophilia and other sex-linked recessives in man, we know that the effect of a mutant gene is so deleterious that a comparatively high mutation-pressure must be postulated to account for its frequency. In other cases, changes in external environment will alter the amount or even the sign of the selection-pressure on the gene. Thus an increase in temperature would favour the spread of the "thermal race" of *Daphnia* mentioned on p. 52, while the lowering of temperature during the glacial period has doubtless led to autopolyploids replacing diploids at high latitudes in many plant species (p. 337).

The same will be true of changes in the internal environment. Genes may have their expression altered by modifiers so as entirely to change their selective value (pp. 68 seq.).

Meanwhile it is important to realize that the frequency of mutant genes represents an equilibrium between mutation-frequency and selection, that variability represents a further equilibrium between recombination and selection, and that the size and structure of the population will have effects on both these equilibria.

We shall revert later to this last point. Here we will merely mention the important conclusion established by Sewall Wright (see Wright, 1940*a*), that the greatest amount of evolutionary potentiality is available to large species divided into partially discontinuous groups (subspecies etc.). The partial isolation between the groups favours diversity by local adaptation and also by drift and the establishment of non-adaptive recombinations; while the fact that it is only partial implies that the variance provided by all the diversity taken together is potentially available to the species as a whole.

Recent work has emphasized the importance of studies of population-structure for understanding the precise way in which evolution will operate in any particular species. Thus to take but two examples, Dobzhansky (1941) points out that certain theoretical calculations as to the relation between the mutation-rate and the number of lethals actually found in a population will only hold in unlimited populations. As the size of the normally in-breeding population is decreased, the number of lethals goes up. In *Drosophila pseudoobscura*, using this method, he was able to show that the size of inbreeding population-groups was quite different in California and in Central America. A region with smaller size of population-groups will show greater divergence between its constituent populations and these will each show greater variability in time; further, in such a region, the type as a whole can only change through the migration and selection of superior genotypes from small colonies. In general, the size of the constituent population-groups seems to be astonishingly small for an organism with such capacities for distribution (see also pp. 371-2).

In *Drosophila hydei* the situation is rather different (Spencer, 1941). This is a tropical species which has become widely established in U.S.A. as a hanger-on of urban man. Each city and town is the focus of a single population-group. Each such population-group passes through tremendous fluctuations in size, becoming quite small in winter. It is improbable that genetic equilibrium is ever reached within such markedly fluctuating groups, and the rapid increases in numbers give abundant opportunity for the spread of new genes even against selection-pressure. Analysis showed, as was expected, that different populations differed markedly in the type and number of mutant genes that they contained.

As Dobzhansky points out, we may say on the basis of such analysis that one of the most important recent evolutionary events has been the merging in the human species of small population-groups in a more or less freely interbreeding whole.

In general it seems clear that from the standpoint of mathematical theory, existing mutation-rates will in moderately abundant species suffice, with the aid of selection, for the distinctly slow processes of evolutionary change to be observed in fossils.*

This statement is a deductive one made on theoretical grounds from the standpoint of mathematical analysis. In the remainder of this chapter we shall deal with more concrete aspects of the relation between Mendelism and evolution.

* In a stock like that of the horses, which shows a functional evolution that by geological standards must be called rapid, the time needed to effect a change of specific magnitude is of the order of 100,000 generations, and to effect one of generic magnitude of the order of 1,000,000 generations (Wells, Huxley and Wells, 1930, Book 4, ch. 8).

2. GENES AND CHARACTERS

A great deal of water has flowed under the bridges of biology since the early days of mendelian work, when mendelian factors were rigidly equated with mendelizing characters when only two states of a given gene were recognized, the dominant being supposed to represent its presence and the recessive its absence, and when all mutations and all mendelian genes were supposed to have considerable and obviously discontinuous effects.*

To-day the notion of mendelian characters has been entirely dropped (see, for instance, Sinnott and Dunn, 1932, p. 301). The term may occasionally serve as a useful piece of shorthand notation, but is in point of fact a false conception. In the first place, a single gene may affect a number of characters, a phenomenon known as pleiotropism. Grüneberg (1938), in an illuminating analysis, points out that pleiotropic effects may be realized in three different ways. In the first place, a gene may exert a direct effect on two or more distinct processes. The example of the effect of the series of white eye-colour allelomorphs in *Drosophila*, which also exert an effect on the shape of the spermatheca, is probably an example of this category. Secondly, a gene may exert a direct effect on a single process, but in many different sites and conditions. This holds for the primary action of the gene studied by Grüneberg (1938) in the rat, which causes hyperplasia and abnormal growth of cartilage in the ribs, trachea, and elsewhere. Another and even more striking case is the array of anomalies in such different organs as eyes and feet, found in a particular strain of mice, which Bonnevie (1934) has shown are due to alteration in a single developmental mechanism, namely the causing of embryonic blebs of fluid at a particular stage of embryonic development.

The most interesting examples for our purpose, however, belong to the third category, of indirect effects. A gene exerts a primary direct effect, and this then causes numerous secondary

---

* A valuable summary of the modern outlook, which treats certain aspects of the problem more fully than is possible in a single chapter, is given by Ford in his little book, *Mendelism and Evolution* (1934).

effects. Grüneberg's gene in the rat has a hyperplastic anomaly of cartilage as its primary effect. But among the secondary effects are such varied "characters" as emphysema, hypertrophy of the right ventricle, blocked nostrils, and incompletely occluded incisor teeth.*

An equally good example is that of the frizzled breed of fowl (p. 118). Here the primary effect is entirely on the feathers; as the secondary effect of the resultant abnormal heat loss, we find (in temperate climates) marked thyroid and adrenal enlargement, subnormal body-temperature, and much increased food-intake.

Such secondary effects are excellent examples of what Darwin called "correlated characters", which may be of great evolutionary importance (pp. 188, 206, 533).

Furthermore, any given character represents the end-result of a great number of genes interacting with the environment during development, and is not inherited as such. What is investigated in any genetic experiment is the inherited basis for a constant character-difference. Thus a *character-difference* may be said to be inherited in mendelian fashion, while the *character* cannot but even so the differential effect of a particular gene on the character need not by any means always be the same. It may alter according to differences in the environment, and also according to differences in the remainder of the gene-complex. As an example of the first, we may take the well worked out case of "abnormal abdomen" in *Drosophila* (T. H. Morgan, 1915). This effect depends on a single partially dominant sex-linked gene: but it is only manifested in moist conditions. In dry conditions flies pure for the gene appear perfectly normal, while intermediates are produced by varying degrees of moisture (see Gordon and Sang, 1941, on the similar case of *antennaless*).

An equally striking botanical case is that of a type of albinism in barley (Collins, 1927), dependent on a single gene. When grown below 6·5° C. the plants entirely lack chlorophyll, while

---

* Waddington (1941a) points out that certain ontogenetic events act as "epigenetic crises", in that quite slight modifications of their course will have a considerable effect on a number of characters. Thus alterations in the pupal contraction of *Drosophila* are involved in mutant characters of legs, wings, bristles, etc.

above 18° C. they are quite normal. Between these limits the mutants produce a graded amount of chlorophyll. Baur's classical case (1923) in *Primula sinensis* has now been shown to be due to faulty experimentation. For other plant cases see Lawrence and Price (1940). In Himalayan rabbits and Siamese cats (both simple recessives) black pigment is produced only below a certain threshold temperature. Normally only the extremities fall below this; but Iljin (1927, 1930) has experimentally produced pale extremities, and black on the body. Another *Drosophila* example is *short-wing*, a sex-linked recessive which at 27.5° C. markedly reduces wing-length and affects eye-development. However, the effect falls away with temperature and is absent at 14° C. (Eker, 1935). Thus environmental changes may either mask or bring out the results of genetic difference. We must therefore distinguish carefully between the *nature* of the gene and its *expression*. The gene itself can only alter by mutation; but its expression can be affected in a number of ways.

The most revolutionary change has come in regard to the way in which the expression of a gene can be altered by other genes. The discovery of this fact has given us the two fundamental concepts of genic balance and the gene-complex. Thus the internal or genetic environment of a gene may produce effects upon its expression which are as striking as those induced by the external environment, and of course very much more important from the point of view of evolution.

By genic balance we imply that individual genes act, not absolutely, in virtue solely of their inherent qualities, but relatively, in virtue of their interaction with other genes. The concept was first reached by studies on sex. It was at one time supposed that in *Drosophila* and other forms with male heterogamety, one X-chromosome automatically determined maleness, and two femaleness. It has since been shown, however, that it is the balance of the X-chromosomes to the autosomes (A) which is operative. A ratio of 1 X to 2 A produces maleness, of 1 X to 1 A produces femaleness; while one of 1 X to about 1·5 A produces intersexuality: Sterile "super-males" and "super-females" are produced by ratios of 1 X to over 2 A and under 1 A respectively. Here we can deduce that sex-determination is effected by the quantitative ratio between sets of male-determining and female-determining genes, though we do not know how many separate genes are involved in each set.

The principle, however, appears to be of universal application: the effect produced by any gene depends on other genes with which it happens to be co-operating. The effects of modifying genes are the most striking examples.

A classical case of the kind is the alteration in the hooded pattern of rats by modifiers (Castle and Pincus, 1928). The basic gene remains the same, but its effects may be reduced to a few specks of black on the head, or progressively extended over the whole back and most of the belly, by the agency of accessory genes. In cotton (*Gossypium*) differences in leaf-shape have been evolved in a precisely similar way (Silow, 1941).

Extending this concept, we reach that of the gene-complex. The environment of a gene must include many, perhaps all other genes, in all the chromosomes. This gene-complex may be altered in numerous ways by mutation or recombination so as to modify the effects and mode of action of particular genes, whether well-established ones or new mutations. We can thus distinguish between the genetic and the somatic environment of genes.

Further, it is now known that a gene can exist in a great variety of allelomorphic forms (alleles), up to a dozen or more being known for single loci. The effects of these usually differ in a quantitative way (though occasionally in a qualitative way as well), and the steps between the various alleles may be very slight. Multiple alleles are, in general, taken to represent different states of a homologous material unit. They thus constitute one type of gene-differences with quite small effects. Many modifiers and cumulative factors such as those involved in quantitative characters also have small effects. In many cases the actual origin of such small differentials by mutation has been observed. Further, where a gene's effect is small, the variations of expression, due to environment and to other genes, may readily cause an overlap with the phenotypic expression of an allele or of another gene with similar type of expression. Thus though genetic variability must be discontinuous, its expression in measurable characters may become continuous.

Even mutations which in one gene-complex are pathological, in another may be perfectly harmless, and in yet another advantageous. A striking example of this is provided by the work of M. Gordon (1931) on generic hybrids between the viviparous freshwater fishes *Platypoecilus* and *Xiphophorus*. Some strains of the former possess a gene for the production of large pigment-cells with black pigment, responsible for a certain type of spotted pattern. When, however, this gene interacts with certain genes in the sword-tail (*Xiphophorus*), the pigment-cells produce cancer-like melanotic tumours (Kosswig, 1929).

Equally striking and curious results may occur as the result of the interaction of two gene-complexes in species-hybridization. As an example of this, we may cite an intergeneric pheasant cross recently described (Huxley, 1941*b*). The cross was between a Lady Amherst pheasant (*Chrysolophus amherstiae*) and an Impeyan pheasant (*Lophophorus impeyanus*), and the hybrid was a male. The coloration of the males of both parent species is not only brilliant but varied. Thus the Lady Amherst cock has a black-and-white extensible "cape" on the head, a striking regional pattern on the body, and elaborately barred central tail feathers; while the Impeyan cock is distinguished by brilliant patches of burnished bronze, green, and blue-back on its upper parts, with white rump and buff tail. The hybrid, however, has most of its upper parts uniformly black, with mere traces of green and bronze iridescence, but neither regional patterning nor brilliant colouring. The lower parts and central tail feathers are mottled with brown, grey and white in various ways. This simple colour-scheme, by the way, cannot be considered to have any rever-sionary or "atavistic" significance whatever: it is simply that the delicately balanced gene-systems responsible for the two elaborate patterns have cancelled out, so to speak, to produce a wholly different and almost uniform coloration. It may perhaps be mentioned that in other characters the hybrid is intermediate (e.g. the shape and size of the cape), and in still others shows obvious dominance (e.g. the blue face-skin of the Impeyan).

What we may call partial gene-complexes may also arise in relation to the separate chromosomes into which the total gene-complex is divided. This has been demonstrated by Mather (1941) as regards what he terms polygenic characters—i.e. quantitative characters dependent on the co-operation and interaction of numerous genes. In *Drosophila*, the number of ventral abdominal hairs can be changed by selection so as to trangress the limits of normal variability in both plus and minus directions (cf. Castle's hooded rats, p. 65). But the effect of selection is exerted in two main stages. During the first two generations, a marked change is effected, which Mather interprets as being due to recombination of whole chromosomes. Then, after a period of relative stability for two or three further generations, a further and more marked change is produced, continuing for a number of generations; this appears to be due to recombination of originally linked genes forming polygenic combinations for hair-number. Different polygenic combinations for this character have arisen in homologous chromosomes in different strains, each combination being balanced in that it contains both plus and minus modifiers of the character. Furthermore, a number of such combinations will tend to co-exist in a species with considerable out-crossing, since the delicacy of the balance (see below) is improved when the genes for a polygenic character are heterozygous. When selection is practised, crossing-over provides new and extreme combinations. (Cf. the more fully isolated partial systems of Darlington; p. 362.)

No such balanced polygenic combinations can be detected in the modifiers of abnormal mutant characters, such as bar eye. Mather suggests that they will arise by natural selection in respect of wild-type characters, in order to prevent too great deviation from the normal, while at the same time affording the possibility of change under selection, through crossing-over providing a limited number of extreme recombinations. Such polygenic combinations, like other features of genetic systems (cf. p. 136), are thus a compromise between immediate individual fitness and long-term evolutionary plasticity.

To sum up the evolutionary bearings of recent discoveries about gene-complexes, we may say that evolution not only need not occur by a series of sharp single steps, but is not likely to do so; each such step is immediately *buffered*, as it were, by ancillary changes in genes and gene-combinations which can act as modifiers for the major mutating gene and adjust it more or less completely to the needs of the organism, though final adjustment may have to wait upon further mutation. In any case, what evolves is the gene-complex; and it can do so in a series of small, if irregular steps, so finely graded as to constitute a continuous ramp.

When we reflect further that it is theoretically possible for a gene to alter its character radically by mutating step by small step from one member of a multiple allelomorph series to another, we shall see that the discontinuity inherent in Mendelian genetics is no obstacle to the visible continuity revealed in paleontological evolution. Discontinuous germinal changes are perfectly capable of producing continuous changes in somatic characters. Nor, as we shall set forth more fully later, is the pathological character of many mutations at their first appearance necessarily a bar to their final evolutionary utilization by the species.

The divergence of two stocks will always involve the accumulation of different genes in the two lines, each buffered by special modifiers and adjusted in its own way to other genes; and this will inevitably lead to a certain amount of disharmony on crossing, the F1 or later generations being less fertile or less viable, or both (see discussion in Muller, 1939, 1940). The fact of internal adaptation within the gene-complex thus automatically helps to bring about the inter-sterility of species.

3. THE ALTERATION OF GENIC EXPRESSION

Let us take some examples of mutations, at first deleterious, being rendered innocuous. One of the most striking cases occurs in the meal-moth *Ephestia kuhniella*. Here a red-eyed mutant is known which shows considerably lowered viability. But when the recessive gene for red eyes is combined with another recessive gene for transparency of eyes, the double recessive is as viable as the normal wild type (Kühn, 1934).

A somewhat similar example comes from *Drosophila*. The

mutation *purple* (eye-colour) causes the duration of life to be considerably reduced. Another mutation, *arc*, affecting wing-shape, produces nearly as great a reduction. But the two in combination cause much less reduction than either separately (Gonzalez, 1923). The figures (for both sexes together) are as follows:

Genes				Length of life (days)
Purple ..	..	..	..	24·54 ± 0·18
Arc ..	..	..	..	26·81 ± 0·29
Purple/arc ..	..	..	..	33·71 ± 0·34
(Wild-type ..	..	..	..	39·47 ± 0·28)

Considering what severe effects are exerted by the two genes separately, the favourable result of their combination is very striking.* Brierley (1938) has worked out a means of determining the "selective index" of any gene-combination, and has obtained some suggestive preliminary results, also in *Drosophila*, on the general viability interactions of numerous genes.

In a number of cases, the restoration of viability occurs gradually in the mere course of maintaining the mutant stock. The classical analysis of this phenomenon is that of the eyeless mutant of *Drosophila*.

Eyeless is due to a 4th-chromosome recessive gene. Its characteristics on its first discovery were that it considerably reduced the size of the eyes, in some cases to complete absence, decreased fertility markedly, and had a depressing effect on viability. After, however, a stock for eyeless had been inbred without any artificial selection for a number of generations, it was found that practically all the flies had normal eyes and showed little reduction in either fertility or viability. On outcrossing to the normal wild type and re-extracting the recessives in F2, it was found that these once more manifested the original characters of eyeless, though in even more variable degree (T. H. Morgan, 1926, 1929).

The explanation of these facts is that the manifestations of eyeless are readily influenced by other genes, and that in general

---

* As the stocks used in this experiment were not "isogenic" in regard to their residual gene-complex, an alternative explanation is possible, by which the increased viability may have been due to modifiers and not to the specific combination of the two main genes.

those modifiers which make for normal viability and fertility also make for normality in eye-size. Thus natural selection acting upon the recombinations of modifiers present in the stock speedily saw to it that the combination making for the manifestation of reduced eyes was eliminated. In competition with its wild-type allelomorph, eyeless would be eliminated; but in stocks pure for eyeless, the genes to be eliminated will be the plus modifiers of the mutation. In broadest terms, there has been a selection of the most favourable gene-complex.

A similar genetic modification of recessive mutations towards wild-type expression was found by W. W. Marshall and Muller (1917) in *Drosophila melanogaster* for the wing-characters *balloon* and *curved*. Still another example from *Drosophila* is the sex-linked mutation *vesiculated*, affecting the wings: this can be brought back to normal expression by means of autosomal modifiers (Evang, 1925). A very similar botanical case is recorded by Harland (1932) for chlorophyll deficiency in cotton; in a way this is even more striking, since the original manifestation of the genes (in this case three pairs are involved) was markedly lethal. Here again inbreeding and selection led to the production of a reasonably viable form, while outcrossing of this to normals caused the reappearance of lethal segregants. The genetic mechanism is similar to that operative in the classical case of Castle's hooded rats and the alteration of their pattern in either plus or minus direction by an accumulation of modifiers (Castle and Pincus, 1928), though the selective implications are of course different.

Selection of this type, it now appears, is a constant and indeed normal process. It has become almost a commonplace in animals used for genetic analysis to find that mutant types, which at first are extremely difficult to keep going, after a few generations become quite viable. This has repeatedly occurred in *Gammarus*, for instance (Sexton, Clark and Spooner, 1930), and Mr. E. B. Ford tells me that it has often occurred in his cultures of other mutant strains of the same species. A recently-described example from *Drosophila* is that of white eye in *D. obscura* (Crew and Lamy, 1932). This recessive mutant was at first very delicate but its viability improved progressively on inbreeding. A precisely similar course of events was observed in the hairless mutant of mice (Crew and Mirskaia, 1931), showing that the phenomenon occurs in mammals. In plants, we have referred to cotton: an analogous case has been found in the nasturtium (Weiss, quoted by R. A. Fisher, 1931, p. 350).

In all cases, the explanation is basically similar to that for eyeless. The experimenter, however, will also attempt to keep the mutant character sharp: he will therefore be selecting for combinations which keep the viability up without altering the visible expression of the gene, so that the process may take a little longer.* R. L. Berg (1941) finds that, owing presumably to this form of selection, dominance becomes more intense in laboratory stocks than in the wild (see p. 75 seq.).

A converse effect is found when a gene, which in one species or variety is harmless, becomes deleterious on outcrossing. The explanation is that the expression of the gene in its normal situation has become so conditioned by favourable modifiers that it exerts no ill-effects; on outcrossing, however, it finds itself in a genic environment lacking some or all of these modifiers, and consequently expresses itself in ways unfavourable to viability. We have mentioned a case of this sort in Gordon's fish crosses (p. 66). A striking example, particularly relevant to our present discussion, comes from Stockard's work (1931, 1941) on dogs. The St. Bernard breed shows various symptoms of hyperpituitarism that simulate the pathological condition known as acromegaly. Matings between St. Bernards give normal litters; but when the St. Bernard is crossed with the Great Dane, a breed that may be regarded as a simple giant type with no hyperpituitary characters, a considerable proportion of the F1

---

* Another method by which viability may be improved is by mutation in the primary gene concerned. As an example, we may take the work of Mohr (1932). Two stocks of vestigial-winged fruit-flies (*Drosophila melanogaster*) were maintained for a long time as inbred cultures. In both of them, the wings eventually became almost normal. Analysis showed that this was due to the selection of a less extreme allele of vestigial which had presumably arisen by mutation from full vestigial, and had then been favoured by selection because of its less extreme effects. An interesting point is that these nearly normal alleles were not identical in the two cases, but represented different steps in the multiple series.

(and later) offspring show serious disturbances during their growth, notably hydrocephalus and paralysis of the hind limbs, these effects being clearly of genetic origin.

Man, it seems, has pushed the St. Bernard breed as far as it can go in the direction of large size, heavy jowl, and other effects of extreme or one-sided pituitary action; and in the process has amassed those combinations of modifiers which will protect the organism against the harmful effects of its exaggerated glandular development. When the breed is outcrossed, the protective genes are diluted to a greater or lesser extent, with corresponding ill-effects. The modern show type of bulldog has similarly been produced by selection for genes causing abnormal thyroid structure and function; here the breed has been pushed still further towards the glandular limit, since a considerable proportion of males are partially or wholly sterile.

An example in which genic expression is altered without noticeable effects on viability is that of the hybrids between *Drosophila melanogaster* and *D. simulans*. About 50 per cent of these lack bristles present in both parent species—i.e. certain combinations of modifiers from the two parent species suppress the expression of certain genes controlling bristle development (Biddle, 1932).

Excellent examples involving artificial selection have resulted from the work of R. A. Fisher (1935, 1938), who by repeated back-crossing introduced dominant or semi-dominant genes from domestic breeds of poultry, into the unselected gene-complex of the wild jungle fowl. Polydactyly varies in its single-dose expression* in domestic breeds. Punnett and Pease (1929) found it to

---

* The term *dominant* has unfortunately been employed very loosely, some authors using it to mean that the heterozygote is indistinguishable from the homozygote, while others call a dominant any gene whose effects in single dose can be distinguished at all: e.g. Bowater (1914) called the melanic form of the moth *Aplecta nebulosa* a dominant, although the heterozygote, as he himself goes on to state, has an intermediate expression; and *all* the so-called dominant mutations in *Drosophila melanogaster* are either lethal in double dose, when, of course, the visible effect of the homozygote cannot be determined, or their heterozygous expression is less extreme than their homozygous (e.g. abnormal abdomen).

For this reason, and because it is in many ways unsatisfactory to have positive and negative terms, like dominant and recessive, to denote gradations in what is really a single scale of positive effects, I would suggest that some other term,

behave usually as a complete dominant, but sometimes as a recessive and sometimes as an irregular partial dominant. To explain these facts, they postulated one dominant inhibitor preventing the expression of the gene for polydactyly, and a second capable of suppressing the action of the first. Hutchinson (1931) pointed out that a simpler explanation is provided by Fisher's theory, according to which there is a single gene which remains constant, but whose dominance-relations differ in different gene-complexes. In the wild gene-complex, moreover, as Fisher showed, the homozygote can be definitely distinguished from the heterozygote by possessing larger extra toes, with more bones. What has happened is that an originally intermediate single-dose expression has, in most domestic breeds, become more complete. The gene for barred plumage behaves in a somewhat similar way. Most interesting are the results with the gene for crest on the head. In the wild gene-complex the crested gene in single dose produces crest alone; in double dose, however, it produces not only an unusually large crest but a cerebral hernia of deleterious character. In the Japanese silky fowl, no hernia is ever produced, and the effect of the crested gene is the same in single and in double dose. Thus firstly, the gene has become fully dominant in domestication in place of intermediate; secondly, its effect on hernia has been suppressed by modifying factors (cf. pp. 70, 79); and thirdly, in the wild gene complex, its two effects are of different type, the harmful hernia being fully recessive, the neutral crest being partially dominant.

Another aspect of the adaptation of genic expression to the needs of the organism concerns the stability of expression of genes. Plunkett (1932), for instance, has analysed the fact, well known in general terms, that wild-type characters are usually much less modifiable by changes in environment than are those determined by mutant genes. His analysis was for the most part

such as *single-dose expression* (or *heterozygous expressivity*) would be more suitable. Full single-dose expression would then be equivalent to true dominance: zero single-dose expression to recessivity; and truly intermediate expression to absence of dominance in which the heterozygote is intermediate between the two homozygotes. Timoféeff-Ressovsky (1934b) deals with expressivity from a rather different angle.

restricted to temperature-effects in *Drosophila*, but the principle can be widely generalized. The explanation is based on the fact that genes are in most cases concerned with the rates of processes (see Goldschmidt, 1938*a*). The curves expressing the rate of the processes are in general obliquely S-shaped, tending to a final horizontal equilibrium-position (Ford and Huxley, 1929). In wild-type genes, the flattening is normally completed before the imaginal state (or corresponding definitive stage) is reached, whereas in the majority of mutant genes, the curve is still in the ascending phase at this stage. Thus quite small disturbances of the curve will have marked effects in mutant genes, but very slight ones on wild-type characters.

There can be no doubt that selection has been at work to adjust the rates of gene-controlled processes so as to produce this result in wild-type genes, thus conferring a high degree of stability on the characters concerned. As Plunkett further points out, the evolution of complete dominance, with which our next section deals, can be regarded as a special case of this principle, viz. that in general natural selection favours the genotype which produces the most stable and therefore uniform phenotype.

Where special circumstances demand the contrary effect, that different conditions shall be met by quite distinct phenotypes, selection has often operated to produce plasticity of genic expression. This plasticity, however, is usually of a special type, operating by some sort of switch mechanism, so that two or a few contrasted phenotypes, each of them relatively stable, are produced. The classical case is that of the environmental control of caste in social hymenoptera, whereby the same genotype can be made to produce either neuter or fertile females, and intermediates are rare aberrations. The same sort of mechanism seems to be at work in regard to the winged and wingless condition of aphids, and in environmental sex-determination.*

* The same result can of course be secured genetically, either by special chromosomal mechanisms, as in genetic sex-determination, or by a selective balance resulting in polymorphism, as especially well illustrated by butterflies with polymorphic mimetic forms (see pp. 101, 122).

4. THE EVOLUTION OF DOMINANCE

R. A.. Fisher (1928, 1931, 1934) has extended this concept of the alterability of gene-expression by modifiers to account for dominance in general, or at least for many features of dominance as found in nature. His argument runs as follows. Mutation is always throwing up new genes; the majority of these will inevitably be deleterious, since. in a delicately-adjusted system like the gene-complex most changes are likely to be for the worse unless compensated. Further, we know as an empirical fact. that the majority of mutations are repeatedly produced. Obviously the great majority of mutant genes will be carried in single dose, so that it will be an advantage to minimize any activity shown by them while in the heterozygous state. Thus, even when a harmful mutation at its first appearance shows considerable single-dose expression, i.e. manifests some or all of its effects when in the heterozygous state, then, if it be repeatedly produced (which is the case with most mutations), the way is open for it to be forced into recessivity by selection acting on the rest of the gene-complex. If it is relatively abundant (and recent studies of wild populations —e.g. C. Gordon (1936), Dubinin and others (1936), and Sexton and Clark (1936a)—have shown the surprisingly high incidence of various recessives which they carry in the fly Drosophila and the shrimp Gammarus respectively), selection may get to work on the homozygous condition, and render it also inactive. In such a way, as Fisher points out, mutations may be reduced to the rank of specific modifiers, normally inoperative, but exerting effects in abnormal gene-situations.*

* · As. showing the intensity of the selection acting against certain recessive mutations, C. Gordon (1935) liberated 36,000 Drosophila melanogaster in England, where they are not endemic. The population originally contained 50 per cent of the recessive gene ebony (25 per cent pure wild-type flies, 25 per cent ebony, and 50 per cent heterozygous for ebony). After 120 days (5 to 6 generations) the frequency of the ebony gene had fallen to 11 per cent. From the data it appears that some heterozygotes were selectively eliminated in each generation, as well as the homozygotes; this is in accordance with the fact that ebony has a slight single-dose expression.

A further important fact is that in nature recessives are almost wholly absent from the X-chromosome of Drosophila, where, of course, they are exposed (in males) to selection in single dose (p. 117).

Dubinin and others (1936) found more than one detectable mutant (recessive)

In support of this view, we will cite some of the array of facts that show how readily the degree of dominance of a gene may be altered by the presence of other genes. The classical case is that of horns in domestic sheep (Wood, 1905). The difference between horned and hornless breeds depends on a single gene-difference, but whereas a single dose of the gene for horns will produce horns in rams, a double dose is necessary in ewes. The same gene is thus dominant in the internal environment of males, but recessive in that of females. In fowls, Landauer (1937) found that the gene for frizzled plumage, whose effects are normally incompletely dominant, is converted into an almost complete recessive by the presence of a particular recessive modifier in double dose. Dunn and Landauer (1934, 1936), with the gene *rumpless*, which reduces the tail and posterior end of the body, were able to go further and to show that this could be converted either into a dominant or a recessive by crossing to different stocks, followed by selection for dominance or recessivity respectively. In mice, on the other hand, the gene for black, which is normally a complete recessive, can be converted into an incomplete dominant by modifiers (Barrows, 1934). In *Drosophila virilis*, the dominant gene for rounded wings converts the gene for ruffled bristles from a recessive into an incomplete dominant (Lebedeff, 1933). Mather and North (1940) describe a gene in mice whose only known effect is to modify the dominance-relations of the *agouti* gene.

A case of some historical interest is that described by Federley (1911) of the behaviour of white spotting in the larvae of the moth *Pygaera*. In *P. anachoreta* an unspotted variety is found, and this behaves as a simple recessive to the normal spotted condition. In *P. curtula*, however, only the unspotted condition exists. In the F1 of a cross between the two species, using the spotted form of *P. anachoreta*, spotting is expressed in an intermediate form, i.e. its dominance has been partially abolished. Twenty-five years ago, this fact seemed so remarkable that an authority such as

allele in each wild fruit-fly! They also showed that various mutant genes altered in their frequency during three years, some becoming more and others less frequent.

Sturtevant (1912) was disinclined to accept it: to-day, however, such alteration of gene-expression by modifiers has become a commonplace.

We need not multiply examples. It is clear that the dominance of a gene can be radically modified according to the genic environment in which it happens to find itself.

The next step is to show that this undoubted fact of the modifiability of the degree of dominance has been utilized in the course of evolution to make most commonly-recurring mutations recessive, so as to reduce the degree of their heterozygous expression, including that of the decreased viability which accompanies most mutations at their first appearance.

In cotton, Harland (1933) and Hutchinson and Ghose (1937) have studied the mutation *crinkled dwarf*. This occurs in the Sea Island variety of *Gossypium barbadense*, and is there a complete recessive. When crossed to unrelated strains of the same species, it is not completely recessive but shows a low degree of single-dose expression.

When, however, the mutation was introduced from G. *barbadense* into the related species G. *hirsutum* (upland cotton) there proved to be a complete absence of dominance of the normal type. The F1 is intermediate, so that at first sight we might imagine the single-dose expression to be about 50 per cent; but the fact that the F2 gives a large and unclassifiable range shows that the degree of dominance must be under the influence of a number of modifying genes. This is confirmed by the results of back-crossing the F1 species-hybrid bearing the crinkled dwarf gene to various strains of G. *hirsutum*. In certain lines, complete or almost complete recessivity of crinkled dwarf was re-established, while in others the single-dose expressivity was rendered accurately intermediate, the heterozygote class being clearly separable from either homozygote. As Hutchinson and Ghose have clearly shown, the results entirely support R. A. Fisher's views. Later work (see summary by Harland, 1941) has shown that it also occurs as a very rare mutant in G. *hirsutum*. The *barbadense* crinkled shows intermediate single-dose expression in the F1 with *hirsutum*, but is recessive when transferred to a pure *hirsutum* gene-complex. When, however, *hirsutum* crinkled is transferred to a pure *barbadense* gene-complex, it behaves as an intermediate.

Harland (1941) develops the thesis that the dominance of normal alleles in cotton may be built up in a considerable variety of ways. Thus the character *petal spot* in both *barbadense* and *hirsutum* is based primarily on a main gene which, however, exists in different allelic forms in the two species. But whereas in *barbadense* the action of this main gene must be reinforced by a number of plus modifiers to produce its full effect, in *hirsutum* the main gene is stronger, and requires no (or few) modifiers. As corollaries of these facts we find (1) that in *barbadense*, the modifiers exert some positive action (a small spot) even in the absence of the main gene; (2) the gene for *barbadense* spot transferred to the *hirsutum* gene-complex has a very weak effect, and the petals are barely spotted; (3) the gene for *hirsutum* spot transferred to the *barbadense* gene-complex is reinforced by the modifiers there present, and produces a spot which is larger and more intense than any previously known; (4) crosses of the spotted forms of the one species with the unspotted of the other give a graded F2 with all intensities of spotting; (5) the F2 from the unspotted forms of the same two species produces some spots as large as normal *barbadense*—i.e. due to recombination of modifiers only, presumably from both species. In G. *arboreum* yet a third method of producing the spotted character is found: there is no main gene, but spotting depends on the genes that in *barbadense* act as modifiers, but here must be called a multiple factor series or polygenic combination.

Harland suggests that if a character is of advantage to the species, it can be more readily retained, in spite of recessive mutation, if its expression depends on several genes. However, this conclusion does not seem justified. The advantage of the method of using a single main gene together with modifiers would rather seem to lie in keeping the expression of the character relatively constant in the normal range of environmental conditions, but retaining a considerable reserve of potential variability to meet new or extreme conditions. The single-gene control will give greater stability, the purely multifactorial control (by "modifiers" only) will give greater plasticity. Single-gene control will permit the character to be more readily lost under the influence of selection or by drift. Presumably in correlation with this, in *hirsutum*, where spot depends on one gene only, the spot character has been lost in all but a few rare varieties.

To return to crinkled dwarf, the same principles apply. Normality (non-crinkled) in *barbadense* depends on a single strong allele, like spot in *hirsutum*. Normality in *hirsutum*, on the other hand, depends on a weaker main non-crinkled allele, together with a number of modifiers. These not only encourage the dominance of normal over crinkled, but make the pure crinkled forms more normal, both in appearance and viability. By rigorous selection, new combinations of modifiers have been obtained which render the *hirsutum* crinkled practically indistinguishable from normal. When the two species are crossed, using the normal of one and the crinkled form of the other, F2 ranges from forms which are phenotypically normal through all grades of crinkling to "super-crinkled" types which are almost lethal. The petal spot experiments demonstrate two types of dominance. In *hirsutum* the Fisher effect is clearly operative, with modifiers aiding a weak "normal" gene, and also modifying the recessive towards normality. Recessive modification is much harder where a nearly dominant main gene exists, as in *barbadense*. This may then be due to an extension of the Haldane effect (p. 82), by selection of "stronger" normal alleles. Harland and Atteck (1941) consider that this also operates for *crinkled dwarf* in some species, but the evidence is not decisive. They further point out that the Haldane effect is likely to be more important in self-fertilized forms, where the Fisher effect cannot so readily be produced (Haldane, 1939a). Where both types occur, as in *Gossypium*, doubtless "accidental" events such as the time of occurrence of suitable mutations, will determine which mechanism evolves (see also Silow, 1941).

An important empirical fact which was among those that led Fisher to promulgate his theory is that of the behaviour of multiple alleles. In almost every case so far investigated, the wild-type allele shows complete dominance over all the lower members of the series, whereas these when crossed with each other show intermediate expression. Thus the normal red colour of the eye in wild *Drosophila* is completely dominant over white, ivory, eosin, cherry, and all the other members of the white allelomorphic series: but white crossed with eosin, or ivory with cherry, gives an FI with eyes intermediate in colour between the two parents.

The exception proves the rule: and the exception to this rule, to which attention was first drawn by Ford (1930), concerns the effect of this same series of genes upon an internal character of apparently no selective value. Dobzhansky (1927) had shown that the genes of the white-eye series affect the shape of the spermatheca to a small but constant degree. Whereas, as we have seen, the genes are all recessive to wild-type as regards their effects on the eye, they show intermediate expression as regards this secondary effect on the spermatheca. The body-colour genes of the ebony-sooty series show the same effect on the spermatheca, and the same differential expression as regards their effect on the external and the internal character (except that ebony body-colour is not wholly recessive). The most obvious explanation is that selection has been operative in modifying the expression of the disadvantageous external character, whereas no such effect was called for, or has been produced, with regard to the harmless secondary internal effect. We may also compare the different dominance-relations of the deleterious and harmless effects of the *crest* factor in fowls (p. 73).

It is worth noting that this differential expression of the gene as regards two characters affected by it cannot be reconciled with any rigid form of the "inactivation" theory of recessiveness. This extension of the old Presence and Absence theory, which is obviously untenable in its original form, claims that the degree of recessivity corresponds to the degree of partial loss or inactivation suffered by the gene in mutating to one or other of its recessive allelomorphs. It is clear from what we know of actual deficiency-mutations, in which a portion of the chromosome is missing, that loss may produce effects of the same nature as gene-mutations (see, e.g., Mohr, 1920, who showed that that loss of the *white* locus produces an *ultra-white* effect more intense than *white* itself), so that the inactivation theory may sometimes apply. But the demonstration that some genes can become dominant or recessive according to the gene-complex shows that it can at best have a partial application. It is also noteworthy that the true absence of a gene in *ultra-white* produces some effects (spermatheca shape) which are not recessive!

As R. A. Fisher (1931) points out, the majority of the characters of most domestic breeds, or at least of the most obvious characters, especially of pattern and colour, depend on mutations recessive to the wild type. It would seem clear that man has here taken advantage of two facts, first that more or less recessive mutations are commoner in nature and secondly that they can be readily fixed by mating two similar individuals, in order to utilize striking and more or less recessive characters during his selection. Furthermore the natural tendency to concentrate for breeding purposes on individuals showing a character in more extreme form will, in the case of genes originally largely recessive, then automatically encourage the production of complete recessivity. If, however, the gene had more than intermediate single-dose expression, selection would tend to make it more dominant. Thus in general man's artificial selection will tend to encourage either complete dominance or complete recessivity, though for reasons quite other than those operative in nature. But, as mentioned, the distinguishing characters of domestic breeds in most species are usually recessive.

The chief exception occurs in poultry, where the majority of "domestic" characters are partially or wholly dominant. Fisher (1931) suggests that this difference is due to the fact that in the countries of their origin, the domestic forms, even to-day and more so in earlier times, would frequently be mated by wild cocks. In such a case, recessives could not readily be fixed, whereas partial dominants would at least reappear in every generation; thus dominants would tend to be bred into the race by a natural selection of man's selective processes. A further effect would be that the degree of their dominance would be increased, through the new varieties being almost wholly heterozygous, and through man selecting the most striking individuals from which to breed.

We have seen (p. 72) that his experimental tests have confirmed this hypothesis.

Marchlewski (1941) has recently confirmed Fisher's theory in dogs. Here, black was originally dominant over yellow; however, in the dingo and in various domestic breeds, yellow has become dominant through the selection of modifiers.

The recessivity of characters in other domestic species is not so nearly universal as Fisher was at first inclined to think (Castle, 1934, on various species; J. A. F. Roberts and White, 1930, and J. A. F. Roberts, 1932, on sheep). It seems clear, however, that man, by his breeding methods, has modified the single-dose expression of wild-type genes in his domestic animals, accentuating the recessivity of those with low, and the dominance of those with high single-dose expression; and that while this will result in most species in a preponderance of recessive breed-characters, in poultry it will tend to a preponderance of dominant ones.

It should be stated that Wright (1934a) does not agree with Fisher's views on the evolution of dominance, but wishes to ascribe recessivity to partial inactivation of the gene (p. 80). An alternative hypothesis for the origin of the recessive character of most mutations has been given by Haldane (1930; and see 1939a). This is based on an interesting view as to the mode of action of genes, namely, that different multiple allelomorphs produce different amounts of some substance, but only up to a certain saturation value: beyond this they can produce no phenotypic effect. Thus any mutation in a minus direction below this level can be detected, but those in a plus direction cannot. In consequence a number of different multiple alleles of different strength, but all above that needed to give the saturation value, may readily accumulate without being phenotypically detected. If now minus mutations occur, Haldane suggests that, in order (I speak teleological shorthand) to prevent their visible and viability effects from being manifested in the heterozygote, those higher alleles will be selected which in combination with the mutation will not fall below saturation level.

In other words, higher members of the series will be selected, and visible dominance will be the result. Ford, however, has pointed out that the saturation level itself will be determined in relation to the residual gene-complex, so that even here the action postulated by R. A. Fisher may be operative, though in some cases in addition to the Haldane mechanism. In any case both suggestions involve selection acting upon other genes than the mutant. Since the above was written, Ford (1940b) has shown that the Fisher effect can be artificially produced. The currant-moth, *Abraxas grossulariata*, has a single-gene wild variety (*lutea*) with yellow instead of white ground-colour, which normally gives an intermediate F1 with wild type. By four generations of plus and minus selection, Ford has conferred both complete dominance and complete recessivity upon the gene.

Sewall Wright (1929, 1934a) attacks Fisher's general conception on the ground that the selection-pressure available will be inadequate to achieve the results envisaged. However, there seems little doubt that dominance of the "normal" wild-type allele has been evolved; and Plunkett and Muller independently (see Muller, 1935) have shown how the need for stability of gene-expression in development will secondarily result in the evolution of dominance.

Whatever the precise method employed, it seems clear that dominance and recessiveness must be regarded as modifiable characters, not as unalterable inherent properties of genes. Dominant genes, or many of them, are not born dominant: they have dominance thrust upon them. Mutations may *become* dominant or recessive, through the action of other genes in the gene-complex. The evolution of dominance is thus seen to be in large measure an adaptation to the deleterious nature of most mutations.

R. L. Berg (1941) points out that the intensity of dominance will be selectively balanced against the accumulation of deleterious recessives which it makes possible, and that it will tend to be decreased in species consisting of incompletely isolated groups. The extra plasticity thus conferred upon such species will be in addition to that deduced by Wright (p. 229).

As another example of an adaptation of the genetic mechanism itself, Fisher (1930a, p. 15) cites the plasticity conferred by sexuality.

For one thing, it will permit evolutionary advance by the combination of new mutations. If several favourable mutations occur in a population in a given time, then in a sexual cross-fertilizing species they can be combined. But if the species is asexual, they will almost certainly remain isolated, each confined to one line; for them to be combined, one mutant must be selected until it has become the main type, and only then will a second favourable mutation have a chance of becoming combined with the first.

In the second place, it will permit recombination to throw up new gene-combinations and so to use the existing genetic variance of the species to alter the type quickly in relation to changed conditions. Thus it promotes both progressive specialization (see Chapter 9) and plasticity in response to the changes and chances of the environment. In addition, as Fisher (1932) stresses, it has a function to perform in relation to the deleterious nature of most mutations. For, by allowing recombination, it permits mutations to appear in homozygous form, and thus facilitates the elimination of the more deleterious. Elimination will be greater when the frequency of homozygosis is increased by inbreeding or self-fertilization. Thus variations in the type of sexual reproduction will alter the emphasis of its evolutionary function (Darlington, 1939): evolutionary plasticity will be more encouraged by cross-breeding, evolutionary stability by inbreeding. Inbreeding will also promote both the rejection of unfavourable and the spread of favourable mutations (see also pp. 136, 140).

Recombinational plasticity will be especially valuable when conditions vary and become less favourable. This is doubtless the reason why so many organisms adopt some method of asexual reproduction (which is more efficient *qua* reproduction) so long as environmental conditions are favourable, but resort to a sexual process as soon as they become unfavourable. This is so, for instance, with many protozoa, rotifers, lower crustacea, and aphids.

The biological meaning of this has been clearly brought out by careful genetic studies on *Paramecium* and other ciliates (Jennings, 1929). It has been found in general that conjugation causes an increase of genetic variability in the resultant population, and that while (as in higher organisms) the majority of the new type may be regarded as unfavourable, some are actually or potentially better-adapted than those prevailing before conjugation. Thus conjugation will in many cases provide an increased chance of throwing up a recombination better able to cope with unusual and unfavourable conditions. Precisely similar results have been obtained with lower crustacea by Banta and his colleagues (see Davenport, 1933).

Attention is elsewhere drawn (p. 113) to the action of the impulse to migrate in unfavourable conditions. This also confers plasticity on a species, but in this case by increasing the range of environmental opportunities available to a given hereditary constitution, instead of increasing the range of hereditary constitutions available to cope with given environmental conditions. This, however, can hardly be called an adaptation of the genetic mechanism.

On the other hand, the peculiar reactions of the crossing-over mechanism to temperatures may well, as Mr. E. B. Ford has suggested to me, fall into this category. In *Drosophila*, the best-investigated case (Plough, 1917), crossing-over is least at temperatures close to the optimum for the species, and increases rapidly both with increase and with decrease of temperature. Increased crossing-over will, of course, have the effect of increasing the recombination of the genes located in a single kind of chromosome, and this will have a considerable effect in a form like *Drosophila* where the chromosomes are few in number. Unfavourable temperatures will thus increase the genetic variance available to a population.

The discovery of the position-effect (pp. 48, 92) allows us to deduce certain ways, previously quite unsuspected, in which the evolutionary mechanism must itself have evolved. If, as now seems established, it is the case with some or all genes that interaction with near neighbours in the same chromosome affects their expression in an important way, then it is clear that all the genes within a given chromosome must be delicately adjusted to each other so as to produce a harmoniously functioning whole.

Any given gene must be adjusted to its neighbours within a certain chromosome-distance either way; the genes at the limit of this range will be adjusted both to the gene at our hypothetical starting-point and to others further away, thus conferring a certain organization on the chromosome as a whole.

This involves a new conception of chromosomes. Up till quite recently, it was possible and usual to regard them as mere vehicles for the carriage and distribution of the hereditary constitution, without any functional organization of the genes they contained. These were assumed to be arranged at random, like coloured beads picked up haphazard by a blind man and threaded on a string; and their positions in the chromosomes were not supposed to have any relation with their effects on visible or other characters.

With the discovery of the position-effect, however, this assumption, as a hard-and-fast principle, has gone by the board. Although many genes affecting one character are scattered irregularly through the chromosomes, and genes affecting different characters are often contiguous, yet some degree of non-random arrangement does occur (Morgan, Schultz and Curry, 1940). Basically, and in origin, their arrangement doubtless is random, and what we know of the frequency of sectional rearrangements (pp. 90, 362) shows that genes must often change their neighbours in an essentially accidental way. But this randomness must then be given a functional polish: neighbouring genes must be adjusted to each other by new mutation and by recombination. To continue our metaphor, the blind man's necklace is looked at, and colour disharmonies are got rid of by choosing new beads of the same general colour but slightly different shade.

The same general type of adaptation to position-effects has been necessary as with dominance in relation to gene-mutation. Indeed, the "weakening" of genes in abnormal positions (Dobzhansky, 1936, p. 376) indicates that a disproportionate fraction of the single-dose expression of dominant genes is determined by their relations with their immediate neighbours. In addition, functionally-balanced groups of genes affecting polygenic characters will be evolved within the separate chromosomes (Mather, 1941: see p. 67). We must to-day consider chromosomes not as being purely mechanical gene-vehicles, but to a certain degree as organic gene-arrangements.

5. TYPES OF MUTATION

So far, under the head of mutation, we have been considering only gene-mutation or point-mutation, i.e. the substantive alteration of a definite unit-region of the chromosome outfit. But various other kinds of mutation are also known to occur and we must devote a brief section to these.

In the first place, there are *genome-mutations*, involving one or more whole sets of chromosomes and therefore of gene-outfits. The normal diploid complement of chromosomes of a species may become doubled (autotetraploidy). Or reduction may fail to occur, and a diploid instead of a haploid gamete may be formed. Or, as a result of the union of a normal gamete with a diploid one, however formed, auto-triploid forms with three genomes may result.

Tetraploidy in nature may also result from a cross between two species, when the corresponding chromosomes from the two parents do not pair before meiosis and the hybrid is therefore originally sterile. If, however, the chromosomes of a cell divide but not the cell-body itself, all descendants of this cell will be tetraploid, and the two members of each kind of chromosome can act as mates at reduction. The result will be that the gametes have complete genomes from either parent. This is known as allotetraploidy, and its actual origin has been observed in *Primula kewensis*, the fertile hybrid between *P. floribunda* and *P. verticillata*. In this case the original hybrid was sterile, and the fertile type, with larger leaves and flowers, arises sporadically in cuttings, from a cell in which chromosome-doubling has occurred. Allotetraploidy is almost confined to plants, because of the favourable conditions provided by their vegetative growth for the rare chromosome-doubling to occur and to give rise to reproductive tissue, and because of their lack of the sex-chromosome mechanism normal to animals, which would not function after chromosome-doubling (Muller, 1925; see also p. 142). For polyploidy in animals see Vandel (1937).

The presence of six, eight, and more genomes in a strain or species is also known, again almost entirely in plants; presumably the condition is usually consequent upon species-crossing (Chapter 6; and Darlington, 1937, p. 65).

In all genome-mutations, the genome-units may be approximate only, sometimes with loss and sometimes with gain of one or a few chromosomes (aneuploidy).

Triploid and other anisoploid strains with an odd number of genomes are relatively rare in nature, and cannot normally reproduce themselves sexually, since the chromosomes of one genome cannot find mates. But allopolyploids and other strains with an even genome-number can maintain themselves.* Such polyploidy has undoubtedly been of considerable evolutionary importance in plants. One method of species-formation is by allotetraploidy after crossing (p. 341). But apart from this, polyploidy of any kind, so long as not excessive, by multiplying the number of gene-pairs of each kind in the hereditary constitution, confers long-range potential variability and plasticity on the species. For different gene-pairs may mutate in slightly different ways, giving a gradation of new recombinations. High autopolyploidy, however, by virtually suppressing the chance of manifestation of recessives, reduces plasticity. It appears that the phenomenon has been of importance in the evolution of higher plants, where series of related forms with two, four, six, and higher numbers of genomes often occur. Polyploidy has also undoubtedly contributed to the evolution of many cultivated plants, notably the cereals and cotton. (See also pp. 335 seq.).

The second type of chromosome-mutation is that of the addition or subtraction of single chromosomes. This again appears to be much commoner in plants than in animals. It has been

---

* Autopolyploids will originally produce many inviable gametes, owing to the aggregation of chromosomes by fours instead of by pairs before meiosis. But there is evidence to show that this condition, too, may be adjusted by selection, leading to reasonably true-breeding forms (Darlington, 1937; Müntzing, 1936).

thoroughly investigated in the Jimson weed, *Datura stramonium*, by Blakeslee and his collaborators (1928). The commonest case is where one kind of chromosome is represented three times instead of twice in the hereditary outfit. Such *trisomic* mutants, as they are called, show greater differences from normal than do ordinary gene-mutants. They also show reduced viability due to the quantitative upset of gene-balance which they cause.

In *Datura*, these types cannot become fixed, since no pollen with an extra chromosome is viable. Thus all viable pollen-grains will contain n chromosomes, while the ova will be either n or $n + 1$.

It would seem, however, that in the evolution of some plants, the condition has become stabilized; but this is always in polyploid forms, where imbalance is not so readily brought about (p. 349).

The third type of chromosome-mutation is the sectional, involving only parts of chromosomes. For its occurrence and evolutionary bearings in *Drosophila*, see Muller (1940). One form of this is known as *deficiency* and involves the loss of a portion of a chromosome. This is known to occur not uncommonly in *Drosophila*, but is here and probably elsewhere of little evolutionary significance, since homozygous deficiency is usually lethal.

The converse is known as *duplication*, when a portion of a chromosome comes to be repeated, occurring twice instead of once, either in the form of a translocation to another chromosome, or of a "repeat" within the same chromosome, often immediately adjacent to its original position. Small "repeats" of this type have been shown by the salivary gland technique to be not infrequent in *Drosophila*, and are of considerable evolutionary importance. They are of immediate importance, since the alteration in genic balance would usually produce definite but not deleterious effects. They are of much greater ultimate importance, since they constitute the chief method by which the number of genes is increased, thus providing duplicate factors, and the opportunity for slight divergent specialization of homologous genes, giving great delicacy of adjustment. In this respect they would appear to be a good deal more important than the earlier-detected and more spectacular process of duplicating whole genomes by autopolyploidy (see pp. 334 seq.).

The next type of sectional chromosome-mutation includes all cases involving spatial rearrangement of sections of two kinds of chromosomes. The most important form of this is *reciprocal translocation* or segmental interchange. When this occurs, two chromosomes break and exchange fragments. The precise mechanism need not concern us. It can be induced with greater frequency by X-rays, and appears to occur where chromosomes actually or almost touch each other. It is known to occur or can be deduced to have occurred in a number of plants, and in *Drosophila* and certain other animals.

In *Datura*, over forty so-called "prime types", which differ from each other merely by rearrangement of segments of the chromosomes, and which appear to owe their origin to reciprocal translocations, are known to occur in nature; they do not show visible differences. Different prime types differ in their geographical distribution.

Owing to certain peculiarities of chromosome behaviour, these prime types in *Datura* tend to persist as such, even after a cross. This is in effect a form of isolation and should eventually give opportunities for mutation and selection to produce visible differences between the various chromosomal types.

After crossing between two prime types, the hybrid type will, owing to certain chromosomal peculiarities, be reproduced as such in later generations, without rearrangement due to crossing-over, as well as the two pure types. If now a recessive lethal mutation occurs in one of the chromosomes which have suffered segmental interchange, the prime type containing that chromosome cannot be reconstituted, as a double dose of the lethal is *ex hypothesi* fatal. Since lethals are relatively common types of mutation, one may readily occur also in corresponding portions of the chromosomes derived from the other prime type. If so, and if we are dealing with an inbreeding group, we shall have a condition of "balanced lethals", and only the hybrid chromosome-combination will be capable of survival.

Wherever much segmental interchange has occurred, followed

by long-continued intercrossing between the resultant prime types, we may expect to find balanced-lethal and therefore permanently hybrid combinations. And once these come into existence, they can differentiate still further by the accumulation of gene-mutations.

This, in actual fact, is what appears to have occurred in the evening primroses, *Oenothera* (see Renner, 1925, and Cleland, 1928; and summary e.g. in Dobzhansky, 1937). One known species (*O. hookeri*) is of normal chromosomal behaviour, but all the others present balanced-lethal chromosome combinations of greater or lesser extent. The chief evolutionary significance of these phenomena would appear to lie in its providing a special method of species-formation (see pp. 139, 329), It is, however, of historical interest since occasional crossing-over will give apparent mutations (really recombinations of large blocks of genes); and on the basis of these de Vries advanced his mutation theory.

Small translocations of various types seem to occur quite frequently in *Drosophila*. They have probably been of some, though secondary, importance in initiating the differentiation of species (Dobzhansky and Tan, 1936; and see p. 362).

As final form of sectional chromosome-mutation we have *inversion*, in which one segment of a chromosome becomes reversed within the chromosome as a whole. Quite large or very small portions of the chromosome may become inverted. Here again the frequency of the process may be accelerated by X-rays.

Crossing-over, of a type which will give viable offspring, cannot occur in the inverted section of a chromosome paired with a normal mate. This being so, inversion may produce a distinct type, homozygous for the inverted chromosome, in addition to the normal; in some cases, in fact, hybrids between the two types will not be able to reproduce so freely, because of the death of cross-overs. The resultant isolation of the two types of chromosome will permit their differentiation. More than that, selection will tend to erect barriers to intercrossing, so that the resultant waste due to the reduced fertility of the hybrids may be avoided. In consequence, the two types may develop into distinct species. This method of speciation is discussed in Chapter 6 (p. 329).

We may here again mention the curious and unexpected phenomenon of the position effect, according to which the mere fact of rearrangement of genes produced by inversion, etc., may cause a difference in their visible effects, thus simulating mutation (Dobzhansky, 1936). Indeed, studies like those of Muller (Muller, Prokofyeva, and Raffel, 1935) make it probable that a large number of the genetic changes in *Drosophila* previously ascribed to gene-mutation are in reality due to such "position-effects", produced by inversions of very small sections of a chromosome.

It has been suggested by some authors that what are normally called gene-mutations are in reality only the effects of small rearrangements. However, Mackenzie and Muller (1940) have recently demonstrated that there is a real distinction between the two types of mutation, since ultra-violet radiation can produce true gene-mutation, but not the chromosome-breakage needed to effect sectional rearrangements, however small. This is *prima facie* evidence that the substantive changes due to true gene-mutation do (as is to be expected) play a part in nature, in addition to the organizational changes due to rearrangement of pre-existing units.

From the point of view of evolution, however, the significance of such changes will be very similar to that of true or substantive mutation; the changes produced will be inherited according to Mendelian laws, and will be of small extent.

Muller (1930) has also pointed out that if two homologous chromosomes with different but overlapping inverted regions are brought together by crossing, crossing-over will result in a new type of chromosome containing one region in duplicate. Such small duplications will have visible effects, and may also be employed as sources of evolutionary change. Recently the discovery of the giant chromosomes in the salivary glands has converted *Drosophila* from a very bad to by far the best material for detailed chromosomal study, permitting the cytologist to produce a detailed map of the visible structure of its chromosomes and to detect even minute inversions and other rearrangements. It is as if an astronomer armed only with Galileo's telescope had been suddenly equipped with a 50-inch reflector.

The use of this method has shown that rearrangements of

segments of the chromosomes are far commoner, and have played a much larger part in evolutionary processes, such as the differentiation of species, than was previously supposed. We have just mentioned the important role of small inversions within a single species. When we compare related species (e.g. Dobzhansky and Tan, 1936; Dobzhansky, 1937), we find they are distinguished by numerous characteristic differences in segmental arrangement. *Drosophila pseudoobscura* and *D. miranda*, for instance, are so closely related that they will mate and produce healthy (but sterile) offspring. The chromosomes of the one are approximately homologous with those of the other, but some segments have been translocated to other chromosomes, and numerous segments have been inverted, so that some sections of certain chromosomes show "profoundly different patterns". Other sections, however, remain approximately similar. On the other hand, it is probable that such changes only pave the way for full separation, the later stages of speciation being effected by a series of single gene-mutations (see p. 359, and Muller, 1940).

In barley, however, Gustafsson (1941) finds that induced sectional rearrangements occurring simultaneously with induced gene-mutations are most likely to give favourable results, as providing a new internal environment for the new gene (cf. pp. 67, 552).

But in spite of the frequency of these larger types of mutation, it would seem that gene-mutation, together with the "pseudo-mutation" due to position effects, is the most important source of evolutionary change.

6. SPECIAL CASES: MELANISM; POLYMORPHISM; FLUCTUATING POPULATIONS

Before proceeding further in our main argument, however, we must turn aside to discuss certain special cases which illustrate various points concerning neo-mendelism and selection.

(a) Melanism in moths

The first of these concerns the phenomenon of melanism in moths, which has played a prominent part in recent evolutionary discussions. The facts may be summarized as follows:

In the first place, there is no doubt that melanism among many species has become much more frequent during the last century, and that this change has been associated with industrialization: the predominance or abundance of melanics occurs in large cities and in industrial areas.* In some cases the entire population of an area has become melanic. Descriptions of the historical course of events have been given for Britain by Harrison (1920*b*, 1932), and for the continent by Walther (1927), and by Hasebroek (1934). A summary of their genetic basis is given by Ford (1937).

As regards their origin, Harrison (1928, 1935) claimed that he had been able to cause melanic forms to appear, in two species belonging to different genera, by means of incorporating lead and manganese salts in the food, and that the induced melanism behaved as a mendelian recessive, as does the naturally-occurring but very rare melanism of these species; (in a third species in which natural melanism is dominant, and has shown industrial spread, he abandoned the work after only preliminary results).

However, repetition of the work on a large scale by Hughes (1932) and Thomsen and Lemcke (1933) has failed to confirm these results. R. A. Fisher (1933*a*) has also criticized Harrison's views as involving a mutation-rate much higher than any obtainable by X-ray treatment. Further, all industrial melanism is due to dominant genes (see below). It would seem best to assume that some error has been at work, and that no true induction occurred. If so, then melanic mutations must, like other recurrent mutations, have been thrown up sporadically for a long period, but have spread owing to the altered selective conditions of an industrial environment. Numerous cases of sporadic melanism which have not become more frequent recently are known in moths as in

* It has been claimed by Harrison that melanism is also commoner in coastal areas: Ford (1937), however, shows that this conclusion is certainly not universal.

Hardy (1937) states that slight but definite darkening has occurred in the house-sparrow (*Passer domesticus*) in the Liverpool area. It will be of interest to see whether this change, too, will show progressive spread. Sporadic melanism has occurred in the passerine West Indian bird *Coereba flaveola*, producing four separate melanic island subspecies. In some cases the replacement of the normal by the black form has been followed during recent historic times. Furthermore, almost all island forms of the genus are somewhat darker than the mainland forms (Lowe, 1912). Two cases of recent spread of melanic mutants in mammals are considered later (pp. 103, 104).

other groups. An interesting case is *Boarmia extersaria*. This shows industrial melanism in Germany; but in Britain it does not enter industrial areas, and the melanic type has remained sporadic. A survey of industrial melanism reveals that the intensity of darkening varies from species to species. As regards its genetic basis, no case of recessive melanism is known to have shown industrial spread. Industrial melanism always depends either on a single dominant gene, or on multiple factors each exhibiting complete or partial dominance (Ford, 1937).

As regards its physiological effects, numerous authors have shown that dominant or partially dominant melanism confers extra hardiness and viability. Ford (1940b) has shown in *Boarmia repandata* that in highly unfavourable conditions (feeding on alternate days) the ratio of melanics emerging (on an expectation of 50 per cent) goes up from about 54 to about 70 per cent. He has also (1937) pointed out that, in spite of this physiological advantage, dominant melanic forms in non-industrial areas have not shown any spread or increase in frequency.

He accordingly concludes that recessive melanism is due to genes which have been forced to become recessive by selection of modifiers, on account of their deleterious effects on viability. Dominant melanism, on the other hand, has favourable effects on viability, but in normal conditions is kept in check by counter-selection operating through natural enemies, the type forms being definitely cryptic in coloration, while the melanics stand out sharply against the normal background. A balance is thus reached, with a low percentage of melanics.

In industrial areas, however, the counter-selection in favour of the type is not so strong, since the background is darker. It has been suggested that in some cases ecological selection would here be reversed, and the dark forms become better protected by background resemblance. Detailed counts by Harrison, however, have shown that in some species at least this is not the case. In industrial areas it is further to be expected that many natural enemies of the adult would be reduced in numbers or absent, so that selection for concealment would be less stringent. As a still further possibility, it appears probable that in the chemically unfavourable environment of industrialism, the greater hardiness of melanics would have an increased advantage.

In any case, according to Ford's general hypothesis, the balance between opposed selective forces is in industrial areas tilted in favour of the melanic variety, with the result that this has speedily increased and in some cases has completely ousted the original type. The strength of the selection acting against melanics on account of their coloration is shown by the fact that in one species, although the melanic is more cold-resistant, and has spread in industrial areas, it is not found so far north as the normal.*

It would appear that on no other hypothesis can the lack of spread of dominant melanics in rural areas and their spread in industrial areas be reconciled. If so, we have one of the most striking demonstrations of the efficacy of selection.

(b) Genetic polymorphism

Genetic polymorphism, or the co-existence of two or more genetically-determined and well-defined forms ("phases") of a species in the same area, presents certain peculiar problems. We speak of polymorphism when the difference between the various forms is sharp, or at least expressed as a bi- or multi-modality in a frequency curve of variability; when the equilibrium between them is relatively stable; and when the frequency of the least abundant is high enough to make it certain that it is not due merely to mutation-pressure (see Ford, 1940a). Polymorphism must be clearly distinguished from normal variability, however extensive, which will be grouped in a single unimodal frequency curve. The existence of separate forms or distinct modes is an essential characteristic of polymorphism.

Since we are here concerned only with genetic polymorphism, we can neglect all such cases as those of the social hymenoptera, the seasonal forms of certain butterflies, etc., which are determined environmentally. We can also neglect the particular type of

* In certain cases, the melanic form has spread from its original industrial area into surrounding non-industrial country, with a decreasing frequency-gradient. If the selective balance in favour of non-melanics in non-industrial areas is slight, this is to be expected as the result of mere population-pressure: cf. Sumner's views on population-pressure in subspecies of *Peromyscus* (p. 187).

genetic polymorphism involved in the genetic determination of two sexes, since this is primarily maintained not by a selective balance but by the inherent nature of the genetic-reproductive mechanism; the same applies to heterostyly in plants. Paulian (1936) applies the term *genetic* to certain cases of polymorphism in male insects where the forms are discontinuous and not to be explained by simple allometry (heterogony). Until, however, the developmental basis of this phenomenon has been ascertained, it is better not to assume that it must be genetically determined: see also Huxley (1932, Chap. 2, § 5).

The interest to the evolutionist of genetic polymorphism within a freely interbreeding population is that, as R. A. Fisher (1930a) was the first to point out in general terms, it must always involve a balance of selective advantages between the different types. For, *ex hypothesi*, mutation-pressure alone will not account for the facts, and it can readily be shown that in the absence of selective balance, one type would rapidly oust the other from any considerable representation in the population.

There are two distinct methods by which this balance is actually effected—genetical and ecological.

(i) In the case of genetical balance, the heterozygote is more viable or enjoys some other selective advantage over either of the homozygotes. (For simplicity's sake we will consider only cases involving dimorphism: trimorphism will occur, as in certain species of foxes, when the heterozygote differs in appearance from either homozygote, or in other cases, as in *Papilio polytes* and *P. memnon*, when two interacting gene-pairs are involved (Ford, 1937), and polymorphism when two or more non-interacting gene-pairs are involved.) This may occur in two ways. Either the gene itself is less viable or even lethal in homozygous condition; or it is closely linked with a recessive lethal, which exerts no effect in single dose but is lethal when homozygous.

Owing to the difficulty of proving a negative, no certain case of the former conditions is known, though the mutant *curly* in *Drosophila melanogaster* is a possible example. In the conditions of ordinary laboratory cultures, this maintains itself indefinitely, giving a dimorphism with wild-type. It does this because it is almost fully lethal when homozygous, but usually rather more viable than wild-type when heterozygous. As, however, it is located within an inversion, the possibility of linkage, either with a lethal or with the genes for the increased viability, is not excluded. Of linkage with a lethal, however, two examples have been thoroughly worked out. In the case of the butterfly *Argynnis paphia*, over most of its range an occasional second form of female occurs, known as *valesina*, in which the ground colour is dull green instead of rich brown. This form is usually rare, but in some localities constitutes 5 to 15 per cent of the female population. Goldschmidt and Fischer (1922) showed that *valesina* depends on a dominant gene closely linked with a recessive lethal; they were able to break the linkage, thus obtaining broods with all females of the *valesina* type. In China and neighbouring areas almost all the wild females are *valesina*. This well shows the relativity of the term *normal* as applied to organisms in nature.

A similar situation exists in the American Clouded Yellow Butterfly, *Colias philodice* (Gerould, 1923). Here a white female variant exists, and normally constitutes 4 to 20 per cent of wild females. As with *Argynnis*, the rarer form is due to a dominant gene linked with a recessive lethal, and Gerould was able to separate the two genes. In one area the white type is the more abundant. The situation as regards selective advantage is complex. The lethal must have some advantage (*a*) when heterozygous, as it is (in *Colias*) more widely spread in the population than the dominant colour-gene; (*b*) in association with the dominant colour-gene, since the linkage, though not very close, survives in nature in most areas. The dominant colour-gene must also have some advantage in association with the lethal to balance the wastage arising from homozygosity. Where it is homozygous in nature, the advantage must come from association with some other gene.

Numerous cases, as yet unanalysed genetically, are known in nature where polymorphism, as with *Argynnis paphia*, exists in one area of the range of the species but not in another. A familiar example is the common red squirrel, *Sciurus vulgaris*, which is always red in some areas, e.g. Britain, but both red and black in mountainous parts of Europe (Lühring, 1928). Other cases are mentioned in Chapter 5 (pp. 184, 203). In some it would appear that a new area has been colonized exclusively by individuals of one type, which presumably then is not linked with a full lethal, but either is linked with a gene somewhat reducing viability, or is the type which is less advantageous than the lethal-linked form. In other cases the lethal linkage may have been broken, as with *Argynnis* and *Colias*.

Highly polymorphic species exist in nature among land-snails, such as the common *Cepaea nemoralis* and *C. hortensis* (A. Lang, 1908), with their vast range of ground-colour and degree of banding; grasshoppers (grouse-locusts, etc., Nabours, 1925; grasshoppers, Rubtzov, 1935*); and certain fresh-water fish such as *Lebistes* (Winge, 1927). In these cases the polymorphism appears to depend on the phenomenon of close linkage within each chromosome or of the obligatory association of many whole chromosomes to produce a similar effect to close linkage (Fisher, 1930b; Diver, 1932). In these circumstances, a recessive lethal will prevent the free recombination of any favourable mutations in the same chromosome. Thus, since recessive lethals are common types of mutation, whole chromosomes will have to compete with each other, instead of selection being able to act so as to produce an approximation to a single "best" combination of genes. Further, since homozygotes cannot live, there must be at least two different forms of each of the chromosomes which contain lethals; the different combinations of these will of necessity give a variety of forms; and this variety will itself be subjected to selection so as to give the best balance, and the least waste through excess mortality of one or some of the forms. In the land-snails, the interesting fact thas been discovered that the frequency of the different types of banding has remained about the same since the neolithic period (Diver, 1929), showing that the balance is an enduring one. The problem, of course, remains as to why the close linkage has become a characteristic of the species in the first instance, since no obvious advantage inheres in such a

* Parallel variations occur here as in *Cepaea*, but in much more striking fashion, since they affect a large number of related species and indeed genera (p. 516).

condition. Haldane (1930; and see discussion in Ford, 1934, p. 84) has suggested that it is due to translocation of segments from one chromosome to another. The unusual phenomenon of the dominance of the mutant types over a "universal recessive" would then also be accounted for, since the mutants would possess the translocated segment in duplicate, both in its original and its new position. Further, if, as is to be expected and as appears actually to be the case, the translocation is less viable when homozygous, we could dispense with lethal genes as an explanation of the selective balance reached.

The common sea-anemone *Metridium senile* exists in a number of strikingly different colour-varieties. D. L. Fox and Pantin (1941) enumerate eight, including white, red, brown, grey, and various combinations of these; in addition, there is much variation in the intensity of the colours. The different forms occur in different proportions in different localities. The various colour-types depend on the interrelation of (1) lipochrome, giving colours from red to yellow; (2) brown melanin, restricted to the ectoderm; (3) black melanin, restricted to the endoderm. There seems no doubt that the main types are genetically determined, and differ in their metabolic properties, and also that the colour is here adaptively non-significant, but correlated with some basic physiological difference. Fox and Pantin conclude that selection is weak as between the different colour-varieties, and that this will account for the existence of the numerous phases. We have seen, however, that a selective balance is required for this, and experiments on the physiological and ecological differences between the varieties should yield interesting results. There are the additional complications that asexual reproductions occurs, and that single individuals can persist for great lengths of time, perhaps even indefinitely.

In the Mexican fresh-water fish *Platypoecilus maculatus*, M. Gordon (1939) has found well over 120 patterns in a state of nature, mostly dependent on the recombination of 15 gene-pairs. This is a remarkable degree of polymorphism for a wild species, especially as collections dating from 1867 indicate that it is a balanced one. Furthermore, as in the other examples we have cited, related species and genera (*Xiphophorus*) present much parallel variation. Some of the excessive variation, however, is apparently due to the fixation of "accidental" characters by drift (see pp. 58, 128). A quite different type of balance occurs in variable plant species which consist of numerous ecotypes (pp. 275, 276).

(ii) Ecological balance, on the other hand, depends either on a diminution in the degree of selective advantage due to increase of frequency of one or all of the polymorphic forms above a certain level, or on an alternation in the amount or type of selection due to alteration in the environmental conditions. The best examples of the former concern mimetic butterflies. Either all the forms are mimetic, or one is non-mimetic and the other or others mimetic. If a mimetic form happens to become too abundant relative to its model, the protection afforded by the resemblance will diminish. Where certain mimetic forms are wholly absent, the corresponding models are also found to be missing. In any area, a balance will thus be struck, depending on relative abundance of models, intensity of predation, and viability factors (p. 191).

Among the best-analysed examples are those of *Papilio polytes* and *Hypolimnas dubius*. In the former case, only the females are polymorphic, existing in three forms, two mimetic and one non-mimetic. The species is a successful one, able to live outside the range of its models: it is then, of course, monomorphic, all females being non-mimetic.

It seems clear that where models are available, mimicry confers a definite advantage, but one which diminishes rapidly with increased frequency of the mimetic forms.

In *Hypolimnas dubius*, both sexes are alike, and are dimorphic, with two mimetic forms (see pp. 123–4). For the details of the genetic basis of the condition, readers are referred to Ford (1937). In general the equilibrium due to ecological selective balance may be broadly compared with the effects of mass action in chemistry.

As a matter of fact, *Papilio polytes* appears to illustrate a combination of genetic with ecological control, since the two mimetic forms, both of which are dominant, are more viable in the heterozygous than in the homozygous condition.

Various authors have regarded as a theoretical difficulty the fact that such enormous differences in pattern, and even shape and habit, obviously involving many independent characters, can be controlled by a single gene. It should, however, be clear that once a mutant type is established, conferring even a small mimetic advantage, the residual gene-complex can undergo evolution of the same nature as what we have discussed in previous sections (pp. 98 seq.). But here the extent of such modification may be pushed much further, with a result that is best described, not as a modification of the visible effects of the original gene, but as an addition of various new effects, all of which, however, are dependent for their expression on the presence of the original gene. Presumably this change in the gene-complex will depend more on new mutation and relatively less on recombination of previously existing genes than in e.g. alteration of dominance (see Ford, 1937).

We may put it in another way by saying that the original gene-difference comes to act as a switch controlling the action of numerous mutant modifying and modifiable genes, precisely as occurs in the case of the primary sex-difference in regard to genetically sex-limited characters. There is no reason for, and every reason against, postulating the sudden origin of the whole pattern by one mutation. Further, the frequent superficiality of the characters by which mimetic resemblance is achieved shows that the resemblance cannot have arisen through parallel mutations occurring and being preserved owing to similarity of conditions (see Punnett, 1915; Cott, 1940, p. 405). The apparently cryptic colour-polymorphism of certain stick-insects and mantids may have a similar ecological basis. The egg-colour polymorphism of the cuckoo, *Cuculus canorus*, is largely related to the risk of ejection by the host (Jourdain, 1925; Huskins, 1934). The different egg-colour strains are presumably balanced in relation to host-abundance.

In the ruff (*Machetes pugnax*) polymorphism is confined to males in the breeding season, and the number of distinctive types is extraordinary. No other bird rivals it. Ford (1940a, p. 501) suggests that the cumulative effect on females of display-stimulation by numerous males at a common courting-ground, (p. 480 Darling, 1939; Huxley, 1938a) promotes maximum variability. Mayr and Rand (1937) cite a peculiar and striking dimorphism in tail-coloration in the bird *Rhipidura brachyrhyncha*.

Polymorphism is much commoner than usually realized, e.g. in birds and mammals only, it exists among squirrels, foxes, bears, cats, owls, herons, hawks, skuas, etc.

Next we come to cases where changes in external environment determine the ecological balance, not those in internal conditions (relative abundance of the separate types). We have mentioned the common squirrel (p. 99. For plant ecotypes, see p. 275).

Elton (quoted by Ford, 1934, p. 83) has found that in the red fox (*Vulpes fulva*), which shows trimorphism, the "cross" type being apparently a heterozygote between red and silver, the rare silver type changes in its relative frequency in a regular way during each of the 10-year cycles of abundance to which the species is exposed (p. 111). In this species, Cross (1941) finds a rough polymorph-ratio cline (p. 222), red being commoner to the S., silver and cross to the N. (and see p. 185).

The arctic fox (*Alopex lagopus*) is dimorphic in winter (blue or white). Only the white type occurs in Kamchatka, and only the blue in certain Alaskan islands; while on the Alaskan mainland a N-S gradient is found, the white type decreasing in frequency with latitude. (See also p. 217.)

Here any selective advantage afforded by the white coat in winter must presumably be offset by some disadvantage, probably connected with viability, for the blue type to be able to exist in numbers at all. The primary basis of the dimorphism (as in the red fox) is thus a genetic balance. But environment may somewhat alter this equilibrium, so that the balance is in part also ecological.

A remarkable case where the relation with environmental conditions is more direct is that of the hamster (*Cricetus cricetus*), as described by Kirikov (1934) and Timoféeff-Ressovsky (1940). About 150 years ago the naturalist-geographer Lepekhin noted that in a certain region of Russia black hamsters were unusually prevalent. Since then, the statistics of the Russian fur-markets have enabled biologists to trace the steady spread of the black type, until to-day, throughout a broad zone along the northern border of the range of the species, black forms are in the majority and in some areas are present to the total or virtual exclusion of the typical greys. This area coincides with the sub-steppe (wood-steppe) climatic zone, and is cooler and moister than the steppe region proper, which forms the main home of the species. In the steppes the black type occurs only as an occasional aberration. It seems clear that the black form enjoys some selective advantage in the sub-steppe area, while it is at a disadvantage in the drier steppes.

In the bird *Coereba*, the recent replacement of the typical by the melanic form on certain West Indian islands appears to be similar (pp. 94 n, 203). In other cases, although the actual process of spread has not been followed, we can be certain that it is taking place. For instance, in the brush opossum (*Trichosurus vulpecula*), melanic variants are very rare on the Australian main-land. In the Tasmanian subspecies, however, they are common. Pearson (1938), from an examination of many thousand skins, was able to plot a contour ("phenocontour") map of the relative frequency of the black type, with contour lines ("isophenes") marking regions of a given frequency. In the first place, he was able to show that neither an isolated small island off the north-west, nor another on the north-east on the course of the sub-merged land-bridge from Australia, contained black animals except as aberrations; this demonstrates that the abundance of the black type must have arisen after the isolation of the sub-species in Tasmania. The north-west corner of Tasmania contains only black opossums, while on parts of the east coast the pro- portion is under 25 per cent. There is no correlation of the frequency of blacks with climatic gradients. The suggestion that the black type appeared (whether by new mutation or by the crossing of two carriers of the black gene in single dose) in the north-west, and is gradually extending eastwards, is confirmed by conditions on the narrow-necked Tasman peninsula. This shows a markedly lower frequency of blacks than the adjacent zone of the main island: it seems clear that the extreme narrowness of its neck has hindered the spread of the black gene.

It is interesting to note that Tasmania is cooler and moister than Australia, so that the similarity to the case of the black hamster is very close. Humidity also favours melanism in *Coereba*.

Another case where a phenocontour map of a mutant type has been plotted, and examination of the map shows that spread of the mutant is occurring and is being impeded by geographical barriers, is that of the *simplex* condition of the teeth in the field-vole *Microtus arvalis* in north-central Germany (Zimmermann, 1935). The aberration here consists in the absence of the last ridge of enamel on the molar. Here the *simplex* condition occurs in over 90 per cent of individuals in Schleswig-Holstein, with zones of decreasing frequency to west, south, and east. The mountains of central Germany have proved a complete obstacle, while certain large rivers have obviously hindered the spread of the character. This case is genetically slightly more complex, since various gradations in the expression of the character occur, and not only is the character more frequent in the presumed centre of origin, but also more extreme in type. It is further worth noting that the gradient in *simplex*-frequency bears no relation to another character-gradient or cline (see p. 206) within the species, namely, the gradual east-west darkening and reddening of the coat-colour across the north German plain.

In the last two cases, the polymorphism may be regarded as transient, since the species or subspecies appears to be moving from a condition in which a given character is rare, maintained only by mutation-pressure, to one where it is universal, again apart from the rare and sporadic occurrence of its allele. This is theoretically to be distinguished from true polymorphism, in which a state of balance between the contrasting types is indefinitely maintained, but it will not always be possible to distinguish the one condition from the other (Ford, 1940a). Thus Southern (1939) has shown that the bridled variety of the guillemot (*Uria aalge*) increases northwards from 0.5 per cent or lower to well over 50 per cent of the total population, in a fairly regular gradient. There is, however, no way as yet of telling whether the two types are indefinitely balanced against a climatic gradient, as with the arctic fox, or whether the bridled type is spreading at the expense of the "normal". The owl *Megascops* shows a centrifugal cline between red and normal (grey) forms in U.S.A. (Hasbrouck, 1893); while that between dark and light fulmar petrels is rather more complex (p. 217).

Mather (1941) has recently propounded a possible genetic explanation of clines in such apparently non-adaptive characters. He suggests that the gene responsible is linked with one of two balanced polygenic combinations within homologous chromosomes (see p. 67), affecting some other character, and that this is related to some environmental condition. The mean development of the character will be adjusted by the relative frequency of the two combinations, and thus the frequency of the linked gene will also vary in relation to the environmental gradient concerned. One may add that the same result would be obtained if one of the genes in the polygenic combination were pleiotropic and also produced the visible effect (e.g. bridling).

A frequent condition found in nature is that of regional or geographical polymorphism, when two or more contrasted forms are confined to different regions. Thus in the moth *Spilosoma mendica* (Ford, 1937), the normal condition is for the male to be dark, the female white. In Ireland, however, the males as well as the females are white, and this condition (variety *rustica*) is known sporadically on the European continent. Such a state of affairs may represent the final stage of a transitory polymorphism, in an area which favours the spread of an alternative type (cf. the brush opossum, p. 104), or be due to colonization by one only of the two forms (and see p. 262). Elsewhere, the condition may represent the end of a dimorph-ratio cline. Thus, in *Accipiter novae-hollandiae* (p. 184) such a cline culminates at either end in an area exclusively inhabited by one of the two forms. Again, the white form of the palearctic moth *Leucodonta bicoloria*, abundant in the east, decreases westwards and is absent in the extreme west (Suomalainen, 1941).

We may conclude by referring to the floral dimorphism of higher plants, even though that is solely or mainly environmental or developmental in its determination, not genetic. Floral dimorphism is concerned with the relation between cross- and self-pollination. (See Kerner and Oliver, 1902, for a good general but somewhat out-of-date account; Uphof, 1938, for cleistogamy; p. 140 for gynodioecism; Mather, 1941, for heterostyly.)

Strictly speaking, the term dimorphism should perhaps only be employed when whole plants of distinct type are found. This occurs in most cases of gynodioecism, e.g. in the common plantain *Plantago lanceolata*, the viper's bugloss *Echium vulgare*, etc., where some plants produce normal hermaphrodite flowers, while others have only female (pistillate) flowers, which are sometimes smaller than the hermaphrodite ones; in a few cases of cleistogamy, such as the balsam *Impatiens noli-me-tangere*, where in addition to plants exclusively producing the normal showy flowers, others may occur bearing only the inconspicuous and permanently closed cleistogamous flowers adapted solely to self-pollination (as well as still others with both types); and in heterostyly. Mather (1941) has an interesting discussion on the evolution of heterostyly (see also Mather and de Winton, 1941). He points out that an illegitimacy reaction appears to be compulsorily associated with heterostyly, and is the chief bar to inbreeding. Homozygous thrum plants, which normally do not occur in nature, are less viable than the heterozygotes or the recessives (pms). This reversal of the usual relations of dominance to viability must be due to the accumulation of deleterious mutations, in the region adjacent to the thrum gene, which will only exist in nature in a heterozygous condition; this is similar to the accumulation of loss mutations in the Y-chromosome, which has led to its almost total inertness (p. 138).

If conditions demand greater stability and therefore increased inbreeding, in some cases selection may reverse the intensity of the illegitimacy reaction. Since commercial seed-raisers prefer selfing, this has occurred with cultivated species, e.g. *Primula sinensis*. Here the fertility of illegitimate relative to that of legitimate pollinations has almost doubled since the experiments of Hildebrand and Darwin in 1864 and 1877. Another possibility is the selection of mutants giving homostyle plants which are then capable of self-pollination. This has occurred in nature (see pp. 222, 313).

In a few cases of heterostyly, such as certain species of *Primula*, the two types of flowers also have different-sized corollas. In some cases the "pin", in others the "thrum" type is thus distinguished. The meaning of these last conditions is obscure. Kerner and Oliver (1902) suggest that the smaller size of corolla is associated with the type where autogamy is more prevalent, and cross-pollination accordingly less essential; but this Dr. Mather informs me is not in accord with experimental facts.

It is also quite logical to use the term dimorphism for types in which two distinct types of flower are produced on the same individual plant, as occurs in most cleistogamous forms (species of *Viola*, *Glechoma*, *Lamium*, *Oxalis*, *Helianthemum*, *Juncus*, many grasses, etc.). Further, it is perhaps even legitimate to extend the concept to cover the frequent combination, in one and the same flower at different times, of definite devices to secure cross-pollination and self-pollination. This would then constitute what we may perhaps call a dimorphism in time, since in the great majority of cases the plant produces flowers which are adapted to ensure cross-pollination, but if this does not occur, it transforms these same organs into what is virtually a new type of flower adapted for self-pollination.

Furthermore, in all these cases, a selective balance is at work. However, the balance is a complex one. In plants whose flowers change from exogamy to autogamy, as well as those which produce both showy and cleistogamous flowers, it used to be supposed that all that was involved was what the experimental embryologists style "double assurance" (*doppelte Sicherung*) to secure pollination. Cross-pollination was assumed to be in some way better, but if, through lack of suitable insects or other reason, it chanced not to be effected, then the plant fell back on its second line of defence, in the shape of self-fertilization. This in itself would constitute a selective balance of an ecological nature. The advantages accruing from cross-fertilization are offset against the disadvantage of its not being always possible; the disadvantage of having to produce a second type of flower (or to develop new adaptations within the original flower) is offset against the advantage of assured seed-production.

Ecological factors may further complicate the picture. Thus certain species produce solely or almost solely cleistogamous flowers when growing in deep shade, where few insects are likely to visit them, but go to the reverse extreme when grown in sunny open localities. In *Viola*, cleistogamous flowers are much more abundant in high latitudes; this is due to a photo-periodic response (Borgström, 1939). Along these lines, the course of evolution of the cleistogamous condition is readily envisaged. Cleistogamy in the strict sense implies a special type of flower which not only does not open, but shows other adaptations; usually the petals and stamen are reduced in size, and the pollen-grains are not liberated from the anthers but germinate *in situ*. This condition has doubtless followed on one of "pseudo-cleistogamy", where, in certain ecological conditions, the normal flowers simply fail to open and self-pollination occurs.

This, however, is not the whole story. Autogamy, it is now realized, is not merely a *pis aller*. It has certain advantages, in perpetuating unchanged a vigorous and well-balanced genetic constitution once this has been evolved. This stability, however, will only be advantageous so long as conditions also remain unchanged: in addition, an entirely stable type loses the possibility of invading new environments. Thus the provision of devices for both cross- and self-fertilization constitutes a balance between the advantages of plasticity (with its disadvantage of wasteful production of less well-adapted recombinations) and of stability (with its long-term disadvantage of absence of adjustment to new conditions). Some forms are exclusively of one or the other type; but in a large number, probably the majority, of flowering plants, the two have been brought into balance, with consequent floral dimorphism of one sort or another.

A third type of selective advantage concerns the degree of waste of gametes associated with a particular mode of reproduction. This wastage is especially marked in monoecious plants, and its implications are discussed in reference to the selective balance involved in gynodioecism (p. 107).

It is difficult to evaluate the precise shares of these various advantages and disadvantages in floral dimorphism. We must be content to observe that a selective balance is involved, and that the dimorphism is thereby maintained.

In other cases the dimorphism is between sexual and vegetative reproduction. Dr. W. B. Turrill informs me in a letter that in the lesser celandine, *Ranunculus ficaria*, the following types of reproduction occur: normal amphimixis, apomixis, abundant vegetative multiplication (of two types; one variety is wholly or almost wholly vegetative in its reproduction), and plants with only male, only female, and only hermaphrodite flowers. Different populations show different proportions of these various types. Here, in the field of reproduction, we may perhaps have something akin to the balance of ecotypes in many plant species (p. 177).

We may in fact conclude that polymorphism always involves a selective balance, whether it is determined genetically, or environmentally, or internally by the processes of normal ontogeny, as when two or more kinds of persons or organs, adapted to different functions, are formed by the same colony or individual (for social hymenoptera see p. 482 n).

Finally in view of its peculiar evolutionary interest as inevitably involving a selective balance and as in some cases leading by way of ecological regional differences, to sharp geographical differentiation, genetic polymorphism deserves the most intensive study, especially in cases where the ratios of the types are geographically graded, since here we may hope not only to measure the intensity of the selective forces at work, but also to discover something as to their nature.

(c) *Selection in fluctuating populations*

Elton (1930) has pointed out that the customary assumption of a population approximately constant from year to year is very far from the truth for many, if not most, species. A stable "balance of nature" does not exist. Fluctuation in numbers, rather than constancy, is the rule. This fluctuation may be broadly progressive towards increase or decrease, it may be irregular, or it may be cyclic and regular.

Animal species subject to such regular or periodic fluctuations include lemmings (*Lemmus*), snowshoe rabbits (*Lepus americanus*), mice, voles, jerbils and other Muridae, foxes (*Vulpes, Alopex*), lynxes (*Lynx*), and other fur-bearing carnivores, certain birds, such as ptarmigan (*Lagopus*) in Labrador and nutcrackers (*Nucifraga*) in Siberia, some invertebrates, land and marine, and probably certain antelopes and other larger mammals. The period of the fluctuation from crest to crest of abundance varies from 3 to 4 years in the smaller rodents, to 10 to 11 years in the snowshoe rabbit, and probably a good deal longer in certain ungulates. The difference in abundance between crest and trough may be very great. In the snowshoe rabbit the ratio of high to low population numbers in extreme cases must reach at least 100 : 1. An interesting point made by Rowan (1931, p. 62) for Canadian birds is that migrant species are not affected by these cycles. In years when the grouse population has been reduced to a minimum, the migrants are present in normal numbers. This fact must, in combination with others peculiar to migrants, have important evolutionary consequences restricted to migrant forms. However, it seems not to be of universal occurrence.

Elton has pointed out certain important evolutionary consequences of these facts. In the first place, both the intensity and the type of selection will vary continuously during the cycle. During the period of rapid increase, when numbers are low and conditions favourable, the intensity of selection will be very low. During the peak period, intraspecific selection due to pressure of competition will be high. Since the catastrophic fall in numbers is normally due to infectious disease, selection during this period will mainly concern disease-resistance. And in the subsequent period of unfavourable environmental conditions (for all these cycles seem to have an external determination) selection will be concerned with resistance to cold and hunger and similar aspects of the struggle for existence. To use Elton's metaphor, the species is put through a series of examinations, with easy times betweenwhiles, and the different examinations test different capacities.

Apart from special resistances, such varying selection will promote a general elasticity of response.

Elton also made the suggestion that periodic fluctuations would allow greater scope for chance in evolution, since if a rare mutation or gene-combination happens to be present in the much-reduced minimum population, it will be automatically reproduced in the same proportion during the period of rapid increase when the struggle for existence is light and the intensity of selection low.

His views have been criticized on mathematical grounds by Haldane. However, the proof of the pudding is in the eating, and the studies of Ford and Ford (1930) make it clear, first that selection-intensity may actually be relaxed during a period of rapid increase, and secondly that when it is once more tightened up, the resultant type may differ from that obtaining in the proceeding period of abundance. They observed a sharply isolated colony of the small Greasy Fritillary butterfly, *Melitaea aurinia*, for thirteen years, and obtained records and specimens for a total period of forty-nine years. The population was increasingly abundant from 1881 to 1897; it then decreased, and became scarce by 1906 and extremely rare from 1912 to 1920. A rapid increase to abundance then took place to 1924, from when until 1930 it showed a progressive slight further increase.

Variability was slight during the first relatively stable period of abundance. During the period of rapid increase after scarcity, however, (I quote from Ford, 1934, p. 77), "an extraordinary outburst of variation occurred. Hardly two specimens were alike and marked departures from the normal form of the species, both in size, shape and colour, were very common. A high proportion of these were deformed in various ways, the amount of deformity being closely correlated with the degree of variation."

With the colony entered on its second period of abundance, the abnormal types and extreme variants practically disappeared, and the population settled down again to a uniform type. This, however, was not the same as before, but recognizably distinct.

It seems clear that the relaxation of selection during the recovery period allowed an excess of variability; and that when it again became rigorous, the new stable type was slightly different, owing to the accidental incorporation of different genes. R. L. Berg (1941) has demonstrated a similar effect in micropopulations of *Drosophila melanogaster*, aberrations increasing with decreased intensity of selection.

Sewall Wright (1932), in discussing such problems in more general terms, concludes that there must be available to most species a number of gene-combinations all of about the same survival-value; he compares them to peaks, separated by "valleys" of intermediate combinations which are less favourable. Normally it is difficult or impossible for selection to shift the type from an established peak to another, although this might be equally satisfactory if reached: but when the intensity of selection is reduced (or when low size of population promotes the accidental survival of genes and gene-combinations: pp. 58, 199), many "valley" combinations are realized, the species can cross dryshod to other peaks, and it will be a matter of chance on which Ararat the type eventually remains perched when the rising tide of selection again floods out the valleys.

Elton draws a further interesting conclusion from the facts of periodic fluctuation. He concludes that it will have promoted the migratory impulse which is so strong in so many types of animals when in unfavourable conditions. At first sight, the existence of this impulse seems hard to explain on any selective hypothesis, since, in the more spectacular mass emigrations, such as those of locusts, lemmings, or certain butterflies, all, or all but a negligible fraction of the migrants perish, while the population is renewed from among those which do not manifest the impulse and stay in their original habitat. One would thus suppose that migratory tendencies would be strongly antagonized by selection.

However, although such migrations are exceedingly striking and have thus received a disproportionate share of attention from biologists, they are, in fact, but extreme and in a sense abnormal manifestations of a much more widespread phenomenon, namely, an impulse to react to unfavourable conditions by changed behaviour, notably by movement away from an environment which has become unfavourable. This does not normally result in mass migration on a vast scale, but in an irregular movement that disperses the population over a wide area. When lemmings are scarce in the Arctic, snowy owls (*Nyctea nyctea*) descend into north temperate latitudes in search of food (Elton, 1927, p. 123). When the cedar-cone crop fails in Siberian forests, the Siberian nutcrackers (*Nucifraga caryocatactes macrorhynchus*) leave their usual haunts and may reach western Europe (Formosov, 1933). And many quite small and inconspicuous movements of animal population are going on all the time.

When migration is of this less extreme type, many individuals which would otherwise die will survive temporarily in regions beyond the normal range of the species and be able to return later to their original habitat, while others may survive by reaching and remaining in other parts of the normal range. In addition, some individuals may be able to survive and to remain in areas outside the normal habitat of the species, either by adopting slightly different habits and so colonizing different habitats within the original geographical range, or by colonizing areas outside this range. This extension of habitat may in the first instance be dependent on a non-inherited modification of behaviour, mutation and selection later stepping in to fix the change genetically (the "organic selection" of Baldwin and Lloyd Morgan, pp. 304, 523); or genetic variants may find themselves in surroundings to which their constitution is better adapted than was the normal environment of the species (pre-adaptation, see p. 449). In either case, migration will have been advantageous to the species as well as to the individual.

Elton (1930, p. 52) draws an illuminating comparison between the sexual process and the migratory urge. Both are extremely widespread, and both confer additional evolutionary plasticity on a species. The sexual process enables the species to exploit to the fullest extent the mutations, old and new, which are carried by the species or which crop up during its evolutionary career, by making possible every kind of recombination of them. The migratory impulse, in relation to unfavourable conditions, has a precisely analogous effect, in increasing the range of environmental conditions with which any genetic variation that exists can be brought into contact. The two are complementary and often mutually reinforcing processes, and both have their most important function in times of stress.

Fluctuations in numbers, both irregular and periodic, thus may have important evolutionary consequences.

7. MUTATION AND EVOLUTION

There remains the difficulty that most mutations so far investigated are deleterious. If mutations are the raw material of evolution, it is clearly not enough that they should be as it were sterilized and rendered innocuous; some of them must sometimes be, or become advantageous. However, this also is not so serious as at first sight appears (pp. 68 seq.). Since the gene-complex is an elaborately co-ordinated system, any changes in it are much more likely to act as defects rather than as improvements. Further, the larger the change the less likely is it to be an improvement; and inevitably the geneticist will detect large changes more readily than small. The detailed analysis of the last ten or fifteen years, however, has revealed large numbers of gene-differences with extremely small effects, down almost to the limit of detectability. It is not only possible but highly probable that among these are to be sought the chief building-blocks of evolutionary change, and that it is by means of small mutations, notably in the form of series of multiple allelic steps, each adjusted for viability and efficiency by recombinations and further small mutations, that progressive and adaptive evolution has occurred. Indeed, in cases where fertile species-crosses are possible, this contention has been definitely proved, as for instance by the prevalence of multiple-factor (polygenic) differences, each factor with only a small effect, as the basis for specific difference in *Antirrhinum* (Baur, 1932), *Phaseolus* (Lamprecht, 1941), cotton (*Gossypium*; Silow, 1941), etc., and in wolf-dog crosses (Iljin, 1941). Many sub-specific characters have a similar genetic basis, e.g. in the plant *Camelina sativa* (Tedin, 1925), in deermice (*Peromyscus*), gipsy-moths (*Lymantria*), etc. (see Dobzhansky, 1937, Chapter 3). Specific differences in *Drosophila* depend on many single genes, often grouped in polygenic systems (pp. 358 seq.; Mather, 1941).

The very large number of genes with small effects involved in the inheritance of quantitative characters has been stressed by "Student". With reference to Winter's experiments (1929) on oil-content in maize, R. A. Fisher (1933b) writes: "all commercial varieties must be segregating in hundreds, and quite possibly in thousands, of factors." With this amount of available variance, Winter was able to select high and low lines differing *sixfold* in oil-content. Silow (1941) estimates that in cotton (*Gossypium*) the closest species differ in over half their genes.

It must be admitted that the direct and complete proof of the utilization of mutations in evolution under natural conditions has not yet been given. Even the case of industrial melanism, apart from its concerning the results of man's interference, will not be complete until the induction of melanic mutations has been finally disproved. On the other hand, a complete and direct demonstration is inevitably very difficult to provide. The mutations concerned will normally have small effects. Thus the species concerned must be easily bred, and should have been subjected to detailed genetic analysis: otherwise small mutations will not be detected. The species must then be followed through a period of evolutionary change, and during this period selection must be proved to have been operative on certain mutations.

Thus it is inevitable that for the present we must rely mainly on the convergence of a number of separate lines of evidence each partial and indirect or incomplete, but severally cumulative and demonstrative.

These different partial lines of evidence may be summarized as follows:—

(1) *The existence of small mutations.* This has been proved in every organism subjected to detailed genetic analysis. While most of these are deleterious, it should be remembered that reverse mutations to wild type have frequently been demonstrated, both "spontaneously" and under the influence of the same agency (e.g. X-rays) used to induce the original mutation. Thus it cannot be maintained that the process of mutation is of its nature deleterious, since the "abnormal" can mutate to the

"normal" Position-effects due to small sectional rearrangements (p. 92) must for our purpose be included in this category.

(2) *The existence of mendelizing variations of small extent constituting the differential characters of subspecies and species.* This has been shown in many cases, though it can, of course, only be demonstrated for species where fertility and segregation occur after an inter-specific cross. However, the cases of this are fairly numerous (see Haldane, 1932a, Chap. 3; Goldschmidt, 1928, Chap. 15; Dobzhansky, 1937, Chap. 3).

This point is important, since the presumption is very strong that all mendelizing variations owe their origin to mutation.

(3) *The existence of selection-pressure against small unfavourable mutations.* All cases of reduced viability in culture and of elimination of deleterious mutants in nature fall under this head. One of the best proofs is the low incidence of mutant genes in the sex-chromosome of wild-caught individuals as compared with their incidence in the other chromosomes (autosomes), as discovered by C. Gordon (1936) and by Dubinin and his co-workers (1934, 1936) in *Drosophila*.

Recessive mutations in the autosomes will not exert their effects unless in double dose, and they cannot occur in double dose unless two individuals heterozygous for the gene happen to mate, which will be a very rare event. Sex-linked mutations, on the other hand, will immediately exert their effects on a number of males, since these possess only a single sex-chromosome, so that any recessive genes located in this chromosome can exert their effects in single dose, not masked by their normal allelomorphs. If the effects comprise reduced viability, selection will at once be brought into play and will tend to eliminate the gene from the constitution of the species.

Thus both the recessivity of most mutations (pp. 75 seq.) and the scarcity of sex-linked recessives are consequences of selection.

A special case is the proof by Gerould (1921) that the normal grass-green larvae of the butterfly *Colias philodice* enjoy a selective advantage over the blue-green recessive mutant type in relation to the attacks of bird enemies, no doubt on account of their close resemblance in colour to the food-plant.

(4) *The existence of mutations which from the outset are non-deleterious, and especially of those which are potentially favourable.* In view of the recurrent nature of mutation, it is extremely unlikely that in an experiment mutations should arise which are markedly favourable at the outset, in normal conditions; for in most cases such mutations would long previously have been incorporated in the constitution of the species.

Of mutations which appear to be potentially favourable—i.e. capable of being immediately utilized by selection in certain conditions (see pp. 52, 449 ff.)—there are numerous examples. We may mention the mutations in seed-weight of beans found by Johannsen (p. 52); those modifying hooded pattern in rats (p. 65); the mutation altering temperature-resistance in water-fleas by Banta (p. 52); and that in tobacco adjusting flowering to a different rhythm of light and darkness (p. 52). Some of the mutant genes found by Dubinin *et al.* (1936) in wild *Drosophila* might readily increase (or even become the "normal type") under slightly altered conditions. The higher variability of abundant species demonstrates this process in action (p. 58 n.).

Zimmermann (1941) has found numerous recessive genes in the heterozygous state among populations of wild rodents, not only house-mice (*Mus m. musculus*), but also field mice (*Apodemus*) and voles (*Cleithrionomys*). Though some of these were for gross abnormalities, and others for partial albinism or spotting, still others determined characters which might readily be utilized in normal evolution, e.g. a darker type of agouti. In one case (*Cleithrionomys g. glareolus*) a dominant gene was found, changing the normal red of the back to the brown character typical of the alpine subspecies *C. g. nageri*.

An interesting example from domestic animals is that of frizzled fowls. These have a peculiar plumage, with upcurled feathers which do not retain heat well, and are at a great disadvantage in temperate climates. The condition depends on mendelian genes (F. G. Benedict, Landauer, and Fox, 1932). In tropical climates, however, as in West Africa, the breed is extremely common: here the frizzled plumage is an advantage, since it enables the birds to keep cooler than normal birds (pp. 63, 76; Haldane, 1935; Landauer and Dunn, 1930; Landauer, 1937; Landauer and Upham, 1936).

(5) *The existence of genetic polymorphism within a species.* This, as we have seen (p. 97), can only occur where there is a selective balance. Since both the visible and the lethal characters involved are known to mendelize in all cases properly investigated, the presumption is that they always do so, and the further presumption exists that they owe their origin to mutation.

Beautiful examples of the action of selection in causing the spread of favourable mendelian characters are seen in those cases of genetically-controlled polymorphism where one type, when freed from its linked lethal, has ousted the other (p. 98), as well as in those where a mutant or rare allele spreads in certain environmental conditions, as in the industrial melanism of moths, and in other cases (pp. 94, 104, 203).

Polymorphism must be distinguished from normal variability, however large, grouped in a single normal curve of error, or at least one without sharply defined modes. When, however, wide normal variability exists, it appears, in so far as it is genotypic, to depend on mendelizing factors and their recombinations, since when a cross is made between extreme variants, the F2 is much more variable than the F1. The adaptive reasons for the existence of high variability of this unimodal sort are unknown, though it would appear that in some cases they must exist. Possibly it supplies the same kind of plasticity in relation to a wide range of environmental conditions as is found in plant species with numerous intergrading ecotypes (p. 275).

(6) *The effect of variation of conditions in altering the incidence of selection on* (a) *mutations, or* (b) *naturally-existing genetic differences.* In some cases mutations, which in what may be described as normal conditions are deleterious, may become advantageous in other conditions.* A good example is that of the vestigial-winged mutant of *Drosophila*, studied by Spencer (1932). In conditions near the optimum, vestigial is much shorter-lived than wild-type. But if vestigials and normals are kept together without food

---

* When this is so they fall conveniently under the heading of pre-adaptations; this subject is expanded in Chapter 8, p. 449.

and water, the vestigials survive longer. Thus in environments which occasionally become very unfavourable the vestigial type might even oust the normal. It is worth noting that the advantage or disadvantage concerns the viability characters: the size of the wings would thus be a "correlated character" of no immediate selective value (pp. 63, 206). On the other hand, reduced size of wings may have a direct selective value in certain conditions. Thus L'Heritier, Neefs, and Teissier (1937) also working with vestigial, found that flies with this character survived better than wild-type *Drosophila* when subjected to constant wind. This, as they rightly conclude, has a bearing on the prevalence of insects with reduced or functionless wings on oceanic islands (p. 453).

Variation in the environment often leads to selection of certain types from among the range occurring naturally. This may refer either to continuous or discontinuous variations. An example of the former is the case described by Harrison (1920a) of the selection for depth of pigmentation in the moth *Oporinia autumnata*. The relative abundance of lighter and darker forms in a dark pinewood and an adjacent light birchwood was quite different, and so, but inversely, was the intensity of selection, as revealed by the number of wings left by birds. The result was that in the dark environment the darker types had become sixteen times the commoner, while in the light environment the lighter types were six times more abundant than the darker. (See also p. 469).

As an example of selection between sharply-delimited types we may mention the experiments of extreme interest carried out by Sukatschew (1928) on pure lines in dandelions (*Taraxacum*). He found that altering the density of total numbers of plants per plot might completely alter both the survival of the seedlings and the fertility of the survivors, so that a pure line which was inferior in one set of conditions would oust the rest if the conditions were changed.

We may also consider selection as between related species. Here, similar results to those with varieties of dandelions have been obtained by Timoféeff-Ressovsky (1933) with the competition between the larvae of two species of *Drosophila* at different temperatures; by Tansley (1917) on the varying results of competition between two species of bedstraw (*Galium*) according to the type of soil on which they are growing; and by Beauchamp and Ullyott (1932) on the decisive effect of temperature in bringing about the selection of one or other of two species of competing planarian worms.

Sukatschew's detailed analysis is entirely in accord with the elaborate ecological work of the Stapledon school, showing the effect of varying intensity of grazing on the survival of different species and strains of pasture plants.

In bacteria, the alteration of type with culture-medium appears not to depend upon any lamarckian or modificatory effect, but upon the selection of variants (to use a non-committal term), though the method of origin of these is still obscure. Again, selection has different effects on different pure lines of yeast according to conditions (Gause, 1934).

The diminution in size and other changes which occurred over a period of 150 years in a stock of horses placed on Sable Island, Nova Scotia, appear almost certainly to be due to selection in relation to the somewhat unfavourable conditions (Gates, 1930). This doubtless has a bearing on the evolution of dwarf forms of large mammals on islands or near the limit of their range, for instance the very small Spitsbergen race of reindeer (*Rangifer tarandus*), the pigmy elephants, now extinct, of Malta and other Mediterranean islands, the Corsican subspecies of the red deer (*Cervus elaphus*), etc.

(7) *The interaction of two or more unfavourable mutations to produce a neutral or beneficial effect.* We have spoken of the cases of the mutations for red and transparent eyes in *Ephestia* and for purple and arc in *Drosophila* (p. 69). Another case, of a rather different kind, is that of the recessive *facet-notched*, which produces a notch at the free end of the wing in *Drosophila*. Its allelomorph *facet*, also a recessive, produces irregular ommatidia in the eye, together with a slight irregularity of the wing-types. When, however, the heterozygous combination of the two is synthesized, it is found to produce no visible effects. The combination of the two recessive alleles restores the appearance and viability of the wild type (Glass, 1933, who cites other cases of the same phenomenon).

Such a state of affairs might lead to the establishment of genetically-conditioned trimorphism.

(8) *The effect of selection of the gene-complex in altering the expression of mutations, and especially in abolishing their unfavourable action while retaining other effects.* We have dealt with numerous cases of this phenomenon earlier in the chapter, both as regards natural and artificial selection. The most striking cases are *eyeless* in *Drosophila* (p. 69), the crest character in fowls (p. 73) and the restored viability of red-eyed meal-moths when the mutant gene responsible is combined with another recessive gene (p. 68).

(9) *The existence of genetically-determined adaptations.* Once more the presumption is that these, if genetic, have arisen by mutation. If they are truly adaptive, the presumption is that they have arisen by selection (see Chapter 8 for a development of this argument and for examples).

(10) *The correlation between the incidence and type of genetically-determined variations in different parts of the range of a species with variation in the conditions and with the incidence and type of selection.* Some of the best examples concern polymorphic mimetic butterflies. We have first the adjustment of the frequencies of the different mimetic forms to the frequency of their respective model species; secondly, the adjustment of the pattern of the separate forms to the geographical variation of the models, or to the replacement of one species of model by another species; and thirdly, the relaxation of close mimetic resemblance in areas where the mimic outnumbers the model (p. 101). None of these phenomena can be explained except on selectionist grounds. Another equally good example concerns the replacement of the "normal" type of the species in certain parts of the animal's range by a type which remains rare in other regions, e.g. black *Coereba*, black hamsters, black opossums, voles with *simplex* type of teeth, melanic moths, bridled guillemots, etc. In all such cases, there are general grounds (p. 97), and in some cases particular grounds (p. 95) for believing that selection is at work.

These various lines of evidence all converge to support a neo-mendelian view, some showing that small mutations occur, others that selection is active, that some mutations are potentially beneficial, that through selection of the gene-complex, mutations can be adjusted to the needs of the organism, and that adaptations are genetically determined and vary in type and accuracy with direction and intensity of selection.

Three further general points of considerable importance must be mentioned. In the first place, R. A. Fisher (1930a) has provided mathematical proof of the interesting theorem that the combination of mutations to provide adaptive improvement in an organ or process in which the harmonious adjustment of many independently varying characters is required, is much more readily effected by mutations with small than by those with large effects.

Secondly, both Fisher (1932) and Haldane (1932a) have shown the enormous superiority, in the light of existing knowledge, of selection to other suggested agencies of evolutionary change, such as true orthogenesis (Chap. 9, p. 509).* Even if genes were to mutate repeatedly in the same direction, this could have no evolutionary effect unless they had no influence on viability and general fitness. A reduction of one-tenth of one per cent in viability would result in adverse selection which would override mutation at the highest rate ever yet observed in nature. Similarly, if a mutation caused an increase of viability of only $0 \cdot 1$ per cent or over, its spread would of necessity be mainly due to favourable selection. The same argument applies to the slow accumulation of lamarckian effects postulated by some believers in the inheritance of acquired characters: if this is so extremely slow as to escape detection in the course of an experiment covering a few generations, as they often assert, it would be overridden by selection-pressure whenever any but the most trifling differences in viability existed (pp. 457 seq.).

Thirdly, variability varies inversely with selection-pressure (pp. 324 seq.). The butterfly *Papilio dardanus* provides a striking example. This possesses several polymorphic female forms. Most of these are mimetic and highly invariable, except when, for special environmental reasons, they are able to live outside their

---

* Haldane (op. cit., p. 142) qualifies this view by pointing out that the paths open to selective guidance are limited by the nature of variation. This restrictive or subsidiary orthogenesis we shall discuss later (p. 510).

models' range. The rare form *dionysos*, however, is non-mimetic, and highly variable (Ford, 1936).

In the field we are discussing, of the relations between genetics and evolution, perhaps the most important single concept of recent years is that of the adjustment of mutations through changes in the gene-complex. Before this had been developed by R. A. Fisher and his followers, notably E. B. Ford, the effect of a mutation was assumed to be constant. A given mutation, we may say, made an offer to the germplasm of the species, which had to be accepted or declined as it stood. And the data on laboratory mutants at the time indicated that the great majority would have to be declined.

To-day we are able to look at the matter in a wholly different way. To continue our metaphor, the offer made by a mutation to the species is not necessarily a final offer. It may be merely a preliminary proposal, subject to negotiation. Biologically, this negotiation is effected in the first instance by recombination and secondarily by mutation in the residual gene-complex. It can lead to a marked alteration in the effects of the mutation, which may make the proposal acceptable to the organism.

Ten years ago evolutionary change, on the neo-mendelian view, depended on the co-operation of two processes only—the presentation of ready-made building-blocks by mutation, and the utilization of certain of them under the influence of selection. To-day we have been brought to realize that a third process is at work—change, primarily recombinational, in the residual variability of the gene-complex; and this can shape the building-blocks so as to enable them to fit in better with their neighbours and with the general plan of the building.

Thus evolutionary change, in so far as Darwinian, is not due simply to the co-operation of mutation and selection; a third, intermediate agency is involved in the shape of the residual variability of the species. Adjustment intervenes between presentation and acceptance.

CHAPTER 4

GENETIC SYSTEMS AND EVOLUTION

1. THE FACTORS OF EVOLUTION

A discursive treatment of mutation, as adopted in the previous chapter, has at the present time a certain historical justification. Darwin's theory of the mechanism of evolution was extremely abstract and generalized. Next to nothing was known in Darwin's time of the nature of variations or of the mode of their inheritance, let alone of their differences in various groups of organisms. The idea of selection remained equally generalized. Darwin admitted but two types of selection, natural and sexual. We now realize that there are many kinds of selection, often antagonistic in their effects, and not all operative in the same way on all organisms.

Finally, Darwin had little inkling, apart from his reference to the greater variability of abundant species, of the evolutionary effects of differences in the nature of the evolving groups. We now know, however, that not only these, but also differences in environmental conditions, may be of the greatest importance.

The biggest blank on the evolutionary map, however, concerned variation and its inheritance. The theory of mutation on a mendelian basis is the first adequate attempt to fill the gap. It has met with great resistance, and has itself developed almost out of recognition during its rapid growth from its beginnings only a few decades ago. There is thus every reason in the present state of biology to devote a chapter to mutation treated broadly as embodying Darwin's shadowy "heritable variations" and as representing the raw material of evolution in a generalized way.

It is probable, however, that writers of books on evolution ten or twenty years hence will adopt a different method. They will begin by describing the nature of the physical basis of inheritance, its modes of change by mutation of various kinds and at various speeds, its remarkable general uniformity in all cellular organisms, and its important variations in detail. They will then point out how the nature of this mechanism governs or limits the evolutionary process, and how its variations affect the mode of evolution of their possessors. It is impossible for higher animals, whether arthropod or vertebrate, to evolve in the same way as do higher plants, owing to differences in their chromosomal machinery: non-cellular and non-sexual organisms such as bacteria have their own evolutionary rules.*

It is not only the cytological mechanism of heredity, however, which influences mode of evolution: to use Darlington's useful phrase, there is involved the whole genetic system, meaning by this not only the chromosomal machinery, but the type of reproduction. Parthenogenesis, hermaphroditism, self- or cross-fertilization, in- and out-breeding—all introduce their own modifications.

Recognition of this fact broadens out into recognition that mode of life in general has its influence on evolutionary differentiation. A wide-ranging type will develop a different genetic structure (here we borrow a phrase from Timoféeff-Ressovsky, 1940) from one with limited powers of dispersal. Thus we need an index of genetic mobility, or of its inverse function, isolation. The spread of genes will be different in linear populations, as in those inhabiting rivers or shore-lines where range is essentially unidimensional, from what it is in the usual two-dimensional species (Sewall Wright, 1940, p. 172); it will be different, as Sewall Wright (1931, 1932) has also shown, in small and in large populations.

Competition by males for mates or for territory will have

* These topics are discussed at greater length in recent books, such as Darlington's *The Evolution of Genetic Systems* (1939).

evolutionary results, some of them rather unexpected (see R. A. Fisher, 1930a, Chap. 6; Huxley, 1938a); so will competition between pollen-tubes in the higher plants, or that between litter-mates in higher animals (see Haldane, 1932a); so will the intensity of general competition, whether exercised through predators or rivals or through the inorganic environment (see pp. 324, 426, 469).

Nor will general organization and mode of development be without its evolutionary consequences. The meristematic growth of flowering plants permits a fuller evolutionary utilization of many types of mutation than is possible to higher animals. In animals, allometric growth has evolutionary consequences which in their turn must be differently adjusted according to whether general growth is limited or unlimited (Huxley, 1932; Gold-schmidt, 1940; de Beer, 1940a). The simple fact that most genes must act by affecting the rate of developmental processes is reflected in the evolution of vestigial organs, in recapitulation, in neoteny (see Chap. 9, § 6; and de Beer, 1940b).

The nature of an organism thus influences the mode of its evolution. This applies at every level. Within the individual, the microscopic machinery of genes and chromosomes, the mode of cellular aggregation and tissue-growth; at the individual level, the type of reproduction, the way of life, the level of behaviour, the method of development; beyond the individual, the size and structure of the group of which the individual is a unit, and its relations with other groups—all these, and many facts besides, have their evolutionary effects.

Evolutionary consequences of this sort were often so obvious that they forced themselves upon the attention of the earliest workers in the field. Darwin (1871), for instance, was fully alive to many of the evolutionary implications of differences in sexual relations in higher animals, and had noted the greater variability of large species (reference in Fisher and Ford, 1928). In the present century, more explicit attention has been given to particular aspects of the question. To take but a few examples, Muller early (1925) pointed out the restriction on polyploidy in animals due to their sex-determining mechanism. Wright (references in Wright, 1940) gave a detailed mathematical analysis of the evolutionary consequences of differences in population-size. Haldane (1932a) discussed the different selective effects of different modes of reproduction, such as the development of a neuter caste in social hymenoptera or of polytocy in mammals; Huxley (1932) pointed out some evolutionary consequences of differential growth.

However, there has been hardly any attempt to survey the problem as a whole. Darlington's *Evolution of Genetic Systems* (1939) is a notable essay in this direction, though limited to chromosomal and reproductive mechanisms (see also Darlington, 1940); and Goldschmidt's *Material Basis of Evolution* attempts the same for modes of development. A small but increasing number of writers realize that such a general approach is not only possible but necessary. Comparative Evolution is destined to become as important a branch of biology as Comparative Anatomy.

In any such general survey, other aspects of evolution would demand the same comparative treatment as that accorded to genetic systems and other peculiarities of the evolving organism. The generalized treatment of selection, as originally developed by Darwin and redrafted on a mendelian basis by R. A. Fisher (1930a), must be particularized. Darwin (1871) made a significant beginning in his separation of sexual and natural selection, and Haldane (1932a) has carried the process a stage further by distinguishing various forms of intraspecific from interspecific selection. The analysis could, however, be extended on a fully comparative basis, with every effort to introduce quantitative treatment at the same time. Selection will act differently in autopolyploids because of the reduced availability of recessive mutations (p. 143). The balance between selection, mutation, and chance recombination will be quite different in large and in small interbreeding groups, the difference in some cases being so great that mutation may exert a directive effect (Wright, 1940a, his p. 173). Certain types of reproductive mechanism or population structure may lead to an immediate rapid differentiation and evolutionary success, to be paid for later by loss of plasticity and widespread extermination of types, as in *Crepis* (p. 376), others to accidental non-adaptive change or to extinction, as in small isolated groups (p. 58); male haploidy will purge the germ-plasm of many recessives; the development of a reproductive caste will permit selection for altruistic qualities; familial selection will promote rapid growth and large size (for both points see Haldane, 1932b); inter-male competition when success may mean more than one mating will produce male characters of display or combat which may be deleterious in the individual struggle for life (p. 426; Huxley, 1938b). The development of social life, with consequent inter-group struggle within the species, may produce the most peculiar selective results, as is especially to be seen in our own species (see R. A. Fisher, 1930a, Chaps. 10 to 12). Isolation from potential enemies or rivals may permit unusual specialization, as in flightless island birds, or encourage variability and degree of adaptive radiation, as in the fish of certain African lakes or the marsupials of Australia (p. 324). According to environmental conditions and to the genetic structure of the group, selection may act either as a stabilizing force or as an agent of change, and may decrease or increase internal variability. We need a comparative study of selection as well as of genetic systems.

Our last examples remind us that the environment, too, has its evolutionary effects. Ecology has listed and analysed the chief types of environments, major and minor habitats, and ecological niches. It has also pointed out one evolutionary result of environmental difference, in the adaptive correlation between organisms and the environments they inhabit (p. 430; Hesse, Allee, and Schmidt, 1937). But it has not undertaken detailed analysis of the effects of environmental difference on evolution. Here and there a beginning has been made. The study of the results of the glacial period—the extinction of some species, the disjunction of others, the subsequent divergence of their separated portions, and their behaviour on re-meeting—has already thrown a flood of light on the evolutionary results of violent climatic changes, and revealed to us that we live in a time when evolution is operating at exceptional speed (p. 243). The study of the marginal zones of species is showing that they are often characterized by a peculiar genetic structure of the population (Vavilov, 1927) or by special adaptations (Reinig, 1937), and is also throwing light on the evolutionary functions of the harmoniously stabilized gene-complex (Huxley, 1938d, 1939a and b). The so-called geographical rules, when analysed in detail, reveal that the sharp discontinuities of species and subspecies are often superposed upon continuous gradients of change (clines, p. 206), delicately adjusted to the external gradients of the inorganic environment (p. 208). Differences in ecological preference may isolate groups as effectively as geographical barriers or mere spatial distance, often with the production of cryptic species (p. 299). Perhaps most important of all, we are beginning to realize that the effective environment of an organism may be and usually is altered by genetic change: as Darlington (1939) pithily puts it, "a dwarf bean does not meet the same environment as a scarlet runner."

Pre-mendelian evolutionary theory arranged its facts and ideas under three main heads: variation, heredity and selection. This was necessary to clarify the generalized theorems of evolution —natural selection and consequent adaptation; it is still necessary to-day. But to-day we can go further. Evolution can no longer be a matter of generalized theorems only: it is itself a major field for comparative study. The comparative study of the reagent— the varying, evolving organisms: the comparative study of the medium—the graded, fluctuating environment: and the comparative study of their interaction—the processes of selection and their consequences: it is along some such lines as these that the evolutionary text-book of the future must be written.

The time is not yet ripe, however, for such a treatment of the subject. In this volume, all that can be attempted with regard to selection and environment will be some incidental comparative discussion in later chapters. With regard to the nature of the reagent, however, the situation is rather different. The spectacular advances of cytology in the last two decades now permit the use of deductive methods on a large scale. Our knowledge of chromosomal machinery and of mode of reproduction allows us to make prophecies concerning genetic detail which may take years to verify empirically, and to draw accurate conclusions as to the type of selection which will operate. Thus it seems worth while to give a brief summary (largely based on Darlington's book (1939) and the relevant chapters in those of Dobzhansky, 1937, and Waddington, 1939) of the evolutionary effects of differences in genetic-reproductive systems. In a later chapter other effects of the nature and mode of development of the reacting organism will be given (p. 525), though a full treatment of this type of consequential evolution is not yet possible.

2. THE EARLY EVOLUTION OF GENETIC SYSTEMS

There is an astonishing similarity in the genetic systems of the great majority of organisms. Their hereditary machinery is organized into discrete chromosomes of definite size, shape and genic make-up. The chromosomes divide normally by mitosis, and at one point in the life-cycle undergo meiosis which is accompanied by crossing-over. This applies to all higher plants and all higher animals and to many quite lowly forms as well.

The genetic system must have had a long evolution behind it before it reached what we may call the meiotic stage, with its elaborate mechanism. Two prior main stages may be distinguished, the pre-mitotic and the mitotic, and organisms still survive which are equipped with genetic systems of these earlier patterns.

Bacteria (and *a fortiori* viruses if they can be considered to be true organisms), in spite of occasional reports of a sexual cycle, appear to be not only wholly asexual but pre-mitotic. Their hereditary constitution is not differentiated into specialized parts with different functions. They have no genes in the sense of accurately quantized portions of hereditary substance; and therefore they have no need for the accurate division of the genetic system which is accomplished by mitosis. The entire organism appears to function both as soma and germplasm, and evolution must be a matter of alteration in the reaction-system as a whole. That occasional "mutations" occur we know, but there is no ground for supposing that they are similar in nature to those of higher organisms, nor, since they are usually reversible according to conditions, that they play the same part in evolution. We must, in fact, expect that the processes of variation, heredity, and evolution in bacteria are quite different from the corresponding processes in multicellular organisms. But their secret has not yet been unravelled (p. 302).

One guess may be hazarded: that the specificity of their constitution is maintained by a purely chemical equilibrium, without any of the mechanical control superposed by the mitotic (and meiotic) arrangements of higher forms. We may also guess, with Darlington (1939, p. 121), that the so-called "plasmagenes" which have been detected in a few higher plants, and which also seem to be controlled in their reproduction only by a chemical equilibrium, are survivals, though possibly specialized in their own way, from the pre-mitotic level of evolution.

The mitotic but pre-meiotic stage is represented to-day by a few Algae and Protozoa. These may be degenerate in having abandoned sex and meiosis, or they may never have acquired them. In any case, the rarity of such cases implies that this stage must have been somewhat transitory. Apparently once the detailed differentiation of the germ-plasm into accurately-divisible chromosomes had been accomplished, it was comparatively simple to alter the timing of the various processes involved in one cell-division, so as to produce meiosis; and this was fraught with such advantages that it was all but universally adopted.

It is in any case interesting to reflect on certain peculiarities of this stage, which must indubitably once have been passed through. The existence of mitosis, of however simple a nature, presupposes the need for accurate mechanical division of the hereditary substance; and this in its turn would not be necessary unless the hereditary substance were differentiated into specialized parts each with their appropriate functions. Thus the mitotic organism has reached a stage of particulate inheritance, based on spatial differentiation of the germplasm. Yet it would be improper to speak of the organism possessing genes, in the sense of definitely quantized units. Such units may have existed, in the sense that there was a real division between two adjacent regions of a chromosome performing different functions. But no method which we can yet envisage would be able to detect this. Genes as we know them are mechanically delimited by the lines of potential crossing-over (p. 49), so that the attainment of meiosis is a prerequisite for their detection. It may be that another type of subdivision existed in the chromosomes of pre-meiotic organisms. If so, we can only say that it is likely to have been profoundly modified by the superposition of a mechanical jointing, for we can safely deduce that selection would tend to adjust the two functions, and convert the mechanically-determined genes into physiological units as well.

Purely mitotic organisms may have enjoyed a more elaborate genetic constitution, with its parts more accurately adjusted, than pre-mitotic ones. But from the evolutionary standpoint their behaviour will be similar. They are compelled to forgo most of the advantages of their genetic complexity for lack of the sexual-meiotic process which permits the recombination of the genetic units.

The attainment of the meiotic stage was thus the most important single step in the evolution of genetic systems, comparable in its evolutionary effects to that due to the attainment of a cumulative tradition, and thus of a new form of heredity, in our own species.

Mere numerical reduction of the chromosomes to prevent doubling of their number in each sexual cycle could perfectly well have been secured simply by a failure of chromosomes to divide at the first meiotic division. This may have been the first step towards true meiosis, and something of the sort occurs (though doubtless secondarily) in the meiosis of the heterogametic sex of some organisms, such as *Drosophila*.

Such a process would also secure recombination, but a recombination of whole chromosomes only—in other words a recombination of perhaps a few tens of units instead of one of hundreds or even of thousands. The evolutionary advantages of a greater degree of recombination are so great that this condition, if it ever existed, has been entirely supplanted by true meiosis, which implies crossing-over as well as numerical reduction. It is the merit of Darlington (see Darlington, 1937) to have shown that crossing-over is not merely the occasional accompaniment of meiosis, but its invariable and necessary condition. It is through crossing-over that the bivalents are held together after each member of a pair has divided into two chromatids: if it were not for the mechanical union thus provided, they could drift apart, since attraction only operates between pairs of homologues, and could not hold four together. Chiasmata thus have both a mechanical and a genetic function: they provide at one and the same time the cross-junctions needed for the cytological process of meiosis, and the sectional separations which give rise to mendelian recombination of genes.

Meiosis at its first origin was without doubt a process inserted into the life-cycle immediately after fertilization. Not only are various primitive organisms haploid throughout their existence except for the brief moment after syngamy, but it can be deduced on general grounds that any mechanism for reducing the diploid number of chromosomes would in the first instance be likely to come into action as soon as and whenever that diploid number was reached (Darlington, 1939). Its delayed onset in all higher organisms must have been secondarily evolved.

Thus diploidy, far from being the normal inevitable condition we are apt to imagine, was originally an embarrassment to be got rid of as soon as possible. Measures had to be taken to prevent the doubling of chromosome-number at each fertilization, and the simplest way was to reduce it again as soon as possible.

But this apparently commendable promptness had its drawbacks. For diploidy has a manifest advantage over the haploid state. It endows the stock with a much higher degree of plasticity by permitting it to carry a store of recessives in its germplasm. In a haploid, these would be exposed to the full rigours of selection in each generation, and the majority of them would be weeded out. In a diploid, thanks to the full evolution of dominance which diploidy must automatically have brought about (pp. 75 seq.), they can be carried in evolutionary reserve in reasonable quantity without being phenotypically expressed, and so exposed to selection, except in a trifling number of individuals. If conditions change, some of them may be employed, either unaltered in expression, or "improved" by combination with other reserve genes.

So it came about that pure haploidy is now confined to certain Protozoa and simple Algae, and diploidy has been prolonged elsewhere for a number of cell-generations—about 10 in rotifers, about 50 in our own species. Diploidy has arisen in two ways. In the Basidiomycete fungi, the two gametic nuclei do not fuse, but persist side by side: as Darlington (1939, p. 11) puts it, the organism is diploid although all its nuclei are haploid. In all other forms, the haploid gametic nuclei fuse to form diploid zygotic nuclei, which persist through the rest of the diploid phase.

The haploid phase is reduced in all Metazoa to the resting-stage of a single cell-generation. In plants, this extreme is never reached. In Bryophyta the haploid stage is the main phase of the life-history, both in size and duration. In the Pteridophyta it is still independent, but it is now both smaller and briefer than the diploid. In seed-plants it has become much reduced and confined to one or two cell-generations. But even here a fundamental distinction from the metazoan condition remains, notably on the male side. While the nuclei of spermatozoa appear to be quite inactive genetically, so that they merely transport their freight of genes without being affected by its peculiarities, this is not true for pollen-grains, in which particular genes may cause marked differences in capacity for germination, rate of growth of pollen-tubes, etc. Doubtless the great majority of genes in higher plants have no or negligible effects upon the haploid phase, since most of them will have been primarily selected for their effects on the much more elaborate diploid phase: none the less, haploid selection will definitely curtail total plasticity.

It appears that lethals may act during animal meiosis and the early part of the transformation of the reduced cells into spermatozoa; but once formed the sperms are not affected in their function by particular genes. In this respect the genetic systems of animals are more advanced than those of plants, since the reserve of recessives which they are able to carry must be somewhat larger. By similar reasoning we may deduce that in regard to evolutionary plasticity seed-plants must be somewhat superior to ferns and horsetails, and these in turn to mosses and liverworts —a conclusion which seems borne out by the facts.

3. THE MEIOTIC SYSTEM AND ITS ADJUSTMENT

In general, however, the diploid meiotic system is remarkably uniform throughout its very wide range of occurrence. Once established, various internal adjustments are effected between the parts of the system. In the first place, two conflicting advantages must be balanced. It is in general an advantage to an organism to have its normal constitution as harmonious as possible, with its main genes buffered by modifiers to a maximum efficiency and viability (p. 67) and mutually adjusted to each other's activity, and neighbouring genes harmonized through an optimum position-effect (p. 85). Even with organisms that show polymorphism or excessive variability, it will be an advantage for the central core of the constitution to be buffered and adjusted in this way. But it is also in general an advantage to an organism to possess a considerable amount of evolutionary plasticity. The former is a short-term advantage, giving the closest possible adaptation to existing conditions, the latter a long-term advantage, coming into play if conditions change or even enabling the stock to extend the range of conditions in which it can thrive.

Stabilization of internal adjustment can be achieved by decreasing recombination, plasticity by increasing it. Low recombination is best effected by keeping a large number of genes (here regarded as mutational units) together in mechanical union —in other words by a reduction in the number of chromosomes and a low chiasma-frequency. High recombination implies the reverse—an increase in chromosome-number and in crossing-over. Extreme reduction of chromosome-number is difficult owing to the mechanics of meiosis and mitosis—a single centromere cannot efficiently cope with more than a certain length of chromosome (Darlington, 1939, p. 77), and in point of fact we find a negligible fraction of species with a haploid number below 4. Similarly, chiasmata normally have an essential function in keeping bivalents together in the later stages of meiosis, so that there will be a minimum crossover-recombination due to this mechanical cause. There is also a mechanical upper limit set to the number of chiasmata within a single chromosome, which is revealed genetically by the phenomenon of interference.

For this and other reasons we shall not expect the adjustment of what Darlington (1939b, p. 77) calls the recombination-index to the conflicting evolutionary needs of the organism to be at all close. That it is not so is shown by the variations in mode of life shown by organisms with similar recombination-indices, and conversely by the variations in recombination-index shown by closely-related organisms with similar mode of life.

None the less, some adjustment undoubtedly exists. Chiasma-frequency in general tends to lie below its mechanical upper limit, thus reducing possible recombination. On the other hand, those forms in which recombination is markedly reduced or absent (e.g. translocation-hybrids such as *Oenothera*; high auto-polyploids such as *Rumex lapathifolium*; apomicts, hybrid or otherwise, as in *Taraxacum* and *Crepis*) are for the most part doomed to eventual extinction as conditions change and they suffer in competition with more plastic rivals. Thus in the evolutionary long run the forms with reasonable recombination will survive to constitute a majority, and at any given time those with recombination markedly reduced or absent will be new and relatively short-lived types, and will be in the minority.

Adjustment of the two conflicting needs thus tends to be effected in two rather different ways. The need for stability will be met by keeping chromosome-number and chiasma-frequency below the maximum possible; the need for plasticity by the differential extinction of the less plastic types.

Plasticity will obviously be affected by mutation-rate as well as by recombination-index. We know that genes exist which affect the mutation-rate of other genes (see Sturtevant, 1937, for summary), even though the number yet described is very small. Though detailed mathematical analysis is desirable, it is clear in principle that in a slow-growing organism like an elephant or a tree, mutation and recombination will give a much lower production of novelty and plasticity than in an insect like *Drosophila* with a dozen or more generations annually.

We may thus expect with reasonable assurance that mutation-rate also will be in some degree adjusted to evolutionary needs.

On the other hand, here too there is bound to be a great deal of lag, and much of the adjustment will concern life as a whole, operating by the eventual extinction of the inherently less plastic, instead of concerning the separate species and operating by changing their separate mutation-rates. Comparative studies in this field will be of the greatest interest. Meanwhile, we can point to the much greater observed diversification of herbs than of trees, of insects than of fish or mammals, as a probable evolutionary consequence of high plasticity due to more rapid succession of generations. If the slower-breeding forms have attempted to compensate for their disadvantage by increased mutation-rate (see p. 54), the compensation has been a very imperfect one.

Interesting results are observed when single chromosomes or chromosomal regions are debarred from recombination with their homologues. The most obvious case is that of the differential segment of the Y-chromosomes in organisms with a specialized chromosomal sex-determining mechanism. Here, the homologue (X) behaves as a normal chromosome, since it can cross-over in the homogametic sex. Thus not only do Y-chromosomes suffer a loss of plasticity, but degenerative mutations, if recessive, can accumulate in them, shielded from selection by their dominant alleles in the partner chromosome or region. This process has much more intense effects than mere loss of evolutionary plasticity and leads rapidly to the region becoming converted into genetically "inert" material (though it may retain important metabolic functions: Schultz, Caspersson and Aquilonius, 1940). As Muller pointed out in 1918, the fact that (part or all of) the Y is debarred from recombination by absence of crossing-over has allowed "loss" mutations to accumulate in it until it has become genetically vestigial. In man and *Drosophila* it still contains a few active genes; in Drosophila XO males are sterile (abnormal vas deferens); "bobbed" and ever-sporting eye-colour (Gowen and Gay, 1933) are also Y-borne.

As with somatic vestigial organs, the Y-chromosome is very variable in size in closely related species and even within the same species. Further, once it ceases to contain effective genes, a mechanical accident at mitosis or meiosis may cause its loss without this bringing any untoward consequences in its train. Thus the XO condition has frequently evolved from the XY.

Somewhat different conditions are provided when recombination is equally reduced in all representatives of a chromosomal region. This occurs generally, and perhaps universally, in the portion of the chromosome immediately adjacent to the centromere. For simple mechanical reasons, breakage and interchange is unlikely or impossible within a certain distance from the centromere. It is interesting to find that here, too, complete or considerable inertness has been a frequent result. Evidently, the shielding of recessives from selection, while it is bound to accelerate the tendency to inertness, is not the only condition for it to occur; the complete or almost complete debarring of a region from recombination may be sufficient condition for it to become inert.

On the other hand, in other circumstances, it may not. This is clearly so whenever structural hybridity, whether dependent on inversion or translocation, has become a characteristic feature of a species. In the regions adjacent to the centromere, there is always a reduction in crossing-over. But with sectional rearrangements, only the heterozygote is affected: crossing-over continues undiminished in both homozygote types. The heterozygous combination will therefore not become the sole or the dominant type unless it is endowed with some countervailing advantage. Such an advantage may very well accrue from heterosis, since, granted that an inversion or translocation persists at all, its genetic isolation from its homologous region will force it to diverge and allow selection to differentiate it further as a regional stabilized system (p. 362). Once heterozygosity is endowed with selective advantage, it will become the dominant or sole phase; and further, inertness will no longer be encouraged in one or both of the partner regions, since the selective value of the condition depends on the activity of both regions in combination.

In such cases, the loss of plasticity due to lack of recombination will be adjusted, if at all, by the extinction of the type. The great variability in the degree of interchange hybridity in *Oenothera* seems to be evidence of the recent development of the condition in this genus; while the state of affairs in *Rhoeo*, where all the chromosomes form a ring, and only a single species remains, "restricted in distribution and almost invariable in form" (Darlington, 1939*b*, p. 92), indicates that this genus has been paying the penalty for its loss of plasticity.

Mather (1940) has recently discussed the evolutionary implications of monoecism and dioecism. Complete separation of the sexes promotes outbreeding, but leads to wastage of gametes except where, as in higher animals, discriminatory mating occurs. In higher plants minimum wastage is best secured by monoecism combined with devices to prevent self-fertilization. Such subsidiary devices are more readily changed if increased inbreeding is required (cf. Lewis, 1941, on the flexibility of cytoplasmic as against genic control of male-sterility).

In gynodioecism, purely female individuals occur as well as monoecious ones. As in other cases of dimorphism (p. 97), this rests on a flexible selective balance, determining the proportion of female plants (p. 107). The advantage of outbred offspring is set off against the disadvantage of producing only one kind of gamete.

Inversions and translocations can be considered from another angle—as one of the aberrations to which the diploid meiotic machinery is subject. Some of these aberrations need not be considered here, since, like the production of acentric or dicentric chromosomes, they are lethal, and so cannot play any part in evolution. Those which interest us are the types which are capable of survival and therefore of being promoted from aberration to norm.

The most obvious of such changes is polyploidy, and the most obvious fact about polyploidy is its rarity in higher animals as opposed to its abundance in higher plants. It appears probable that nearly half the species of flowering plants are polyploids.

Permanent anisopolyploidy is inevitably associated with some form of non-sexual reproduction, since triploids and the like are incapable of perpetuation by sexual means. Thus, since both vegetative reproduction and apomixis are very much commoner in plants than animals, the same is true of anisopolyploids.

This holds also for tetraploids and other isopolyploids. It is at first sight less clear why this should be so. However, there are several reasons. In the first place a single autotetraploid individual has much less chance of establishing a tetraploid strain in animals owing to the rarity of self-fertilization in them: autotetraploids are often sterile with the corresponding diploids, and even if fertile, the offspring are triploid and therefore sexually sterile. In cross-fertilized species, vegetative reproduction and apomixis will also tend in the same direction. When facultative, they may multiply the original single tetraploid many times, and so increase the chances of two meeting when sexual reproduction supervenes. This, however, will not wholly account for the facts. Autotetraploids are always initially handicapped by reduced fertility, since the four homologous chromosomes of a set by no means always separate in pairs at meiosis, and when three separate from one, chromosomally unbalanced types result which often display reduced viability or fertility. Autotetraploids are thus most unlikely to establish themselves except in types with some form of non-sexual reproduction—in other words, except in plants.* The rare cases found in animals are usually parthenogenetic (e.g. the moth *Solenobia* and the crustacean *Artemia*).

Allotetraploids are not always restricted to forms which can carry on by means of non-sexual reproduction. Thus in certain moth hybrids (e.g. *Pygaera*), pairing does not occur at meiosis, but the chromosomes all remain as univalents which divide twice by mitosis, giving diploid gametes. However, this is irrelevant from the evolutionary point of view since behaviour-barriers to mating prevent hybridization in nature.

In various plant species-hybrids, too, pairing fails to occur in all or almost all chromosomes at meiosis, and unreduced gametes thus result (though one of the two meiotic divisions is suppressed). This occurs, for instance, in the celebrated radish-cabbage hybrid *Raphanobrassica*. In other cases, however, as in *Primula kewensis*,

---

* In higher plants there are of course great variations in the degree to which non-sexual reproduction is available. Thus, as Darlington points out (1939, p. 105), since autotetraploids are very unlikely to establish themselves in nature except where such methods of reproduction are available, "by discovering their occurrence among plants, we are therefore indirectly discovering the degree of importance of sexual fertility in the life of the species, a matter to which little attention has been paid in the past."

the diploid hybrid is sterile *because* its chromosomes show regular pairing. The chromosomes of the two parent species, *P. floribunda* and *P. verticillata*, have differentiated sufficiently (largely we may presume, through translocations) for them to be no longer functionally equivalent, so that a haploid set consisting of mixed chromosomes from the two species will not be viable.

Fertility can here only be restored by means of somatic doubling of chromosome-number, resulting in a tetraploid shoot. The pairing attraction between chromosomes of the same species is greater than that between those of different species, so that diploid gametes each with two complete or functional haploid sets are produced, and fertility is restored. But the production of a tetraploid shoot is a rare phenomenon: in *P. kewensis* it did not occur until after many generations of vegetative propagation. Nothing of the sort could have occurred in a higher animal. Finally, there is the existence in all or almost all higher animals of a chromosomal mechanism of sex-determination. This, as Muller pointed out many years ago, will in most cases fail to function in a tetraploid individual, giving numerous intersexes or other sterile forms. It is true that in the white campion *Melandrium*, which has an XY sex-determining complex, this still functions in the tetraploid (Warnke and Blakeslee, 1939); but this is due to special quantitative relations between the sexual valency of the X-chromosome and the autosomes, which are unlikely to occur generally.

But animals are not wholly debarred from enjoying any of the benefits polyploidy may bring. They do so through the method of "repeats" or reduplications of small sections of chromosome, which bring about what may be called a partial polyploidy. As M. J. D. White says (1937, p. 107), "that part of their gene-complex which is tetraploid is possibly less subject to the conservative effect of natural selection and is consequently in more active evolution." This was not discovered until recently, and the extent to which it occurs has, up till now, been investigated only in *Drosophila* and other Diptera in which the enlarged salivary gland chromosomes permit direct examination. However, its widespread existence in these forms, coupled with general theoretical considerations on sectional rearrangements, makes it possible for such an authority as Muller (1940) to assert that even in plants it must have played a more important evolutionary role than straightforward polyploidy.

4. THE CONSEQUENCES OF POLYPLOIDY

We must now consider the evolutionary effects, immediate and secondary, of polyploidy (pp. 334 seq.). In autopolyploidy, an obvious immediate effect will be the restricted evolutionary function of recessive mutations. In most cases these will not exert any phenotypic effect unless they are present in all four of the homologous chromosomes (though cases exist where three recessives dominate over one dominant), so that the chance of a recessive character reappearing after a cross is reduced to that for a double recessive combination in diploid organisms. This effect increases by powers of two for successive steps in chromosome-doubling, so that in high autopolyploids with 16*n* or higher number of chromosomes, recessives virtually cease to have any effect on the organism, either in regard to their single effect or in recombination. Such forms have their stability-plasticity balance tilted over in favour of stability, and cannot be expected to survive if environmental conditions change to any considerable extent.

Meanwhile, however, if repeated chromosome-doublings do not take place too rapidly, and if the species does not rely solely or mainly upon vegetative reproduction, counteracting tendencies are likely to operate which will convert the phylogenetic autopolyploid into a functional allopolyploid, at the same time restoring its sexual fertility (p. 335).

One method by which this is achieved is by reducing the number of chiasmata to one per chromosome, which automatically operates to prevent the formation of quadrivalents as in *Tulipa* (Upcott, 1939). If any genes exist or later appear which alter the differential pairing attraction of either of the two members of any chromosome-pair of the original diploid set, not only will fertility be restored but some degree of genetic isolation will arise between the two chromosome-pairs of the tetraploid and will tend to be self-reinforcing. Presumably this effect, if strong enough, could operate *ab initio*, without prior reduction of the chiasma-frequency, but cases of this are not yet known. In any case, once such genetic isolation has been established, it will open the door to a functional differentiation between the two homologous pairs as regards their externally adaptive effects.

Another method involving adjustment of the number and behaviour of chiasmata is found in *Dahlia*, in this case permitting multiple pairing but compelling regular segregation (see Darlington, 1939, p. 39).

In any event, sexual reproduction in an autopolyploid implies natural selection for fertility, and this automatically tends to convert the species into a functional allopolyploid.

Polyploidy may be expected to increase delicacy of genetic adjustment in certain respects, by increasing the number of multiple factor systems. In an octoploid, for instance, every kind of gene has four homologous representatives. Where all contribute something to a phenotypic result, a very flexible system is available (see Winge, 1938, on genic replication in general).

In general, the evolutionary consequences of polyploidy may be roughly compared with those of metameric segmentation in Annulata: a number of homologous parts are available, between which functional division of labour is then possible. The fact that the division of labour is genotypic instead of phenotypic is irrelevant. The chief difference is that in metamerism the parts are initially repeated a large and indefinite number of times, and their later divergence is accompanied by a reduction and definition of their number. In polyploidy, on the other hand, the parts are never repeated indefinitely, nor, indeed, many times over, and functional divergence may and does begin when they are merely doubled. Nevertheless, the analogy is a real one.

In allotetraploids, some degree of functional autopolyploidy often remains. The reason for the fertility of a form like the tetraploid *Primula kewensis* is not any inability of the homologous chromosomes of the two parent species to pair, for they do pair regularly in the diploid hybrid. It resides in a differential pairing affinity as between identical and merely homologous chromosomes: where tetraploidy has provided two identical chromosomes of each sort, these will normally begin to pair with each other rather than with either of their two homologues from the other species, and the rapidity of pairing usually does not allow other chromosomes to be drawn in to form multivalents.

Occasionally, however, some mechanical accident permits the pairing of non-identical chromosomes or the formation of quadrivalents. In such cases, a new *type* of variation occurs. Segregation takes place between chromosome-segments of the two ancestral species (pp. 343, 345; Darlington, 1939, p. 38). Since the ancestral species may be phylogenetically quite remote, the variational consequences may be unusual and considerable. Here again, it is to be expected that selection will automatically step in to reduce the frequency of such behaviour, since the extreme variants are likely to be less viable than normal. Accordingly, the "interspecific segregation" is more frequent in relatively recent alletraploids, such as *Triticum vulgare* or *Nicotiana tabacum*.

The interaction of the two gene-complexes will also produce various new effects, sometimes unfavourable, sometimes favourable (pp. 66, 341 seq.).

It remains to mention one other selective adjustment which occurs in both auto- and allotetraploids, namely, the abolishing of much of the physiological effect of polyploidy. Polyploids at their first formation appear invariably to show some degree of gigantism, and often vary from the diploid in respect of their general vigour, temperature-resistance, and flowering period. These latter properties have often proved to be pre-adaptive, in that through them polyploids have extended their range beyond that of their ancestral diploids. With respect to their gigantism, however, the general rule has been for this to be reduced or wholly abolished in the course of evolution. Even octoploid forms exist which are identical in size and appearance with the diploid (e.g. in *Silene ciliata*: see Darlington, 1939, p. 39). This fact can only be due to adjustment through selection, and is strong evidence for concluding that the mean size of a plant species is an adaptive characteristic. Darlington suggests that the absence of polyploidy in certain genera (e.g. *Ribes*) may be due to the failure of these secondary genetic adaptations.*

* The absence of polyploidy in Gymnosperms and in various Angiosperm genera is apparently due to its being mechanically impossible where chromosomes are too large relatively to cell-size (see Darlington, 1937, p. 84).

5. SPECIES-HYBRIDIZATION AND SEX-DETERMINATION:
CONCLUSION

It remains to consider other modifications of the basic meiotic system, and their consequences. Fertile species-hybrids, quite apart from any questions of polyploidy, appear to be much commoner in nature among plants than among animals. This is due to two quite different causes. In the first place, they are much more readily formed in plants, owing to their passive methods of cross-fertilization by wind or insects, and to the consequent absence in them of reproductive barriers based on mating-preferences, which are all but universal in higher animals.

In the second place, they are more likely to be fertile owing to the absence of the delicately adjusted sex-chromosome mechanism. In animals, the heterogametic sex in species-hybrids is often wholly or partially sterile (Haldane's rule) owing to imbalance between the single sex-chromosome derived from one parent species and the autosomes derived from both.*

Where the ranges of diverging plant species overlap, selection will normally step in to erect genetic barriers between them. But where they have differentiated in isolation from each other, then fertility on crossing will often remain. Species-hybrids are thus only likely to occur on a large scale where circumstances cause species to be brought together secondarily. The recent geological past is a period when this has been happening on a very large scale, owing to the high degree of range-change consequent on the alterations of climate since the beginning of the last glacial period. During the recent historical past an additional agency promoting species-hybridization has been at work, in the shape of human interference. This may be direct and intentional as when new species are deliberately introduced; or direct and unintentional, as when they are accidentally transported to new areas (cf. the production of the hybrid species *Spartina townsendii*

---

* This is by no means universal, as is shown by the high fertility of species-hybrids in, e.g., ducks and pheasants. Here, however, the formation of species-hybrids in nature is prevented by mating barriers. In other cases, such as fresh-water fish (Hubbs and Hubbs, 1933), species-hybridization occurs not infrequently in nature, in spite of resultant infertility and upset of sex-ratio.

owing to the accidental importation of an American species of the genus to Europe; p. 341); or indirect, as when species meet owing to changed ecological conditions caused by man's interference. Deforestation in the Balkans, for instance, has provided opportunities for many plant species to meet and hybridize (p. 258); the extension of cultivation has allowed many weeds of cultivation to spread far from their original home.

These two causes taken together have resulted in a degree of species-hybridization which must be unprecedented in evolutionary history. Confining our attention for the moment to fertile species-crosses, one result has been the production of "hybrid swarms". These have been described on a large scale in the New Zealand flora (p. 355; Allan, 1940), but it is probable that this is primarily due to the accident of the existence of New Zealand botanists interested in the problem, and that equal attention would reveal comparable phenomena in other parts of the world.

Sometimes the hybrid swarm has a mean which is intermediate between the parents, though of course with excessive variability. In other cases, as with *Centaurea* hybrids in Britain (p. 258), the result in some localities is the virtual disappearance of one parental type, save for the modification and enrichment of the other by a certain number of its genes. In any case, we have here another example of a mode of evolution to all intents confined to higher plants.

When species-hybridization is combined with polyploidy and apomixis, more complex phenomena result. When hybridization is solely or mainly initial, the result is the formation of numerous collections of apomicts each centring round a certain mean, as discussed for *Crepis* on p. 375; and see Turrill (1938c) for *Taraxacum*. Where, however, some of the products of initial hybridization continue to cross, we obtain elaborate complexes such as those of *Rosa, Rubus*, etc. (p. 351), in which a number of initial forms are combined in an evolutionary reticulum. Reticulate evolution in this form appears to exist only in plants. In animals, it occurs on a much more modest scale and at a lower taxonomic level, being usually restricted to the formation of "hybrid swarms" between a limited number (usually only two) subspecies. The only case in which it has reached larger scope is in our own species, where excessive migration, coupled with a breakdown of purely instinctive mating-barriers, has caused it to operate on a world-wide scale, producing a phenomenon not found elsewhere either in plants or animals.

We have several times found the presence of the chromosomal sex-determining mechanism operating to prevent the occurrence in animals of this or that phenomenon found in plants. Its presence, however, also has certain positive consequences. Some of these, like dosage-compensation of the effects of sex-linked genes, or indeed the phenomenon of sex-linkage itself, do not seem to have further evolutionary effects. There are, however, other effects. For instance, the need for suppressing crossing-over between the differential segments of X and Y has brought with it, apparently as secondary consequence, a lower cross-over value in all chromosomes of the heterogametic sex. The reduction may be slight, or it may be total as in *Drosophila*. Unless this is compensated for by an increase of crossing-over in the homogametic sex, the evolutionary plasticity of the species will be correspondingly lowered.

The genetic isolation between X and Y leads to a progressive increase of inertness in the Y, and often to its total disappearance. Especially in early stages of differentiation, an XY may switch over to a WZ (female heterogamety) mechanism, as is seen in cyprinodont fishes. Even in highly specialized forms such as *Drosophila*, the role of sex-chromosome may be taken over by different parts of the whole chromosome-complex in different species of the same genus (see Muller, 1940; Waddington, 1939).

In such an essentially unstable system situations often arise by which there are more than one pair of either X's or Y's produced, and in some cases astonishing complications such as that found in the fly *Sciara* (with its elimination of whole chromosomes, in different lines producing broods of different sexual types, etc.; see e.g. Metz, 1938). But none of these effects is important from the evolutionary point of view.

There is another method of sex-determination, however, which does have interesting evolutionary consequences, and that is the method of male haploidy, where the haploid condition determines maleness, the diploid condition femaleness. This is best known in the Hymenoptera, where it is certainly widespread and possibly universal, but has been independently evolved in Thysanoptera, in two families of Hemiptera, and one of Coleoptera, in certain mites, and in rotifers (tabulated in M. J. D. White, 1937). The origin of this mechanism is still obscure, though work on the parasitic wasp *Habrobracon* shows that it here operates in conjunction with female heterogamety and differential fertilization.

Its consequences, however, are obvious enough; all recessives will be subject to much more stringent selection through being robbed of any shelter from their dominance whenever they pass into the male sex. We might at first sight expect this to result in the purging of virtually all recessives from all the chromosomes, in the same way that unisexual haploidy of the sex-chromosome has led to the virtual absence of sex-linked recessives in natural populations of animals with an XY mechanism (p. 117); which in its turn would reduce the evolutionary plasticity of the type to a very low level.

This may have been the effect in certain cases, but it is difficult to believe that it has occurred in the Hymenoptera, where forms showing this method of sex-determination have achieved a great amount of adaptive radiation and have given rise to some of the highest and most successful types known among animals. We should hesitate to believe in the general value of diploidy if it had been in truth almost entirely sacrificed in this group.

Doubtless male haploidy does very speedily purge the germ-plasm of obviously deleterious recessives; and this, combined in social Hymenoptera with the intense mating competition among the males, must result in a genetic constitution that is extremely efficient for immediate purposes. Meanwhile recessives can still be carried by the diploid females, which, be it remembered, usually enjoy an actual or an effective predominance over the males, either through the existence of temporary parthenogenesis or through the social organization in social forms. We must accordingly presume that recessives of evolutionary value are retained in the constitution through some form of dosage-compensation analogous to that which obtains within the X-chromosome in forms with an XY mechanism.

*   *   *   *   *

There remain certain essentially minor types of evolutionary modification of the genetic system. One of them, that culminating in the production of true-breeding translocation hybrids, has received a great deal of attention owing largely to the historical accident that its existence in *Oenothera* led de Vries to enunciate his theory, which later proved to be erroneous, of evolution by large mutations. We now know that this method, for all the complications of its working and the intense interest which its analysis has provided, is both rare and of restricted evolutionary importance, since it condemns the types which practise it to loss of plasticity and so to eventual extinction (p. 139; Darlington, 1939).

The analysis could be pushed much further. Facultative and obligatory apomixis, facultative and obligatory self-fertilization each impose their own evolutionary consequences; so do the various degrees of gametic and zygotic mobility and other factors affecting the freedom of movement of genes within a population; so, as we have already pointed out, do the different intensities of selection to which a type is subjected. Space, however, will not permit us to pursue the subject. Enough has been said to show that each major group, and various minor groups within the major, will have their own peculiarities of genetic system and accordingly their own characteristic modes of evolution. We must not expect plants to evolve along the same lines as animals. Flowering plants will differ from mosses in their modes of speciation, trees from herbs, Hymenoptera from Crustacea, corals from higher vertebrates. The variety of genetic systems and of modes of evolution is as important a fact of biology as the variety of morphological types.

CHAPTER 5

THE SPECIES PROBLEM; GEOGRAPHICAL SPECIATION

I. THE BIOLOGICAL REALITY OF SPECIES

Our third chapter was in the main concerned with the *modus operandi* of natural selection in a mendelian world. We must, however, beware of thinking that the conclusions thus arrived at cover the whole field of evolution. There is a danger that the undoubted and in some ways spectacular success of mathematical and deductive methods in clarifying our vision and defining the course of one type of evolutionary process may distract attention from others of equal or at least of major importance.

Deduction and mathematical generalization can only achieve valuable results with the aid of a firm foundation of fact: the history of science abounds with examples. Indeed, the history of this particular subject is especially instructive on the point. The biometrical school, inspired by Galton and carried on by Karl Pearson and his disciples, such as Weldon, applied mathematical methods of extreme delicacy and ingenuity to the study of evolutionary problems. But the foundation on which they built was one of assumptions. When these were not simply erroneous, like the assumption of blending or of non-particulate inheritance, they were extremely incomplete or partial, like the assumption of genetic regression, or that of the truth of Galton's so-called Law of Ancestral Inheritance, which have validity only as statistical formulations and even at that are no more than first approximations. As a result, it is not unfair to say that on the biological side (as opposed to the mathematical, where definite progress occurred) no fundamental advances were registered through the employment of the biometric treatment. This is in strong contrast with the rapid and steady advances which followed on the discovery of the mendelian facts of segregation and recombination.

The more recent fruits of evolutionary mathematics have been of far greater value, because mathematical treatment has in this case been applied to a firm basis of fact. This basis of fact, however, has been for the most part confined to the elementary behaviour of genes—segregation and recombination; dominance and recessiveness and their possible origins; gene-mutation and its frequency, in relation to total numbers.

There is no doubt that the conclusions deduced from these data are of extreme importance: but it is equally certain that they do not cover the whole field. It has been known for some time that genome-mutations (polyploidy) play a considerable role in higher plants. Later research has shown that aneuploidy, hybridization, segmental interchange, and other processes affecting the chromosomal mechanism of heredity are also of importance in plants, and the most recent work on *Drosophila* has shown that many of them have had their part to play in animals too. These points have been dealt with in the preceding chapter.

So far, almost the only attempt to generalize these facts and to use them as a basis for large-scale deduction is that of Darlington (1937): it seems clear, however, that this is a necessary next step. Evolutionary mathematics in the pre-mendelian era was little more than a chimera bombinating in a biological vacuum. In the transitional period, with which the name of R. A. Fisher is especially associated, genes have been the grist for its mill. The time is now approaching when the chromosomal and genic apparatus in its entirety, with all the peculiarities of its behaviour, can be utilized as factual basis.

Meanwhile discovery has already progressed far enough to show that these peculiarities of chromosomal behaviour are of great importance in evolution. We may discover eventually that they have something to say in regard to long-range evolutionary trends, to the initiation of new evolutionary possibilities, and other major processes. So far, however, their chief importance appears to lie in producing diversification through species-formation; and it is to this process of species-formation that we must now turn.

Darwin himself happened to confuse the issue by calling his greatest book the *Origin of Species*, though this is but one aspect of evolution. Evolution must be dealt with under several rather distinct heads. Of these one is the origin of species—or, if we prefer to beg no questions, we had better say the origin of biologically discontinuous groups. Looked at from a rather broader angle, this problem presents itself as the origin of minor systematic diversity, including the origin of what taxonomists call varieties and subspecies, species, genera, and perhaps families. Another is the origin of adaptations. A third is extinction. And a fourth, and in many ways the most important, is the origin and maintenance of long-range evolutionary trends.

It is, of course, true that these all overlap and interlock. A long-range evolutionary trend cannot take place without involving the origin and apparently the extinction of many species, or without involving the origin and improvement of many adaptations. Most adaptations themselves involve at least subspecific or specific change, and many subspecific and specific characters are adaptive. None the less, the distinctions are real and important. The origin of minor systematic diversity in general seems to have little to do with the major processes of evolutionary change; and, as various authors have shown (see especially Robson, 1928; Robson and Richards, 1936), specific and other minor systematic characters frequently have no discernible adaptive significance.*
Accordingly, I propose to deal with each of the topics in turn.

* I say *discernible*. This is partly because much of speciation is concerned with invisible, physiological characters; partly because taxonomists deliberately prefer to base their diagnoses on non-adaptive characters; and partly because many non-adaptive characters are correlated with adaptive ones. But even so, a number of non-adaptive specific characters would seem to remain.

First, then, we have the problem involved in the origin of species. As a preliminary to that, logic demands that we should define the term. It may be that logic is wrong, and that it would be better to leave it undefined, accepting the fact that all biologists have a pragmatic idea of its meaning at the back of their heads. It may even be that the word is undefinable. However, an attempt at definition will be of service in throwing light on the difficulties of the biological as well as of the logical problems involved.

In the first place, although, as we shall see later, the degrees of discontinuity represented by good species and by certain types of subspecies constitute favoured equilibrium-positions in the process of taxonomic differentiation, so that borderline cases are rendered less frequent than we should otherwise expect, yet there cannot be any hard-and-fast distinction between a species and a subspecies or variety, since in many instances one arises gradually out of the other in the course of evolution, and it must often be a matter of taste and convenience where the line is drawn.

Secondly, a very important fact for our discussion, there are a number of quite different *kinds* of animal and plant species, differing in their mode of origin and in their biological characteristics. The remainder of this and of the following chapter will be mainly concerned with amplifying the evidence for this fact and drawing conclusions from it. Here we will merely mention a few points. In so far as species are biological units, marked off from related units by partial or complete discontinuities, they may originate in several different ways (see e.g. Rensch, 1939a): the most important are the geographical, the ecological and the genetic. With geographical differentiation, spatial separation is the primary factor, paving the way for biological divergence and subsequent discontinuity. With ecological differentiation the primary factor is divergence in functional specialization, which may lead to full speciation with complete biological discontinuity even within one and the same geographical area. And with genetical differentiation, the primary factor is some alteration in the genetic machinery underlying heredity, sex, and reproduction. This acts at once and automatically, either to prevent intercrossing between the two types, or to render them or their hybrid offspring partially or wholly infertile.

Each of these main types of speciation produces species with somewhat different biological characteristics. Related geographical species tend to be distinguished by broad and general adaptations to climate, and to lack special genetic or behaviour mechanisms evolved for the prevention of intercrossing: when geographical accidents produce complete spatial discontinuity, this will tend to produce a greater degree of biological discontinuity than would otherwise have occurred.

In addition, when isolation is relatively complete and when, in addition, the isolated populations are small, non-adaptive is superimposed upon adaptive divergence, often to a marked degree, chiefly owing to what we have called the Sewall Wright effect, or drift. Related ecological species tend to be characterized by detailed adjustment to special habitat and mode of life, and often by special adaptations to prevent intercrossing. And genetic species, especially those which are biologically more or less completely discontinuous from the outset, will owe their success initially to general and intrinsic characters like vigour, not to gradually-evolved adaptations, whether general or special; further, the differences in morphological, and other, "characters" by which they are distinguished from their closest relatives will often be, relatively speaking, small (see p. 385).

Species will also differ from group to group and from area to area, both for intrinsic and extrinsic reasons. The nature of the reproductive and sexual mechanisms found in a group will have an influence on the nature of species that constitute it. When asexual reproduction exists, either exclusively or side by side with sexual, certain possibilities of species-formation are open which are not available to exclusively sexual forms. Similarly the typical animal method of sex-determination by dissimilar sex-chromosomes almost entirely rules out certain methods of speciation found in plants (p. 142).

Again, sedentary and less mobile forms will differ, especially as regards the degree of geographical speciation, from more mobile types (p. 239). And ecological speciation is encouraged by a decrease of biological competition (p. 323). Of course, these various differences of origin, nature, and environment may overlap and combine, so that there will be great variation in the size, discontinuity, and distinguishing characteristics of species in different groups and different regions.

It is this fact, of the existence of different kinds of species and of different degrees of speciation within each kind, which makes it difficult to give a satisfactory definition of a species, and makes us sometimes wonder whether the term itself should not be abandoned in favour of several new terms, each with a more precise connotation. However, we may here reflect that the term species has a practical as well as a theoretical aspect. It is necessary for the museum systematist to have some criterion by which he can allot specimens to the pigeon-holes of named taxonomic units. Frequently he has to give an opinion on a few preserved specimens sent for identification. His work may often have important practical bearings: it is necessary for practical reasons to be able to distinguish between a mosquito that transmits malaria and one that does not, or between two plant species in only one of which the essential oil is commercially valuable. Thus, whatever refinements of method he may call to his aid in regard to favourable material, whatever niceties of ecology, genetics, or cytology he may wish to evolve in his theoretical studies, the fact remains that for his practical routine he must have some rule-of-thumb criterion for distinguishing related forms and deciding when they deserve separate names. It is inevitable and right that minor systematics shall be a compromise between the complexity of biological fact and the logic of practical convenience.

One of the most important tools of taxonomy is nomenclatorial terminology. Incomplete or incorrect nomenclature may indeed involuntarily distort the factual data. For instance, if, as at present, current taxonomic practice operates almost exclusively by giving names to areal groups, and does not provide terms for continuous gradations, then what are really arbitrary stages in a gradation will often be given names, implying that they are uniform groups with a definite distribution (p. 226). The basic theoretical aim of taxonomy is obviously the accurate description of organic diversification in nature. Although for reasons of convenience it is desirable to have a general terminology, like that of species and subspecies, applicable to the majority of organisms, yet it must be recognized that this does not apply at all in certain exceptional cases (p. 353), and that it must in many groups be supplemented by additional terminology. However, although certain new terms should probably be incorporated into the nomenclature, yet practical reasons dictate that most of such additional terminology should be purely supplementary, adopted as an additional means of analysis for this or that special purpose (p. 405; Turrill, 1938a).

A quite reasonable definition of the term species is that given some years ago by Dr. Tate Regan when Director of the Natural History Museum at South Kensington—namely, that "a species is a community, or a number of related communities, whose distinctive morphological characters are, in the opinion of a competent systematist, sufficiently definite to entitle it, or them, to a specific name" (Regan, 1926). The difficulty with this definition lies in the term *competent*, which is what we have recently learnt to call the "operative" word. And experience teaches us that even competent systematists do not always agree as to the delimitation of species.

Furthermore, in view of what we have previously said as to the existence of different kinds of species, it is clear that the competence of a systematist in this respect must be in the main confined to groups which he himself has studied in detail; for other groups may differ in their prevalent mode or degrees of speciation, or in other characteristics of the species of which they consist. It is no good asking a systematist who has drawn his experience from a higher animal group such as birds to apply his competence directly to a plant group such as the Compositae, still less to one like the brambles or the roses, in which, as we shall see (p. 351), wholly different processes are operating to produce group-differentiation.

And even in groups with the same general biological character-istics, and therefore the same general type of speciation, experience is needed to decide what characters are of value to the practical systematist in separating his groups. Sometimes these appear arbitrary enough. For instance, in the group of fossil fish known as Paleoniscoids, it is customary to use differences of body-scale ornament as diagnostic of species, those of head-scale ornament as diagnostic subspecies. In fish, again, the fusion of the lower pharyngeal bones to form a single plate is used in the perches as a generic diagnostic, while it is used as an ordinal character for the order Synentognathi (see Norman, 1936).

Such examples once more remind us of the pragmatic aspect of taxonomy involved in the need for quick and simple pigeon-holing. In general, systematists prefer non-adaptive (or apparently non-adaptive) characters as bases for their diagnoses, so long as they are readily visible. Such characters are less likely to be obscured by parallel or convergent evolution in response to selection-pressure (p. 357). In passing, we may note that this very natural preference goes a considerable way towards explaining the assertions of the non-adaptiveness of speciation that are made by many systematists. But what precise characters shall be chosen as predominantly suitable for classificatory diagnosis must in each case be discovered anew by experience. What works in one group may have no pragmatic taxonomic value in another, even though closely related. Chapman (1924) has studied the question carefully in birds. He considers that hard-and-fast rules should not be followed. The variability and evolutionary plasticity of the group and the degree of its adaptability in habit, must be taken into account, and differences in voice and behaviour are to be regarded as of equal or sometimes greater importance than those in morphological characters. If so, then even in the absence of adequate collections throughout the whole range, the systematists should be able to classify specimens much more successfully by such comprehensive methods than by rule-of-thumb procedure.

None the less, even when the differences between groups and the claims of practical pigeon-holing have been allowed for, this definition of Regan's must be taken into account, for there *is* some reasonable measure of agreement among competent systematists as to the criteria they adopt for classifying organisms in different species. These are first, visible (morphological) resemblance between members of a group, of such a nature as to be consonant with the view that the group is actually or potentially an interbreeding one; secondly, lack of intergrading with other groups; thirdly, a geographical area of distribution consonant with the idea of a common ancestry for the group; and fourthly, where data are available, infertility on crossing with related forms.

The first three criteria can be evaluated on the basis of preserved specimens and records of their provenance. They may be modified in various ways according to special circumstances. For instance, as regards resemblance, experience has taught that in some cases large differences in appearance are possible within an interbreeding group. The colour-phases of some birds and mammals (p. 184) are examples; but the most striking cases are those of polymorphic mimicry in butterflies (p. 102). The older entomologists were shocked at the idea that such diverse types might belong to a single species. Thus Hewitson (1874) wrote with regard to *Papilio merope* (now called *P. dardanus*) and its polymorphic female forms, each then regarded as a distinct species:—

"Mr. Rogers has sent me a second collection of butterflies from Fernando Po, containing *P. merope* and *P. hippocoon* taken by him in copulation, another illustration of the saying that 'truth is stranger than fiction'. I find it very difficult even with this evidence to believe that a butterfly, which when a resident in Madagascar has a female the image of itself, should in West Africa have one without any resemblance to it at all."

But breeding tests have proved that the older entomologists were wrong.*

Systematists have also learnt to discount occasional mutant forms, though here again, in the absence of actual breeding

* Actually, the difference between the two sexes of one and the same species may be far more extraordinary, as in the worm *Bonellia*, or in certain anglerfishes. But we are so accustomed to this type of difference that it no longer strikes us as remarkable, although in point of fact the genetic and developmental mechanisms by which this difference is maintained shed light on the origin and maintenance of other kinds of intra-specific variation such as mimetic polymorphism.

experiments, individual opinion must enter into practice (see Chapman, 1923, 1928; Stresemann, 1923-6; Bateson and Bateson, 1925). A constant average morphological difference from other groups is thus the first criterion (Regan, 1926), though, as we shall later see, it is not an indispensable one, and, as Mayr (1940) has pointed out, subspecies may differ visibly more than do good species.

As regards intergrading, a number of quite different situations present themselves.* What we may call simple intergrading is shown by subspecies inhabiting a continuous land area, when these intergrade by freely interbreeding in narrow zones at the margins of their ranges. In some of these cases careful analysis has shown that there exists a cline or continuous gradient of change in subspecific characters, which is gradual within the main areas of the subspecies, but much steepened across a narrow intermediate belt (p. 187): it is possible that the majority of cases of true intergradation will prove to consist in such a steepening of general gradients of change (p. 209).

Sometimes, owing to physical barriers, there is little or no interbreeding at the margins of the group-areas. This may lead to complete discontinuity of type, as with island forms such as the St. Kilda wren (*Troglodytes t. hirtensis*), although in other cases the mean differences between the two populations may be no greater than when intergrading occurs. In some cases, however, complete physical and genetical isolation may exist with slight or even no character-difference between the types.

In still other cases there is an interbreeding zone in which, instead of the phenotypically simple gradation between two not

---

* The term intergrading is here used in the sense of geographical intergrading, usually along a marginal zone delimiting populations of distinct mean type (although irregular types of intergradation mentioned also occur). Such geographical intergradation appears always to rest on genetic mixture of types. In systematic literature, however, the term is sometimes used to denote that two populations of different mean type overlap in their visible characters, irrespective of whether one population actually passes into the other by means of a change in mean character. To avoid confusion, this should rather be styled *morphological overlap*. Marked morphological overlap may occur between two quite discontinuous populations (e.g. an island and a mainland form), where accordingly there is no geographical intergrading, and genetic intergrading is absent or negligible.

very dissimilar types, which we have just been considering, we find obvious mendelian recombinations involving the characters of two markedly distinct types on either side of the zone, as in flickers and other birds (p. 250). If we want a special term, we may call this a zone of recombination (though we must remember that recombination must also be at work in the zones of simple intergradation between subspecies that differ only slightly and in quantitative ways). When it occurs, it may be taken as evidence that two groups which have undergone considerable differentiation in complete isolation from each other have later extended their ranges so as to come into contact, owing to climatic or geographical changes. A still further complication is provided by forms such as the brambles or the hawkweeds (pp. 352, 372), in which irregular reticulation, apparently due to widespread crossing, recombination, and apomixis, occurs between various main types over a large area and not only along a marginal zone between the areas of two uniform types.

A quite other form of intergradation is seen when two groups differ in the percentage of two or more strikingly different forms or "phases". Thus the different band- and colour-types of the snails *Cepaea nemoralis* and *C. hortensis* exist in different proportions in different localities, as do the percentages of white and blue arctic foxes (*Alopex lagopus*) or of bridled and non-bridled guillemots (*Uria aalge*; Southern, 1939), etc. In some of these cases, such as the guillemot, there exists a regular geographical gradation (cline) in the ratio of the two forms (pp. 105, 217), whereas in others, e.g. *Cepaea*, the distribution of types appears to be wholly random. Limiting cases are also known, where a type exists in two forms in some parts of its area, but in only one of them in other regions (p. 184).

Finally, gradual clines in modal character (not in the ratio of sharply distinct types) may be exhibited over considerable areas (p. 220). In some cases the presumptive evidence supports the view that the phenomena are due to hybridization, but is more often against it. Classical taxonomy has for the most part concerned itself only with the intergradation to be observed in narrow zones; but, as we shall see later, large-scale clines of various types, though of different significance, are probably of equal importance.

With regard to the criterion of geographical area, matters are in most cases fairly simple. Difficulty arises, however, when there is considerable crossing between well-differentiated forms.

Before evaluating these criteria further, we must mention the classical criterion of infertility, which of course is not available for most museum specimens. It was at one time considered that this was crucial. "Good species" were those which were either directly infertile, or yielded infertile hybrids: fertility between two types proved that they were not species but only varieties.

This view, however, is no longer tenable. Undoubted species may cross and yield fully fertile hybrids (see Goldschmidt, 1928, p. 392), while forms which are partially or wholly infertile with each other may be so similar in appearance as to be barely distinguishable (*Drosophila simulans* and *D. melanogaster*, p. 333; the two "races" of *D. pseudoobscura*, p. 323; certain "biological races", p. 295; the peculiar "races" of mosquitoes, p. 317; etc.).

Dobzhansky, in his recent book (1937, p. 310), seeks to overcome the inherent difficulty of definition by substituting a dynamic for a static concept of taxonomic categories. For him the species is "that stage of the evolutionary process, at which the once actually or potentially interbreeding array of forms becomes segregated into two or more separate arrays which are physiologically incapable of interbreeding". The dynamic point of view is an improvement, as is the substitution of incapacity to exchange genes for the narrower criterion of infertility: but even so, this definition cannot hold, for it still employs the lack of interbreeding as its sole criterion. "Interbreeding without appreciable loss of fertility" would apply to the great majority of animals, but not to numerous plants. In plants there are many cases of very distinct forms hybridizing quite competently even in the field. To deny many of these forms specific rank just because they can interbreed is to force nature into a human definition, instead of adjusting your definition to the facts of nature. Such forms are often markedly distinct morphologically and do maintain themselves as discontinuous groups in nature.

If they are not to be called species, then species in plants must be deemed to differ from species in animals in every characteristic save intersterility (see also p. 342).

Dobzhansky is perfectly aware of these difficulties, but is inclined to minimize them. He concludes that if groups at this level of evolutionary definition are not to be called species, they do at least demand some name. This may be granted, yet it may be preferable to employ subsidiary terminology for such one-criterion categories (cf. the term *commiscuum* proposed by Danser, 1929).

We have just noted that certain authorities have attempted to erect infertility on crossing into an absolute criterion of species. Others have done the same for lack of geographical and genetic intergradation, irrespective of the degree of visible difference between the two types. This, indeed, is a common practice of many American systematists. It is, however, very difficult to justify any such hard-and-fast rule as a matter of principle, since it can only be a mere rule of thumb. There are many cases where the extremes of a chain of intergrading varieties are far more different than, say, an island and a mainland form which happen for geographical reasons to be unable to intergrade. It appears quite illogical to erect the latter to the rank of species while leaving the former as subspecies: the one may be more likely than the other to differentiate later into a full species, but that is another matter. The question has been ably discussed by Chapman (1924), who emphasizes the need for a broad biological outlook in minor systematics. Stresemann (1927) adopts the same biological standpoint.

As regards geographical variation within the species, modern practice is tending more and more towards the adoption of the principle embodied in the German term, introduced in 1926 by Rensch, of the *Rassenkreis*.* This may be stated as follows. When one form is replaced by another very similar form in a different

* For a discussion of this and similar terms see Rensch (1934). As Rensch points out, the term *Formenkreis*, proposed by Kleinschmidt, suffers from various disadvantages in that he includes under it undoubted species as well as subspecies, and does not insist on the principle of replacement. Mayr (1940) refutes the view of Kinsey (1937) that the title of species should be given to the lowest distinguishable systematic category, which will in fact usually be the subspecies.

geographical area, the two should be considered as subspecies, whether they show intergradation or not, unless the difference between them is so marked that we should be justified in presuming that they would not cross if present in the same area in nature, or that they or their hybrids would be infertile on crossing. Even so, we may find our rules inadequate. Sometimes the end members of a single chain of intergrading subspecies will not breed together (see p. 244). Such cases merely emphasize the fact that there can be no sharp line between subspecies and species, and that discontinuity between groups may arise gradually. The converse fact that forms showing much less difference in visible characters than that between undoubted subspecies may live in the same area without interbreeding and must therefore be regarded as good species, shows that we must not make a hard-and-fast rule on the basis of visible differentiation either.

In general, it is becoming clear that we must use a combination of several criteria in defining species. Some of these are of limiting nature. For instance, infertility between groups of obviously distinct mean type is a proof that they are distinct species, although once more the converse is not true.

Thus in most cases a group can be distinguished as a species on the basis of the following points jointly: (i) a geographical area consonant with a single origin; (ii) a certain degree of constant morphological and presumedly genetic difference from related groups; (iii) absence of intergradation with related groups. Where evidence is available, infertility with related groups will be extra evidence for specific distinctness, but its absence will not be conclusive as evidence against such distinctness. The actual absence of interbreeding in nature is in some ways of greater importance than infertility. The lack of interbreeding may depend on mere geographical separation, on psychological barriers, on ecological separation, on difference in breeding dates, etc.; but such absence will in point of fact isolate groups, whether or not in abnormal circumstances they can be made to mate and their matings are then fully fertile. The absence of interbreeding connotes absence of intergradation; and both can be summed up under the head of isolation. Our third criterion above, if translated from the terminology of the museum to that of the field, may thus be formulated as a certain degree of biological isolation from related groups. When two morphologically and geographically distinguishable groups will under no circumstances produce fertile offspring, the biological discontinuity is both complete and absolute. When they produce a reduced number of offspring, or offspring with reduced fertility, the discontinuity, though absolute, is partial. When, however, they do not normally interbreed, though they are capable of free interbreeding under changed geographical, ecological or other circumstances, the discontinuity, as found in normal circumstances, is complete but relative.

In most cases a species can thus be regarded as a geographically definable group, whose members actually interbreed or are potentially capable of interbreeding in nature, which normally in nature does not interbreed freely or with full fertility with related groups, and is distinguished from them by constant morphological differences.

This is in general satisfactory, but difficulties sometimes arise. These difficulties differ with different methods of species-formation. With geographical speciation, one difficulty concerns the extent of morphological difference: there are bound to be borderline cases. Another difficulty arises when forms which have differentiated in separate regions or habitats are enabled to rejoin each other. Intercrossing productive of obvious recombination involving numerous characters may then result (p. 249), rather than phenotypically continuous and simple intergradation. It is in such cases that the criteria based on interbreeding and inter-fertility may both break down, and we must lay chief weight upon degree of difference.*

* This must be unusually prevalent at the present time, partly due to the violent changes of climate since the beginning of the glacial period, partly to the post-glacial rise of man to biological dominance. Owing to the activities of man, many species and other groups which could otherwise have remained completely isolated from each other, have met and hybridized, often with full fertility. This may be due to indirect results of a changed ecological balance, to deforestation, cultivation, or accidental transport, to deliberate introduction or deliberate hybridization. The results of the sweeping range-changes produced by fluctuating climate must have been almost as extensive (see pp. 146, 258 seq.).

At the opposite extreme are cases where related groups are entirely isolated from each other in nature, and normally never cross, but yet show very little morphological difference, in some cases indeed none whatever (p. 296 seq.). Other striking examples are those where genetic isolation (p. 333) has occurred: here, more attention must be paid to criteria such as geographical distribution, but even so, doubtful cases will remain. Here convenience may dictate the verdict: if it is impossible to distinguish forms on the basis of preserved specimens, it is of dubious utility to give them separate specific names.

In plants, polyploidy and asexual reproduction complicate the picture. Most botanical authorities to-day would classify forms differing solely in the number of chromosome-sets as "varieties" or genetic subspecies, not as species, even if their inter-fertility is lowered or absent. Similarly, authorities differ greatly as regards their treatment of forms with purely asexual reproduction, like the majority of the dandelions (*Taraxacum*). Some wish to designate every recognizable form as a species; this, however, if pushed to its logical conclusion, would imply that each new surviving mutation should be accorded specific rank. Turrill (1938*b*) suggests that for practical convenience a number of well-marked forms should be recognized as species (*agamospecies*), each comprising a number of separate asexual lines to be designated by the non-committal term *biotype*. Degree of mutual resemblance and of distinctness from related populations here become the main criteria of species, while the idea of the inter-breeding group has completely disappeared.

Where ecological divergence of two forms has occurred within the same geographical area, spatially overlapping groups may be kept from interbreeding by slight differences in mating habits, food-preferences, or breeding dates, and so remain separate in spite of the complete or almost complete absence of morphological differences. In many such cases again (e.g. in "biological" or "physiological" races), the allocation of specific rank must be a mere matter of opinion and convenience. Finally, where free hybridization occurs, as in roses and brambles, the ordinary categories of systematics, which are adapted to divergent and not to reticulate evolution, break down (p. 353). If the term *species* is to be retained in such groups, it must be employed mainly or merely on a basis of convenience.

Thus we must not expect too much of the term species. In the first place, we must not expect a hard-and-fast definition, for since most evolution is a gradual process, borderline cases must occur. And in the second place, we must not expect a single or a simple basis for definition, since species arise in many different ways. On the other hand, if we ask whether there is any greater biological reality corresponding to the term species than to higher systematic units such as genus, family, or order, we must reply in the affirmative. Thus Dobzhansky (1937) is in entire agreement on this point. As he writes (p. 306): "There is a single systematic category which, in contrast to others, has withstood all the changes in the nomenclature with an amazing tenacity. . . . In most animal and plant groups, except in the so-called difficult ones, the delimitation of species is subject to no dispute at all." And again (p. 309): "Despite all the difficulties encountered in classifying species in certain exceptional groups of organisms, biologists have continued to feel that there is something about species that makes them more definite entities than all other categories. W. Bateson has expressed this vague feeling quite concisely: 'Though we cannot strictly define species, they yet have properties which varieties have not, and . . . the distinction is not merely a matter of degree.' " Diver (1940) confirms this from the angle of the ecologist, and Mayr (1940) from that of the taxonomist: "It is quite amazing that in well-worked groups there is hardly ever any doubt what is a species and what is not"; and investigation has steadily reduced the number of cases where there is doubt as to the objective existence of specific or subspecific groups. The number of "difficult" species in birds is below 1 per cent. Again, of 755 birds listed as species by the American Ornithological Union, only two are seriously disputed (probably geographically isolated colour-phases). A further 94 are considered subspecies by "lumpers"; but even so, these are objective natural groups. Allan (1940) agrees that species, in spite of widespread hybridization, are "a reality of nature".

We cannot give any single reply such as that a species is an interbreeding group completely isolated from breeding with other similar groups: that would be an over-simplification. But we can say that living things, instead of showing continuous intergradation, as might perhaps be expected *a priori*, tend to be broken up into discontinuous group-units, distinguishable by recognizable genetic differences in their characters, and that practical convenience demands that these units, even though they are of several types, originating in different ways and differing in character and magnitude, be given specific names.

The scale on which this process of speciation operates to introduce discontinuity into the vital continuum, may be better appreciated if we give a few figures concerning the approximate number of species already described in different groups. Linnaeus in the 10th edition of the *Systema Naturae* described under 4,400 species of animals. This number has now been increased two-hundred-fold. Hesse (1929), in a careful review, estimates the total number of metazoan animal species recognized in 1928 as between three-quarters of a million and slightly over one million. Of this figure, the single class Insecta accounts for a minimum of 500,000 and a maximum of 750,000. The estimates for other main groups are as follows:—

Sponges	4,500
Coelenterates	9,000
Echinoderms	4,200
Annelids	7,600
Other Worms	9,000
Molluscoidea	3,300
Molluscs	80,000–104,000
Crustacea	15,500
Myriapods	8,100
Arachnids	28,000
Vertebrates	40,000–70,000

The variation in the estimates depends chiefly on whether the principle of geographical replacement (p. 174) is adopted or not. If adopted, the number of species is reduced, but many become polytypic. The number is being steadily added to by the process of discovery at an increasing rate which is already over 10,000 per annum in insects alone! (Smart, 1940). In the well-worked birds, however, Mayr (1940) estimates that under 100 undiscovered species remain to be added to those already described.

Usually the identity of the discontinuous group and its delimitation from other groups is preserved by interbreeding, though in some cases, as in non-sexual forms like dandelions, the delimitation is presumably achieved by selection-pressure. Sometimes the group is only potentially an interbreeding one: in other cases the discontinuity which separates it from other groups is not complete. In general, however, such discontinuous groups, characterized by a particular area of distribution, and by discontinuity in interbreeding or in degree of resemblance or in both, do exist: and to them we can legitimately apply the term species.

An interesting analysis could be made of the general problem of discontinuity in biological phenomena. Life is and must be a continuum because of its basic process of self-reproduction: in the perspective of time all living matter is continuous because every fresh portion of it has been produced by pre-existing living matter. However, discontinuities of various sorts have been introduced into the continuity. The chief of these discontinuities are those of the cell, the multicellular individual, the species, and the ecological community. The last-named type of unit is very instructive: in spite of continuous variation in environmental factors, ecological communities are quite sharply separated, as any one knows who has passed from the tree zone to the treeless zone above it in mountain country (for a discussion on this point, see Elton, 1927, Chap. 2). This type of discontinuity was a constant source of preoccupation to Bateson (e.g. 1913, Chap. 8), who also drew the attention of biologists to many others, such as meristic variation.

Longley (1933) points out that if the quantitative relation found by Willis (1922) between the frequency of genera in a given group and the number of species they contain, can be generalized on a firm basis, it would provide independent evidence for the biological reality of species.

In all cases, the discontinuity, though fundamental, is never absolute. Every biologist knows the limitations of the cell-theory and the impossibility of giving a rigid definition of organic individuality, yet cells (Wilson, 1925) and individuals (Huxley, 1912) remain as essential biological units.

The same applies to species. Just as syncytia constitute an exception to any rigid cell-doctrine, so large multiple inter-breeding groups, such as those found in willows or in man, form exceptions to the usual rule of specific discontinuity. Intercellular protoplasmic bridges find a parallel in the occasional exchange of genes between otherwise discontinuous groups. The problem of individuality in colonial organisms with moderate division of labour between the zooids is matched by the problem of speciation in groups intermediate between a *Rassenkreis* and an *Artenkreis* (pp. 179 n., 407). Yet species, too, remain as essential biological units.

Owing to the historical and philosophical association of the word *species*, it might be thought desirable to employ some other term in biological nomenclature. Owing to the fact that various types of species exist, and that they exist in various degrees of differentiation, it might be thought more scientific to replace one by many technical terms. But *species* is hallowed by long usage and so ingrained in practice that it would be virtually impossible to replace it. Species, envisaged in this way as largely or wholly discontinuous groups, are thus normally, though not universally, realities of the biological scene: and it is our business to see what is known of the methods by which they originate and by which their distinctness is maintained.

2. THE DIFFERENT MODES OF SPECIATION; SUCCESSIONAL SPECIES

It is logically obvious, on the postulate of evolution, that every existing species must have originated from some pre-existing species (sometimes, as we shall see, from more than one), but equally clear on the basis of recent research that it may do so in one of several quite different ways. A single species as a whole may become transformed gradually to such an extent that it comes to merit a new specific name. Or it may separate, also gradually, into two or more divergent lines whose divergence eventually transcends the limits of specific distinction: sometimes the separation into mutually infertile or otherwise distinct groups may occur suddenly, but the subsequent divergence may yet be gradual. Or it may hybridize with another species and their hybrid product may then, by chromosome-doubling, at one bound constitute a new species, obviously distinct from the outset: here, instead of one species diverging to form two, two converge to form one. (It is possible that such sudden origins of new species by means of chromosome or genome aberrations may also occur without hybridization, from a single instead of a dual origin.) Finally, in certain groups of plants, the minor systematics are in an inextricable tangle, so that no two authorities agree even approximately as to the number of species involved and their limitations: in these cases hybridization, apparently involving many more than two forms, together with back-crossing, recombination, chromosome-doubling, and apomixis, appear to have been and still to be at work.

Thus species-formation may be continuous and successional; continuous and divergent; abrupt and convergent; or what, following a recent writer (Turrill, 1936), we may call *reticulate*, dependent on repeated intercrossing between a number of lines and thus both convergent and divergent at once.

We may thus classify the types of species-formation in various ways—whether they are gradual and continuous or sudden and abrupt; whether they are divergent or convergent; what kind of isolation has been operative; what barriers to fertility have been developed; and to what environmental factors, if any, the process of species-formation is related.

We can distinguish four main kinds of factors which have been decisive in bringing about the discontinuity leading to speciation. These four factors are time, space, function, and intrinsic mechanism. The four resultant modes of speciation are transformation in geological time, geographical divergence, ecological or adaptive divergence, and separation through genetic accident. Thus, if we wish, we can distinguish four main kinds of species, the successional, the geographical, the ecological, and the genetic. Naturally, the decisive agency in each case may be assisted in a subsidiary way by the other agencies. In geographical speciation, for instance, there is normally an adaptive element, while lapse of time and changes in genetic mechanism are inevitably involved; but the factor of separation in space is primary and deci:.ve, that of adaptive functional change subsidiary, and those of temporal and genetic transformation merely consequential and secondary.

Let us deal with these four modes of speciation in more detail. The first three are always gradual, while the fourth may be, though it is by no means always, abrupt.

Our first major factor is time, producing successional speciation. In this process a given stock gradually changes its characteristics, so that forms meriting different specific and generic titles succeed each other in time. Paleontology provides numerous evidences of really gradual specific transformation; these have been preserved almost exclusively in aquatic animals such as ammonites and other molluscs, sea-urchins and other echinoderms, though also in a few land vertebrates such as the horses and titanotheres; but similar changes must, it is clear, have been generally at work. In some cases, as in the shift of the mouth of the sea-urchin *Micraster*, the change seems definitely to have been an adaptive improvement—except possibly during the last phase, when some authorities maintain that the original trend was prolonged orthogenetically although by this time useless or deleterious (Hawkins, 1936). Furthermore, whenever the species-transformation is part of an adaptive trend, as in the horses or elephants (Chap. 9) it must itself be essentially adaptive.

We cannot be completely certain that a given trend as revealed by fossils is unilinear and not divergent, since this would presume a knowledge of other areas that we cannot expect to possess. We may, however, reasonably presume that unilinear trends have occurred in certain abundant and widespread types. In any case, the important point is that a long-continued trend exists, in the course of which types meriting systematic distinction succeed each other in the same stock, whether or no the stock also splits to form other species showing broadly parallel evolution: the type is successively transformed. The subject of long-range trends is of such importance that we deal with it in a separate chapter (Chap. 9). Our analysis there will show that the great majority of such trends are adaptive. Thus the main agency here in producing successional speciation is selection, though it is possible that orthogenesis (p. 504) may in some cases be at work.

It might accordingly be considered that time can never be the primary factor in speciation. If orthogenesis is at work, the primary factor would be genetic: it would be ecological when the transformation is adaptive. It is true that time can never operate alone to produce speciation, in the way that is possible with alterations in genetic mechanism. Nevertheless it can rightly be regarded as the major factor, or one of two major factors working in combination, in all cases where we are considering the transformation of a single stock. The transformation of the horse stock from the three-toed into a one-toed type was undoubtedly in the main adaptive. Nevertheless, what separates the forms along the single transforming line is time. It is the length of time that has elapsed between the genesis of one form and of the next form meriting a separate name that has permitted their specific distinction. This is because, in successional speciation, we are dealing with stages in an evolutionary trend, not with mere divergence in relation to peculiarities of the local environment or of the genetic constitution; and evolutionary trends are normally long-continued, involving steady change in a single direction over long periods of time.

To put it in another way, the distinction between two related successional species is primarily a function of their separation in time; while that between two related geographical species is primarily one of their separation in space; that between ecological species, of their divergence in mode of life; and that between genetic species, of changes in their genetic mechanism. Of course here, as in every aspect of evolution, we are dealing with processes of multiple causation. For instance, successional adaptive transformation within a trend cannot proceed at all when a certain limit of specialization has been reached

(p. 494); and its rate will be dependent on the stage of specialization reached by the evolving type, as well as on environmental
conditions, in the same sort of way as the degree of ecological
speciation is dependent on predator-pressure (p. 324). In any
case, long-range evolutionary trends, considered as affecting
groups and manifested as adaptive radiation (p. 487), are primarily affairs of ecological divergence. But each trend, considered
separately, is primarily an affair of successional transformation,
in which the successive forms owe their distinctness to the lapse
of time by which are separated their positions in the evolutionary
trend.

According to certain authorities, successional speciation often
proceeds, partly or wholly, by discontinuous changes of small or
moderate extent. These are usually called "Mutations of Waagen"
after the paleontologist who first drew attention to them. However, as Rensch (1933a) has pointed out, a much more probable
explanation of these is that a climatic or other environmental
change has produced a shift in geographical distribution, causing
a given stage in the stratigraphical sequence to be replaced by a
related subspecies or species which has differentiated in another
region.

There are comparatively few cases in which environmental
conditions appear to have remained constant over a long period
in one area. But whether this be so or not, the change in the
fossils may be continuous, as with the sea-urchin *Micraster* during
a considerable portion of the Cretaceous; in such cases we must
be dealing with intra-specific selection towards a higher degree
of adaptation. In the absence of evidence to the contrary, we are
probably right in thinking that successional transformation, in
the abundant species which alone can provide satisfactory fossil
series, is always or at least normally a gradual and continuous
process.

3. GEOGRAPHICAL REPLACEMENT: THE NATURE OF
SUBSPECIES

Next we come to cases in which divergence subsequent to some
type of isolation is the primary fact leading to the formation of

new species. The divergent splitting of species and genera must clearly be postulated to have occurred on a large scale in the past, if only to account for the rapid increase with geological time of the number of types and taxonomic units in newly-evolved groups, such as the orders of higher placental mammals. Most of the divergence seen in such adaptive radiations of groups (p. 489) is ecological, concerned with adaptation to different environments and especially to different modes of life. It is, however, not easy to obtain from paleontology *direct* evidence of divergence, since this demands good series in at least two separate but crucial areas.

We shall return in a later chapter to ecological divergence as illustrated from existing organisms. Here, however, we will begin by dealing with geographical isolation, since a study of geographical distribution reveals what are without question all stages of geographical divergence. Furthermore, the data on this subject are extensive, and have been subjected to thorough analysis.

In all cases, the basis on which we presume geographical divergence, i.e., the evolution of a common ancestral form into two or more different forms in different geographical areas, is what has been called the principle of geographical replacement (see, e.g., Rensch, 1929, 1933*a*). Under this we include the numerous cases where closely-related but distinct forms (species or subspecies) are found in different areas of the world's surface, but do not (with certain exceptions to be discussed later) overlap; on the contrary, one replaces the other as we pass from one area to another.

Such forms which replace each other geographically show all stages of diversity, from dubious and intergrading to sharply defined subspecies,* and thence on to species and genera. As we should expect, the percentage of groups which, though clearly owing their origin to geographical differentiation, do not exhibit

---

* It is highly desirable to restrict the term *subspecies* to groups that are isolated geographically or in other ways (e.g. physiologically) and also not to use the term *variety* as synonymous with subspecies, but, if it be employed at all, to restrict it to forms which occur together within the same geographical or other group, as in polymorphic species (p. 99).

strict geographical replacement, but have overlapping areas of distribution, is very low among subspecies (pp. 273, 291), but may be considerable in higher taxonomic units which are intersterile and have had time for extensive range-changes (pp. 241, 243 ff., 285).

Almost every group of organisms investigated reveals some examples. Geographical divergence has been, perhaps, most carefully worked out in birds: our own avifauna provides excellent examples, with the St. Kilda and the Shetland wren (*Troglodytes t. hirtensis* and *T. t. zetlandicus*), the British subspecies of tit (*Parus*), jay (*Garrulus*), wagtail (*Motacilla*) and many other forms, and the specific distinction of our red grouse, *Lagopus scoticus* (see Witherby, 1938–41). This last form, it should be noted, has not only diverged specifically from the willow grouse (*L. lagopus*) but has itself differentiated into a separate subspecies in Ireland. Hartert's classical work on palaearctic birds (1903–35) illustrates the use of the systematic principle for a wide range of forms, while Lynes' exhaustive and elaborately illustrated study of the passerine genus *Cisticola* (1930) provides an example of its application to a single type. In this single genus he recognizes 40 species, with 154 subspecies. The genus is of sedentary habits, so that the number of subspecies per species is about 50 per cent higher than in related but migratory genera (see p. 239) such as *Phylloscopus* (studied by Ticehurst, 1938) or *Sylvia*.

Mammals, however, provide as good an array of examples. We shall later refer to the thoroughly-investigated case of the deermice (*Peromyscus*) (pp. 186, 188, etc.), but squirrels and other rodents (e.g. Grinnell, 1922, on the kangaroo rats, *Dipodomys*), antelopes, monkeys, and many other types behave in just the same way. Insects, notably butterflies, have also received much attention from this point of view. As an exhaustive study we may refer to Warren's monograph on *Erebia*, in which 69 species, many with marked subspeciation, are recognized (Warren, 1936); while Ellers (1936) has made an elaborate investigation of the subspecies of a single species, the swallowtail *Papilio machaon*, and Zarapkin (1934) and Endrödi (1938) of the beetles *Carabus granulatus* and *Oryctes nasicornis* respectively. Zarapkin's study is based on quantitative measurements of over 100 characters. We shall later also have occasion to refer to the geographical variation of various mimetic and other butterflies, of moths, beetles, reptiles, amphibia, snails, crustacea (see Chevais, 1937) and other animals.

Plants do not seem so prone to geographical subspeciation as animals, but a number are known which show the phenomenon. Among plants an excellent example is *Gentiana lutea*, the large yellow gentian. *G. l. lutea*, with free anthers, is widespread in central Europe, while *G. l. symphyandra*, mainly distinguished by its united anthers, is limited to the Balkans and their neighbourhood: there is a slight amount of intergradation in an intermediate zone. Gregor (1938a) has found geographical (as well as ecological) differentiation in *Plantago maritima* (p. 223).

Fish are just as susceptible to the process as other animals. Even deep-water species may show geographical differentiation, as has been shown by Hubbs (1930), who finds that three forms of *Hymenocephalus striatissimus* can be readily distinguished, intergrading at the margins of their areas. The "races" of herrings appear to be geographical subspecies, although the differences between them have to be evaluated by biometrical as opposed to ordinary taxonomic methods (see Schnakenbeck, 1931); and marine littoral types may be markedly differentiated into subspecies. Again, according to Schilder and Schilder (1938) all the 165 species of living cowries (*Cypraeidae*) are divisible into geographical subspecies, the number per species ranging from two to seven or eight. Similarly the marine gastropod *Turbinella pirum* shows well-defined geographical variation (Hornell, 1916).

Naturally, however, the process is better illustrated by types with geographically discontinuous ranges, for instance, by the differentiation of the tree senecios in Africa, where nearly every high mountain has its own characteristic form (Fries, 1922). An admirable example from animals is provided by the different forms of char (*Salvelinus*) which inhabit various British and Irish lakes. Where the char is still migratory, living in the sea and ascending rivers to spawn, as in the northernmost parts of its range, it is comparatively uniform; but when non-migratory and landlocked in a lake, geographical differentiation sets in. Regan (1911) distinguishes fifteen forms in Great Britain and Ireland. All these we should to-day classify as subspecies; for, as Regan says in a later paper (1926), "Once you begin giving specific names to lacustrine forms of char you never know where to stop." On the other hand, "if we were to exterminate the char in our islands and on the continent, except in a dozen selected lakes, we should have left a dozen well-marked forms which it would be convenient to recognize as species."

The biologically more or less irrelevant differences arising from isolation are in this case sometimes associated with certain adaptive differences. For instance, the Loch Rannoch char, inhabiting a very deep lake, has unusually large eyes; the habitual bottom-feeders have blunter snouts and more rounded mouths. Thus, the differentiation is partly geographical, partly ecological (see p. 227). The whitefish (*Coregonus*) and the cisco (*Leucichthys*) also show geographical differentiation in different lakes (see Worthington, 1940).* This lacustrine subspeciation of freshwater fish can only date back to glacial times, when the lakes were formed. The differences between trout and sea-trout and their local differentiations are also of interest in this connection, though too complex to summarize here.

Again, a large number of subspecies of rainbow trout are restricted to single lakes or rivers in the western United States. These last are described by J. O. Snyder (1933) as separate species. This is a result of his adopting the principle we have already noted (p. 163), of employing lack of intergradation between geographical forms as an absolute criterion of specific rank. This, however, must lead to the pigeonholing of types which are in point of fact at similar stages in the process of evolutionary divergence, in different systematic categories. Absolute isolation of groups will facilitate divergence: but that is a different point.

* Some of the variants which have been given subspecific rank may prove to be purely modificational forms. Thus Hile (1936), working on the North American cisco (*Leucichthys artedi*), finds that allometric growth, together with its alteration owing to seasonal differences in food-supply, etc., may induce form-differences as great as some of those found in named subspecies. However, while this points the need for more careful analysis, we can be certain that the majority of the described forms have a genetic basis.

We shall here accordingly adopt the view, which is becoming increasingly the basis of modern taxonomic practice, that forms which replace each other geographically and the differences between which do not transcend those between intergrading varieties, are (unless they are proved infertile by experiment) best regarded as subspecies of a large species. The application of this principle has much reduced the number of species recognized in well-investigated areas. Thus the twenty-six palaearctic forms of wagtails (*Motacilla*) originally accorded specific rank are now classified in four species with thirty subspecies: and instead of nine species of palaearctic jays (*Garrulus*) one only is now recognized (Rensch, 1933*a*). The total number of bird species has been rather more than halved by the application of this principle (Hesse, 1929).

When related and obviously "good" species replace each other geographically we must conclude that the process of geographical divergence has continued until the differences are of specific magnitude. For groups of species related in this way Rensch (1933*a*) proposes the name of *Artenkreis*, which we may perhaps in English call a geographical subgenus.*

The *Artenkreis* is a novel concept in systematics, but according to Rensch it is a widespread fact of nature. Stresemann (1931) applied the principle to the bird genus *Zosterops* (white-eyes). In the genus as a whole he distinguishes twenty-two polytypic species (*Rassenkreise*, or species with geographical subspecies) and thirty monotypic species (without geographical differentiation). Of these, he grouped fourteen polytypic and eighteen monotypic species into six geographical subgenera (*Artenkreise*).

Similar phenomena are known in plants. Turrill (1929) gives a number of examples of apparently good species from Crete which are represented by closely allied species on the mainland.

---

* Some English-speaking authors translate *Artenkreis* by the term *superspecies* or *supraspecies*. However, this should be restricted to intermediate cases, in which the majority of the forms in a *Kreis* of groups showing geographical replacement are clearly subspecies of a polytypic species, but a few have diverged further until they are probably or certainly to be regarded as separate monotypic species. It is in any case quite illegitimate to equate *Rassenkreis* and *Artenkreis*, as is done by Schilder and Schilder (1938, p. 189), or, as they also do, to use the term *superspecies* for polytypic species composed entirely of obvious subspecific groups.

Examples of "geographical species" from North America are the Canada and the Oregon jays (*Perisoreus canadensis* and *P. obscurus*); and the mourning and MacGillivray's warblers (*Oporornis philadelphia* and *O. tolmei*). The two members of either pair are both very similar, differing almost solely in details of colour, and they inhabit different areas; they thus jointly constitute an *Artenkreis*.

A similar example from Europe is that of the meadow and red-throated pipits (*Anthus pratensis* and *A. cervinus*). The common and Carolina chickadees (*Parus atricapillus* and *P. carolinensis*) are borderline cases: in some regions they overlap without intergrading, but in central New Jersey do interbreed (Chapman, 1924).

Although in general, systematists who adopt the same principles of classification will classify groups in the same way, there are bound to be dubious cases. A well-known example is that of the Japanese pheasant, characterized by metallic green coloration. This is by some authors classified as a separate species, *Phasianus versicolor*, but by others as a marked subspecies of the widely-ranging common pheasant, *P. colchicus* (discussion in Rensch, 1933*a*, p. 28).

Numerous examples are to be found of *Rassenkreise* whose extreme subspecies are so distinct that they would rightly be classified as separate species if the intergrading connecting types were not known. The char provide a case of this (p. 177). Among the numerous further examples cited by Rensch (1933*a*) we may mention the beetle, *Carabus monilis*. Here the different subspecies, in addition to large differences in size, shape, colour, ornamentation, etc., are characterized by differences in copulatory organs, which should prevent interbreeding. Some examples are known when migration has brought extreme subspecies of a *Rassenkreis* together and they prove not to interbreed. These are cited on pp. 243 seq.

A borderline case from plants is that of the bugles, *Ajuga chamaepitys* and *A. chia* (Turrill, 1934). Here, cultivation ecotypes seem to have been selected out and to have spread with agriculture to the N.W., until the extreme types have become radically different from the original Near-Eastern polymorphic forms (p. 267).

The divergence of the marine fish fauna on either side of Central America since the last union of the North and South American Continents, probably in the early Miocene, provides examples of a larger degree of divergence. In this case (Regan, 1906–8) the fish are hardly ever identical on the two coasts. Usually a given form is represented by a pair of species, one from either side, but sometimes the differences are so slight that the two forms can only be accorded subspecific rank. It is of considerable interest that although all the forms have been separated for the same length of time, the degree of visible divergence varies considerably from one species-pair to another.

The independent development of certain elements of the fauna in large isolated lakes such as Baikal (see, e.g., Korotneff, 1905–12) and Tanganyika (see Yonge, 1938a; Worthington, 1937) provides examples of another kind of differentiation, in which certain groups branch out into many types which have not evolved elsewhere (pp. 324, 492). In such cases geographical isolation, notably when combined with reduced selective pressure from predators or competitors, opens the door to further differentiation of the original type by means of ecological, especially ecobiotic, divergence.

Different major groups, and different minor groups within them, show differences in their proneness to diverge geographically; doubtless due to differences in their modes of life and their environments; but it is clear that geographical divergence is a general evolutionary phenomenon.

In wide-ranging species, different geographical races, or subspecies as they are now generally called, may occur over a large land-mass, intergrading genetically at the margins of their areas. Where there are definite barriers, such as mountain ranges or deserts, the intergradation may be absent, just as it often is with island forms. All stages in the restriction of gene-flow between adjacent groups may of course be observed.

The house-wrens (*Troglodytes*) of South America, studied by Chapman and Griscom (1924), provide a good example. Noteworthy in many subspecies of this group is the wide degree of individual variation found. Distinctions between subspecies may be based simply on alterations in the means of such varying characters. Thus the subspecies often overlap in regard to their characters and are definable only on the basis of long series. Steep character-gradients (genoclines; p. 253) occur in the mixed zones along the borders of contiguous subspecific ranges.

Numerous cases of subspeciation in birds have been analysed with great thoroughness. We refer later to A. H. Miller's work on shrikes (p. 236). Here we may mention that of Swarth (1920) and of Linsdale (1928) on the fox sparrow (*Passerella iliaca*). Linsdale studied the skeletal characters and found that these show just as much variation (often in the form of geographical character-gradients or clines; see p. 206) as do the plumage and the general size. Some of these, e.g. those subserving flight, appear to be adaptive: in every case the sedentary or relatively sedentary subspecies have smaller bones in the wings and pectoral girdle than do those with long migration routes. Linsdale could not assign any adaptive significance to the considerable differences in skull and bill, though these may be "correlated characters" (p. 206). No part of the skeleton was exempt from geographical variation, and there was a considerable though not complete correlation between the geographical variation of skeletal and of plumage characters.

In all these cases, the subspecies are relatively constant over large areas, and the subspecific areas are separated by relatively narrow intergrading zones. This state of affairs may be taken as the ideal pattern of geographical subspeciation. Frequently, however, full details are unknown, and subspecific names are assigned to forms from different areas simply because they are different. In some cases, however, we know that there is no sharp delimitation of subspecies by means of an intergrading zone, but only a gradual delimitation; and, further, the "subspecies" itself may be by no means constant, but merely represents the mean of many differentiated local populations. This is so with some forms of deermice (*Peromyscus*), as shown by Dice (1939), although in other cases in the same genus the ideal condition is realized (see below). Eventually it will be desirable to distinguish these two types of intraspecific differentiation by appropriate terminology.

The geographical variation in song demonstrated by Promptoff (1930) in the chaffinch, *Fringilla coelebs*, appears to concern local populations rather than being of true subspecific type (p. 308).

In other cases, excessive taxonomic zeal applied to insufficient material in variable species has resulted in individual varieties being erroneously named as subspecies. This is well instanced by the spotted hyena (*Crocuta crocuta*). No fewer than 19 forms of this have been named, most of them originally as full species; but the detailed study of Matthews (1939a) has shown that none of these can be regarded as valid, though it is possible that two or three geographical subspecies may be established later if sufficient material is forthcoming.

Warren (1937) draws attention to the fact that in the large butterfly genus *Erebia*, different subspecies show very different degrees of variability. Facts of this sort clearly merit detailed study in relation to ecology, selection, and population-size; we need not at the moment accept Warren's hypothesis of an inherent recurrent cycle of variability.

Isolation of land forms by water, as occurs with groups inhabiting islands, often leads to greater divergence, such subspecies being unusually distinct (as with the St. Kilda wren) or having developed into full species (as with the British red grouse). It is worth mentioning that among the fifty-six species and subspecies of mammals found in Scotland, more than half show a degree of difference meriting taxonomic distinction from their continental relatives—eight as full species and twenty-two as subspecies (Ritchie, 1930).

The effect of complete isolation in promoting divergence is especially clear in archipelagos where different islands often harbour distinct forms (see p. 324). Examples of this fact occur on the Galapagos (see, e.g., Swarth, 1931, 1934), and on the Hawaiian Islands (e.g., in the birds known as sicklebills, *Drepanididae*, p. 325; Lowe, 1936, discussions in A. Gulick, 1932, and Mordvilko, 1937). Again, G. S. Miller (1909) points out that the Malayan mouse-deer (*Tragulus*) exhibits only one form in the whole of Sumatra and Borneo, whereas in the Rhio Linga Archipelago off the tip of the Malay Peninsula, with 1/150th of the land area and with less rather than more diversity of environmental conditions, seven subspecies are to be distinguished. In a subsequent section (p. 295) we deal with similar cases where the barriers are of different nature. The high degree of differentiation in these cases is doubtless due to the small size of the island populations, which promotes "drift" and non-adaptive divergence (cf. p. 200).

An interesting type of geographical divergence is one arising out of the fact of dimorphism (or polymorphism). A species which in most of its range exists in two (or more) distinct forms, shows only one (or fewer) in certain restricted areas (see also p. 104). For instance, the common squirrel (*Sciurus vulgaris*) of the European continent exists in two forms, black and red, but the British subspecies, besides showing certain quantitative peculiarities, is monomorphic, without any blacks (p. 98). Stresemann (1923–26) refers to several analogous cases among birds. The South American hawk *Accipiter ventralis*, for instance, occurs in its "normal" phase over the whole of its range, in a lighter and reddish (phaeomelanic) phase over the whole range except for a limited area, and in a dark (eumelanic) phase in a limited area only. An even more clear-cut case is that of *Accipiter novae-hollandiae*. Here a N-S dimorph-ratio cline in the proportions of dark and white birds extends across Australasia; but on certain islands to the extreme north only dark forms occur (Mayr, 1931–40, no. 41), and only white forms in Tasmania (p. 106; Stresemann, 1923–6). In such cases we must assume that the dark form is the original: it is accordingly interesting to find that in the snow goose *Anser coerulescens* the dark form is now restricted to a very small area of the total range.

The phenomena of local melanic subspecies of *Coereba*, etc., are referred to elsewhere (p. 203). A further refinement of differential geographical dimorphism is seen in the cases where the proportions of the two types vary regularly in space (dimorph-ratio clines: see pp. 104, 161; the case of *Accipiter novae-hollandiae* falls into this category, though the proportions here change abruptly).

The common red foxes present an interesting case (see Iljina, 1935). An Old World and a New World species are often distinguished (*Vulpes vulpes* and *V. fulva*), but most modern practice regards them as highly differentiated subspecies, or rather groups of subspecies, since large numbers of minor subspecies of ordinary type are recognizable. In addition, polymorphism exists in almost every subspecies, due primarily to combinations of three major distinct gene-pairs together with modifiers: the polymorph ratios vary geographically. One major colour-differentiation has a geographical basis: the true silver fox depends on a gene found only in Canada. The black foxes of the Old World are slightly different in appearance, and contain a different gene: this, however, is also found in Alaska to the exclusion of the Canadian "black" gene.

Complete geographical separation may also occur for ecological reasons. Thus the moth *Thera juniperata* feeds in the larval stage entirely on juniper. Owing to the absence of juniper from the English Midlands, the British forms of this species are restricted to two separate areas, one in the north, the other in the south, and as a result subspeciation has occurred.

Wherever experimental analysis has been undertaken, it has shown that the main differences between subspecies are of genetic origin, and not due to environmental modification. Indeed, we must lay down as a principle (although a decision may often not be possible in practice) that non-genetic differences cannot be accepted as a basis for subspecific distinction.

Recent analysis on neo-mendelian premises (see especially Muller, 1940) has shown that complete or almost complete geographical isolation (i.e. permitting no or negligible exchange of genes with other groups) must be *expected* to lead, with the lapse of time, both to morphological divergence and, usually later, to physiological (genetic) discontinuity. This depends on the fact that evolution proceeds by the incorporation of numerous small mutational steps, and that each mutational step demands buffering and adjustment through "internal adaptation", by means of modifiers (p. 67). The improbability that such mutations will be identical in two isolated groups, even when environmental conditions are similar, is immense; and when the two forms are subjected to different conditions, the divergence from identity will be more rapid and more obvious. Similarly, the internal adaptations of the germ-plasm will not be identical, and disharmonies will arise leading to partial and eventually to total reproductive disharmony between the two groups, either by way of reduced mating, reduced fertility of P1 or F1, or reduced viability of F1 or later generations (p. 360).

It is worth while recalling that under conditions of artificial selection, isolation may frequently lead to divergence. Darwin (1868) gives several examples of this phenomenon in Chapter 20 of his *Variation of Animals and Plants under Domestication*. The most striking concerns two flocks of sheep, both bred from Bakewell's pure stock; after half a century, they had "the appearance of being quite distinct varieties". In such cases, a form of Sewall Wright effect (p. 58) may operate, as well as unconscious selection; but the effect of isolation is beyond question. (See also D. S. Jordan, 1909, pp. 75 seq.)

Analysis also shows that mere separation in space of two parts of a population, even when biologically continuous, with free or only slightly reduced gene-flow between them, will lead to morphological differentiation when the environmental conditions are sufficiently distinct in the two areas, since here divergent selection will operate. The fact of relatively free gene-flow, however, halts the process at the stage of partial biological discontinuity, resulting in intergrading subspecies (p. 209).

Sumner (1932), following up the notable taxonomic study of Osgood (1909), has made a detailed analysis of subspeciation in *Peromyscus*. Perhaps the most striking case concerns three subspecies of *P. polionotus* in Florida. *P. p. polionotus* is dark in colour and inhabits the interior, where the soil also is dark. *P. p. leucocephalus* is extremely pale, and inhabits an island reef of pure white quartz sand; and *P. p. albifrons* is somewhat pale, although inhabiting beaches of the same white sand, but on the mainland.

Here we undoubtedly have an example of the value of isolation in counteracting the effect of migration and in permitting selection to act unchecked. In general Sumner finds it necessary to assume some selective interpretation of the colour of these sub-species, on the basis of its protective (cryptic) value, although he is careful to point out that selection cannot be very intense, since adaptive coloration is not always present in other subspecies of the genus, the coloration often being apparently correlated with other advantages which may outweigh that of cryptic resemblance. It may also be, of course, that certain groups have not been long enough in their present habitats to permit the requisite mutations to appear: with a low mutation-rate, mere chance might make a great difference in the time needed to throw up the required mutations.* On this hypothesis, selection of low intensity is acting on all inhabitants of the white sand; but on the mainland its effects are partly counterbalanced by intermixture with the dark inland race.

There is little doubt that this is part of the truth. On the other hand, statistical investigation reveals that the mainland forms, coastal and inland, not only intergrade but that they both show a gradient of colour-change. This is moderate as the coast is left for the interior. Then, about forty miles inland, follows a narrow strip a few miles wide where the gradient is very steep, and finally a region where the gradient is very gradual indeed. The zone of rapid change must be regarded as the boundary between the two subspecies; interestingly, it does *not* occur at the same place as does a geological change involving a darkening of soil-colour.

To account for these and similar facts in other races, Sumner assumes that each race has a main area, and is subject to large periodic fluctuations in abundance, such as Elton has shown to occur in most small mammals. In periods of over-population, migration will be initiated (Elton, 1930), and will presumably

* A case bearing on this point is that of the local population of housemice (*Mus musculus*) on a small sandy island in Ireland, studied by Jameson (1898). The average coloration of the population was considerably lighter than normal, but with great variability: the paler animals' colour matched the sandy background. Predator-pressure was intense owing to the lack of cover. From a careful study of maps Jameson estimated that the island could not have been isolated for more than 100 to 125 years. Meinertzhagen (1919) mentions that the introduced goldfinch (*Carduelis carduelis*) in the Bermudas now merits sub-specific rank, and that the introduced starling (*Sturnus vulgaris*) in Cape Colony has already lost the migratory habit, though this may be only a modification

be most intense in directions away from the main centre of the population, or as Sumner puts it, in the direction of a falling gradient of population-pressure. Two contiguous subspecies will thus be pressing against each other like two inflated rubber bags, and the boundary between the two will shift according to the relative degree of population-pressure. Just at the boundary, migration will be producing intercrossing. Owing to the principle of harmoniously-stabilized gene-complexes, the zones of inter-crossing will remain narrow even when their location is shifted (p. 209). It is thus quite possible that a subspecies which originally differentiated in relation to some particular area will spread over a much larger area. Thus the type of adaptation which we actually find, namely, a rough general correspondence between adaptive characters and habitat but with numerous exceptions of detail, is to be expected.

It is worth pointing out that such zones of rapid change with intermixture have been found in numerous other cases where sub-specific distribution has been thoroughly investigated—e.g. with numerous types of birds in Lower California (Grinnell, 1928), as well as the wrens and sparrows already mentioned (p. 182).

In general Sumner's hypothesis seems to fit many of the facts very well. As further consequence, it may turn out that certain subspecies occupying a large and diversified area represent the sum of a number of originally separate races which have united by migration: if so, in some cases subspecies may be of poly-phyletic origin, as regards their evolution within the species (p. 291).

Thus it seems clear that some characteristics of the subspecies of *Peromyscus*, such as coloration in some form, must be directly adaptive (see Dice and Blossom, 1937). Others, however, such as absolute and relative tail-length, have no obvious adaptive value. They may be accidental by-products of isolation; or they may be correlated with less obvious but deeper-seated physio-logical adaptations. Yocom and Huestis, for instance (1928), have shown that a coastal and a desert subspecies of *P. maniculatus* differ in important characters of their thyroids, the coastal variety having less active glands with greater accumulations of secretion. These differences in glandular make-up are   quite possibly the direct cause of the differences in colour, which would then be non-adaptive "correlated characters". Sumner (*op. cit.*, p. 98) states that later work shows it to be "just as easy to distinguish these two subspecies by the thyroids as by the pelages". He also finds that certain subspecies are distinguished by constant differences in general activity. Grinnell (1928), on the basis of great experience, believes that the differentiation of subspecies (in birds) is basically adaptive.

In some cases the subspecies are polymorphic, e.g. in *P. maniculatus blandus*, buff, grey, and all intermediate types are found (see Dice, 1933*a*). Here all the colours cannot well be adaptive, but some selective balance must be operative (p. 97).

However, the principle of the correlation of visible and apparently non-adaptive characters with deep-seated adaptive properties is undoubtedly widespread. Dewar and Finn (1909, p. 357) cite a case from domestic pigs and sheep in America. The light-coloured breeds are poisoned by various plants, while the dark breeds are immune. Black pigs, for instance, are not injured by eating the paint-root *Lachnanthes*.

A classical case is that of the *rubrinervis* mutant of the evening primrose *Oenothera lamarckiana*. This, as its name implies, is distinguished by the red colour of the veins on its leaves and elsewhere. But it also shows accelerated pollen-tube growth and increased resistance to cold.

Haldane (1932*a*, 1932*c*) draws attention to other cases in which genetical experiment has proved the dependence of two or more very distinct phenotypic characters on a single gene. Thus in stocks (*Matthiola incana*) hairiness depends not only on two special genes for hairiness, but also on a gene for colour in the flowers (Saunders, 1920). Thus selection for hairiness would, in certain heterozygous populations, automatically eliminate white-flowered plants. A still simpler case is that of the gene increasing the size of the central "eye" in the flowers of *Primula sinensis*: this also reduces the style-length in genetically long-styled plants, producing a homostyle in place of a "pin" flower. Thus the normal arrangement for bringing about cross-fertilization can only operate in small-eyed flowers. Again, many genes in *Drosophila* produce multiple effects, e.g. on bristles and wings. We have already mentioned (p. 80) the effect of the white series of eye-colour alleles on certain internal organs. Haldane also recalls the fact that apparently irrelevant genes may restore physiological balance and viability. We have given examples of this in Chap. 3 (pp. 68 seq.). A further probable case is the increased viability of "arc"-winged mutants when an axillary spot is added. Sometimes the correlated characters are merely modifications, which appear only in certain environments. The best example of this is the frizzle fowl (p. 118), in which the thyroid is enlarged as well as the feathers altered. Investigation shows, however, that the thyroid effect only occurs in cool climates, and is a reaction to the excessive heat-loss caused by the inadequate feathering, which is the only direct genetic effect. (See also p. 533).

Whenever a genetically-determined cline or character-gradient (p. 206) exists in visible characters, even if these are apparently non-adaptive, and is correlated with a gradient in the environment, we are justified in assuming a further correlation between the visible characters and adaptive physiological properties. In all such cases, the onus of proof is on those who would deny the direct or indirect adaptiveness of the graded characters.

It is interesting to note that Sumner began his laborious investigations with a bias in favour of the subspecific characters of deer-mice being due to the hereditary fixation of the direct effects of the environment, and against the view that they were determined by mendelian genes. In the course of time, however, the facts induced him to abandon this position, and he now believes that natural selection has been an important agency in establishing subspecific differences, and that most subspecific characters are not only "genetically determined" but mendelian.*

The long-tailed field-mouse, *Apodemus*, fills the same ecological niche in the old world that *Peromyscus* does in the new. Though it belongs to the murine section of the mouse family, as opposed to the cricetine, it is very similar to *Peromyscus* in

---

* So recently as 1921, it was possible for distinguished ornithologists to express the view that most subspecific characters in birds were mere environmental modifications (Lowe and Mackworth-Praed, 1921). To-day all would agree that the great majority are genetically determined.

appearance, and also shows marked geographic variation. Mr. Hinton tells me that he believes this genus would show a very similar correlation of type of geographic variation with climate and soil, but the detailed analysis has not yet been made.

In general, it appears that some at least of the distinctions between subspecies are adaptive, but, when not obviously cryptic, in relation to local background, are usually of a general nature, in some relation to climate. Such a relation may be direct, as in cases of differing temperature-resistance, or indirect, as in the greater prevalence of migratory habit in bird subspecies from higher latitudes. Goldschmidt, in an exhaustive series of studies (summary and references in Goldschmidt, 1934), has shown that trivial and apparently useless differences between geographical races of the gipsy-moth *Lymantria dispar* are accompanied by physiological and reproductive differences of great significance in relation to climatic conditions (p. 436).

Timoféeff-Ressovsky (1935) has shown that the widespread population of *Drosophila funebris* in Europe, though showing no visible subspecies, is geographically differentiated in regard to temperature-resistance. The adaptation is a delicate one. Thus the Western European strains are especially susceptible, the Russian and Siberian ones especially resistant, to the extremes both of heat and of cold, while those from the Mediterranean are resistant to heat but susceptible to cold.

A curious case is that of the chat *Oenanthe lugens*. In Egypt both sexes are alike, with conspicuous coloration; but in the Algerian subspecies, though the males are very similar, the females are of a sandy colour. Here there seems to be a local protective adaptation of the female only. This case from birds is paralleled by various butterflies, notably the swallow-tail *Papilio dardanus*. In the subspecies inhabiting Madagascar, both sexes are alike, resembling the male of the other subspecies. In those from the African mainland, however, the females are nearly always mimetic, often polymorphically so (p. 123), except in a few special areas (Eltringham, 1910). It would appear that where the struggle for existence is more intense, the female, with her greater biological value, is often protected before the male (as undoubtedly occurs in many birds: Huxley, 1938c), although it would also appear likely that selection is acting to keep the male uniform, so that any stimulative or recognitional function exerted by his coloration in regard to mating may be preserved, unimpaired by any break-up into several forms of different appearance.

The view that subspeciation is in any large measure adaptive is not universally held. Only recently D. M. S. Watson (Watson and others, 1936) wrote, "It is probable that the differences between geographical races (which have only a statistical meaning) have no adaptive significance," a statement which is only a little less sweeping than his earlier one: "I do not know of a single case in which it has been shown that the differences which separate two races of a mammalian species from one another have the slightest adaptive significance." Quite apart from the statement concerning the merely statistical nature of the distinction between subspecies, which is by no means always or even usually true, this dictum would not correspond with the consensus of biological opinion (see, for instance, Grinnell, 1928). It is unlikely that mammals and birds would differ in this respect, and apart from the mammalian case of *Peromyscus*, we have that of the crested larks (*Galerida*) and other birds of semi-desert country in which Meinertzhagen (1921) has shown a strong correlation, undoubtedly protective, between colour of plumage and colour of soil. Moreau (1930) finds similar phenomena in some Egyptian bird subspecies. Again, in the African buffaloes, the gradual reduction of body-size and of relative horn-size shown by C. Christy (1929) to occur with increased density of forest is clearly adaptive. It is noteworthy in this case that skull-size is little affected: the difficulty of moving rapidly through dense forest would depend much more on body- and horn-size than on this.

In the African squirrel *Heliosciurus gambianus*, Ingoldby (1927) has shown a marked correlation between climatic conditions and visible characters, the forest forms being saturated in colour and larger, the savannah forms pale and smaller, and with all gradations between. The adaptive nature of these particular characters is not apparent, but the close correlation of environmental and character gradients makes it impossible to believe that the characters are the result of chance: they are presumably, when not mere modifications, correlated with non-apparent adaptations (pp. 63, 206).

In this case, by the way, Ingoldby maintains that many forms do not have definite geographical areas, but recur sporadically as the climatic conditions dictate. This would be contrary to our experience in cases like that of *Peromyscus* which have been very thoroughly worked out, and it is likely that in the squirrels, in addition to these more obvious characters of pigmentation and size, others will be detected which will enable a truly geographical (as well as an ecological climatic) distribution to be worked out. The squirrels of the genus *Callosciurus* of Lower Burma (Thomas and Wroughton, 1916), which also show great colour-variation, do conform to such a scheme, certain species being sharply separated by the Chindwin River. Curiously enough, differentiation has been much more active on the east than on the west bank of the river; the differentiation, however, appears to take the form of a number of clines instead of well-defined subspecies (p. 219).

The increase in wing-length of open-country subspecies when contrasted with forest forms of the same species, as found by G. L. Bates (1931) in West African birds, is a clear case of adaptive difference. Similar adaptive differences in wings and tail have been found in the subspecies of fox-sparrows and shrikes by Linsdale (1928) and A. H. Miller (1931) respectively (pp. 182, 236).

Bates also found various cases of clines or character-gradients correlated with environmental gradients. We shall give further examples of such character-gradients later (p. 206). As already pointed out, these, in so far as they are genetic, must be either directly adaptive or correlated with some internal physiological adaptation.

Undoubtedly genetic accident plays a part in determining the characters of subspecies; but its role will be most important in small and entirely isolated groups, whereas with groups showing continuous distribution over larger areas it will tend to be overshadowed by the influence of selection. We refer elsewhere to some examples of the Sewall Wright effect, or drift (pp. 200, 242). From the wealth of facts available, we cite a couple more here. Murphy and Chapin (1929) find two subspecies of goldcrest (*Regulus regulus*) in the Azores, one generally distributed except on the island of San Miguel, where alone the second form exists. Using elaborate genetic analysis, Dobzhansky (1939*a*) finds that *Drosophila pseudoobscura* has smaller effective breeding populations in the north of its range than in Mexico and Guatemala, and that this has led to the northern populations showing reduced genetic heterogeneity (see pp. 60, 371–2).

We often know the approximate date at which isolation of an island has occurred, and can see that broadly speaking, though with a considerable amount of variation (pp. 200, 324; and below), the degree of divergence is proportional to the time that has since elapsed, as well as to the effectiveness of the isolation. It is thus a perfectly legitimate deduction that geographical variation of the type we have been considering provides us with a cross-section of a temporal process and that isolational divergence has been constantly operative throughout evolution, as an agency promoting minor systematic diversity. Moreau (1930) on the basis of the known facts concerning post-glacial changes in geology and climate, has discussed the age of various Egyptian subspecies of birds. He finds that several cannot be older than 10,000 years, while one or two must have an age of only 5,000 years or slightly less. He is inclined to put 5,000 years as the normal minimum time for distinct subspeciation, on the ground that lower Mesopotamia, where the land has only come into existence during the last 5,000 years or so, shows no endemic passerine subspecies, and very few others. Approximately similar periods would hold for the subspecies of birds and mammals found on islands off Scotland, which can only have been colonized in post-glacial times; the same applies to the differentiated races of frogs (p. 235). However, goldfinches (*Carduelis carduelis*) introduced, apparently recently, into Bermuda are now appreciably darker (Kennedy, 1913), and the facts concerning rats and mice (pp. 187n, 257) show that subspecific differentiation may sometimes occur much more quickly.

In particular, the Faeroe house-mouse, *Mus musculus faeroensis*, which was introduced into the islands not much more than 250 years ago, is now so distinct that certain modern authorities have assigned full specific status to it (see Evans and Vevers, 1938).

Rabbits have been isolated on Skokholm island (S. Wales) for about six centuries. They now average 120 g. below mainland weight, and are blacker above. This is moderately rapid differentiation, though the result does not yet merit subspecific naming (Lockley, 1940).

Temperature must influence the rate of differentiation to a certain extent. Thus Hubbs (1940b) finds that the subspeciation and speciation of fish populations isolated by the desiccation of the American desert is more rapid in warm springs than in pools at normal temperature.

Accidental "drift" in small populations may, of course, rapidly bring about slight differentiation. Thus a colony of the heath fritillary butterfly (*Melitaea athalia*) deliberately introduced into Essex within the present century, is already noticeably smaller and darker than the Kent strain, from which it was derived (Stovin, 1937). Harrison (1920a) showed that in the moth *Oporabia autumnata* two local populations inhabiting ecologically distinct woodlands, became quite distinct in size, colour, and certain physiological characters in a very short period of years. Salomonsen (1938) gives evidence to show that the white-headed form of the barbet *Lybius torquatus*, which is localized to the east and south of Lake Nyasa, has spread westwards in the last forty years. This form (originally described as *L. zombae*) appears to have originated by at least two mutational steps, as pink-headed types, intermediate in various degree, are also found. At Somba in the eighteen-nineties about half the population still had light red heads, though no dark-red birds were present. In 1933, however, no light reds occurred, and, apart from an occasional light pink, all the birds were white. Salomonsen considers this as evidence of the transformation of a whole population by the spread of mutant genes, though Meise (1938, p. 68) thinks it represents the shifting of a zone of hybridization between two well-marked subspecies as a result of population-pressure.

An extremely interesting point is brought out by Swarth (1920, p. 106, map), concerning the migratory habits of the fox-sparrow, *Passerella iliaca*. The *unaleschensis* group of sub-species breeds along the north-west coast of North America. Five well-marked subspecies succeed each other as we pass north-wards along the coast. The southernmost (*P. i. fuliginosa*) is to all intents and purposes a resident. The others are migratory, but in their migrations play leap-frog over the intervening forms. Thus No. 2, reckoning in breeding range from south to north, winters just south of No. 1 (*fuliginosa*). No. 3 breeds north of No. 2, but winters to the south of No. 2's winter range; and Nos. 4, 5, and 6, whose breeding ranges succeed each other to the north-west of No. 3's, winter together in the extreme south of the winter range of the group.

The obvious explanation is that the resident subspecies persisted in its present range throughout the last glacial period. As the ice receded, No. 2 invaded new breeding territory, but was forced to winter south of the already occupied range of No. 1: Nos. 3, 4, 5, and 6 repeated the process, but the last three were crowded together into a single winter area close to the southern limit to which the species is adapted. If so, the differentiation of the northernmost subspecies must have been effected during the last 10,000 years or less.

In numerous instances, forms meriting classification as species are found geographically isolated from their nearest relatives, and must be presumed to have owed their origin to an extension of the divergence that leads to subspeciation. Naturally, they will tend to occur more often where the isolation is more thorough. We have mentioned the red grouse of Britain, *Lagopus scoticus*, whose nearest relative is the willow grouse of Scandinavia, *L. lagopus*; it should be recalled that one of the most important specific distinctions in this case is adaptive, namely the willow grouse's winter change of plumage to white, and the absence of this feature in the less extreme climate of Britain. The ptarmigan (*Lagopus mutus*), which is a bird of higher latitudes and altitudes, becomes white in winter in both regions.

Another case is that of the snail, *Truncatellina britannica*, closely allied to and doubtless derived from the continental *T. rivierana*. Excellent examples from plants are found in the European Gesneriaceae, notably in the genus *Ramondia*—e.g. *R. serbica* from Serbia and neighbouring areas, *R. heldreichii* from Thessaly, and *R. pyrenaica* from the Pyrenees. These would thus constitute an *Artenkreis* (p. 179). Numerous other plant cases may be found in books such as Willis's *Age and Area* (1922) or in phytogeographical works such as Turrill's *Plant Life of the Balkan Peninsula* (1929). In some cases the geographical variation appears adaptive, but in others, as for instance the marked fruit variation in *Clypeola jonthlaspi*, no adaptive interpretation can be given (Turrill, in Watson and others, 1936).

We must, however, mention the view of Goldschmidt (1932, 1935, 1940) that the formation of geographical subspecies and that of true species are wholly distinct processes. The former, according to him, involves only quantitative modifications of a basic genetic pattern, while the latter involves the formation of a new inherent pattern. This production of a new type of equilibrium, he is inclined to think, is achieved abruptly. While this may apply in some cases (though there is no direct evidence for it as yet) it would appear impossible to deny that the divergence which produces subspecies does in fact often lead on to the production of species, more especially since the distinction between subspecies and species is not (and indeed cannot be) a sharp or universally agreed one (see p. 456).

A rather different type of geographical subspecies may occur in rare species. Rare species will not normally be spread more or less continuously over a wide area, but will often exist in pockets here and there, whether because they have not been able to spread or because they are in process of being ousted by other species. In such cases there will already be considerable isolation of groups. Thus any selective agencies can work without being counteracted; further, even new non-adaptive mutations and recombinations can establish themselves much more readily in a small group (Wright, 1931, 1932, 1940). Indeed, in certain cases, the course of evolution may possibly be determined by mutation-pressure (Wright, 1940). We may distinguish these as *local* subspecies from the *areal* or *regional* subspecies of abundant species, and it may be expected that they will owe their divergence more to chance recombination and less to selection; their distinctions will tend to be trivial and useless rather than adaptive. Bateson (1913) gives numerous examples of both types.

We have already mentioned the case of the fern, *Nephrodium spinulosum* (p. 33). A slightly different example, since the range covered is greater, is afforded by the rare moth, *Rhyacia alpicola*. This occurs only in small restricted areas, in each of which considerable differentiation has occurred. One subspecies exists in Lapland, another in Ireland and Scotland, a third in the Shetlands, and a fourth in the Carpathians.

Some of the local groups of the genus *Sorbus* (service-trees, etc.) seem to be local subspecies in this sense (Wilmott, 1934). One well-marked form, for instance, occurs only in the Avon Gorge, another in the Wye Valley, another only near Minchead, and so on.

An interesting case of local variation, presumably mutative, is given by Salaman (Watson and others, 1936). The wild potato-like plant, *Solanum demissum*, in one part of its range is genetically resistant to common blight (*Phytophthora infestans*), but is susceptible in another area. The resistant strain occurs in a region where blight is not found, so that we have here an example of potential pre-adaptation (pp. 450 seq.).

The jimson-weed, *Datura stramonium*, shows geographical differentiation in regard to its chromosomal structure, various "prime types" produced by segmental interchange (p. 90) having a well-defined distribution (Blakeslee, Bergner and Avery, 1937). It is possible that they may all originally have shown geographical replacement, but the fact that the species is a readily-distributed weed has confused the distribution; in any case, some regions now contain two or more chromosomal races (p. 329).

Some abundant species show highly localized varieties which may also be called local subspecies—for instance the common thyme, *Thymus serpyllum*, and the sea-campion, *Silene maritima*. The reason for such localized differentiation in these cases is obscure, as is the reason for the local existence of obvious single-gene mutants, such as white-flowered plants, in patches or in isolated valleys.

Among birds where a presumed large mutation has become diagnostic of a taxonomic form is *B. brunneinuchus*, a wide-ranging species of sedentary habits (Chapman, 1923). *B. inornatus* differs only in its slightly smaller size, and in the absence of the black breast-band characteristic of the former. Its habits and ecological preferences appear to be the same. It exists in a rather isolated valley in the centre of the range of *B. brubbeinuchus* and there replaces its relative. There can be little doubt that it represents a geographical form (probably a subspecies, not a species, however) of which the chief characteristic is the presumably abrupt (mutational) loss of the breast-band. In *B. assimilis* sporadic individuals of one well-marked subspecies show characters diagnostic of other subspecies or species: see also Chapman (1927). In the Papuo-Melanesian bird *Formenkreis Lalage aurea* (Mayr and Ripley, 1941, Amer. Mus. Novit. no. 1116) barred plumage of underparts has been independently lost at least five times, and independent mutation seems to have occurred in other clear-cut characters such as eyestripe.

The buttercup *Ranunculus allegheniensis* appears to have differentiated in a way essentially similar to *Buarremon inornatus* (Gates, 1916), since it is found abundantly in a comparatively small area within the range of the widely-distributed *R. abortivus*, which it there replaces and from which it differs by a few minor characters and one striking, probably mutational distinction in the shape of its achenes.

In passing, a curious case of geographical difference in *Drosophila* may be mentioned. Timoféeff-Ressovsky (1932*a*) finds that the wild-type alleles of the white-eye series in European and American *D. melanogaster* are not identical. The American allele mutates nearly double as often with the same dose of X-rays, and gives a higher proportion of full white genes among its mutations. Here we have a geographical difference in intrinsic capacity to vary.

The proof given by Wright, that non-adaptive differentiation will occur in small populations owing to "drift", or the chance fixation of some new mutation or recombination, is one of the most important results of mathematical analysis applied to the facts of neo-mendelism. It gives accident as well as adaptation a place in evolution, and at one stroke explains many facts which puzzled earlier selectionists, notably the much greater degree of divergence shown by island than mainland forms, by forms in isolated lakes than in continuous river-systems. We have given numerous examples of such phenomena. Turesson (1927) uses the term "seclusion types" for such forms in plants. Recently Kramer and Mertens (1938a) have provided a quantitative demonstration of the principle, in their work on Adriatic lizards (*Lacerta sicula*). Surveys were made of the lizard population of a number of islands, and the degree of their divergence from the uniform mainland type was determined on an arbitrary scale. At the same time, the depth of water between each island and the mainland was noted; this can be regarded as a measure of the time during which the population has been isolated, since the islands have been formed by subsidence. Further, the area of the island can be used as a measure of population-size. It was found that degree of divergence showed definite partial correlations, both directly with length of isolation, and inversely with size of island. The table opposite, based on Kramer and Merten's data, brings out the point. Island-size is denoted on a logarithmic scale, subdivided in its lowest part, since the intensity of the Sewall Wright effect increases rapidly with decreasing size of population.

o indicates identity with the mainland form, 4 the greatest divergence found. The least divergence is shown on large islands, the greatest on rather small islands after long separation; very small islands may show considerable divergence after very short separation (see also pp. 187 n., 195).

In the white-eyes of the wide-ranging bird genus *Zosterops* (see p. 179 and Stresemann, 1931) the degree of differentiation of island species (or subspecies) appears to be correlated with a considerable number of factors—(*a*) directly: with (1) the age of the island, (2) the inherent mutability of the stock; (*b*) inversely: with (3) the size of the island, (4) the predator-pressure and degree of competition from related forms, (5) the degree of migration.

It should be noted that if a population is subjected to cyclical fluctuations of abundance, the determining factor is the size of the *minimum* effective breeding population. In extremely small populations, the Sewall Wright effect may even fix deleterious mutations, and so result in extinction. Various of the cases where protection of the remnant of a once-abundant species have failed

DIFFERENTIATION IN ISLAND LIZARDS

area (arbitrary units)	0–6	6–12	12–18	18–24	24–30	30–36	depth (m)
0·5	2½		2½				
0·5	I	I					
I–5	I, 2	I, 2	2, 2½, 2½, 3	3		4	
5–10	I						
10–100	0		2				
100–1,000			0				

to prevent further decline and eventual extinction are probably due to this cause. The best-documented example is the extinction of the subspecies of the prairie chicken known as the heath hen (*Tympanuchus c. cupido*), in spite of the most elaborate protective measures (Gross, 1928). Conservationists should take note of this. If their efforts to save a dwindling remnant of a species do not bring about a rapid increase of numbers, they are likely to be in vain: early action is essential.

Geographical differentiation may be carried far beyond the stage of broad subspecies to a high pitch of local detail When small populations are completely or almost completely isolated

from each other, almost every such population may develop
its own distinctive characters. This is so, for instance, with
Partula and other snails of the Pacific Islands (p. 232), with the
insular lizard populations of the Adriatic and elsewhere (p. 200),
with certain flightless grasshoppers of arid regions (Uvarov, *in
verbis*), etc. Hubbs (1940*b*) finds marked differentiation in quite
small populations of freshwater fish (a few hundred individuals),
isolated in pools as a result of the desiccation of the American
desert. Differentiation is then often apparently non-adaptive.
Frequently the differences, though definite, are not considered
by experienced taxonomists to merit a subspecific name: e.g.
some of the insular lizards; various insular birds, such as the
Fair Isle wren (see discussion in Huxley, 1939*a*, and in J. Fisher,
1939*a*) and others cited by Mayr (1931–38), etc. But in other
cases, as in the grasshoppers just mentioned, the differentiation
is considerable, and the only difference from ordinary subspecies
lies in the small size of the groups. If a general term is needed
for such cases, *microsubspecies* is perhaps preferable to that of
micro-race proposed by Dobzhansky (1937). Goldschmidt (1940)
uses the rather awkward term "*subsubspecies*".

Microsubspecies are preferably not to be given names subject
to the international rules, since this would complicate the nomenclature unnecessarily.

Even finer differentiation may occur. Thus Diver (1939) in
the snail *Cepaea* finds that the proportions of the various types of
colour and banding vary from colony to colony, almost always
in an arbitrary, non-graded way; he also gives similar examples
from other land and freshwater molluscs. Lloyd (1912) and
Hagedoorn and Hagedoorn (1917) found that among the rats
of India and Java respectively there occurred highly localized
groups with distinctive characters, often consisting of a few
individuals only. Sometimes the distinctions seemed to be mono-
factorial, sometimes to depend on several different genes; in
some cases the groups disappeared after quite a short time. In
this case we have to do apparently with the effect of chance
inbreeding on one or a few recessive genes; it is of interest,
however, in demonstrating the high potential of variation avail-

able, through which geographical differentiation may appear in the event of complete isolation or of partial isolation accompanied by differential selection.

Gilmour and Gregor (1939) have recently proposed the term *deme* for "any specified assemblage of taxonomically closely related individuals". This should be useful to replace such cumbersome phrases as "local intrabreeding populations". The ultimate natural unit in sexually reproducing species is then the deme, and analysis is needed to show to what extent demes are isolated from each other (see also Buzzati-Traverso *et al.*, 1938).

In some instances, new types have been thrown up which spread from their centre of origin owing to some selective advantage, thus causing local differentiation of a peculiar type. When this occurs in an isolated population, the new type may oust the old within the area. This has happened with the melanic form of certain species of the bird *Coereba* in the West Indies (p. 94 n; Lowe, 1912), and is in progress with the melanic type of the opossum *Trichosurus vulpecula* in Tasmania (p. 104). It may, however, also occur in large or continental populations, as with the *simplex* tooth-character of *Microtus arvalis* in N. Germany (p. 105). Whether the resultant gradient in proportions of *simplex* and normal teeth will reach an equilibrium, or the *simplex* character will infect the whole species, remains for future generations of taxonomists to determine (p. 105).

In general, we may be sure that the analysis of invisible physiological characters, and the more intensive study of visible ones, will reveal that species are much more diversified geographically than is now generally recognized (for further examples, see Timoféeff-Ressovsky, 1940).

Wherever there is any appreciable isolation, not only will non-adaptive distinctions accumulate, but adaptation to local conditions will be able to proceed to a further pitch than where counteracted by free gene-flow. Further, internal (intra-group) clines (p. 220) will doubtless be revealed within populations of species which are not too mobile.

Out of these minor local differences, the processes of differentiation will create the obviously distinct groups which we call subspecies and species, and the obvious regularities of inter-group clines. But those which merit taxonomic naming will form but a small fraction of the total amount of geographical diversification.

Mention should here be made of the views of Willis (1922, 1940). Chiefly on the basis of studies of geographical distribution, he entirely rejects the selectionist view, and concludes that evolution is a largely automatic affair of differentiation produced by large mutations, followed by spread of the new type at a more or less constant rate, and by further differentiative variations in due course.

Unfortunately most of Willis' conclusions are vitiated by his failure to take account of modern work. Thus he continues to accept Fleeming Jenkin's criticism of Darwin, namely, that new variations will be swamped by crossing, whereas, as R. A. Fisher in particular has shown (see p. 55), this objection has been entirely obviated by the discovery that inheritance is particulate. He adopts, in exaggerated form, de Vries' idea of large mutations, and appears to be unaware of the modern conception of the adjustment of mutations to the needs of the organism (p. 67). He does not refer to polyploidy as an evolutionary agency in higher plants. He makes a sharp distinction, which is quite unjustified on general biological grounds, between structural and functional adaptations. He concludes that, since localized endemic forms, e.g. on islands or mountain-tops, appear to have no adaptive value, they must have arisen by sudden mutation, whereas "drift" due to accidental recombinations in small populations will clearly account for a great many of such cases (p. 58). It seems, further, that he has not adopted the principle of geographical replacement as a basis for taxonomy. If this were done, many of his endemics would doubtless turn out to be, not new full species, but new subspecies produced by "drift", and it would be much easier to distinguish between such products of recent diversification and true relicts. He practically ignores zoological facts, notably in paleontology, which contradict some of his general conclusions such as that gradual adaptive improvement does not occur, that no important change is to be found in major groups during geological time, and that the distinctive characters of moderately large taxonomic units are not adaptive. He does not distinguish between euryplastic and stenoplastic forms (p. 519), or between those which are narrowly adapted and those which succeed by virtue of general vigour and viability. In conclusion, he neglects all the evidence that new types may arise in several quite distinct ways, and maintains that there is only one mode of evolutionary differentiation.

If the extensive data which he has assembled could be analysed in the light of modern knowledge, instead of being lumped together to produce a heterogeneous mass from which purely statistical consequences can be drawn, it is probable that certain valuable conclusions could be reached. It is likely, for instance, that his general idea of "age and area", or progressive increase of range with time, would prove to hold for a number of forms, and to have interesting consequences. The further conclusion, arrived at in conjunction with Yule (Yule and Willis, 1922) that differentiation is also a function of time, and that genera tend to split into two at more or less regular intervals, may also be of importance, though, as examples such as *Lingula* or *Nautilus* demonstrate, it is certainly not universally valid.

He has also collected a number of very interesting facts concerning the number of species in different genera of a family. The average number of species per genus in flowering plants (apparently without taking into account the principle of geographical replacement) is 14 or 15. But there are in all families a very large proportion of unispecific genera. Thus more than a third of the genera of Compositae (446 out of 1143) and of those of Caryophyllaceae (29 out of 78) are monotypes, with only one species each, indicating a very peculiar form of differentiation. Further, the largest genus of a family is always relatively enormous in the number of species it contains, in over 40 per cent of cases (235 families) comprising half or more than half the total number of species in the family. Facts such as these demand the most careful consideration. However, we can be sure that their meaning will not be elucidated by the purely statistical methods used by Willis, but must wait upon the fullest analysis, notably ecological and cytological.

4. CLINES (CHARACTER-GRADIENTS)

The delimitation of named subspecies in different areas, each with their own distinctive mean and range of variability in respect of a number of characters, provides one means of pigeon-holing the data of geographical differentiation. But, as we have already seen in discussing such cases as that of *Peromyscus*, this method does not cover a certain aspect of the facts, namely the frequent tendency of characters to change gradually and continuously over large areas.

In point of fact these character-gradients, or *clines*, to give them a convenient technical name (Huxley, 1939*a*, 1939*b*), appear to be much commoner than is generally supposed. Indeed, on any general Darwinian view, we should expect to find them as one of the general features of organic variation. Natural selection will all the time be moulding life adaptively into its environment; and since gradients in environmental factors are a widespread feature of the environmental mould, we should expect organisms to show corresponding adaptive gradients in their characters.

The adaptive characters directly affected may be visible characters such as absolute size, or relative ear-size in warm-blooded animals; or they may be invisible, physiological features with no outward sign in the characters usually employed in taxonomy (e.g., the difference in temperature-resistance in different regional populations of *Drosophila* (p. 191); or the temperature-preferences of the races of the beetle *Carabus nemoralis* (Krumbiegel, 1932); or, as with the phototropism of the same species, they may be associated with slight differences in eye-structure; or finally, and it appears most frequently, they may be physiological features reflected in non-adaptive but taxonomically convenient correlates such as proportion of parts, or colour.

Broad environmental gradients exist in numerous general climatic factors, in relation primarily to latitude and altitude. Such graded climatic factors include temperature, humidity, solar intensity, relative day-length, and so forth. More restricted gradients are found in ecological factors, in relation to the change from one habitat to another—gradients in salinity or water-content, in height of vegetation, in edaphic conditions, and so on. There is, of course, no sharp line to be drawn between geographical and ecological gradients. The gradient up a steep mountainside may be better styled ecological; but in many features it will repeat the general geographical gradient from the base of the mountain to higher latitudes. The point is that such gradients exist, and that they are of every size, from those of largest scale between the equatorial and polar regions, to those of extremely small scale like that in decreasing moisture round a pond.

How may we expect life to accommodate itself to these graded features of its environment? In the first place, their scale has an influence. Because of the rate of gene-flow through a population, a cline cannot usually establish itself as a characteristic of an interbreeding group unless the group covers a considerable area. The only way by which clines on a genetic basis may be established over small distances is by having a highly variable population of which different types are adapted to different ecological conditions. Selection will then automatically see to it that different proportions of the various types are found along the environmental gradient, even when this is quite short. Short clines of this type do exist, as we shall see later, in certain plants, e.g., *Plantago maritima* (p. 223). They are not, however, enduring characters of the species, but come and go within its plastic framework with the changes in ecological conditions. They will also tend to be repeated, *con variazioni*, in many localities, while large-scale climatic clines will be few in number, and will constitute characters of the species as definite and enduring as its measurements or its geographical range.

With regard to large-scale clines, the biological peculiarities of the species will of course have an influence, large size and high mobility tending to make them less prominent, and vice versa (see p. 239).

Any continuously-graded variation will tend to be broken up by various factors. In the first place the accidents (biologically speaking) of complete or almost complete geographical isolation will introduce discontinuities. These will interrupt gene-flow, and so not only allow local selection to act more effectively (as we saw with the island subspecies of *Peromyscus polionotus*, p. 186), but also permit the Sewall Wright effect of non-adaptive differentiation to occur wherever the isolated populations are small. The first effect will tend to break up a continuously sloping cline into sharp steps, while the second will impose non-adaptive features upon it, sometimes quite obscuring any underlying regularity.

Biological discontinuities will also break up the continuity of clines. Here again, neo-mendelian principles have pointed the way to important deductions. We have shown in an earlier chapter how the effects of major genes are selectively adjusted, individually and mutually, by means of combinations of modifiers to suit the needs of the organism, notably in giving maximum vigour and fertility. There is an internal adaptation of the gene-complex as well as an external adaptation of characters. This extension of the principle of genic balance we may call the principle of harmoniously-stabilized gene-complexes.

Let us now consider what will happen within a continuous population spread over a large area in which markedly different climatic conditions occur in different regions, but with the extremes connected by environmental gradations. Selection will then be operative and will tend to adapt the population locally; however, this local adaptation will be impeded and graded by gene-flow. But wherever some accident, such as temporary or partial isolation, allows selection full scope, local adaptation will be intensified, and the major adaptive genes will be fortified by internal adaptation until a local harmoniously-stabilized gene-complex is built up. Once this occurs, the resultant extra vigour and fertility will permit the bearers of this gene-complex to spread beyond the area to which they were originally adapted.

If several such gene-complexes arise within the area of the species, they will tend to spread until they meet. As Sumner (1932, p. 76) has stressed, local groups must be regarded as in a dynamic equilibrium based on relative population-pressures. He compares them to a series of balloons in contact, the population-pressures being here represented by the gas-pressures in the balloons. Groups with high population-pressure, resulting from successfully stabilized gene-complexes, will spread, and groups whose relative population-pressure is below a certain threshold may actually be extinguished, their remnants being incorporated into and transformed by the more successful groups (see p. 187).

What his simile does not explain, however, is the permanence of the skin of the balloons—as represented in nature by the relatively sharp delimitation of subspecific groups. As we have seen (pp. 182 seq.), in many cases, adjacent subspecies are separated by a relatively narrow zone of intergradation. What maintains this zone? Why does not gene-flow broaden it and break down the sharp distinction between the two subspecies?

On the principle we have been following out, the answer is simple. Crosses between two harmoniously-stabilized gene-complexes will give relatively disharmonious gene-combinations. The zone of intergradation will constantly be renewed by inter-crossing; but it will as constantly be prevented from spreading by selective elimination in favour of the better internal adaptations on either side, even though it may shift its position (p. 249).

This principle doubtless also explains why the zone of recombination between two markedly distinct yet interfertile forms which have met after differentiating in isolation, in some cases remains so narrow, notably in the crows (p. 248).

We here meet with a new type of biological discontinuity—a *partial discontinuity*, as opposed to the complete discontinuity found between full species. Where the "biological tension" between different portions of a widespread species is sufficient, a condition of equilibrium will be reached, represented by a series of distinct subspecies passing into each other by inter-breeding at narrow zones of intergradation.*

This will be facilitated by partial environmental discontinuities such as partial barriers, or unfavourable zones where population-

---

* A suggestive ecological parallel exists in the way in which relatively uniform biotic communities pass into each other across narrow intermediate zones (see Elton, 1927, ch. 1). Such zones are sometimes styled "tension zones" (cf. Elton, 1938). In both cases, environmental continuity is reflected in partial organic discontinuity.

density is lowered; it will also be facilitated by sharp changes in environmental conditions, as where a mountain range rises abruptly from a plain, or open country gives place suddenly to forest. But—and this is important—it may occur in the absence of any barriers or any abrupt alteration in the environmental gradient: the cause of partial discontinuity is then a purely bio-logical one, due to the nature of the gene-complex.

So far, these deductions, however their validity be supported by the frequent existence of subspecies separated by narrow zones of intergradation, have only been experimentally verified in one instance. Timoféeff-Ressovsky (1932b), studying the geographical varieties of certain lady-beetles, found that their visible peculiari-ties depended on several mendelian genes, and that the combina-tions of these actually realized in wide-ranging geographical groups were almost invariably more viable and more resistant than the recombinations not found in nature, which he produced by crossing. It is much to be hoped that further experimental analysis of this important point will be made in other types. Meanwhile Sumner's data in *Peromyscus polionotus* show that the population of the narrow intergrading zone between *P. p. polio-notus* and *P. p. albifrons* shows a markedly higher coefficient of variation than either pure subspecies (see p. 186, and Huxley 1939a), a fact which is to be expected on the above theory of harmoniously stabilized gene-complexes.

If, as it seems probable, these deductions prove valid, it will mean that subspecies, as found in nature, are in reality of two distinct types. The first we may call independent, and consists of those which are so fully isolated that gene-flow between them and other groups is wholly or virtually interrupted; the second, or dependent, are those we have just been discussing, which interbreed with their neighbours along intergrading zones. Independent subspecies may differentiate into full species, and, with sufficient time, normally will do so. Dependent subspecies normally will not do so, but though they may continue to evolve, will evolve as part of the whole interbreeding complex to which they belong. Thus it is not true to say that subspecies are necessarily "species in the making" (as was done, for instance, by Rothschild and Jordan, 1903): some are, and some are not.

The breaking up of a continuous population into subspecies by the physical discontinuities of geographical barriers and the biological partial discontinuities of narrow intergrading zones will profoundly modify any cline systems present. The continuously sloping character-gradient that simple *a priori* considerations might lead us to expect is converted into a staircase or a stepped ramp, the separate subspecies corresponding with the treads, flat or gently sloping, and these being either united by steep slopes —the zones of intergradation—or, in the case of completely isolated subspecies, remaining unconnected. The mean or modal values for the several subspecies will often fall on a gradient. This may be called an external or intergroup cline; when the characters of a subspecies change slightly or gradually across the area of its distribution, giving a sloping tread in the staircase, we may speak of its showing an internal cline.

Intergroup clines are a very frequent feature of geographical differentiation, and appear usually to be correlated with corresponding gradients in environmental features, though Mayr (1940) cites some clines in tropical birds where no such correlation can be found. A summary of the chief generalizations concerning them is to be found in Rensch (1933a, 1938a), and an excellent discussion in Goldschmidt (1940). The most important of these have been called Bergmann's Rule, Allen's Rule, and Gloger's Rule, after their most important proponents. They lead to much parallel variation in related species, though all of them are broad correlations only; with a considerable number of exceptions.

Bergmann's rule may be stated thus. Within a polytypic warm-blooded species, the body-size of a subspecies usually increases with decreasing mean temperature of its habitat. A detailed statistical study by Rensch showed that in the great majority of cases this rule holds good for birds. For Corvidae and Picidae there are hardly any exceptions, and in general the rule applies in 70 to 90 per cent of cases. The rule also applies to mammals, though here the exceptions are more numerous. It is clear that size may be modified in other ways, e.g. by selection in relation to type and abundance of food. We have already noted the fact that the size-gradient between forest and open-country forms runs in opposite directions in buffaloes and squirrels in Africa. The reason for the greater number of exceptions in mammals is doubtless to be found in various biological peculiarities of the group, such as hibernation, temperature-regulation by means of greater or less growth of hair, nocturnal habit, use of burrows and dens, etc.; thus the burrowing *Microtus* behaves contrary to Bergmann's Rule (Dale, 1940). Rensch has shown (1939*b*) that the correlation in temperate regions is with winter minimum temperature. This is what would be expected, selection being exerted by the most rigorous conditions. It may be prophesied that in semi-tropical areas the correlation will be with the maximum temperature in the hot season.

Recent studies (Salomonsen 1933, Huxley 1939*a*) have enabled a beginning to be made with a quantitative study of Bergmann's rule. Thus for three polytypic species of birds in western Europe, a change of 1 per cent in wing-length requires a difference of 2° N. latitude in the redpolls (*Carduelis flammea*), of just over 1° in the puffins (*Fratercula arctica*), and of only a little over 0·5° in the wrens (*Troglodytes troglodytes*). Other measures of size (beak in puffins, tarsus in wrens) show approximately the same rate of change as the wing, indicating that the effect is on the animal as a whole. The total relative change is least in the wrens (about 12 per cent of lowest wing-length), and highest in the puffins (nearly 50 per cent), but the range of the last-named is from Majorca to Spitsbergen, whereas the size-cline in the wrens is only exhibited between the N. of Scotland and Iceland, the wren population of mainland Britain and western Europe being very stable. Such differences presumably result from differences in selective intensity, but it is difficult at the moment to see why, e.g., there should be less effect in the tiny redpolls than in the relatively large puffins.

In cold-blooded animals, matters are more complex, types often appearing to have an environmental optimum where they attain their maximum size. In frog species, forms from colder climates seem to be larger, with relatively shorter hind legs (Porter, 1941; and see Pflüger and Smith, 1883).

Allen's rule also is correlated with temperature. It states that in warm-blooded species, the relative size of exposed portions of the body (limbs, tail, and ears) decreases with decrease of mean temperature. We have already noted this for *Peromyscus* species. Statistical treatment showed that it applied in 80 to 85 per cent of small mammals investigated by Rensch, and to almost the same extent for wing-length in birds (five families of non-migratory North American birds).

This rule also appears to hold for related species as well as related subspecies: e.g. for ears in foxes (Hesse, 1924). When the temperature is at all extreme, ear-size is of considerable adaptive value, small ear-size reducing heat-loss in cold climates, large ear-size facilitating heat-loss in hot climates.

Rensch (1938*a*) has shown that Allen's rule is in part purely a consequential effect of the negative allometry of the parts concerned, but that this must in many cases have been accentuated by selection in relation to heat-loss (see p. 547).

Both Bergmann's and Allen's rule may be included under the more general principle that in homothermous forms body-surface relative to bulk tends to decrease with decreasing outer temperature.

These effects prove to be genetic in every case as yet tested. It is noteworthy, however, that temperature also has a direct effect of the same type on such organs, but the modification is not permanently inherited (Przibram, 1925).

Pigmentation also shows marked geographical gradients, but these are rather more complex. Gloger's rule applies to pigmentation in warm-blooded species. In its modern formulation it states that intensity of melanin pigmentation tends to decrease with mean temperature (though the operative factor may possibly be light rather than temperature); however, humidity also has an effect, great humidity together with high temperature promoting the formation of the black eumelanins, while aridity together with high temperature promotes the substitution of the yellowish- or reddish-brown phaeomelanins. Phaeomelanins tend not to be found in cooler conditions even if arid. Thus the maximum depth of pigmentation will be found in humid and hot climates, the minimum in arctic climates. Heat and aridity, as in subtropical deserts, will promote yellowish and reddish browns, while lower temperature and aridity, as in steppes, will promote greys and grey-browns.

Among numerous examples, the studies of A. Roberts (1935, 1938) on S. African birds may be cited, though he is inclined to find geographical regularities also in other colours and in striping. Rensch's statistical investigations showed Gloger's rule to apply in 85–90 per cent of cases. We have seen a good example of the results in African squirrels (p. 192). The African buffaloes (C. Christy, 1929), with their red forms in forests and black forms in open country, constitute an exception. Lipochrome pigmentation tends to be of lower intensity in hot arid regions.

Invertebrates also show pigmentation-gradients, e.g. bumble-bees, wasps, beetles, butterflies; but these are complex (see p. 262). Lizards (*Gerrhonotus*) in western North America show distinct clines (Fitch, 1938), size and relative tail-length decreasing with decrease of temperature. Dobzhansky (1933), by genetic analysis in lady-beetles, has made it possible to demonstrate a genetic cline underlying geographical variation in *Harmonia axyridis*.

In all such cases, since related forms will tend to show similar effects, parallel evolution often results. Vogt (1909 and 1911) gives numerous cases among bumblebees (*Bombus*), and G. L. Bates (1931) among West African birds. Aldrich and Nutt (1939) find that in Newfoundland all resident birds which exhibit any geographical variation are exceptionally dark, often more so on the more humid eastern coast. An excellent example is given by Mayr and Serventy (1938) from birds of the Australian genus *Acanthiza*. Several species show a concentric arrangement of subspecies, those in the arid interior being pale, while those on the S.W. coast and a small part of the less humid S.E. coast are very dark. An interesting feature of this case is that the boundaries of the subspecies do not always overlap exactly in different species, but may run parallel at some distance from each other. Mayr and Serventy are inclined to interpret this on the basis of differing rates of evolutionary adjustment to environment. It is, however, just as likely that the pigmentary expression of whatever physiological adaptation is involved, may differ from species to species. See also Rensch (1936).

Another interesting case concerns the crested larks (*Galerida*) of N. Africa and S. Europe (Rothschild and Hartert, 1911). Two closely allied species, G. *cristata* and G. *theklae*, largely overlap in range, but are ecologically differentiated. Both have numerous subspecies, which show parallel variation in coloration correlated with soil-colour (though complicated by polymorphism in G. *theklae*). G. *theklae* also shows a cline in song, which becomes more prolonged as one passes from north to south in Africa.

Numerous other geographical clines appear to exist. The number of eggs in a clutch increases with increasing latitude within bird species, and the form of the wing becomes more pointed (Rensch, 1938b); organisms tend to decrease in size with decrease in salinity (e.g. in the Baltic; but this may be only a non-genetic modification); the number of fin-rays and vertebrae in many fish varies inversely with temperature; relative heart-weight decreases with temperature in warm-blooded species; tropical conditions promote a reduction of stomach- and intestine-size in species of birds with a mixed diet, etc.

The selective interpretation of such clines gives a rational basis to the Geographical Rules of Bergmann, Allen, etc., which we have just discussed; and to the consequent parallel variation. This is well discussed by Goldschmidt (1940), p. 83, who subsumes all the Rules under the head of "parallelism of subspecific clines". This parallelism may lead to forms which are taxonomically indistinguishable being evolved independently in several areas. Under current taxonomic practice, these are lumped together under one subspecific name. Thus the woodpecker type named *Picus canus sanguiniceps* appears to have evolved in the Western Himalayas, Southern Malacca, and Cochin China (Danis, 1937); and Mayr and Greenway (1938) state that in the bird *Mesia argentauris* three populations which "differ, though too subtly for formal description", although probably not genetically related, will all have to be called M. *a. argentauris*. This is a clear case for subsidiary taxonomic terminology (p. 405), whether specified in the form of clines or descriptive ecological terms.

In addition to such general or widespread gradients, manifested in many related and unrelated species, others appear to exist which apply only to limited groups (Rensch, 1933a). From among the wealth of possible examples we may adduce a few more concrete instances to illustrate the principle.

We have mentioned the geographical variation of the gipsymoth, *Lymantria dispar*. Goldschmidt (1934, p. 170) summarizes the geographically-varying characters which he has investigated genetically. These include (i) characters which, in his view, are definitely adaptive:—the male and female sex-factors, which differ in potency; the length of larval development; the length of the diapause; (ii) characters which Goldschmidt considers undoubtedly to be correlated with other distinctions which are adaptive:—the number of moults (four in both sexes; four in the male and five in the female; five in both sexes); the total size (weight) of the animal; the larval pigmentation; the colour of the imaginal abdominal hair; and (iii) characters which seem to have neither direct nor indirect (correlated) adaptive value:— the imaginal wing-colour.

Clines appear to exist in regard to many of these characters: in general these are very gentle in the main holarctic land-mass but much steeper, and with more tendency to sharp breaks, in the eastern Asiatic region. However, the clines for different phenotypic characters are not always coincident.

This species is the only one in which a full mendelian analysis has been made of the genetic basis for geographically-varying characters. It is interesting to find that most are controlled by a series of multiple alleles, whose effect is often reinforced by cytoplasmic influence. Length of diapause, however, and colour of abdominal hair are determined by a set of independent multiple (polymeric) genes; and wing-colour appears to be determined partly by a series of multiple alleles, partly by four other independent genes. (In *Peromyscus*, Sumner found that almost all subspecific differences depended on several genes, which he considered to be independent multiple factors.)

A peculiar cline is found in the insular populations of the deer-mouse, *Peromyscus maniculatus*, on the islands of Georgia Strait, British Columbia (Hall, 1938), in relation to distance from the mainland. Within a mere fourteen miles, body-length increases from 84 to 103 mm., and tail-length decreases from 94 to 66 mm., almost halving the tail-body ratio. It seems impossible to correlate this with any of the usual geographical rules.

The small copper butterfly, *Heodes phloeas*, analysed by Ford (1924), shows distinct gradients in certain regions, while in others the distribution is irregular, and in still others, such as North America, there is hardly any variation over large areas. Ford considers that this last fact is due to the species having only recently colonized the region, so that there has been inadequate time for geographical differentiation. Certain characters of the swallowtail butterfly, *Papilio dardanus*, show a graded distribution (Ford, 1936), as do some of *Acraea johnstoni* (Carpenter, 1932). In this and other butterflies with polymorphic females, a poly-morph-ratio gradient in the proportions of the forms may often be observed (Eltringham, 1910; Carpenter, 1932), as is also the case in the polymorphic foxes (p. 103), the guillemot (p. 105), etc. The fulmar petrel, *Fulmarus glacialis*, shows a condition intermediate between the dimorph-ratio cline (in the propor-tions of two sharply distinct forms), and the continuous gradation (J. Fisher, 1939b). Here there is a primary distinction between pale and dark (blue) forms, but the blue types exist in various degrees of intensity, and there is a cline towards a greater pro-portion of the deeper blue types in the far north.

The fox-sparrows studied by Swarth (1920) show character-gradients, but these are by no means simple. The sharp steepening of the gradients at the zones of intergradation between subspecies is again prominent. In some regions, different trends occur in different directions. Finally, there are certain apparent anomalies in the trends. Swarth suggests that these depend upon migratory habit, since the type would be influenced (whether by selection or otherwise) by conditions in their winter range as well as by those in their breeding quarters.

The zebras of the Burchell's zebra group (*Equus burchelli*) show an interesting cline (see Shortridge, 1934). The equatorial forms, covering two-thirds of its north-south range, are fully striped; south of the Zambesi the striping is progressively reduced, first on the tail and legs (*E. b. burchelli*), and then on the hinder half of the body (*E. b. quagga*, the true quagga, now extinct, and often regarded as a separate species). Here a threshold value for striping has been reached at a certain latitude.

An interesting case is that of the cole tit, *Parus ater*. One of the characters by which the Irish subspecies, *P. a hibernicus*, is distinguished from the British, *P. a. britannicus*, is the amount of yellow lipochrome pigment in the plumage, manifested especially in the yellowish colour of its under-parts. Occasional specimens, however, lack this feature and these are more common towards the north-east of Ireland; and occasional specimens from Wales show varying degrees of the characters of the Irish form (Witherby, 1938–41). It would seem that the Irish Channel has introduced a considerable discontinuity into a coloration-gradient (see Huxley, 1939a).

In this case, it is interesting to note, the various forms appear to differ primarily in regard to rate-genes (p.528 ff) affecting the rate of deposition and final amount of lipochrome pigment. This seems also to be the case in the African buffaloes just mentioned, though here the pigment concerned is melanin (see discussion in Huxley, 1939a). A similar case is that of the *Rassenkreis* of the palearctic goshawk *Accipiter gentilis* (Gladkov, 1941). The subspecies to the N. and E. are lighter, and in them the young birds, which are always darker than the adults, show an earlier onset of the lightening process. This species also obeys Bergmann's rule.

In the case of *Parus ater* we have apparently an approximation to the condition of the stepped ramp, in which the subspecies show internal clines. A similar example has already been mentioned in *Peromyscus polionotus* (p. 187). In both these cases the internal clines of certain subspecies appear to be confined to the margins of the areas of distribution, while in *P. polionotus* a pigmentary cline is continuous across the whole subspecific area.

Among the silver pheasants (Beebe, 1921), *Gennaeus* shows

large-scale colour-clines in all the main species. In addition, there has been considerable hybridization along the boundaries of species or marked subspecies, producing irregular genoclines. The internal cline in the moth *Platysamia* (Sweadner, 1937) appears to be a genocline, due to hybridization between two distinct forms brought together by post-glacial migration. The clines in the frequency of blood-group genes in man across the Palearctic (Haldane, 1940) are also undoubtedly due to migration; where natural barriers occur, the slope of the clines is much steepened.

Løppenthin (1932) describes a continuous cline in the colour of the under parts (from chestnut to pure white) in the common nuthatch (*Sitta caesia*) from several hundred miles from west to east across north-central Europe. At either end, the cline passes over into forms which are stable over considerable areas—i.e. geographical subspecies. It is possible that here, too, we are dealing with a genocline resulting from hybridization between two distinct forms which have met subsequently to differentiation; possibly, however, it is a true geographical internal cline related to an environmental gradient, and such clines may turn out to be commoner than now supposed. The differentiation of the squirrel *Callosciurus sladeni* along the Chindwin river is considered by Thomas and Wroughton (1916) to be into numerous subspecies: their own data, however, make it probable that it is really into two colour-clines, separated by a tributary (see p. 227). Again, Fleming and Snyder (1939) in the song-sparrow *Melospiza melodia* find a continuous N.W.–S.E. colour-cline across Ontario.

L. L. Snyder (1935), in a study of the sharp-tailed grouse (*Pedioecetes phasianellus*) of North America, finds that, in addition to distinct subspecies of the usual type, there is a colour-cline from north to south over the Great Plains. He hesitates whether to give trinomials to various forms within this cline. Although, as he says (p. 59), this would be quite a normal procedure according to present taxonomic practice, this does not mean that it would be justified (see p. 226).

We may be sure that many forms have been accorded subspecific rank because the conferring of a trinomial was the only accepted method of distinguishing them, whereas in reality they represent only points on a continuous cline. Once the idea of clines is generally accepted, we may safely prophesy that an increasing number of cases of clines will come to light, often replacing series of subspecies.

Examples of continuous (internal) geoclines within extensive populations are as yet infrequent, doubtless because they are less readily detected. However, a very interesting case is that of the honey-bees, studied by Alpatov (1929). In the plain of European Russia, a gradient occurs in tongue-length. This increases from north to south so regularly that the change can be reasonably well represented by a mathematical equation connecting tongue-length and latitude ($y = 10 \cdot 3219 - 0 \cdot 07559x$, where y = tongue length in mm., and x = degrees of N. latitude). The tongue-length ranges from $5 \cdot 726$ mm. to $6 \cdot 733$ mm.

A north-south gradient towards smaller absolute body-size, larger relative leg-size, relatively broader wings, lighter abdomen-colour and other characters, including certain points of behaviour, is also apparent.

In the Caucasus, this gradient is continued with decreasing latitude for tongue-length and relative leg-length, but is reversed (presumably in relation to decrease of temperature with altitude) for abdomen-colour and relative size of wax-glands. This shows how valuable the specification of character-gradients may be as an additional method of taxonomic description, as does the fact previously cited (p. 217) that in fox-sparrows (*Passerella*) different character-gradients run in different directions; the same is true for *Lymantria* (Goldschmidt, 1940, pp. 69–70, 84).

No such graded variation is to be found in North America: this is due to the fact that the honey-bee is there a recent importation. The geographically-graded characters are all or mostly genetic. Some of them appear to be adaptive, e.g. the tongue-length in relation both to the type of flora and the average level of nectar in the flowers.

Another interesting case is that of the lady-bird beetles (*Coccinellidae*) studied by Dobzhansky (1933). In many of these, polymorphism exists, several qualitatively distinct non-intergrading types being found within the species. Character-gradients of two sorts are found in the group, one concerning the frequency of the different qualitative types, the other affecting the quantitative development of a single character of a particular type or types. Humidity, and to a certain degree low temperature, appear to favour depth of pigmentation, though the correlation is by no means complete. Various species show well-marked pigmentation clines around centres of light and of dark forms.

This example is interesting as combining the two types of internal or intra-group clines—in quantitative characters and in polymorph ratio (p. 103).

A similar combination seems to exist in the gyrfalcon (*Falco rusticolus*). Its various forms may prove to be better represented by a single cline (involving an increase of size and in percentage of light-coloured birds with increasing N. latitude) than by the usual method of subspecific naming. Witherby (1938–41) distinguishes a very dark subspecies from Labrador, a moderately dark (typical) subspecies from the north of the western palearctic, a moderately light subspecies from Iceland, and a very pale subspecies from N. Greenland, as well as others from Siberia and Arctic Canada.

However, in some localities a certain number of contrasted types occur. Thus a minority of N. Greenland birds are indistinguishable from the typical Iceland form. In Iceland, there is a considerable range of variation, and a typical Iceland form and one similar to the pale Greenland type have been recorded in the same brood. The S. Greenland population is indistinguishable from that of Iceland. The "subspecies" from Siberia and Altai show great variation, and can only be separated on the basis of the relative abundance of the various types they contain.

Bird and Bird (1941) state that the very dark forms are in the great majority in Labrador, but that some occur in S.W. Greenland. Variation is at its lowest in N.E. Greenland, and they wish to restrict the N. Greenland subspecies to this area, while admitting that some birds from Arctic Canada are as pale. They lump all the birds from Labrador, Arctic Canada, and S. Greenland into one subspecies, in spite of the great local variation, and in spite of the identity in colour of the S. Greenland with the Iceland birds.

It would appear much more logical to include the whole population in a single cline; the relative lack of variation in the N.E. Greenland birds would then be due to their being close to the limit for pale colour.

Juveniles are always darker than adults, but those forms with lighter adults have lighter juveniles. The variation is therefore quite possibly genetically dependent, like those in buffaloes and cole tits (p. 218), on rate-genes affecting the rate of deposition of pigment.

Polymorph-(dimorph-)ratio clines have a special interest for the selectionist, since the continued existence of two or more sharply marked types within a population implies a selective balance between them (p. 97; and see Ford, 1940a). When a cline exists in the proportion between the two, the geographical conditions along it may give a clue to the selective factors involved.

A recent study of primroses (*Primula vulgaris*) by Crosby (1940) shows how the origin of a mutation with positive selective value may give rise to a temporary polymorph-ratio cline. Primulas normally show heterostyly with the two types, pin and thrum, approximately equal in frequency. In one area, however, large numbers of long homostyles were found. If, as seems probable, these are normally self-fertilized, their numbers will increase, and those of the other types decrease, thrum more so than pin. If the mutation arose in one centre, it would spread, and the ratios of the three types would change with distance from the centre and with time. The preliminary counts so far made are not conclusive, but do not contradict this hypothesis (see p. 313).

A remarkable cline in regard to sexual dimorphism, but affecting species instead of subspecies, is found in the flycatchers (*Pomaea*) in the Marquesas. The northernmost species, *P. iphis*, has pied black-and-white males and brown females; the central *P. mendozae* has black males and probably pied females; and the southernmost *P. whitneyi* is black in both sexes (Murphy, 1938).

Colman (1932) has made careful measurements on the shells of the periwinkle, *Littorina obtusata*. He finds great variability in size and form, but the populations from the two sides of the

Atlantic cannot be distinguished statistically. Here and there, distinct gradients occur. For instance, in passing up the New England coast a marked change in shape occurs along a portion of Maine, the shells becoming thinner, with taller spires. Biometric investigations of this sort on molluscs with a wide range should provide useful data linking ecology with systematics.

The application of the principle of geographical replacement to plants is revealing intergroup clines. Thus Rensch (1939c) finds a west to east increase in the divided condition of the leaves in a *Rassenkreis* of the pasque-flower, *Pulsatilla*.

We may next consider ecological clines (ecoclines). In general, as already pointed out, these will tend to be repeated, with variations in slope, form, and extent, in numerous regions of a distribution area. The increase of shell-thickness with aridity in land snails appears to be one such example (see instances in Rensch, 1932). There appear to be numerous examples of altitudinal clines, notably in size, in bird species: see Chapman and Griscom (1924) for wrens (*Troglodytes*), Danis (1937) for woodpeckers (*Picus*), Dementiev (1938) for various genera, and Mayr (1931–40, No. 41) for the honey-buzzard (*Henicopernis*).

Schmidt (1918) demonstrated a gradient in number of vertebrae in the sedentary fish *Zoarces viviparus* in various Norwegian fjords, the number decreasing with distance from the open sea. Vertebral number and other characters in fish appear often to show a broadly graded distribution (Regan, 1926; Hubbs, 1934).

In many plants, very short ecoclines may exist. Gregor's investigations on *Plantago maritima* (1938a, 1939) indicate that these are produced anew in each generation by selection from among a wide range of ecotypes present in the species—an important general conclusion. The differences involved may be considerable; thus scape-length runs from just above 20 cm. in waterlogged coastal mud types to nearly 50 cm. in those from maritime rock. In addition, large-scale geographical clines (which Gregor calls *topoclines*) exist for certain characters which do not show ecoclines, e.g. the ratio of scape-length to spike-length increases from west to east from western America (3.2) via eastern America and Iceland to western continental Europe (4.9).

Topoclines have been shown to exist in *Pinus* (Langlet, 1937) and *Iris* (Anderson, 1928), and will doubtless prove a common feature of plants as more attention is directed to the subject.

A case of abrupt steepening of a gradient is seen in the silver pheasant, *Gennaeus*. The areas of two well-marked forms, one with dark and the other with vermiculated plumage, are separated by a more sparsely populated region where no two individuals seem to be alike. Baker (1930, p. 295) puts this down to the rapid variation in geographical and climatic factors in the intermediate region. It is more probable, however, that these are two forms which have met after differentiating in separate regions (pp. 243 seq.): they are in any case so different that Baker places them in different species (*Gennaeus h. horsfieldii* and *G. lineatus oatesi*). See also Ghigi (1909), Beebe (1921), and p. 218. *Gennaeus*, as a form open to genetic analysis, merits intensive investigation.

Numerous other examples of clines of various types will be found in Robson and Richards (1936); but enough will have been said to demonstrate their widespread existence and their importance in many groups of organisms.

As Rensch points out, the various empirical rules concerning gradients enable us to prophesy with considerable accuracy what will be the appearance of subspecies from areas as yet uninvestigated.

Although some of these effects (pigmentation; altered proportion of extremities, etc.), may be induced experimentally as pure modifications, it appears certain that most of the differences seen in nature are determined genetically. As regards their biological meaning, while some of them, such as change in relative size of heart, of digestive organs, and of ear-size, appear to be, in whole or in part, directly adaptive, many must be presumed to be correlated with less obvious but more fundamental adaptive changes in metabolism and activity, such as those evidenced by the thyroid of *Peromyscus* subspecies (p. 188).

It is clear that, since humidity and temperature often vary in different ways, gradients in pigmentation will often run across each other. Doubtless many other character-gradients may run in different directions. A. H. Miller (1931) has demonstrated this independence of character-gradients for some characters of the shrikes (*Lanius*) that he studied, and so has Swarth (1920) for the fox-sparrow, *Passerella* (see pp. 182, 196, 217, 220).

It should be mentioned that geographical clines do not always occur. When a population is thus uniform over a large area, the uniformity may be correlated with uniformity in environmental conditions, e.g. in the wood-mouse *Peromyscus leucopus noveboracensis* (Dice, 1937).

Again, marked gradients sometimes exist for some characters, but not for others. Thus in South American wrens (*Troglodytes musculus*), Chapman and Griscom (1924) find a distinct increase of size with altitude (doubtless a temperature effect), but little correlation of colour with any environmental factor. This latter fact they put down to the supposedly very recent date of the extension of the species over the continent (cf. *Heodes* in North America: p. 217). If so, then selection for increased size in low temperatures must be more intense and therefore more rapid in its effects than selection, e.g. in humid areas,. for whatever characters produce changes of coloration as their correlates.

It should be mentioned that Reinig (1939) has criticized Rensch's views as to the adaptive origin of the clines connected with the Geographical Rules, and substitutes a theory according to which they are due to selective elimination of genes during postglacial migration from glacial "refuges". While this explanation may hold good for some forms, such as the red deer *Cervus elaphus*, or the swallowtail *Papilio machaon*, it would seem certainly not to be of general application. His views, however, are another reminder that clines are of common occurrence, and originate in numerous distinct ways.

The general existence of character-gradients within species and groups of related species is a fact of major biological importance which has been fully established only within the last few decades. As detailed work proceeds, and is backed by genetical and ecological study, we may prophesy that the mapping of character-gradients will provide an important method of taxonomic analysis, complementary to that afforded by the characterizing of named subspecies. It should, for instance, be possible to show on a map the lines of maximum change for different characters.

If the extreme values for different populations of the species are designated o and 100, the plotting of intermediate values (pheno-contours or *isophenes* (p. 104) will give a contour map of the character-change.

Such mapping will obviously permit of important studies in comparative systematics—the determination of regularities and differences in the correlation of character-gradients with environmental gradients, the tendency for subspecific boundaries to occur in certain regions (Reinig, 1938; Grinnell, 1928), the relative variability of different species, and so forth. The specification of inter-group clines will permit biologists to obtain a much clearer picture of the inter-relationships of the subspecies of a polytypic species, especially when (as will probably prove to be the rule) clines for different characters run in different directions.

In most cases, clines should be employed as a terminology which is purely subsidiary to that of the trinomial naming of genera, species, and subspecies. The description of clines can provide a clarification of the taxonomic picture, as well as greater detail of analysis, but must follow and supplement the description of species and subspecies, not in any way replace it. Occasionally, however, clines must be regarded as taxonomic categories in their own right, to be employed as part of the nomenclature, in place of subspecies. This will be so when a well-marked gradation of characters extends without sharp break over a considerable area, as in the nuthatches mentioned on p. 219. Løppenthin, it is true, assigns subspecific names to arbitrary stages in the cline, but this would appear to be quite indefensible.

Subspecies, by definition, should mean something of the same general nature as species—i.e. unique groups, with definite characters shared by the whole population, and definite areas of distribution; the distribution may be either geographical or ecological. Clines, on the other hand, may be repeated a number of times; and even when they have a definite single area of distribution, by definition show a gradation, not a uniformity, of characters. It is suggested (Huxley, 1939a) that when a cline has a large single distribution area, and thus constitutes an infra-specific category equivalent to a subspecies, it should be denoted

by a hyphenated Latin name, preceded by the abbreviation *cl.*
It is further suggested that where doubt exists as to whether a
series of forms represents a single internal cline or a set of subspecies which can be arranged in an intergroup cline, they should
be provisionally named as clines. Thus in the Burmese squirrels
(*Callosciurus sladeni*) referred to on p. 219, the northern series
of forms, instead of being divided into four separate subspecies
C. s. shortridgei, fryanus, careyi, and *harringtonii,* as is done by
Thomas and Wroughton (on the basis of collections from six
stations only, one of which yielded types intermediate between
two of the "subspecies"!), should, pending further investigation,
be styled *C. s. cl*. *shortridgei-harringtonii.*

The cline concept can also be employed in a formal sense, to
express the gradation of forms produced by species-hybridization,
even when no geographical gradation exists. Such clines have
been called hybrid clines or *nothoclines* by Melville (1939), and
have been used by him in his analysis of the bewildering variety
of forms found in the elms (*Ulmus*).

The giving of a name to a particular group inevitably tends
to endow it with greater fixity and uniformity than may be
warranted; and if one infra-specific group be just sufficiently
distinct to merit subspecific naming, another not, the named
group will tend to be thought of as having a greater "reality".
The employment of clines in taxonomic description will tend to
correct this, by stressing gradational changes and the orderly
inter-connexions of groups, and will help towards providing a
truer and fuller picture of organic diversity.

5. SPATIAL AND ECOLOGICAL FACTORS IN GEOGRAPHICAL DIVERGENCE

We may now consider in more detail the various methods by
which geographical isolation may operate. It is clear that, whenever the areas inhabited by different geographical groups differ
either in their physical or their biological environment, then
adaptive changes may, and usually will, occur, superposing some
degree of ecological divergence on what we may call the pure

geographical, due to non-adaptive changes. In order to discuss these adaptive processes adequately we must anticipate some of the later conclusions and point out that ecological divergence may be of three main types. There is first, adaptation to the broad physical features of a region, including climate: this we may call *ecoclimatic*. Secondly, there is adaptation to the detailed features of a particular type of habitat within a region, which may be called *ecotopic*. And in the third place there is *ecobiotic* adaptation, to a particular mode of life within a habitat.

In ecological divergence, adaptive differentiation is primary, whereas in geographical divergence, spatial separation is primary. Naturally, there are many borderline cases; but the distinction is often a real one. Ecological divergence may be superposed upon geographical, e.g. in cottons of the genus *Gossypium* (Silow, 1941).

In this section we shall confine ourselves to geographical divergence, where the primary factor permitting or promoting partial or complete speciation is the spatial separation of the groups concerned. This, however, may operate in various ways. (1) In the first place, geographical changes may introduce a discontinuity into a previously continuous range. This will occur when subsidence isolates groups of a land form on islands; when elevation separates groups of a marine form on two sides of an isthmus; when a change of climate isolates groups on mountain-tops; when ecological conditions cause a discontinuity of a necessary food-plant; or when an anadromous fish species becomes land-locked in several separate lakes.

Such barriers are non-biological accidents superposed on the biological continuum. They may be ecologically neutral, when the environment is similar on both sides of the barrier. If, however, it differs on the two sides, the barrier will be ecologically significant, and, by preventing gene-flow, will facilitate greater divergence than would otherwise have occurred.

The discontinuity may erect a complete barrier to the inter-breeding of the two groups, as with the case of the isthmus or the lakes; or the barrier may be partial, as with a bird population on an island close to the mainland. Divergence in small isolated populations may depend solely or mainly on the isolation, and be due to the "accidental" incorporation of non-adaptive mutations and new chance recombinations—the Sewall Wright effect of "drift".

(2) A similar state of affairs may arise when sharp geographical barriers, such as rivers or mountain ridges, exist *ab initio* in the path of a species which is extending its range. The species may be able to surmount the barriers by migration, but the migration is of small extent: thus the resultant groups remain essentially isolated, as with *Partula* (p. 232).

(3) A somewhat different picture is afforded by wide-ranging species whose range is not cut up by sharp physical discontinuities. In such cases, the whole can form a single interbreeding group without any marked barriers, even though mere distance prevents the intermingling of the remoter portions of the population. Divergence may then occur, as with *Peromyscus*, in relation to the broad features of various regions—humidity, temperature, colour of background, etc. Essentially adaptive subspecies will be produced, but further divergence into full species is prevented by interbreeding at the margins of the subspecific areas. The subspecies may of course differ also for accidental "isolational" reasons.

Such subspecies will remain dependent, as parts of a single evolving *Rassenkreis*. They have reached the equilibrium-point of partial biological discontinuity, which is maintained thanks to the establishment of harmoniously-stabilized gene-complexes in the subspecific populations, with consequent restriction of interbreeding to narrow zones (p. 210). This condition, as pointed out by Sewall Wright (1940), is the most favourable for the adaptive evolution and plasticity of the group as a whole.

This type of divergence may readily be combined with the types outlined under (1) or (2) above, and (5) below. In such cases, full species may arise, and divergence proceed further.

(4) When a species has been widespread and becomes restricted, or when it is very local, interbreeding between local groups becomes reduced, and accidental divergence, fostered by isolation and by reduction of numbers, can play a greater part.

(5) When ecologically very distinct regions within a larger area are colonized, distinct subspecies or species may be formed in each such area. We may think of woodland as against open country, upland as against lowland, desert as against well-watered country, sea-coast as against inland. Groups diverging in this way will in general be spatially separated, but the process differs from ordinary geographical subspeciation, as under (3) above, in certain important ways. In the first place, such ecological regions may each be markedly discontinuous (e.g. regions over a certain height), whereas those inhabited by typical geographical sub-species are normally each well-defined as a continuous single area. Secondly, the principle of geographical replacement may break down, distinct groups within a region being kept apart by ecological preferences (pp. 270 seq.). Thirdly, the ecological adaptation is here on the whole primary, the spatial separation secondary. These facts may have a further consequence, namely that there may be relatively more zones where the two groups may come into contact, though there will be sharper adaptive distinctions between them. Then, as we shall see, selection will promote barriers to interbreeding, so that full speciation is more likely to result.

This type of divergence thus forms the transition to ecological divergence, and is on the whole on the ecological side of the dividing line. We shall accordingly treat of it in a later section.

(6) When the biological environment of an area inhabited by a group is very different from that of other areas inhabited by related groups, the type of divergence which results from geographical isolation may be quite distinct. On oceanic islands, for instance, a very restricted fauna and flora is usually found, so that selection will act in quite a different way from the original habitat of the species on the mainland (pp. 324 seq.). The same may apply to large and well-isolated lakes.

In such cases the struggle for existence will in general be less intense, both as regards competitors and as regards enemies. This will allow greater play both to accidental divergence and to ecobiotic differentiation of a rather special sort (p. 325). In addition, the environmental factors will often be so different that ecoclimatic and ecotopic divergence also will be promoted above the ordinary.

(7) The nature of the group that is spatially isolated may also play a part in determining the type and extent of divergence, in addition to the nature of the isolation and the nature of the physical and biological environment in which it is isolated. For instance, migratory forms are less likely to show geographical divergence than sedentary ones (p. 239).

(8) Next, there are the effects of migration. Sometimes we have the simple expansion or contraction of the distributional area of a group. A particularly interesting process is that of the migrations of two or more distinct groups subsequent to their divergence. A process that is in a sense the converse of (1) occurs when geographical change, such as elevation or change of climate, permits subspecies or species that were differentiated in complete isolation to meet once more (p. 243). The result will be quite different according to whether they are or are not still capable of breeding together. Of rather a different nature are the alterations in range of subspecies that have always been in contact at the margins of their areas, as a result of changing population-pressure (p. 209).

(9) Finally, we have numerous range-changes due to human interference, such as introductions, deliberate or accidental, of alien types. It is probably fair to say that most biologists are unaware of the number and extent of such range-changes now actually in progress.

We may now consider these general points in the light of actual examples. Cases where divergence appears to be largely non-adaptive, due either to the accidental after-effects of isolation, or to the equally accidental initial process of colonization by a non-representative sample, are seen in various island forms, in the differentiation of different races of char in European lakes (p. 177), and in the divergence of the flora of the high mountains of East Africa. In this last case, it appears that during the pluvial period the present high mountain forms occurred at much lower levels and accordingly had a continuous distribution: with increased aridity, they were pushed up the mountain-sides into isolation. As a result the giant senecios, lobelias, tree-heaths and other plants usually differ specifically or subspecifically from one mountain to another. The same occurs with birds in South America, two well-marked subspecies of the mountain humming-bird *Oreotrochilus chimborazi* being found on Chimborazo on the one hand and Cotopaxi and neighbouring mountains on the other. The ranges of the two forms are separated by about sixty miles. A rare intermediate form, however, appears to exist on a ridge midway between the two: if so, this provides a beautiful example of partial isolation (Chapman, 1926, p. 301). In these cases, differentiation, whether accidental or adaptive, appears to have occurred wholly or mainly subsequent to isolation, not by initial sampling.

A similar phenomenon, here apparently altogether due to non-adaptive subsequent differentiation (the Sewall Wright effect), was described by Kammerer (1926) for lizards on isolated islands in the Adriatic. In one case, the two halves of one island are biologically isolated through the isthmus being exposed to salt spray: and the lizards on the two halves are of a different colour. A well-known case is that of the special variety of lizard found on the isolated rocks known as the Faraglioni close to Capri. We have referred (p. 200) to the quantitative evaluation of geographical differentiation in insular lizards recently undertaken by Kramer and Mertens (1938a).

The most remarkable cases, however, are those of various land-snails in the Pacific, as described by J. T. Gulick (e.g. 1905), Pilsbry (1912–14), and Crampton (1916, 1925, 1932). We may take *Partula* on the Society Islands as an example. The interior parts of the islands are mountainous, cut up into deep wooded valleys separated by knife-edge ridges. Snails can and do migrate from one valley to the next, but this is an occasional phenomenon only, since they are adapted to warm, moist conditions, and are normally not found either in the dry coastal strip, the cold peaks, or the cold dry ridges between valleys. Thus the populations of different valleys are virtually isolated in a genetical sense, except for rare and more or less accidental migration.

Numerous species of *Partula* are distinguished, with different degrees of intra-specific variation. The most complex species described is *P. otaheitana*, with eight subspecies and their varieties of primary, secondary, and tertiary degree. These varieties include dextral and sinistral types, giant and dwarf types, and numerous types differing in colour and form of shell.

The different characters and varieties occur in different proportions in different valleys, some often being wholly absent in particular areas. In certain cases the course of migration can be deduced. For instance the population of Fantaua Valley shows a remarkable degree of variation, and appears to have been the source for the colonization of a number of other neighbouring valleys: for the populations of all of these show a reduction in the number of "unit-characters" as against the Fantaua assemblage, but each possesses a different combination of these characters. Thus local reduction of variability by colonizing through small random non-representative samples seems here to have been an important method of increasing geographical diversity. On the other hand, other evidence points strongly to some of the diversity being due to the "accidental" incorporation of new mutations or recombinations, in the populations subsequent to their isolation.

An important feature of Crampton's work is that he was able to demonstrate the process of change in operation (Crampton, 1925). He himself had been collecting since 1908, and a detailed record had been made by Garrett from 1861 to 1888. During this period, several changes have occurred. Extension or alterations of range have been not infrequent. Colour-types and giant and dwarf forms unrecorded by Garrett have become well-established in certain valleys. Forms showing reversal of spiral have become established in colonies recorded as exclusively dextral or sinistral in the nineteenth century.

The largest change occurred with another species, *P. clara*. Garrett described this as "very rare", and restricted to a small southern area of Tahiti. By 1909 it had covered almost four-fifths of the island, and both in its old and its new areas showed a much greater degree of variation in size, shape, and colour.

Similar phenomena were found with *P. suturalis* in Moorea

Island. Here we have a curious fact. While the species in Garrett's time was almost exclusively dextral, and remains so to-day in its original area, it becomes progressively more sinistral in the newly-colonized areas. (The physiological peculiarities of sinistrals (p. 316) may favour their spread in certain conditions.) Again, *P. mirabilis*, so rare in Garrett's time as to have escaped detection by him, now covers quite a wide area, and exhibits an extremely high degree of general and local variation. Comparison of Crampton's earlier and later data show that the process of spread and differentiation deduced for the period before 1907–9 had been continued in the further sixteen to eighteen years.

Very similar results have been found by J. T. Gulick (1905; and see Pilsbry, 1912–14, and Welch, 1938) with the Achatinellid land-snails from the Hawaiian Islands. It appears that a similar, though not quite so excessive, differentiation has occurred among the amphibia of the mountainous islands of the Antilles (see Barbour and Shreve, 1937). In other parts of the world, where these peculiar conditions favouring isolation are not operative, the geographical differentiation of land-snails proceeds along more normal lines (see, e.g., Rensch, 1933b).

An interesting case from mammals is that of the African cob-antelopes (*Kobus*) studied by Hamilton (1919). On the east bank of the Nile there is a gap between two distinct forms (well-marked subspecies), while on the west bank the two grade into each other both geographically and in appearance. The reason for the greater isolation on the east is not clear.

The ecological and geographical factors in the distribution and differentiation of birds are interestingly discussed by Palmgren (1938).

By far the commonest method of geographical divergence and probably of divergence in general, is that which we may call eco-geographical, in which the primary fact of spatial separation of groups is combined with adaptation to the peculiarities of the areas in which they find themselves.*

We have already given examples of this from a mammal

* Rensch (1933a), indeed, considers this the only important method of speciation, but he fails to deal with genetic isolation, and unduly neglects ecological divergence or includes certain aspects of it under the geographical head.

(*Peromyscus*) and a moth (*Lymantria*). What is probably another example comes from amphibia. Witschi (1930) has studied sex-differentiation in the common frog of Europe. In this animal, different geographical races have different methods of gonad development. In the differentiated races, sex-differentiation is clear-cut from the outset. In the undifferentiated races, all individuals develop as females until metamorphosis, after which 50 per cent become transformed into males. In the semi-differentiated races all individuals start as females, but the transformation of the genetic males to phenotypic maleness occurs earlier.

A study of types from many localities brought out the fact that the undifferentiated races are confined to the regions of Central and Western Europe, which were not glaciated in the Ice Age, while the differentiated types are found both in the north and in Alpine valleys, with the semi-differentiated in an intermediate zone. The divergence of the various races must then have taken place since the end of the Ice Age. In addition, the races show obviously adaptive difference in habits. On arriving at a pool or being brought into tanks in the laboratory, the differentiated or short-summer races lay eggs immediately, while the undifferentiated may not lay for one or two weeks. The time-relations of spermatogenesis are also adaptive. Witschi believes the differences in sex-differentiation to be determined in some orthogenetic fashion, but they are probably correlates of fundamental adaptive processes such as rate of metabolism, promptness of egg-laying, etc. Local colour-varieties occur, but have no relation to type of sex-development. The physiological differentiation of the beetle *Carabus nemoralis* has already been mentioned (p. 206).

Witschi's case is similar in its general evolutionary significance to that of the geographical adaptation to different temperature-conditions found in *Drosophila funebris* (p. 191). It is probable that further research devoted to this point will reveal numerous other cases of such climatic adaptation in morphologically invisible but biologically important characteristics. Porter (1941) has demonstrated different egg-cytoplasm effects on early development in two geographic races of frogs. It will be interesting to discover whether such differentiation normally shows the phenomenon of partial discontinuity with relative uniformity of character over considerable areas (p. 209).

Baily (1939) has exhaustively analysed the physiological peculiarities of two morphologically indistinguishable local populations of the water-snail *Limnaea columella*, and finds that they differ quite considerably in inherent mortality and longevity, fecundity, and rate of growth. One very curious fact is that, under the optimum conditions provided by laboratory culture, one type only was able to grow regularly into a large form of peculiar shape, which conchologists dignify as a separate variety: here we have a good example of inherent difference in developmental potentiality. Further research will be needed to show whether such physiological differentiation is sporadic and local, or if well-marked types (physiological subspecies) extend over large regions.

A case where isolation has enforced new habits, but not as yet new genetic adaptation, is that of the situtunga antelope (*Tragelaphus spekii*) on Nkosi island in the Sese archipelago of Lake Victoria (Carpenter, 1925). This species is normally an inhabitant of papyrus swamps; but there are no swamps on Nkosi, so the buck on this island have become virtually bush-buck in habits. Their hoofs are short, not elongated as is normal, but this is presumably a mere modificational difference in wear; they do not bark in the usual way, and are exceedingly tame. If the Nkosi situtunga should eventually become a genetically-adapted subspecies, we should have an example of organic selection (p. 304) following on isolation. Somewhat similarly, the feral camels of southern Spain, released over a century ago, have become restricted to marsh life, and have not colonized neighbouring sandy areas (A. Chapman and Buck, 1893).

An excellent example from birds is the widespread North American shrike, *Lanius ludovicianus*, the distribution and ecology of which has been thoroughly investigated by A. H. Miller (1931). Of this species he describes eleven subspecies, distinguished by differences in colour, size, proportions, and habits; apart from correlation of colour with climate (see above, p. 213) he finds certain features which appear to be definitely adaptive. Certain subspecies are migratory, while the others are not; the former are more efficient fliers, as measured by a higher ratio of wing-length to tail-length (differences of 4 to 5 per cent). One subspecies is migratory in the northern part of its range, resident in the southern: the same type of difference is shown here, though as would be expected the differences are much less (about 1·5 per cent in the ratio).

Then some subspecies inhabit more wooded country, others more open and more arid country. The latter must fly longer distances from perch to perch and in pursuit of prey (a deduction checked in two subspecies by field observation). In correlation with this they have greater manœuvring capacity, as evidenced by greater length of both wings and tail relative to total weight (e.g. in the best worked-out case about 3 per cent longer wings and tail with a 6 per cent lighter weight). The island races show slightly reduced wings and tail, and larger feet: this is in accord with the character of island birds and insects in general, which in extreme cases are wingless. An interesting point is that the size of the breeding territory varies, sometimes markedly, in different subspecies, in relation to habitat and food supply: it would be interesting to ascertain if this is a genetic trait.

In this species Miller finds that isolation *per se* has little effect compared with spatial restriction to ecologically different areas: this is well illustrated by one of the island subspecies.

In general, he concludes that there are three factors governing the magnitude of the subspecific differences found: first, and most important, the degree of difference in the environment; secondly, the effectiveness of isolation against interbreeding at the margins of the area; and thirdly, the migratory or non-migratory nature of the group and of neighbouring groups. Sewall Wright's work has made it clear that the size of an area also has an influence, small size of area implying smaller population and therefore greater scope for accidental variation. We have noted this effect at work in mouse-deer (p. 183) and in lizards (p. 200). Stresemann (verbal communication) has given me another example of this. Java, Sumatra, and their outlying small islands were all isolated from the mainland and from each other at approximately the same time in the quite recent geological past. While numerous distinct bird subspecies exist on the small islands, the corresponding forms of the large islands show no or much less divergence from the mainland types. Here the accidental type of change must be decisive, since mere size of area should not inhibit adaptive change.

An important problem is raised by the empirical fact that some species or genera show greater geographical variation than others. That exhibited by *Lanius ludovicianus*, for instance, is characterized by Miller as "only moderate". Miller and McCabe (1935) have studied this question in the Lincoln sparrow (*Passerella lincolnii*), which shows much less geographical differentiation than its close relative the song-sparrow (*P. melodia*) and the fox-sparrow (*P. iliaca*). It has only three subspecies as against over fifteen in the same area for each of the other species.

Miller and McCabe reach the interesting conclusion, which might have been deduced by the selectionist on theoretical grounds, that this is not due to a lack of inherent variability in the more uniform species. Its actual variability is in point of fact quite high; but the variations have not been sifted out into markedly different combinations by selection. Miller and McCabe ascribe the difference chiefly to a difference in what must be called temperament, *P. lincolnii* tending to remain confined to a narrow ecological niche, while the other two species are "adventurous" in relation to range and habitat expansion; in addition, *P. lincolnii* is more migratory.

In general, ducks show comparatively little subspeciation. This is correlated with a high "activity-range", as Timoféeff-Ressovsky (1940) styles the area within which individuals of a single generation may move. For instance, common teal (*Nettion crecca*) bred in England were recovered next year as far west as Iceland, as far east as the Urals (Timoféeff-Ressovsky, l.c., p. 112). This species has only two subspecies, one holarctic, the other nearctic. The name "abmigration" has been given by A. L. Thomson (1923) to describe northward departure in spring, for a new summer area, on the part of birds which have made no corresponding southward journey in the previous autumn. Abmigration is found in other ducks besides the teal, such as mallard (*Anas platyrhyncha*), tufted duck (*Nyroca fuligula*), and shelduck (*Tadorna tadorna*). A high activity-range must clearly be, in part, a corollary of this habit of abmigration.

Rensch (1933*a*) has approached the problem on broader lines than Miller and McCabe. Taking Hartert's standard work on palaearctic birds (1903–22) as source, he has tabulated the ratio of monotypic to polytypic species (i.e. those without and with geographical subspeciation), and also the number of subspecies

Type of animal	Per cent monotypic of total no. of species	Number of subspecies per polytypic species*
1. Large birds	54·5	1·6
2. Small birds, migratory ..	39·9	3·2
3. Small birds, non-migratory ..	29·6	7·2
4. Bats	82·5	2·6
5. Insectivores	71·9	3·5

* The number of subspecies refers to the palaearctic area only. Some of the polytypic species are polytypic when their whole range is considered, but have only one subspecies within the palaearctic.

per polytypic species, in groups which differ in habit. He took (1) large birds, with consequently a greater mobility, and in general also a smaller population-size per given area (five families —herons, storks, ibises, bustards, and cranes—with forty-four species); (2) migratory small birds (nine families, including shrikes, warblers, thrushes, swallows, flycatchers, and wagtails, with 288 species); and (3) non-migratory small birds (six families

—crows, tree-creepers, nuthatches, tits, wrens, and woodpeckers —with 115 species). He applied the same method to flying *versus* related non-flying mammals (bats and insectivores, from G. S. Miller (1912, 1924). The results are striking (p. 239). Schaefer (1935) shows that the distribution areas of races are much smaller in small mammals than in birds. (See also p. 176.)

Similarly Stonor (1938) has shown that in Birds of Paradise, the excessive development of display plumes has resulted in an unusually high degree of geographical speciation, by restricting

FREQUENCY OF DIFFERENT TYPES OF SPECIES IN HABITATS AFFORDING DIFFERENT TYPES OF RANGE. (AFTER MAYR, 1940)

Type of Species	Specific Ranges		
	Almost all continuous (Manchuria: 107 species)	Both continuous and discontinuous (New Guinea: 290 species)	All discontinuous (Solomon Islands: 50 species)
	%	%	%
(1) Monotypic species with restricted range	1·9 ⎫	11·7 ⎫	18·0 ⎫
(2) Monotypic species with wide range	14·0 ⎬ 15·9	7·2 ⎬ 18·9	2·0 ⎬ 20·0
(3a) Polytypic species with feebly differentiated sub-species	55·1 ⎫	40·7 ⎫	22·0 ⎫
(3b) Polytypic species with markedly differentiated subspecies	28·0 ⎬ 83·0	29·0 ⎬ 69·7	24·0 ⎬ 46·0
(4) Superspecies	1·0	11·4	34·0

the power of flight and rendering the birds more sedentary. On the other hand, the very mobile ducks (*Anatidae*), as we have just seen (p. 238), with few exceptions show no subspeciation, The same is true for other active birds such as snipe (*Gallinago*, etc.) and for the very large and mobile whalebone whales (Discovery Committee, 1937). Again, degree of subspeciation is inversely correlated with powers of dispersal in the rabbits (Orr, 1940).

Mayr (1940) has made similar tabulations, but in this case in relation, not to peculiarities of mode of life, but to the geographical features of the environment (see Table, above).

In the continental area of Manchuria, where almost all specific ranges are continuous, polytypic species are in the great majority. The internal differentiation of subspecies, however, is not carried very far, doubtless because of the number of intergrading as opposed to isolated subspecies, so that species with markedly differentiated subspecies are only half as numerous as those with slight subspecific differentiation, and superspecies are very rarely produced. Of monotypic species, those with restricted range are very rare.

On the other hand, where an old tropical archipelago provides the extreme of geographical discontinuity, as in the Solomon Islands, the category of superspecies is the most abundant, and monotypic species are not only more abundant than in Manchuria, but it is those with extended ranges which now are rare. The promotion of differentiation through isolation is shown not only by the frequency of superspecies (pp. 179 n., 407), but by polytypic species more often showing marked than slight subspecific differentiation. Once a superspecies has differentiated into an *Artenkreis* (p. 179), its constituent forms will come to overlap, and will be listed in one or other of the stages of a tabulation such as Mayr's.

New Guinea, where islands and mountains introduce a considerable degree of range-discontinuity, provides an intermediate picture. The only exception is the slight excess of markedly polytypic species over that seen in Manchuria: however, in the *ratio* between markedly and feebly differentiated polytypic species, New Guinea preserves its intermediacy.

Such work is an important contribution to the as yet embryonic science of Comparative Systematics, which is undoubtedly destined to yield results of the greatest importance for general biology.

The same type of conclusion, though not expressed in numerical terms, has been arrived at for the fish of American rivers (Thompson, 1931). Large, strongly-swimming and actively migratory species of fish show great uniformity of character. Smaller fish show much greater diversity when populations from different localities are compared, and the differences are greater when such species are restricted to small head-water streams than when they occur in streams of all sizes. The differentiation is not graded along the course of the rivers, but is random, presumably a result of the Sewall Wright "drift" effect.

Although, as we have said, the most frequent mode of geographical differentiation is broadly adaptive, there are many cases in which apparently non-adaptive differentiation has occurred, either predominantly or superposed on a general adaptive divergence, or as a correlate of invisible physiological adaptation.

The diversification of the Hawaiian land-snails and probably that of the Galapagos ground-finches appears to be largely "accidental" in the biological sense. The colour polymorphism of various *Peromyscus* races (p. 189) shows that colour in these forms is not always of direct selective value. The markings of the local species (or subspecies) *Buarremon inornatus* (p. 199) appear to be non-adaptive, and in any case show no intergradation with the normal type.

There are quite a number of cases in which subspecies of a *Rassenkreis*, or geographical species of an *Artenkreis*, show sharply contrasted colour-distinctions which are apparently non-adaptive and mutational. For instance, the northern and southern Indian robins (*Thamnobia*), which do not appear to interbreed in their zone of overlap, are sharply distinguished by the colour (brown *versus* black) of the back of the males (Dewar and Finn, 1909, p. 378). Chapman (1927) and Stresemann (1923-6) give other examples. Spatial isolation, we may say, permits a varying degree of accidental divergence to be superposed on the complex geographical grid of broadly adaptive character-gradients.

A number of different effects are all illustrated by the fauna of the Galapagos (Swarth, 1931, 1934; Lowe, 1936). Here, the mocking-birds (*Mimidae*) and ground-finches (*Geospizidae*) illustrate the extreme of mere isolational divergence, while in the latter the release from competition has permitted what can only be described as an abnormal variability and multiplicity of forms (p. 326). The land-tortoises also illustrate isolational divergence, while their gigantism is ecological, an evolutionary response to island life and its absence of predators and competitors, as is the flightlessness of the Galapagos cormorant and the genetic tameness of almost all the endemic birds. The flightlessness of so many insect inhabitants of oceanic islands is similarly an example of ecological differentiation, after divergence was made possible in the first instance by isolation; but the type of differentiation is here more directly in relation to the physical than to the biological environment, winglessness in insects constituting an adaptation to prevent being blown out to sea.

Thus while geographical divergence always depends for its initiation on spatial isolation, it may subsequently be linked in varying degrees with ecological divergence of an adaptive nature, and also, in small populations, with non-adaptive divergence due to the genetic accident of "drift".

6. RANGE-CHANGES SUBSEQUENT TO GEOGRAPHICAL DIFFERENTIATION

As geographical changes may isolate groups and thus permit them to diverge, so, after a certain degree of divergence, further geographical changes may permit the differentiated groups to meet again. (We are using the term geographical in the broadest sense, to denote climatic changes as well as elevation and subsidence or physiographic alterations.)

This phenomenon appears to have had very widespread effects upon existing forms, as we should expect from the rapid changes of climate and of sea-level that have occurred since the beginning of the Pleistocene, and still more those which have taken place since the end of the last glacial period, some 20,000 years ago. Some of its results are at first sight very surprising. In what follows, we shall consider not only eco-geographical divergents, but also those produced in relation to regional ecological (ecoclimatic) differentiation, since the effects of subsequent migration are essentially similar in both.

In the first place, range-changes may bring together end-members of a chain of subspecies. A striking example of this, cited by Rensch (1928, 1933a), concerns the great tit (*Parus major*). There are three main groups of subspecies of this large *Rassenkreis*, extending from west to east across the Old World —the *major* group in Europe and Western Asia, the *bokharensis* group from Persia to Malaya, and the *minor* group from China to Japan: each is well characterized, but the central *bokharensis* type intergrades with both its neighbours along broad marginal zones at either end of its range.

However, the western or *major* group also extends far to the eastwards, along a strip north of the areas of the other two groups and quite separated from the *bokharensis* group by desert and mountain regions, and finally overlaps with the area of the *minor* group near its northern boundary in the Amur region. This eastward extension doubtless is secondary and has only become possible through the amelioration of climate since the end of the last Ice Age. However, where the *major* and *minor* groups meet, they do *not* interbreed, but live side by side as perfectly distinct "species". Nothing could better illustrate the relativity of the terms species and subspecies. Rensch also points out that the end forms of a chain of subspecies may be much less alike than good species living side by side.

Again, *Larus argentatus* (Stegmann, 1934; Schweppenburg, 1938) forms a circumpolar chain of subspecies. But the herring-gull (*L. argentatus sensu stricto*) now lives in W. Europe as a "good" species side by side with the lesser black-backed gull ("*L. fuscus*") though occasionally interbreeding. The two differ markedly in temperament as well as appearance (Richter, 1938).

An equally good case is that of the buck-eye butterfly of America, *Junonia lavinia* (Forbes, 1928, 1931). This species shows marked geographical subspeciation. There are three main groups of forms—North American, Central American (including a northern strip of South America), and South American. These intergrade at their boundaries. However, the island of Cuba is inhabited by two types between which intergradation does not occur, and which do not appear to interbreed. Among several other distinctions, these differ in the presence or absence of a red semicircle round the upper "eye-spot" of the hind-wing, a character diagnostic of all the North American group of forms.

Apparently the island has been colonized from the north by the North American group, and from the south by the Central American group (by two subspecies, which do intergrade with each other on Cuba). Thus members of the two groups remain as separate species in Cuba, while in northern Mexico they interbreed. Here the distribution is in the form of a chain bent round into a circle: in the centre of the chain the two types intergrade, but the two ends have differentiated far enough to become biologically discontinuous. Other similar examples are given by Rensch (1929). Similarly the warbler "species" *Phylloscopus plumbeitarsus* and *P. viridanus* are the overlapping but non-interbreeding end-forms of an intergrading chain (Ticehurst, 1938).

These examples also illuminate numerous cases from Central Europe, which on first inspection appear very puzzling, where extremely similar species live side by side in the same area. The most striking case is that of the two species of tree-creeper, *Certhia familiaris* and *C. brachydactyla*. The latter has a longer beak, a shorter but more bent hind claw, and is rather darker. There are also differences in the colour of the eggs. The two forms are so alike that their distinctness was for long disputed. However, they appear to behave definitely as two separate species, and not to interbreed, in spite of much individual variation (Hartert, 1903–35). *C. brachydactyla* appears to be more plastic, judging from the degree of subspeciation.

C. familiaris (which alone is found in Britain) is a more northern and mountain form, while *C. brachydactyla* has a more southerly distribution; but the two overlap over a large part of their range. The more northerly form alone exists in North America. This occurs also with the marsh and willow tits (p. 270), and it may prove that these too owe their separate differentiation and later overlap to the same causes (see below, p. 246), though their overlap region is more extensive.

It is of interest that elsewhere one of the two species of tree-creepers just mentioned shows an incipient stage of the same phenomenon. Dementiev (1938) mentions that *Certhia familiaris* in Persia and neighbouring areas exists as a well marked subspecies, *C. f. persica*, while to the north the type subspecies is found. In the region of the Caucasus, however, the two sub-species have re-met, presumably after some degree of glacial isolation, with consequent intercrossing and great variability.

Similarly, we have the true nightingale (*Luscinia megarhyncha*) and the northern nightingale or sprosser (*L. luscinia*). Although these will cross if kept together in captivity, they remain perfectly distinct in the region between the Vistula and the Oder where they overlap. The yellow-bellied and red-bellied species of the fire-bellied toad *Bombina* (*Bombinator*) behave in a similar way, and so do the two closely-allied land-snails, *Clausilia dubia* and *C. bidentata*.

The explanation of all such cases appears to be simple. In the last Ice Age the extensions of the northern ice-sheet of the Alpine glaciers isolated many species into a western or southern and an eastern or north-eastern group. The exact type of separation would have been different for different species. This permitted eco-geographical divergence in adaptation to a mild or oceanic and a severe or continental climate respectively. Divergence pro-ceeded so far that when later the ice receded and the two forms were able to extend their range so as to meet, they did not breed together. Doubtless this failure to cross depends mainly on psychological barriers; the two species of tree-creeper and of nightingale have distinctive notes. Further, the two nightingales will mate if kept together in captivity: none the less, they do not in actual fact mate in nature and must therefore be regarded as "good" though very closely-related species (see also p. 254).

Probably the common and mountain hare (*Lepus europaeus* and *L. timidus*) differentiated in a similar way after glacial isolation and were afterwards able to colonize the same areas. In this case, however, the two species are separated ecologically, even where they overlap geographically, the mountain hare, as its name implies, being an upland animal as contrasted with the lowland common hare. A fact which throws an interesting light on regional restrictions of an ecological nature is that in Ireland, which was isolated as an island before the common hare could reach it, the mountain hare is found in the lowlands as well as the uplands. Habitat may thus be as much a matter of competition as of close physiological adaptation. However, the Irish form has differentiated into a distinct subspecies, which may perhaps have been adapted to take advantage of the habitat left open by the absence of its competitor.

The past differentiation and present distribution of the very distinct northern and southern forms of the water-beetles *Deronectes* and *Gyrinus* (see Omer-Cooper, 1931) appears to be due to the same cause. These both occur separate in certain parts of their ranges, but intergrade in central Britain. It is interesting that on the continent the two types of *Gyrinus* occur together without intergradation, as if differentiation had here proceeded further, to full speciation.

Other interesting examples come from monkeys of the African rain-forest. According to Schwarz (1928, 1929), groups were here isolated by the large inland lake that previously filled the Congo basin. When this disappeared, they were able to meet after previous differentiation. One small area of overlap occurs between two markedly distinct types of Mona monkeys in the Cameroons, and two similar overlap areas, one of moderate and one of large size, between two well-differentiated types of Colobus monkey, each with several subspecies, in the Lower Congo and in the forest region between Ruwenzori and the Congo river. Schwarz puts all the Mona monkeys into the one species *Cercopithecus mona*, and all the forms of Colobus into one species, *Colobus polykomas*; but since no intermediates or hybrids have been found in these areas of overlap, it seems clear that we should consider the differentiation to be of specific rank in both cases. It is fair to state that some authorities do not agree with Schwarz's taxonomic groupings.

Doubtless with the progress of faunistic work, many similar examples will come to light.

But, clearly, differentiation need not always have gone so far as to prevent the two divergent forms from interbreeding when they meet again. This, it appears, is what has happened in Europe with the subspecies of the long-tailed tit, *Aegithalos caudatus*, and the bullfinch, *Pyrrhula pyrrhula*.

As regards the bullfinch, Stresemann (1919) distinguishes a

northern and eastern form, *P. p. pyrrhula*, from west Siberia, northern Russia and Scandinavia, and a southern and western form, *P. p. minor*, from north Italy and western Europe, including western Germany. In addition, there is the bullfinch population of central Germany and the north of the Alps. This appears to intergrade with both the other forms, and shows an unusually wide range of variation in size. Stresemann considers it as the product of mixture between the other two subspecies, over a broad area into which they have re-immigrated after isolated differentiation.*

The longtailed tits, *Aegithalos caudatus*, show similar behaviour. On the continent of Europe and Asia there is a northern and north-eastern subspecies, *A. c. caudatus*, with white head, and a southern and western subspecies. *A. c. europaeus*, with dark head-markings. Stresemann (1919) and Jouard (1929) have studied these forms. There is a broad zone in west central Europe where excessive variability occurs, apparently due to intercrossing of the two types on meeting.†

Stresemann also considers the cline between the eastern and western European nuthatches (p. 219) to owe its origin to crossing of differentiated types, while other authorities consider that it differentiated, in direct relation with an environmental gradient, within a continuous population. A. H. Miller (1938, 1939) finds that various "subspecies" of birds of the genus *Junco* are the product of fusion between two or more subspecies which have met after preliminary differentiation; subspecific hybridization may here also produce striking recombinations, and small stable populations of new type (see also p. 291).

In these cases, the differences between the two groups are not very great. In the crows, however (Meise, 1928), the differences

---

* It should be noted, however, that Hartert (1903-35, suppl. vol., p. 53) assigns the mixed form entirely to *P. p. minor*. This may make for systematic convenience, but the geographical distribution suggests that Stresemann's view is in principle correct.

† Again it is to be noted that Kleinschmidt (1929) disagrees with this conclusion, and considers that the species as a whole is very variable and that the mixed race does not show abnormal variability. This only shows how hard it is to arrive at final decisions except in clear-cut cases such as the crows and flickers (see below).

are-striking, the carrion crow, *Corvus c. corone*, being entirely black, while the hoodie crow, *C. c. cornix*, has a light grey mantle. So distinct are they at first sight that many ornithologists (e.g. Hartert, 1903–35, suppl. vol., p. 6) still prefer to regard them as full species. It should be noted that if they are to be regarded as subspecies, then we must introduce a still further category, since each of them shows definite geographical differentiation into "regional races". According to Meise, they exhibit no essential differences in behaviour, voice, or ecological preferences, and should therefore be better regarded as subspecies. In any case, where their breeding ranges overlap, they interbreed, and the hybrid population shows what appear undoubtedly to be the results of mendelian recombination, the offspring of a single pair often differing a great deal in regard to the amounts and distribution of black and grey. The geographical distribution of the two forms is at first sight curious, with three zones of inter-breeding, as defined by field observation in the breeding season of birds of obviously mixed origin: one of these runs across central Scotland; a second from near Genoa, along the south side of the Alps, and then passing northwards to reach the Baltic in eastern Schleswig-Holstein; and a third in Asia from near the mouth of the Yenisei, southwards to the Altai, then south-west and west towards the Aral Sea. The total length of these zones is over 5,000 km. and their average width quite narrow, from 75 to 150 km. (Meise considers that the breadth would prove to be considerably greater if an intensive study of skins were to replace field observation.) These zones, it appears, can shift their position; see pp. 188, 209.

Since these crows appear to be ecologically dependent on the presence of trees, it appears quite reasonable to suppose that during the last glacial period the crow population of the Eurasiatic land-mass was segregated into three discontinuous groups, one in the south-west of Europe, a second in southern and south-eastern Europe and the Near East, perhaps as far as the Caspian, and a third probably in eastern Siberia. If we assume that the central group evolved the hoodie pattern, the spread of the three groups subsequent to the retreat of the ice could perfectly well bring them into contact as indicated by the present mixed zones. The hoodie's colonization of northern Scotland from Scandinavia and of Ireland from northern Scotland, fits in with other eco-geographical facts (cf. the distribution of the mountain hare: p. 246).*

An almost more striking example comes from North America, and concerns the eastern and western species of the woodpeckers known as flickers, *Colaptes auratus* and *C. cafer* (Allen, discussed by Bateson, 1913). These are by most authorities regarded as good species and both exhibit distinct geographic subspecies, *C. auratus* ranges over most of the continent east of the Rockies, and in the north extends westwards to Alaska. *C. cafer* is from the Pacific coast. Between the regions in which they are found almost pure is a band, 1,200–1,300 miles in length and at least 300–400 in width, where the majority of specimens exhibit characters from both species in various combinations. Some of the characters in question are striking: for instance, quills yellow *versus* red (in every case the character of *C. auratus* is put first); male "moustache" black *versus* red; female "moustache" absent *versus* brown; nape-patch scarlet *versus* absent; throat brown *versus* grey; top of head grey *versus* brown.

The characters of the "mixed" birds, as Bateson very clearly points out, are only explicable on the hypothesis of crossing followed by the recombination of a number of independent genes. Even birds from the same nest may show marked recombinatory variation (as with human families).

It seems clear that the two species originally diverged at a period when the glaciated Rockies provided a complete barrier between them. With the regression of the ice, the two types could meet along the zone of the Rockies, and *C. auratus* could extend northward and westward in Canada until there' too it met *C. cafer*. The meeting is secondary to the divergence, and the intergradation and interbreeding have not always existed, as seems to be the case with many subspecies of wide-ranging forms like *Peromyscus* (see also p. 291).

* Meise (op. cit.) believes that the black (carrion crow) type is the later-evolved. His reasons, however, are of no genetic or evolutionary validity, and his conclusion would imply the independent evolution of the black type in one American and two separate Eurasiatic areas, which is most unlikely.

Later work (Taverner, 1934, and verbal information from A. H. Miller) indicates that sporadic "mixed" birds are found over a much wider range than earlier supposed. Taverner believes that *auratus* is more "aggressive" and that its characters are spreading westwards faster than those of *cafer* eastwards.

Another North American example concerns the two warblers *Vermivora pinus* and *V. chrysoptera*. These are sharply distinguished by their markings; the former is a southern, the latter a northern form. These show a mixed zone of interbreeding at the junction of the ranges from northern New Jersey to the Connecticut Valley, and casually to eastern Massachusetts: here a wide range of segregants occurs. It is interesting to note that intergrading and segregation also occur in regard to the songs of the two forms. (Chapman, 1924; Bateson, 1913.) Here the history of the two forms and the reason for their initial separation is not so clear (see also p. 254).

Chapman, though stating that no ornithologist would question the specific distinctness of the two warblers and the two flickers, points out that in notes and habits the flickers are very much, the warblers fairly alike—i.e. no or slight psychological barriers to mating have been developed. This is in contrast to the eastern and western meadowlarks *Sturnella magna* and *S. neglecta*. Here differentiation has given rise to quite unlike calls and songs, and where the two overlap after coming together again subsequent to the Ice Age, they do not form a zone of general mixture, though occasional intermediates, apparently due to sporadic hybridizing, do occur.

Another clear-cut case is that of the grackles (*Quiscalus*) in eastern North America (see Chapman, 1936, 1939, 1940). Chapman now regards all the forms as subspecies of one species, Q. *quiscula*. Apparently two populations were isolated during the glacial period, Q. *q. aeneus* in south-eastern Texas and Q. *q. quiscula* in southern Florida. The latter, in its postglacial spread to the north and west, has differentiated into a further subspecies, Q. *q. stonei*. The western form appears to have extended its range more rapidly, now being found in the northern New England seaboard. It has met and hybridized with Q. *q.*

stonei over a long belt extending from western Louisiana north-eastwards to Cape Cod, a distance of some 1,500 miles. The intermixture is similar to that of the flickers, except that the two parent forms are not differentiated by such sharply contrasted single characters, so that the hybrids present a more regular and finely-graded series of intermediates. The hybrid population has been christened Q. *q. ridgwayi*. An interesting feature is that the width of the interbreeding zone increases steadily from about forty miles in the south-west to almost two hundred miles in the north-east. This, it may be suggested, is a time effect. The hybrids may be presumed to be at a slight selective disadvantage as compared with the pure parent forms, which would lead to a restriction of the hybrid zone. But the two types must have met earliest in the south-west, so that selection has not operated for so long in the north-east (see p. 287). A curious minor point is that at the eastern end of Long Island, the great range of hybrid variation is absent, and 90 per cent of the population are sharply intermediate. (For chickadees, see p. 180.)

The red-tailed hawks (*Buteo borealis*) of N. America (Taverner, 1927) present an amazingly complex picture. Two main sub-species exist, in the east and the west respectively, the latter diphasic and also very variable. Both show what Taverner considers incipient geographical differentiation in certain regions. In the north-west, presumably by post-glacial range-change, both the major and both the minor types have come to overlap and interbreed, giving profuse recombination. Finally the bird's nomadic habits appear to disseminate individuals far from their original home (see p. 355). The species would repay exhaustive investigation.

Dementiev (1938) gives numerous examples from eastern palaearctic birds. In the shrike *Lanius collurio* in particular, there exists a large region peopled by hybrids between *L. c. collurio* and *L. c. phoenicuroides*.

Stuart Baker (1930) gives similar examples in pheasants. Bateson (1913, p. 160) cites further examples in birds and butterflies, namely the zones of hybridization between two distinct species of roller (*Coracias*) in India, and between two very distinct species of white admiral (*Limenitis* or *Basilarchia*) along the quite narrow line of junction of their ranges.

In mammals similar phenomena occur in the hartebeest antelopes (*Alcelaphus*) in the rift valley region. Ruxton and Schwarz (1929) give graphs which show that the hybrid forms exhibit bimodal frequency curves, as would be expected, for certain characters. Banks (1929) gives facts which support the idea of hybridization among certain monkey species in Borneo. Here the different forms are separated altitudinally.

In a considerable area of the north-central U.S.A. (Sweadner, 1937), the whole population of the moth *Platysamia* appears to have been produced by hybridization between two distinct species, which again have met owing to post-glacial range-extensions after differentiating during the glacial period. The area here is a triangular one, expanding towards the north. The characters of the hybrid population appear to be graded: if so, we should then have a *genocline*, dependent on a balance between two opposed streams of gene-flow.

Dr. A. P. Blair (1941*b*) has investigated similar though more complex phenomena in the toads *Bufo fowleri* and *B. woodhousi* in the U.S.A.

A case from butterflies that seems very similar to the flickers is that of *Aricia a. agestis* and *A. a. artaxerxes*. After the Ice Age, the two must have met along the coast of Northumberland and Durham. Here marked segregation occurs, giving striking recombinations along a rough genocline (Harrison and Carter, 1924). It is uncertain where the two subspecies originally differentiated. Harrison and Carter suggest Ireland for *artaxerxes*, but there is no evidence for its occurrence there to-day (Donovan, 1936).

A somewhat different phenomenon is recorded by Carothers (1941) for two species of North American grasshopper, *Trimetropis citrina*, a form from sandy river banks, and *T. maritima* from coastal sands. Both of these are remarkably constant in their characters. An intermediate and very variable form has been described from the north shore of Lakes Erie and Ontario, an area separated from the range of either pure species. Carothers has now synthesized all known variants of this in the F2 and backcrosses from crosses between the two pure species. It may be hazarded that the Great Lakes form has been produced by hybridization, but at some earlier date when conditions were different and permitted the two pure species to meet and cross in this locality. When conditions changed, the hybrid form must have been able to maintain itself in this locality, while the others were compelled to retreat. This, however, is purely speculative, and further investigation of this peculiar case is desirable.

Lack (1940b) has an interesting discussion of the role of habitat-preference in speciation, which, in addition to its intrinsic interest, has a bearing on some of the problems we have just been discussing. The origin of a marked difference in habitat-preference must be, in his opinion, due to historical accident—e.g. through a group of a woodland species being isolated in a region with only one particular sort of woodland available, and its behaviour then becoming gradually adapted to this type of habitat. He comes to the conclusion that habitat-preferences are not of significance in originating the isolation leading to speciation, but that, once evolved, they may play a part (together with mating reactions) in maintaining the distinctness of forms which have re-met after differentiation.

Thus the nightingale and sprosser (p. 246) not only differ in their songs, but frequent quite different habitats, dry and very damp woodland respectively. These behave as "good species"; but in the case of the bullfinches and the longtailed tits (p. 248) the habitat-preferences of the two groups have remained similar, and they have therefore remained as subspecies, and interbreed where they have come to overlap.

The North American warblers of the genus *Vermivora* (p. 251) intercross regularly where they overlap, in spite of considerable differences in plumage and song. Their habitat-preferences isolate them partially, *V. chrysoptera* preferring higher slopes, but they overlap considerably. If their habitat-preferences had differentiated somewhat further, they would not have had the opportunity of intercrossing. We shall meet with similar cases in mammals (see pp. 271, 283-4).

Differentiated forms may come to occupy the same area not

only by the process described on pp. 243 seq. but by immigration at different times. This "double invasion" (Mayr, 1940) is commonest on oceanic islands. However, the weasels (*Mustela*) probably carried out a "double invasion" of S. America (E. R. Hall, 1939); and the case of *Parus major* (p. 243) is similar. If sufficient differentiation has occurred between the waves of immigration, the forms will behave as "good species", like the two chaffinches on Teneriffe, *Fringilla coelebs canariensis* and *F. teydea*,* or the three species of white-eye (*Zosterops*) on Norfolk Island. If, on the other hand, differentiation has been slight, the phenomenon will not be noticed, as the new immigrants will blend with the old. If it has been of moderate extent, obvious hybrid populations will result, as in a species of brush turkey, *Megapodius* (Mayr, 1931–40, No. 39).

It is interesting that in certain cases the zones of interbreeding, notably in the crows, are so narrow and apparently so stable in position. That of the flickers, on the other hand, is much wider and its width is quite possibly still increasing. It is clear that a theoretical analysis of the genetical problems arising from the meeting of two distinct types capable of free interbreeding would be of great interest.

In general, we should expect that the development of regionally stabilized gene-complexes, together with the effects of isolation in accumulating differences impairing fertility or viability (p. 360; Muller, 1940), would account for the restriction of the zones of recombination. The greater the impairment of fertility or viability suffered by the hybrids, the narrower and sharper will be the intergrading zone.

According to an interesting verbal communication from Mr. J. Dunbar of Spynie, Morayshire, fifty years ago all the breeding crows near Elgin were hoodies. Soon after this he remembers the first nesting of the carrion crow in the district. To-day the breeding birds are all carrion crows, implying that the zone of interbreeding has moved north-westwards. If so, this would

---

* These two forms are of further interest, since both, in correlation with the oceanic climate, show similar colour-changes, the later immigrant (the subspecies of *F. coelebs*) to a lesser degree than the earlier, which has had time to achieve full speciation (see Meinertzhagen, 1921).

indicate, first that the carrion crow in Scotland enjoys a slight selective advantage as a breeding species over the hoodie, and secondly that these zones of hybridization, as suggested for the genetically similar zones of intergradation between contiguous subspecies, may alter their position without losing their sharpness.

A curious case is provided by the sparrows (Meise, 1936; verbal information from the late F. C. R. Jourdain). Without going into detail, we may say that in Spain the house-sparrow (*Passer domesticus*) and the related *P. hispaniolensis* exist as well-defined and well-localized species, the former near human habitation, the latter in open country. On the other hand, in North Africa and also in parts of the Near East the two are found together, interbreed, and produce every kind of intermediate over considerable areas. The plausible suggestion has been made by Kleinschmidt that *P. hispaniolensis* is an original inhabitant of the countryside in Spain, while *P. domesticus* is a later immigrant and, being more of a parasite of man, has there remained more urban. In Africa and the Near East, on the other hand, he suggests that both arrived more or less simultaneously and began to cross at once, before ecological segregation occurred; and that the mixed types show no sharp habitat-preferences. In any event we have the interesting phenomenon of two good species differentiated in different regions but intercrossing freely when brought together by circumstances (see p. 258).

The two common species of rat provide interesting examples not only of migration after initial differentiation but of further differentiation consequent on migration. A useful summary is given by Hinton (1920). The black rat (*Rattus rattus*) was originally a more or less tree-living animal, yellowish or reddish-brown above and white below, from India, Burma, and neighbouring regions. The brown rat (*R. norvegicus*), on the other hand, had its original home in Asia north of the great mountain-chains, and is typically grey or brown above, with a silvery-grey belly. The two may be regarded as having originally been differentiated as mutually-replacing species of a geographical subgenus (*Artenkreis*).

To-day the black rat is found in three main varieties or subspecies: the roof rat, which is the typical original form, character-istic of India and the Western Mediterranean; the Alexandrine rat, a darker form, with brownish-grey back and dingy belly, characteristic of Asia Minor, North Africa, and certain Indian provinces; and the true black rat, characteristic of cold-temperate Europe, with black back and smoky-grey belly. A black variety of R. *norvegicus* is also known, this too from Western Europe.

Commerce and navigation have carried both species all over the world. The black rat was probably not introduced into Western Europe until the Crusades, the brown rat certainly not until the eighteenth century. The competition between the two types is complex, the brown rat being more vigorous but more dependent on water, while the black rat is favoured by warmth and by environments where climbing is needed. Thus the latter remains the dominant species in countries like India, and also on shipboard, but the brown rat has almost completely ousted it from temperate countries. However, of recent years the black rat is obtaining a foothold in temperate ports, where it obtains access from ships and where modern tall buildings put a premium on climbing ability, while also discouraging the brown rat.

Perhaps the most interesting fact concerns the development of the colour varieties. It seems clear that in the rats (which thus constitute an exception to Gloger's rule), lower temperatures and indoor life both favour darker coloration, and that the Alexan-drine rat differentiated from the original R. *rattus* in moderately cool regions, the true black rat in still cooler climates. The full black form appears to have differentiated in Western Europe by 1530—i.e. in less than five hundred years from its first intro-duction. Once differentiated, the three forms (one may perhaps call them subspecies, though of a rather unusual type) have been still further disseminated by man, and mixed groups of two or of all three types may occur; mendelian segregation may then be found in a single litter.

Most striking is the fact that a black variety of the brown rat has differentiated within the last two hundred years. First described from Ireland in 1837, it has since become commoner and has extended its range in Britain. In E. Africa, *Rattus (Mastomys) coucha* has recently produced black forms, but only in modern buildings (Hinton, 1920, p. 4 n., and *in verbis*).

Undoubtedly many cases of species-hybridization in plants are due to migration bringing differentiated forms together. A good example is that of the knapweeds *Centaurea jacea* and *C. nigra* in Britain (Marsden-Jones and Turrill, 1930). The former is a more recent immigrant, largely introduced by human agency. In various localities extensive crossing has taken place, producing segregants and back-cross types of all kinds, sometimes to the extent that the pure *C. jacea* type has been eliminated, and only its genes remain, in various recombination and degrees of dilution.

Turrill (1929; and in Watson and others, 1936) mentions the fact that the deforestation of the Balkan Peninsula by human agency has not only enabled many non-forest plants to extend their range, but has frequently permitted numerous species that were originally differentiated in separate areas to meet, "and so to hybridize with the production of a wealth of new phenotypes which are the bane of the taxonomist but make material for natural selection".

A wholesale case of crossing after originally separated types had been brought together, in this case wholly by human agency, is afforded by the introduced flora of New Zealand. In the new environment, hybridization has occurred on a considerable scale (cf. the sparrows mentioned on p. 256). Here, however, the position is complicated by the existence of even more widespread hybridization among the indigenous flora (see p. 355), a fact for which it is difficult to give any satisfactory explanation, unless it be correlated with low intensity of selection by herbivores. Similar cases in animals, but concerned with subspecies, have already been referred to (p. 248).

Besides extensive range-changes of this type which alter the degree of isolation, contact, or overlap between forms, we have those which are concerned merely with the extension or retraction of areas of forms which remain throughout in contact with each other. We have already discussed these in *Peromyscus* subspecies (p. 208), and shown that they are probably dependent on variations in population-pressure. Such occurrences are doubtless widespread and when they occur will reduce the closeness of adaptation between subspecies and habitat.

Migration and changes of range have unquestionably been extensive in periods of rapid climatic change like the recent past, and bring many complications into the field of systematics. In some cases we can deduce what has happened; but in others we must remain uncertain. It is, for instance, theoretically possible that many cases which we shall discuss under the head of ecological (ecoclimatic and even ecotopic) divergence are in reality due to geographical isolation, followed first by regional adaptive differentiation, and later by migration. In any event range-change has often been extensive and important, and has contributed to systematic diversity both by introducing pairs of species that normally do not cross (such as the European tree-creepers or the *major* and *minor* forms of great tit) to countries where, apart from such isolation, differentiation, and reunion, the ecological niche would have been filled by one species only; and also by allowing differentiated subspecies to cross and so to produce a wide range of new segregant recombinations.

7. THE PRINCIPLES OF GEOGRAPHICAL DIFFERENTIATION

Out of the accumulation of taxonomic and micro-evolutionary data, illustrated by genetic and mathematical theory, certain general principles of geographical differentiation are now emerging. First, isolation is *per se* a cause of differentiation (Muller, 1940). This is due to the nature of the evolutionary process, which proceeds by the presentation of numerous small mutative steps, and the subsequent incorporation of some of them in the constitution by selection, or in some cases by Sewall Wright's "drift". The improbability of the mutative steps being identical in two isolated groups, even if they be pursuing parallel evolution, is enormously high, so that reproductive incompatibilities will in the long run automatically arise between them. If the direction of selection differs for the two groups, visible divergence will also automatically result, even in the absence of divergence due to drift.

Secondly, non-adaptive or accidental differentiation may occur where isolated groups are small. This "drift", which we have also called the Sewall Wright phenomenon, is perhaps the most important of recent taxonomic discoveries. It was deduced mathematically from neo-mendelian premises, and has been empirically confirmed both in general and in detail (pp. 58, 200, etc.).

Thirdly, and almost equally important, there is the principle of stabilized gene-complexes. R. A. Fisher's extension of the theory of genic balance enables us to deduce that we may expect to find, in addition to the complete biological discontinuity exhibited by species, a condition of equilibrium which may be called *partial biological discontinuity*. In this condition, which will occur in populations spread continuously over a large region, groups showing relatively uniform characters over a relatively large area will be separated by narrow intergrading zones where interbreeding occurs. This is the condition actually found in the subspecific differentiation of many forms. The existence of partial geographical or ecological barriers will promote and accentuate this type of subspeciation, but it may occur even in their absence, provided that the region concerned is large enough, and that there is enough ecological difference between different areas within it (p. 208).

As corollary to this, it becomes clear that geographical subspecies are of two biologically distinct types—those that may differentiate into full species, and those that, unless geographical or climatic conditions alter, will remain as interconnected parts of a polytypic species. We may call them *independent* and *dependent* subspecies respectively.

A further corollary is that, since the intergrading zone is automatically kept narrow by selection, dependent subspecies may be maintained in spite of considerable range-changes: the areas of the different subspecies may expand or contract, but the subspecific groups will maintain their distinctness and the intergrading zones will remain narrow.

Fourthly, we have the phenomenon of graded differentiation, which may be subsumed under the head of *clines*. *A priori* selectionist considerations would suggest that, wherever environmental agencies vary in a graded way, organic variation would be forced into a corresponding gradation. The matter, however, is not so simple. It is complicated by two facts—first, the fact of partial biological discontinuity just discussed, and secondly the fact of migration and range-change. The fact of partial biological discontinuity prevents the realization of a continuous gradation of characters running parallel with the environmental gradient, and substitutes a staircase or stepped ramp for a uniform slope. The mean values for the environmentally correlated characters of the treads of the stair—the subspecies—then show gradation, and constitute an external or inter-group cline. This type of cline has been the subject of the "geographical rules" of Gloger, Allen, etc. The gradation within the several subspecies has been much flattened, and in most cases still awaits empirical verification; when present, it constitutes an internal cline.

It is important to note that clines for different characters may run in different directions. Thus specification by clines permits the construction of a new and more complete picture of variation within the species.

The above statement applies mainly to animals. In plants, broad geographical clines of this type appear to be absent or subsidiary, while there is a much greater prevalence of less extensive ecoclines, which come into existence by selective elimination from a large range of genetic types adapted to different ecological requirements. This distinction seems to be due to the more random and broadcast methods of fertilization and dispersal found in higher plants (p. 276).

Range-changes will clearly tend to obscure the regularity of graded differentiation. If extensive enough, they may obscure it altogether; if moderate, they will destroy the regularity of correspondence between intergroup clines and environmental gradients. Where hybridization occurs, it introduces an additional source of disturbance. A special type of range-change is the cyclical, produced by periodic fluctuations in population-size. These may cause the population to spill over at the margin of its area of distribution and then recede again (see Timoféeff-Ressovsky, 1940).

Fifthly, within the large areal or regional groups of species or subspecies, a much greater degree of localized differentiation occurs than was previously suspected. Where a species is distributed in isolated colonies, each colony may differ from every other, sometimes sufficiently so to deserve the name of micro-subspecies. But even where distribution is fairly uniform, a surprising degree of local variation is to be found if search is made for it, both in visible characters and in the complement of invisible recessives carried. Such incipient geographical differentiation may be more or less stable or permanent, or may fluctuate unstably with time. When local differentiation is combined with periodic population cycles, peculiar results may occur, periods of great variability (during recovery after a population minimum) alternating with periods of stability, but during each period of stability with the type showing new characters (see p. 112 and e.g. Dobzhansky, 1939a).

It is in this field, of population studies on the genetical structure of species, that the most valuable results, for evolution as well as for taxonomy, may be expected in the near future.

POSTSCRIPT.—1. A further possible cause of geographical polymorphism (p. 106) is mutation restricted to an isolated area. This is found in *Corvus corax varius*, the Faeroes subspecies of raven (Salomonsen, 1935). This subspecies was dimorphic, a partly whitish form existing in addition to the normal black. The piebald form was fairly common in the sixteenth to eighteenth centuries, but has now become extinct owing to the depredations of collectors. Here mutation leading to balanced dimorphism seems to have occurred in the Faeroes alone.

2. Hovanitz (1941) shows that pigmentary clines in butterflies (p. 214) present "astounding regularities", but differing for different pigments. We have (1) melanin pigments in all families, (2) ground-colour pterins (orange to white) in Pieridae and Papilionidae, (3) tawny ground-colours in other families. To decreased temperature and solar radiation and increased humidity and rainfall these react thus: group 1, by darkening (increased intensity and extension); group 2, by lightening; group 3, by darkening in intensity, but either increased or decreased area.

CHAPTER 6

SPECIATION, ECOLOGICAL AND GENETIC

I. LOCAL *versus* GEOGRAPHICAL DIFFERENTIATION

When we examine the question of evolutionary divergence more closely, we shall find that two rather distinct problems are involved. We may perhaps begin by looking at the matter historically, and from the point of view of pure taxonomy. Two phases may be distinguished in the history of modern, as opposed to Hellenistic and Moorish, taxonomy. In the first, which begins with Gesner, Gerard, and Caesalpinus, the primary motive was medical. In large measure it sprang from the need for identifying the plants prescribed in mediaeval medicine. Though reinforced and broadened, first by the emergence of commercial seed-production for horticulture in the eighteenth century, and secondly by the deliberate policy of reporting on the flora and fauna of the new English and Dutch colonies (see various reports in the *Phil. Trans. Roy. Soc.*, New York Colonial Documents, Hakluyt's *Voyages*, the official *Hortus Malabaricus* of the Dutch East India Company, etc.), its predominant characteristic and achievement was its preoccupation with the *local* situation. The major contributions were made by naturalists concerned with the animals and plants of their own country.

This regional or local phase reached its climax in the work of Morrison, Ray, and Linnaeus.

The second phase, stimulated by an intensification of the colonial motive and the extension of horticultural enterprise (e.g. the foundation of the Royal Horticultural Society by Thomas Knight), begins with the voyages of Banks and the collections of Raffles. Its special characteristic is the impact of the Australian and remote Oriental fauna and flora on the scientific consciousness of Europe. The subsequent development first of steam navigation, and then of the new colonial policy which followed the break-up of the great trading monopolies, and was more distinctively national in character, conspired to produce a new orientation, in which local preoccupations were swallowed up in a study of broad geographical distribution. This led eventually to the establishment of the great museums, with their vast collections and their staff of professional classifiers and describers. This phase of taxonomy had its social roots, first in the desire to introduce new and useful plants and animals, and later in the need, from the standpoint both of health and of agriculture, especially in the tropics, for identifying disease-bearing animals, insect pests, noxious weeds, and potentially useful crop-plants and trees.

The first phase we may style that of the herbal, the second that of the museum. The first is essentially regional, the second essentially world-wide.

Now let us see what taxonomic problems emerge as a result of these two approaches. In the regional phase, the classifier is confronted with related species either occupying quite distinct ecological habitats or found together over much of their range. In the former case, spatial isolation clearly facilitates ecological divergence. In the latter case, it is generally found that the overlapping species show definite though often slight ecological differences in habitat-preference or in mode of life. This may give us an insight into the adaptive basis for the differentiation of the related forms, but we are immediately confronted by the problem of how they are kept distinct and separate in nature, and still more how they were prevented from breeding together in early stages of their divergence. A frequent feature of over-lapping local differentiation is the sharpness of certain characters differentiating the related forms.

Quite other facts confront the museum systematist investigating the world-wide distribution of a group. What strikes him most forcibly is the phenomenon of geographical replacement, as described in the preceding chapter. Geographical forms, whether species or subspecies, are normally not distinguished by obvious qualitative characters, but by small or general differences, in colour, size, and proportion. Where the differentiation appears to be adaptive, the adaptation is usually or mainly to some broad regional influence such as climate or soil; it is often physiological, and then accompanied either by no obvious morphological distinctions, or by morphological characters which are purely consequential on the physiological adaptation, and not themselves adaptive.

The question of preventing intercrossing between groups of this type does not arise, since geographical separation provides the requisite barriers. On the contrary, the major biological problem has been that of accounting for that fraction of the divergence which is not adaptive, and this would now appear to have been settled in principle, as due to the Sewall Wright phenomenon of drift.

The main preoccupation of taxonomy in the past half-century has been geographical. To-day, however, now that the principles of geographical differentiation have come to be generally recognized and in broad outline understood, attention is once more being focused upon the local situation, but in the light of the new discoveries of cytogenetics and ecology.

2. ECOLOGICAL DIVERGENCE

We shall return later to the basic question of the prevention of crossing between spatially overlapping species. Our immediate problem is the study of systematic diversity which is based primarily upon ecologically adaptive divergence.

We have already pointed out that ecological and geographical divergence overlap,* and have mentioned the main different types of ecological divergence. These may be summarized as follows:—

1. With geographical isolation primary: ecogeographical.
2. With ecological specialization primary:
   (a) ecoclimatic: adaptation primarily to distinct regions, differing in climatic and other general environmental features.
   (b) ecotopic: adaptation primarily to distinct local habitats.
   (c) ecobiotic: adaptation primarily to distinct modes of life.

We have also stressed the role which may be played by range-changes subsequent to differentiation.

Ecogeographical divergence has been treated at length. Where marked climatic difference between two areas is associated with geographical barriers to migration and interbreeding, ecological divergence will proceed more rapidly and good species may differentiate in place of mere subspecies. The primarily ecological divergences we cannot discuss in such detail, since much less is known, or can be deduced, about their early stages.

The most obvious examples of ecoclimatic divergence are those where two species replace each other altitudinally within the same main area. Examples from Britain are the ptarmigan and the red grouse (*Lagopus scoticus* and *L. mutus*), the twite and the linnet (*Carduelis flavirostris* and *C. cannabina*; the ring-ouzel and the blackbird (*Turdus torquatus* and *T. merula*); the mountain and the common hare (*Lepus timid s* and *L. europaeus*) over most of their range; the alpine and the common lady's mantle (*Alchemilla alpina* and *A. vulgaris*). An example from Switzerland is that of the black and common redstarts (*Phoenicurus ochrurus* and *P. phoenicurus*). The difference between a maritime and an inland region provides opportunity for the same type of divergence. We may instance the rock and meadow pipits (*Anthus spinoletta petrosus* and *A. pratensis*), or the two species of bladder-campion, *Silene maritima* and *S. vulgaris* (see p. 268).

---

* Plate (1913) has a valuable discussion of the subject in which he treats the different modes of isolation from a somewhat similar viewpoint.

At first sight it would appear very difficult to maintain any real difference between such ecoclimatic adaptation of distinct environmental regions within a single geographical area, and ecogeographical adaptation to environmentally distinct geographical areas. However, a theoretically important distinction is possible. It may be that in an originally continuous population, those groups inhabiting climatically very distinct regions became closely adapted to the conditions of those regions. If selection in favour of such adaptation were intense, selection would also act to erect barriers to the interbreeding of the groups, since such interbreeding would hinder the adaptive change. There is a real distinction between cases in which spatial isolation, brought about by purely geographical barriers, is primary, and ecologically adaptive divergence is subsequent and secondary; and those in which ecological divergence is primary (even if it occur in different regions of a range) and tends to erect barriers to free interbreeding. This will be reflected in the distribution. In cases where geographical divergence is primary, the range of a geographical group (subspecies or species) will in general be a whole area. Where, however, ecological divergence is primary, the range of each divergent group will in general constitute a type of regional habitat—all mountains above a certain height for ptarmigan, all rocky coastal areas for rock pipits—which will not constitute a single geographical area but will be discontinuous.

An example which well demonstrates the interconnection between ecological and geographical divergence is that of the two species of bugle, *Ajuga chamaepitys* and *A. chia* (Turrill, 1934). *A. chia* is a highly polymorphic species found in the eastern Mediterranean and eastwards into Persia, in various natural habitats. *A. chamaepitys*, on the other hand, is found in Central and Western Europe and parts of North Africa, is on the whole very uniform, and over a great part of its range is a weed of cultivated land. The two forms are connected by every intergradation over a zone of very considerable width. In addition there is a character-gradient (cline) traversing both forms from north-west Europe to the Near East. As one passes in this direction, the plants tend to have a longer duration of life, become more bushy in habit, with shorter leaf-lobes and larger flowers (the gradation reaching from 10 to 28 mm. corolla-length), and tend towards corrugated instead of pitted seeds; the gradient appears to be steepened in the zone of intergradation.

Turrill concludes that the original home of the two forms was in the Near East, and that *A. chamaepitys* has arisen by an extension north-westwards in relation to the spread of human agriculture, selection having operated to reduce the variability of the stock and to adapt it more closely to the status of a weed of arable land. On this supposition the zones of intergradation are not due to interbreeding between two differentiated forms, but to incomplete selective differentiation of the more uniform from the more variable form. On distribution alone the two forms could be regarded as geographical divergents, but since *A. chamaepitys* is so sharply characterized in its ecological requirements, it seems easier to suppose that it was the new ecological niche provided by human agriculture which was the primary factor in stimulating its differentiation. However, this differentiation could not occur in the original range of the species, but only where agriculture was combined with other climatic conditions: thus geographical separation here resulted from ecological differentiation.

It must be, as Turrill stresses, a matter of opinion whether the two forms should be regarded as species or subspecies: their many important differences, however, make it more convenient to give them specific rank.

The detailed analysis of cases of ecoclimatic divergence has rarely been undertaken. However, a careful study has been made of the two species of bladder-campion previously mentioned (p. 266), by Marsden-Jones and Turrill (1930).* Both are highly polymorphic, notably *Silene vulgaris*, as would be expected from the greater ecological variety of inland habitats. *S. maritima* is more restricted ecologically: over most of its range it is confined to the coast, but towards its northern limit it may penetrate far inland, especially on mountains. *S. vulgaris* does not extend so

---

* This case could equally well be regarded as one of ecotopic divergence. The different categories of course overlap.

far north as *S. maritima*. Much of the natural variation is parallel in the two species, but certain variants are found only in *S. vulgaris*. It appears likely that in Britain *S. maritima* survived the Ice Age, while *S. vulgaris* was a post-glacial immigrant.

Although under experimental conditions the two species can be crossed, and then yield fully fertile hybrids, they rarely cross naturally in the main portion of the area of their geographical overlap. Spatial isolation, due to their ecological preferences, thus keeps them apart, and they must be regarded as good species. However, in some smallish northern areas the available evidence suggests that the two have come to overlap regionally, and that here they have been fused to form a still more poly-morphic mixed population. If so, this would be parallel to the case of the sparrows mentioned on p. 256.

The two speedwells, *Veronica spicata* and *V. hybrida*, are very similar in appearance, but are kept separate by the adaptation of the former to a continental, of the latter to an oceanic climate (Salisbury, 1939).

It will obviously in many cases be difficult to distinguish ecoclimatic from ecotopic divergence. A case in point is the crested tit (*Parus cristatus*), which is confined to coniferous forests and to a certain range of environmental conditions. In many areas it thus becomes limited to mountain regions, but elsewhere (e.g. Scotland) it descends lower. The special (ecotopic) rather than the general (ecoclimatic) ecological conditions of the habitat, however, appear to be much the more important.

The evolution of the crested tit in Britain affords an interesting contrast with that of the cole tit (*P. ater*). As has been pointed out by Lack and Venables (1939) and J. Fisher (1940c) both species are typically restricted to coniferous woodland. During the last glacial maximum, coniferous woodland extended across what is now the English Channel into southern Britain, and both species were presumably restricted to this habitat, as on the continent to-day. Later, Britain was cut off from the rest of Europe, and its coniferous forest receded northwards, being replaced by deciduous woodland in the south. The British cole tit adjusted itself to the new conditions by becoming adapted to deciduous as well as to coniferous woodland, so that it is now found over the whole of Britain. The crested tit, however, was for some unexplained reason less plastic, so that the British subspecies is now restricted to the central highland region of Scotland. Various complications of simple ecoclimatic divergences occur. For one thing, altitudinal separation is, of course, often translated into geographical separation at the margins of the range, the form adapted to high altitudes extending to low levels in regions which are too cold for the other form. Numerous examples of this are given in Chapman's notable monograph (1926) on South American bird-life.

A remarkable example of divergence in ecoclimatic preference without morphological differentiation is that of the lesser whitethroat (*Sylvia curruca*) cited by Oldham (1932). In Britain this is a lowland bird, never nesting above 1,000 ft.; but in the Swiss Alps it is not found in the valleys at all, and breeds only above 4,500 ft., in pine forests.

A peculiar case is that of the marsh and willow tits (*Parus palustris* and *P. atricapillus*). These are in many parts of their range extremely similar in appearance. The chief plumage distinction is that the black of the crown is glossy in the former species, dull matt in the latter. The marsh tit rarely if ever excavates its nest-hole, while the willow tit always or normally does so. Further, the notes are distinct. The ranges of the two *Formenkreise* are by no means identical, *P. palustris* not being found at all in America, where the common chickadee is the subspecific representative of *P. atricapillus*. In Western Europe, *P. atricapillus* ranges further north than *P. palustris*, the latter, for instance, being absent from Scotland. In general *P. atricapillus* is the more northern form, and ranges higher in mountainous regions.

In certain parts of the range, as in England, the two are found within the same area, and are extremely similar in appearance. Elsewhere, however, they may be distinct both in distribution and in appearance: for example in the Alps the willow tit is found much higher, and is larger and paler than the marsh tit. Presumably they are ecogeographical species, probably separated in the glacial period (see p. 246). In any case they must have spread extensively since their separation, and under certain conditions now compete within the same area. The distinction in nesting habits is a mark of ecological specialization: in some areas this is also indicated by difference in habitat-preferences, for instance in regard to type of woodland frequented.

A somewhat different case exists in mammals. In the long-tailed field-mice (*Apodemus*) two closely-related species, *A. sylvaticus* and *A. flavicollis*, are generally recognized. The latter is slightly but distinctly larger, and has more yellow on the chest and neck. The osteology also presents some definite distinctions. There is partial ecological isolation, *flavicollis* being restricted to woods and scrub, while *sylvaticus* prefers more open habitats (Zimmermann, 1936). They are found within the same area in much of Western Europe, though *sylvaticus* has a much wider distribution. In some regions, as in Scandinavia, intermediates are found; but here *sylvaticus* is a lowland form, *flavicollis* an upland form, with the intermediates found in the transitional region (Barrett-Hamilton and Hinton, 1910—, p. 545). However, as the two forms are traced eastwards across the Eurasiatic continent they become less distinct, until in Eastern Asia only a single type can be distinguished (verbal information from Mr. M. A. C. Hinton).*

In many cases of apparent ecoclimatic divergence, we must allow for the possibility that the differentiation was in origin ecogeographical, and that subsequent migration later brought the two forms into the same area, where, however, their different ecological requirements segregate them into different regions. We have given examples of this in a previous section. From what we know of the common and mountain hares (p. 246), we must be prepared for the possibility that similar cases, like that of the red grouse (or alternatively the willow grouse) and the ptarmigan, may be of this nature. The fact is that comparatively little is known on the matter; and it would be extremely valuable to be able to distinguish the results of ecogeographical

---

* Sviridenko (1940) has recently shown that in Russia there is an ecobiotic difference, *A. flavicollis* consuming more green food and fewer insects than *A. sylvaticus*.

divergence followed by migration from those of ecoclimatic divergence *in situ*. Systematic mapping of the actual ranges of a number of species and subspecies as found to-day, together with their probable ranges during the last glacial maximum, would shed much light on this problem.

In general, as pointed out by Mayr (Stanford and Mayr, 1940), higher-altitude subspecies of birds are larger and darker than mid-mountain and lowland forms. In S. America and New Guinea the evidence strongly suggests that most altitudinal races have differentiated *in situ*; the types are accordingly often connected by "a graded series of intermediate populations". In two cases in New Guinea, however, the local altitudinal representatives seem to have differentiated in separate localities and to have come into their present close proximity by subsequent range-change (cf. the marsh and willow tits in the Alps, p. 270). The types are then usually sharply distinct, without intermediates. This type of origin seems to have been particularly frequent in N. Burma.

In Nyasaland the two white-eyes *Zosterops virens* and *Z. senegalensis* are separated both altitudinally and ecotopically, the former being restricted to the borders of evergreen forest at high elevations, the latter occurring at lower altitudes and often in the interior of open woodland as well as the borders of evergreen scrub (Benson, 1941). A rather similar difference holds for two species of *Cinnyris*, *C. manoensis* and *C. zonarius*, and for two subspecies of tit, *Parus n. niger* and *P. n. insignis*.

We now come to ecotopic divergence. This clearly overlaps with ecoclimatic. The ecological adaptation of the rock pipit (*Anthus spinoletta petrosus*) is in one aspect ecoclimatic, to a maritime zone, in another ecotopic, to rocky ground (p. 279). The other two common British pipits show ecotopic divergence, the meadow pipit(*A. pratensis*) being a bird of moors and rough meadows, the tree pipit(*A. trivialis*) demanding partially wooded areas.

A case of ecotopic subspeciation in birds where the two forms are kept separate by their ecological preferences is afforded by the very distinct salt-marsh and dry hillside subspecies of the song-sparrow (*Melospiza melodia*) in San Francisco Bay. The king rail (*Rallus elegans*) and the clapper rail (*R. longirostris*) of the U.S.A. are restricted to fresh-water and salt-marshes respectively; here the divergence has reached species level. (Examples from Mayr, 1940.)

The caribou (*Rangifer tarandus*) exists in Canada in woodland and barren-ground subspecies. The former is considerably larger, but has smaller antlers, in adaptation to the obstacles of its habitat. It migrates south in summer, the barren-ground form north. The two are kept sharply apart by their ecological preferences. In fish, two subspecies of bream (*Abramis brama*) differ also in time of spawning; the spring form has a much more restricted distribution (Velikokhatko, 1941).

Ecotopic divergence seems to be considerably rarer in vertebrates than in insects (p. 322).

Plants provide numerous examples. Divergence in relation to the calcium content of the soil is not infrequent, leading to the production of calcicole and calcifuge species (or subspecies). Examples of such species-pairs from Europe include the bed-straws *Galium saxatile* and *G. sylvestre* (the calcifuge type is in each case mentioned first), the gentians *Gentiana excisa* and *G. clusii*, the anemones *A. sulphurea* and *A. alpina*, and cases from *Rhododendron*, *Achillea*, etc. (Salisbury, 1939). It is interesting that the anemones are physiologically buffered against the environmental difference in calcium-content, the ash of the calcicole species containing slightly *less* Ca. In a somewhat similar way, animal species may be buffered with regard to temperature conditions, forms adapted to regions of higher temperature having, at any given temperature, a lower metabolism than close relations living in cooler conditions (p. 435; Fox, 1939; Fox and Wingfield, 1937). In the gentians, however, no buffering has developed, and the calcicole species contains considerably more calcium.

Dr. Turrill tells me that an even greater number of species (or subspecies) pairs are differentiated in relation to serpentine or its absence.

The two bedstraws can both be grown in a wide range of soils, but in nature they are rather rigidly calcicole and calcifuge respectively. This is a frequent phenomenon. Many plants which in the absence of competition show wide tolerance are, under the more intense selection found in nature, confined to a small section of their potential ecological range. Edelweiss grows luxuriantly at sea-level in an English garden: it is a mountain plant in nature, owing to its inferior performance in competition with lowland types, combined with its wide range of tolerance which will permit it to grow in regions above their capacity to colonize. (See also pp. 446-7).

The morphological distinctions between such ecotopic species, as between the "biological species" of various animals (see below, p. 296), may be remarkably slight. Thus the two species of gentian mentioned were long confused. They both occupy the same ecobiotic niche in the Alpine pasture community, and differ visibly only in the presence or absence of green spots inside the corolla tube, and the mode of insertion of the calyx teeth. Such types are normally kept so isolated by their ecobiotic adaptations that they are properly to be regarded as species. However, just as in certain extreme parts of their ranges the two ecoclimatic species of *Silene* overlap and there cross freely (p. 269), so in exceptional circumstances ecobiotic species may hybridize. Salisbury (1939) has shown that the two oaks, *Quercus robur* and *Q. sessiliflora*, are distinguished mainly by preferring heavy and light soils respectively (and see also Watson, W., 1936, *J. Ecol.* 24: 446). Where soils of the two preferred types meet abruptly, a narrow belt of hybrids is found, reminding us of the narrow zones of intergradation found between many geographical sub-species of animals. Where, on the other hand, soils of a truly intermediate nature occur, an entire wood may consist of a mixed population of the two pure forms together with hybrids.

Miller Christy (1897) has described the behaviour of the true oxlip (*Primula elatior*). This species is in Britain rigorously confined to the boulder-clay in its highest and most solid areas. It hybridizes freely where it comes into contact with the primrose (*P. vulgaris*), but for the most part the two species are kept sharply apart by their ecological preferences. Interestingly enough, in some areas the oxlip is being "hybridized out" by the primrose, the zone of intercrossing apparently advancing into the oxlip area. On the continent, the oxlip has not such a restricted ecological preference, and is correspondingly more abundant. The distinction of the oxlip from the cowslip (*P. veris*) is maintained by hybrid sterility, not by ecological preference.

In discussing clines (p. 223) we have mentioned the ecoclines found in such plants as *Plantago maritima*, in which a wide range of genetically different forms is differentially adjusted by selective balance (p. 103) to different parts of a wide range of ecological conditions. These conditions may be artificially imposed, e.g. by the degree of grazing by sheep (see Gregor, 1938*b*).

This typical plant mode of intraspecific differentiation (which of course may, through subsequent isolation, lead on to full speciation) is usually manifest in a broader way, over larger areas. Turesson especially has developed this view. According to him, most or at least many plant species consist of numerous ecotypes, each adapted to a certain range of environmental conditions. Usually the differentiation is ecotopic or ecobiotic, related to habitat conditions. To take but one example, Turesson (1927) finds that the grass *Poa alpina* in Scandinavia comprises alpine, sub-alpine and lowland ecotypes, highly selected in regard to such features as earliness and water-requirements. From his analysis he draws some interesting biogeographical conclusions, e.g. that the lowland ecotypes are not glacial relics. See also Turesson (1930) for more general discussion.

In still other cases, the differentiation may be of the same general nature but with still broader basis, in relation to climate. Numerous examples of this are given by Sinskaja (1931) for Russian plant species. Thus in grasses like *Bromus inermis* there are definite "climatypes" (climatic ecotypes) which each characterize a particular climatic zone. "Outliers" of one climatype within the main zone of another may occur, and are also associated with regional peculiarities of the habitat which make it approximate to the zone normally inhabited by the "outlier" type. Presumably, as in *Plantago maritima*, but over a much vaster area, selection sifts the array of ecotypes present in the species in accordance with the climatic and other peculiarities of the habitat. The difference, though of great significance, is essentially a quantitative one.

In many forms, several ecotypes may coexist in one area, each adapted to slightly different habitats. But where conditions are exacting, only a single main ecotype may survive over a considerable area (see e.g. Stapledon, 1928, on cocksfoot grass). This multiple-ecotype species-structure of higher plants is to be contrasted with the regional differentiation typical of higher animals, and leading to geographical subspecies: the difference is doubtless due to the random methods of fertilization and distribution in plants. Another type of species-structure is provided by the existence of seasonal ecotypes, each adapted to flowering and fruiting at a different time of year: see e.g. Clausen, Keck and Hiesey (1937, p. 15), for the tarweeds *Hemizonia*.

The ecocline mode of differentiation revealed by Gregor's work may also, it appears, sometimes be pushed further until the range of groups is broken up into well-marked ecological subspecies or even distinct species. Salisbury (1939) gives two examples, both interestingly enough from a similar range of environmental conditions. Thus the glassworts *Salicornia dolichostachya*, *S. herbacea* (*sensu stricto*), *S. gracillima*, and *S. disarticulata* are found at progressively higher and drier levels of salt-marshes. An interesting ecotopic complication is seen in that the moderately low zone is characterized by *S. herbacea* when more muddy, but by a closely allied species, *S. ramosissima*, when more sandy. A similar but less complex series is provided by the sea-lavenders, *Limonium* (*Statice*) *rariflora*, *L. vulgare* (*sensu stricto*), and *L. pyramidale*.

Ecological succession may be the agency which keeps such forms sufficiently separate for group-differentiation and eventual speciation to occur, one and the same salt-marsh at different stages in its career being habitable by one only of the types. Frequently, however, conditions are such that two or more of the forms are found at different levels of the same marsh, so that it is difficult to envisage the precise nature of the isolating barriers which must have been operative to effect speciation.

In certain cases there may be a marked segregation of ecotypes adapted to highly specialized habitats. Thus we have prostrate "varieties" of bittersweet (*Solanum dulcamara*), broom (*Cytisus scoparius*), and of the hawkweed *Hieracium umbellatum*, restricted (and highly adapted) to shingle, cliff-ledge, and shifting sand habitats respectively. All three retain their characters in cultivation, side by side with the normal form. In the *Solanum* the prostrate form has a complex multifactorial basis (results shortly to be published by Mr. Marsden-Jones); we may expect the breeding experiments now being carried out by Dr. Turrill to reveal the same general state of affairs in the *Cytisus*.

In the *Hieracium*, Turesson (1922) showed that the dune-type occurs all along a long stretch of dunes, except near the few spots where woodland comes down close to the dunes. He interpreted this as meaning that in these localities, cross-pollination from the woodland form has wrecked the specialized constitution of the shifting-sand form sufficiently to prevent it maintaining itself at all in its difficult habitat (cf. also p. 187).

The considerable gap in characters between the other two prostrate forms and the type would imply that they too are what we may call "all-or-nothing" forms, which may with some justice be called ecological subspecies.

The distinction between them and the less specialized ecotypes would then be that they can only maintain themselves as a relatively pure population, whereas in cases such as that of Gregor's *Plantago maritima*, each population contains numbers of ecotypes, none of them very sharply defined, and all intercrossing and connected by intermediates. In this latter case, the species is polymorphic, the selective balance needed to maintain the polymorphism (see p. 97) being a balance between the selective effect of a wide range of habitats. In the former case, however, true polymorphism is absent, and a highly adapted type is maintained as an ecological subspecies in a special habitat by means of a considerable degree of isolation.

This type of species-structure could readily evolve out of the more usual multiple ecotype structure; doubtless various intermediate conditions will come to light as research proceeds.

The two forms of *Ajuga* (p. 267) have shown us how the

peculiar conditions of cultivated land may combine with climatic selection to cause a partly ecological, partly geographical divergence. In other cases, cultivation may induce purely ecotopic divergence. Thus in some plants, e.g. the weeds *Caucalis arvensis* and the fool's parsley *Aethusa cynapium*, dwarf strains characterize stubble-fields. The taller strains which also regularly appear earlier in the season in the same fields are eliminated each year through decapitation of the flower-heads by the reaping machine before ripening (Salisbury, 1939). It is quite conceivable that good dwarf species may eventually evolve, restricted to the autumnal stubble habitat.

A point of great importance is that, with ecotopic differentiation, the spatial overlap between related divergents may be very extensive. Overlap may occur with ecoclimatic divergence: for instance, the red grouse and the ptarmigan overlap in certain parts of their range over a zone of up to 300 m. in vertical height. But such forms as the chiffchaff and the willow warbler (*Phylloscopus collybita* and *P. trochilus*), for example, though the latter has a preference for more open situations, overlap extensively and irregularly over most of their range; so do the meadow and tree pipits (p. 289), though to a somewhat smaller extent.

Again, though the bell-heather (*Erica cinerea*) is adapted to drier mean conditions than the waxbell (*E. tetralix*), the two are quite commonly found growing together.

It is not uncommon to find a species in the atypical conditions at the margin of its range adopting a peculiar habitat. Thus the reed bunting (*Emberiza schoenichlus*) in north-west Scotland and the Isles is found nesting on small islands in lochs, among low birch scrub (personal observation). This is due to the absence of the marshy willow coverts which it normally frequents, and to its general preference for low shrubby vegetation near water, which here is largely confined to islets, since it is elsewhere grazed down by sheep. The swallow-tail *Papilio machaon*, normally an ordinary open-country butterfly, inhabits fens on the edge of its range, in Britain. In this and other cases, the reason for the changed habitat is unknown—e.g. for the extension inland in the north-western regions of Britain, and notably on St. Kilda, of the rock pipit, which normally is rigidly confined to the maritime zone (Nicholson and Fisher, 1940). As with *Silene* (p. 269), the change of habitat causes an overlap of range with a related species, the meadow pipit. *Gammarus duebeni*, mainly brackish water in Britain, is the chief fresh-water species of Ireland (Beadle and Cragg, 1940).

The rock pipit is of great interest, since this itself is an ecologically differentiated subspecies of *Anthus spinoletta*, most of whose numerous subspecies are styled water pipits, owing to their preference for streams. All are confined to barren country: some, like *A. s. spinoletta*, to alpine areas; others, like *A. s. rubescens*, to mountains or to low barren areas in the far north. This last-named subspecies shows a transition towards the habitat-preferences of the rock pipit (*A. s. petrosus*), since it is rather frequently found on steep slopes above sea-cliffs. The combination of ecotopic and geographical divergence is thus well illustrated by the forms of this polytypic species.

Sometimes the ecological isolation is concerned primarily with breeding-places, the forms often mingling while feeding. This occurs, for instance, with the British Hirundinidae, the swallow (*Hirundo rustica*) nesting only under shelter, usually inside buildings, the house martin (*Delichon urbica*) only on houses (or rarely on cliffs), the sand martin (*Riparia riparia*) only in sand-cliffs, usually along rivers. The house martin, by the way, provides an example of the effect of human agency in altering range. This species was originally confined to cliffs as breeding-places, but its adoption of houses has both changed its type of nesting habitat and much extended its distribution.

The reverse condition is exemplified by the terns, *Sterna*, where several species may show similar nesting habits, but are differentiated in regard to their feeding. Formosov (in Gause, 1934, p. 19) cites a case where four species nest in a single crowded colonial breeding territory (though the species tend to keep separate within the colony), and all co-operate in driving away intruders. But their feeding habits are quite distinct; three fish in different types of water, and the fourth feeds excusively on land.

The house and tree sparrows (*Passer domesticus* and *P. montanus*) may also be mentioned, the former essentially a parasite or commensal of man, the latter restricted to open country away from buildings. However, in certain eastern palearctic regions, outside the range of the house sparrow, the tree sparrow has taken the other's ecological role and constantly associates with man. This shows how ecological distribution may alter in relation to the absence of related competitors, just as was shown for regional distribution in the case of the mountain hare (p. 246).

As mentioned later (p. 322), the small size and rigid instincts of insects appear to favour ecotopic and ecobiotic differentiation to a much greater extent than in higher vertebrates.

Before returning to the biological problem raised by the existence of overlap and the consequent absence of spatial isolation, we will briefly deal with ecobiotic divergence, where the main adaptation is to a mode of life rather than to a habitat. Here the opportunities for overlap are greatest. One may, for instance, find half a dozen good species of *Geranium* or of *Veronica* in one hedge or bank, five good species of blue butterflies (Lycaenidae) on a single chalk down. All the six common species of British titmice may frequently exist together in a single wood, although here they also show ecotopic preferences, a coniferous wood being quite likely to harbour only the cole tit (*Parus ater*), an alder grove by a swamp only the willow tit (*P. atricapillus*), while the longtailed tit (*Aegithalos caudatus*) is somewhat local and tends to frequent rather open bushy country.

Sometimes size is the decisive factor. The greater and lesser spotted woodpeckers (*Dryobates major* and *D. minor*) are extremely similar in appearance and habits, but the one is three to four times the weight of the other. Such differences in size are doubtless correlated with difference in the food taken: this holds for the similar case of the two very similar falcons, the large peregrine (*Falco peregrinus*) and the small merlin (*F. columbarius*). Similar examples from North America include the common and fish crows, *Corvus brachyrhynchos* (*corone*) and *C. ossifragus*, the latter having also well-marked ecological preferences, and the hairy and downy woodpeckers, *Dryobates villosus* and *D. pubescens*.

Mr. M. A. C. Hinton tells me that the same holds for shrews (Soricidae). In Britain we have the common and pigmy species, *Sorex araneus* and *S. minutus*; other size-differentiated sets of species occur within the family. In *Hemicentetes* (p. 287) the differentiation is by tooth-size, not body-size. Other obvious examples are to be found in bats, foxes, toads, Mustelidae (stoat and weasel, *Mustela ermineus* and *M. nivalis*), cats (e.g. jaguar and ocelot, *Felis onca* and *F. pardalis*) and the curlew and whimbrel (*Numenius arquata* and *N. phaeopus*). That the size of predator and prey is often closely adjusted is shown by the experiments with fish and water-boatmen mentioned on p. 469. Presumably the size-difference between pairs of species differentiated on this basis must reach a certain level before the two types cease to overlap appreciably in regard to the prey taken, and so gain maximum advantage by their differentiation. It is relevant that in the woodpeckers, the ratio of size of the smaller to the larger species is very similar in Europe and America, as if a certain degree of size-divergence were necessary to secure the optimum exploitation of the environment by species-pairs of this type. A quantitative comparative study on such size-differences in various groups should yield interesting results.

With reference to woodpeckers it is interesting that in North America the group shows a much greater range of ecological divergence than in the Old World. For instance, acorn-storing, catching insects on the wing, egg-stealing, sap-sucking, etc., are characteristic of American species only (see Bent, 1939). It would be interesting to try to discover the reason for this and other similar cases of differential ecological radiation.

Feeding habits are the commonest source of ecobiotic divergence. For instance, among the British finches, the goldfinch (*Carduelis carduelis*) is the only one to prefer thistle-heads, the bullfinch (*Pyrrhula pyrrhula*) to prefer fruit-buds: the hawfinch (*Coccothraustes coccothraustes*) enjoys berries and green peas, while the crossbill (*Loxia curvirostra*) is almost confined to pine-seeds. Such dietary specialization is naturally often reflected in structure: the huge beak of the hawfinch and the remarkable crossed mandibles of the crossbill are obvious examples.

The birds of prey afford equally good examples. Almost every British bird of prey is, by its wing-shape, mode of flight, beak, claws, size and general instincts, specialized for capturing a distinct type of prey—the peregrine (*Falco peregrinus*) for large birds such as ducks and pigeons, the merlin (*Falco columbarius*) for smaller birds, the buzzard (*Buteo buteo*) for young rabbits, mice and other small animals, the kestrel (*Falco tinnunculus*) for voles and insects, the sparrowhawk (*Accipiter nisus*) for small passerine birds, the hobby (*Falco subbuteo*) for the swiftest victims, including even dragonflies and swallows, the osprey (*Pandion haliaetus*) for fish.

An interesting case of incipient ecobiotic differentiation is cited by Noble (1930) in the common Japanese tree-frog, *Rhacophorus schlegelii*; this normally lays its eggs in holes in the banks of rice-fields, but one form deposits them in frothy masses on leaves overhanging water. There is a very slight degree of morphological difference, but the two types appear to be genetically isolated by their breeding habits, and may be expected to diverge into good species.

Among plants, differentiation of a clearly ecobiotic nature is on the whole rarer than among animals, but adaptation to special modes of pollination, by hive-bees, bumblebees, flies, moths, butterflies, etc., is a case in point. The different degrees of facultative or obligatory parasitism found in the eyebrights (*Euphrasia*) and their relatives provides another example, linking up with the facts discussed in section 4 of this chapter.

The lampreys (*Petromyzon*) show an unusual type of ecobiotic divergence. As Hubbs and Trautman (1937) point out the original mode of life in this group appears to be for the animal after metamorphosis to develop strong sharp teeth and to feed in a semi-parasitic fashion on other fishes, usually in the sea. They grow to a considerable size, and eventually reascend small streams to spawn and die. Several species of this type are known.

A second set of species, however, entirely cease feeding after metamorphosis. Their gut becomes functionless, and the teeth are reduced in size and sharpness and become fragmented. They live in the smaller streams in this dwarf condition for under a year, and then spawn and die.

The dwarfed non-parasitic but degenerate type is thus an adaptation to an adult existence in small streams. Different dwarf species appear to have originated independently from several parasitic ones.

A very different but equally interesting case is afforded by the koala (*Phascolarctus cinereus*). This marsupial exists in several subspecies. The northern, more tropical one is smaller than the southern (Bergmann's rule, p. 211), and is restricted to other species of eucalyptus. According to Pratt (1937) the leaves of the eucalyptus species preferred by the more tropical subspecies are rich in cineol and poor in phellandrene, while the reverse is true of those eaten by the higher-latitude form. Pratt further maintains that this has an adaptive physiological significance, cineol tending to keep body temperature down, and phellandrene keeping it up. If this proves to be correct, we have here a case of geographical subspecies which are strongly differentiated physiologically and therefore ecologically.

An instructive case of the apparent ecological differentiation of geographical subspecies comes from lizards (Kramer and Mertens, 1938*b*). In Istria, *Lacerta muralis* occurs in two subspecific forms, *L. m. muralis* and *L. m. maculiventris*, the range of the latter confined to the west of the peninsula, and its habitat almost entirely restricted to the neighbourhood of human habitations where refuse is to be found, while the former, a wide-ranging form, is found on the east of Istria in woods and thickets far from houses or villages. However, *m. muralis* becomes an associate of man in other areas, but only where the countryside is naturally very bare, and also highly cultivated—as is the case with the part of Istria inhabited by *m. maculiventris*. Thus the ecological differentiation of the two forms in Istria is apparent only, caused by the climatic and edaphic peculiarities of the geographical area of *m. maculiventris*.

Again, the jirds (*Meriones*) of the Arabian desert are differentiated into three ecological species "distinguished from each other by characters of skull and pelage, which appears to be closely correlated in such cases with special habits" (Cheesman and Hinton, 1924). Two are truly desert forms, one nocturnal, and therefore with larger auditory bullae, thicker fur, and less pallid colour, the other diurnal, with opposite characteristics, and the third, less specialized, is ecologically restricted to the cultivated fringe. Examples of this sort could be multiplied almost indefinitely. They show how widespread is the tendency to ecobiotic and ecotopic differentiation—in other words to a specialized sharing out of the environmental habitat and ways of exploiting it among different related species. At the same time they are a challenge to biologists, since the method by which such differentiation originates is by no means clear. The chief clues are the facts concerning "physiological races" in certain animals and plants (p. 295), and the existence of local or sporadic variations in behaviour in certain animals.

3. OVERLAPPING SPECIES-PAIRS

Numerous puzzling cases are presented by extremely similar species which overlap over much of their range and yet remain distinct.

Some of these puzzles, like that of the two European tree-creepers (p. 245), we have already shown to receive their solution in the fact of migration and overlap subsequent to divergence in isolation. It is probable that other examples, like that of the marsh and willow tits (p. 270) and of the pied and collared flycatchers (*Muscicapa hypoleuca* and *M. albicollis*), are of the same nature.

A striking case is that of the two crested larks of North Africa, *Galerida cristata* and *G. theklae*, already referred to on p. 215. These differ only in certain apparently trivial characters, such as the length of bill, and whether the song is given from the ground or on the wing. Their overlap is extensive, but by no means complete. It is quite possible that here, too, migration after ecoclimatic differentiation in isolation has been responsible.

Slightly different cases of overlap arise when two waves of invasion have occurred from different direction at different times (see p. 255). This has been particularly studied in the islands of the Pacific; thus on the Marquesas, Mayr (1940) finds two forms of fruit-dove, which ordinary taxonomic practice would be inclined to regard as subspecies, living together without any hybridization. Then we have overlap due to the end members of a chain of subspecies meeting and behaving as species (p. 244). In all, ten or a dozen examples of this phenomenon are known from birds alone. The distribution of the three subspecies of *Rana esculenta* is very peculiar (H. W. Parker, *in litteris*). Usually they are kept from interbreeding by differences in breeding-times, but in certain zones hybridization occurs. Four-fifths of the species of gall-forming Cynipidae infest the oak (Hogben, 1940). Three species, including two of *Neuroterus*, often occur on the same leaf. Hogben suggests that agamic reproduction has facilitated this divergence.

An interesting case is afforded by the blue butterflies. The chalk-hill blue (*Lycaena corydon*) and the Clifton blue (*L. thetis*) must be ecologically slightly different in their requirements, since the latter is found more commonly near the sea, and even where they overlap, one is usually more abundant than the other in particular spots. On the other hand, they do overlap to a considerable extent, and, although their times of emergence are not identical, they are frequently to be found flying together. The brownish females of the two species are so similar that no entomologist would undertake to assign a single specimen to its correct species merely on its appearance. The males, however, are strikingly distinct, that of *L. thetis* being a rich azure, of *L. corydon* a very luminous pale blue.

An example which has been a source of confusion to ornithologists for over a century is that of the genus *Tachyeres* or steamer ducks, so called from their habit of racing over the surface of the water, churning its surface with their wings like paddle-wheels. In addition, some can fly; and these have long been known to be smaller and to have larger wings.

For many years the belief was firmly held by many authorities that only one species existed, and that the flying stage was passed through in youth. However, Murphy (1936) has definitely established that three distinct species exist—one flightless form from the west coast of southern South America, a second from the

Falkland Islands, and a flying form with a range including that of both the others and also spreading some distance up the east coast. The three forms are distinguishable at all stages. The flightless forms are considerably heavier, especially the mainland type, the males of which are almost double the weight of flying males. An interesting point (derived from an analysis of Murphy's data, but not noted by him) is that the sexual disparity in size is much greater in the flightless species. The $\male/\female$ weight-ratio in the mainland flightless form is 1·47, in the flying form only 1·17. One may conjecture that this is due to sexual selection in favour of more powerful males being no longer counteracted by natural selection in relation to efficiency of flight.

Though the wings of the flightless forms are smaller, the wing-muscles are normal, since a great amount of energy is needed for the "steaming", which is rather faster than in the flying species. The calls of the three species appear to be different and the Falkland flightless species shows genetic tameness.

There is an ecotopic as well as an ecobiotic distinction between the flightless and flying forms, the latter being found on fresh water as well as on all regions of the coast, while the flightless species are restricted to the coast, and to such regions of it as are not subject to strong tidal fluctuation.

It would seem clear that both flightless forms have been derived from the flying form by further specialization of the curious form of surface locomotion which is already well developed in it. But whether they have been independently derived or have differentiated into the mainland and Falkland form subsequent to losing their powers of flight, is uncertain, as is the mode by which isolation between flightless and flying forms occurred in the first place.

The two shearwaters *Puffinus griseus* and *P. tenuirostris* are closely similar except that the former is larger. In New Zealand, only *P. griseus* is found, while *P. tenuirostris* breeds in southern Australia. Wood-Jones (1936) considers that both species breed on the same island off Tasmania. This finding would indicate that the two species have remet after geographical differentiation.

Two close and overlapping species of the insectivore *Hemi-*

centetes seem to be ecobiotically differentiated in relation to size of prey, one having considerably smaller teeth (Butler, 1941).

We now return to the extremely important question of how related species which overlap spatially are in nature prevented from intercrossing. It is clear on general grounds that wherever such crossing is possible, whether it results in fully fertile, partly fertile, or infertile offspring, or is itself wholly sterile, its occurrence will usually be a biological disadvantage. This is obvious whenever loss of fertility is involved: on the average, individuals whose mating produces no offspring, or offspring which themselves show partial or complete infertility, will be less fully represented in later generations than individuals whose matings are fully fertile. But even when the offspring of two distinct types are fully fertile, their production may be a disadvantage. This will be so when the parent types are ecologically well adapted to distinct environments or modes of life: for *ex hypothesi* their hybrid products will be less well adapted.

Accordingly we may expect natural selection to operate to prevent the crossing of related but distinct forms under the following conditions: (1) when the two forms overlap spatially and consequently have the opportunity of interbreeding; and (2) *either*, (*a*) when divergence has proceeded far enough for crossing to be attended with reduction in fertility, of whatever nature; *or* (*b*) when the two forms are subject to strong selection adapting them to distinct environments or modes of life.

We shall, on the contrary, not expect such special barriers to mating to be erected when (1) the two forms do not overlap spatially; *or* (2) they overlap spatially but are capable of producing fully fertile offspring, and are further not subject to strong selection promoting adaptive ecological divergence.

Let us see how these deductions work out in practice. The simplest method by which related forms can be prevented from crossing is by the possession of distinct breeding seasons, and this is frequently found to occur. An inspection of the breeding seasons of the marine animals of the Gulf of Naples shows many examples, and a number of cases are known among flowering plants, moths, etc.

This, however, is not always practicable. In temperate and arctic climates, it is inevitable that the bulk of the bird species, for instance, will breed at almost the same period, and the same will often apply to flowering plants. With flowering plants, various alternatives are possible. Either the flowers may open at different times of day; or a sharp distinction in colour or form of flower may be evolved, which, since bees tend to visit a number of similar flowers in series, will reduce the chance of cross-pollination; or the two forms may become adapted to pollination by different species of insects. Factors making for reduced fertility of foreign pollen may also be encouraged.

With higher animals, the most obvious method will be the encouragement of specific mating reactions. Numerous interesting cases of this exist. In *Drosophila*, no example is known where different species will mate as readily as do individuals of the same species. Races A and B of *D. pseudoobscura* almost certainly differ in the males' stimulating scent. The sprosser and the nightingale will mate in captivity, but do not do so in nature (pp. 246, 254).

In general, it will be found that among birds and other higher animals overlapping and related forms frequently differ markedly in regard to some character connected with recognition. These recognitional characters may be auditory, visual or olfactory, and they may be common to the group as a whole, or confined to one sex. In any case, they often have a function in relation to keeping the group defined and preventing interbreeding with other groups, though they may and normally will have other functions as well. For instance, in gregarious animals, recognitional characters common to all individuals may serve to keep the group together on migration or to give warning on occasions of danger, or may enable the young to recognize their parents or others of the species, or prevent mating with members of closely-related species. Recognition characters confined to one sex, in addition to facilitating recognition by offspring, may serve for recognition between the sexes, or between members of the same sex, or both (e.g. the "moustache" of the male flicker, *Colaptes auratus*, Noble and Vogt, 1935; and see discussion in Huxley, 1938c); or have some sexually selective function, either in regard to choice of mate, as in ruff or blackcock, or in promoting readiness to copulate, as apparently with most monogamous birds. In all such events, however, any marked difference between the recognition characters of related forms will have a function which we may call that of *group distinctiveness*, in that it will promote the unity of the group which it characterizes and give it a sharper biological delimitation from other related groups (see also p. 545).

Lorenz (1935) has emphasized the biological value of distinctiveness as such in all characters serving to elicit behaviour-reactions in other individuals (allaesthetic characters: Huxley, 1938c); but he has not emphasized this frequently superadded function of group distinctiveness, which is of biological value only in so far as it keeps groups apart: see also Lack (1941).*

As examples of distinctive characters serving as barriers against intercrossing, we may note the fact that bird species that are closely similar in appearance and overlap spatially frequently differ strikingly in their calls and songs. This is best exemplified in the songs of the three British species of *Phylloscopus*, the chiffchaff (*Phylloscopus collybita*), willow warbler (*P. trochilus*), and wood warbler (*P. sibilatrix*), notably the first two. It was by their songs that Gilbert White in 1768 was able to be the first to distinguish all three. Other good British examples are the meadow and tree pipits, and the marsh and willow tits (p. 270). As Mayr (1940b) writes of certain almost indistinguishable overlapping species of minivet (*Pericrocotus*), *Cisticola*, etc., "the birds themselves are apparently not deceived, though the taxonomists are", since hybridization seems not to occur.

Song in these forms thus has a dual function. Since its primary function is to advertise the possession of territory, it must be striking; but since a secondary function is to advertise the fact only to members of the same group, the song of related and overlapping forms must be markedly different. It is both distinctive *per se* and also group-distinctive.

* Molony (1937) in a recent book has done useful service by drawing attention, from the standpoint of a field-naturalist, to the group function of recognition marks, especially in keeping the young in the group and within the group tradition.

Heinroth and Heinroth (1924-6; vol. 1, p. 49) have a general discussion of the songs of the thrushes (*Turdus*), which illustrates the same principle.

It is interesting to note that the marked differentiation of the various species in song bears no obvious relationship to their equally striking differentiation in visual appearance. In visual appearance, the original thrush type (brown with spotted underparts) has been modified in various species (primarily in the males) by the addition of striking characters like the black head and chestnut breast of the American robin (*Turdus migratorius*) or by a total transformation as in the blackbird (*T. merula*) or the ring ouzel (*T. torquatus*). This striking differentiation in visual appearance due to the need for specific distinctiveness is seen in many other birds, either in the males only or in both sexes. Obvious examples include that between the whinchat and stonechat (*Saxicola rubetra* and *S. torquata*); the special colorations of the goldfinch (*Carduelis carduelis*) or the redpolls (*C. flammea*) compared with other members of the genus; the white nape-patch of the cole tit (*Parus ater*) as against its absence in the marsh and willow tits; the colour of the crest in goldcrest and firecrest (*Regulus regulus* and *R. ignicapillus*) respectively; the general colour of the blackbird (*Turdus merula*), as against the more typical brown and spotted song-thrush (*T. philomelus*), and the white breast-crescent of the ring ouzel (*T. torquatus*) as against its absence in the blackbird; the strikingly different coloration and pattern of the males in related species of duck— these are all presumably examples of this difference-function. Lack (1940a) has recently shown that one important function of beak-size and -shape in the ground-finches (*Geospizidae*) of the Galapagos is to facilitate specific recognition for mating purposes.

It is tempting to suppose that the striking difference in coloration between the males of the chalkhill and Clifton blue butterflies (p. 285) serve as sexual recognition characters of this type; but experimental evidence is lacking in this case, and what exists for most other Lepidoptera makes it appear that any preparatory visual recognition is of females by males (except in *Hepialus*).

A more directly sexual character keeping related species from crossing is found in the dart or *spiculum amoris* in the overlapping snail species *Cepaea hortensis* and *Cepaea nemoralis*. That of *nemoralis* is bigger and more powerfully ejected than that of the other; as a result, if members of the two species attempt to pair, the weaker fails to provide adequate sexual stimulus, while that of the other is so powerful that it causes the weaker to shrink away (Diver, 1940, p. 326).

In the deermice *Peromyscus*, several cases occur of distinct subspecies sharing the same geographical area but being adapted to different habitats. Thus in *P. maniculatus* (Dice, 1931) members of short-tailed prairie-dwelling subspecies may overlap with members of various long-tailed woodland-dwelling forms. Specimens of *P. m. osgoodi* and *P. m. artemisii* may even be caught in the same traps. We may conjecture that in this last case the discontinuity is here preserved by some difference in mating reactions. The same appears to be true for the two good species *P. leucopus*, the wood-mouse, and *P. gossypinus*, the cotton-mouse, the former northern (and western), the latter southern (Dice, 1940a). Though interfertile in captivity, the two remain perfectly distinct in the small area where their ranges overlap. Dice considers that this psychosexual type of isolation is the major one in *Peromyscus*; ecological isolation may occasionally reinforce sexual, but tends to break down at the margins of habitat zones, where the ecological relations are somewhat abnormal. This is doubtless not general, though Spencer (1940) regards psychosexual and reproductive barriers as primary in the differentiation of *Drosophila*. In the garter-snake, *Thamnophis ordinoides*, ecological differentiation, largely related to terrestrial or aquatic habit, may be primary (Fitch, 1940); aquatic habit, which arises in arid areas, permits much larger size; different ecological subspecies frequently come to overlap geographically.

Where neither psychosexual nor ecological isolation is operative, two (or more) subspecies which meet owing to range-changes may fuse into one. Both Dice and Sumner, the two chief authorities on the biotaxonomy of the genus *Peromyscus*, consider that such polyphyletic subspecies are not infrequent in it (see p. 248).

Besides such sexual characters which act as barriers to intercrossing by promoting assortative mating, non-sexual recognition characters may have a similar effect by keeping members of a species together. The distinctive wing-bars of various related birds (e.g. sandpipers, etc.), or the striking and diversely coloured specula on the wings of different species of ducks will serve as visual examples, while there are innumerable cases of group-distinctive but non-sexual call-notes.

Olfactory characters, of course, will play a part in groups like mammals and insects where the sense of smell is more important than it is in birds. It is probable that such characters are group-distinctive in *Drosophila*.

It must be admitted that there are many cases where no wholly satisfactory explanation of the absence of intercrossing between overlapping and related species is as yet forthcoming. Diver (1940) has enumerated some of these; for instance, that of the numerous and often scarcely distinguishable species of the grass-moths of the genus *Crambus*, many of which may be found on the same ground. We may presume that slight but distinctive olfactory stimuli control the mating-reactions, but this is purely hypothetical; and the problem of initial divergence remains. See also A. P. Blair (1941) on overlapping species of tree-frogs.

These examples will serve to substantiate our deduction that mating barriers of special type, often psychological, will tend to be created between closely-related species which show spatial overlap. But we also drew the converse deduction, namely, that such spatial barriers will *not* tend to arise between closely-related forms which have differentiated in separate geographical areas. For the adaptations involved will not, in general, be of so specialized a nature; and further, since during the early stages of divergence intercrossing will not occur at all, or only at the margins of the range (where environmental conditions also will be intermediate) there will be little or no opportunity for selection to act. We shall accordingly expect a similar degree of character-divergence to be accompanied by fewer and lower barriers to intercrossing.

An important fact supporting this deduction is that when forms which have differentiated in different regions later extend their geographical range so as to overlap, intercrossing may occur freely, and the offspring be fertile.

We have already mentioned examples of this, notably in the flickers in America, the crows and other birds in the Old World, and various plant species (p. 115).

Another excellent case concerns the red grouse (*Lagopus scoticus*) of Britain and the willow grouse (*L. lagopus*) of Scandinavia. These, though generally recognized as "good species", are closely allied, and their considerable differences are clearly the result of geographical divergence. However, there has been no pressure of selection operating to erect barriers to inter-crossing, and accordingly, when either species is introduced into the geographical range of the other, the aliens, contrary to the expectation of the sportsmen responsible for the introduction, have not maintained themselves, but have quickly become incorporated into the indigenous species. A similar lack of barriers may exist between wholly unrelated moths. Mr. Ford tells me he has found male burnets (*Zygaena filipendula*) attracted by female oak-eggars (*Bombyx quercus*). Here the waste arising from the actual production of hybrids is absent, and ecological preference normally isolates the two forms.

Dobzhansky (1937, p. 258, and, more emphatically, 1940) is of the opinion that restriction on interfertility (in the broadest sense) will be brought about *only* by selection, whereas most authors believe that random accumulation of differences in stocks isolated from each other will in the long run inevitably lead to some restriction, whether by reducing the frequency of unlike matings or the fertility or viability of their offspring (p. 371). There is no question that, even if an initial reduction of interfertility may be due to the accidents of divergence, it may subsequently be increased by selection (p. 360). In this connection it is worth noting that in the case of the crows (p. 248) and the grackles (p. 251), the zone of intergradation is narrowest where the two forms are presumed to have been longest in contact, and where therefore selection aimed at the reduction of biological waste will have had more chance to exert its effects. It would be of the greatest interest to test individuals from the most recent and the longest-established areas of contact to see whether they are in point of fact generally different in their psychosexual reactions or in the viability or fertility of their offspring.

★   ★   ★   ★   ★

The problem is not simple. We must remember that related species now found together in one region may have differentiated in quite separate regions and have been brought together later by migration. The British Isles, for instance, contain representatives of three or four regional faunas—Northern, Central European, South-eastern European, and Lusitanian. Only after the end of the Ice Age were these brought together in our islands, so that the original differentiation of many forms, such as the common and mountain hare (p. 246) or the carrion and hoodie crows (p. 248) occurred in different regions.

There is also plenty of evidence to show that, as we should expect, character-divergence shows a correlation with genetic intersterility. In the deermice of the genus *Peromyscus*, Dice (1933*b*) has shown that whereas subspecies are mutually highly interfertile, and "good" species belonging to the same species-group, as defined by morphological resemblance, are moderately so, those belonging to different species-groups are wholly inter-sterile. But the condition appears to differ for different types of animal. In deermice marked intersterility appears with a small degree of morphological difference (sub-generic or "sub-sub-generic"). In pheasants, so far as the evidence goes, it begins with generic difference, and in some ducks at least, even generic crosses may be quite fertile. There is also evidence that different types of Canidae may be interfertile in spite of wide taxonomic divergence. In any case this type of sterility is often associated with readiness to mate, and if so is quite different from the special barriers to intercrossing we have been considering, which usually operate to prevent mating rather than to reduce fertility.

It is clear that many more facts are needed, based on the analysis of a large number of crosses between related species of ecological and geographical type. None the less, the following deductions appear to hold. First, that with the same degree of general character-divergence (excluding characters promoting assortative mating and acting as barriers to interspecific crossing), types which have diverged in geographical isolation will show less effective barriers, direct or indirect, to fertility, than those which show ecological divergence in the same area. But secondly, that as regards characters promoting assortative and impeding interspecific mating, the ecological type of speciation within the same region will accentuate the degree of character-divergence, largely by promoting the evolution of characters accentuating group-distinctiveness (p. 289).

This last point is clearly valid, since such characters are only serviceable if they are immediately recognizable, or at least sharply and qualitatively distinct. It is further likely that ecological but spatially-overlapping differentiation will promote a more rapid and thorough divergence in general characters, since more complete adaptation to the two ecological niches will be an advantage to both species. And for this reason it will be difficult to attach precise meaning to comparisons as to degree of divergence between the ecological and the geographical types of speciation. What we can say, however, is that when the degree of general character-divergence between two overlapping species is slight, and we yet find considerable barriers to intercrossing, we shall expect to find lower barriers between two non-overlapping (geographically isolated) species with the same degree of character-divergence. And this, so far as we can judge on the evidence at present available, is true.

4. BIOLOGICAL DIFFERENTIATION

A special type of ecobiotic divergence, and one which from its practical bearings has recently received a great deal of attention, is that usually known as biological (or physiological) differentiation. By this is meant the divergent adaptation of separate groups of parasites or phytophagous animals to particular hosts or food-plants. Reviews of the subject have been given by Thorpe (1930, 1940), from which we select most of our examples. (References given only for cases not cited from Thorpe.)

The most striking points about this kind of differentiation are as follows. First, all gradations are found from incipient physiological subspecies to full species characterized by complete intersterility and morphological differences. Secondly, however, the visible morphological divergence lags further behind the invisible physiological (including the reproductive) than in any other type of differentiation. Thirdly, barriers to intercrossing, largely it would appear on a psychological basis, appear to be speedily set up by selection between the diverging groups. And finally, the biological differentiation in its early stages appears usually to depend upon an interesting form of organic selection (the Baldwin and Lloyd Morgan principle; p. 304) operating in its modificational phase through olfactory conditioning.

Let us now examine some well-analysed cases in the light of these principles. The maggot of the Dipteran known as the apple fly (*Rhagoletis pomonella*) is very destructive to certain fruits. It appears originally to have been a parasite of a species of hawthorn (*Crataegus*) in North America, but this genus is now but rarely attacked. It exists in two main forms, differing in no visible characteristic except size, but confined to different host-plants, the larger attacking apples and related fruits, the smaller blueberries and huckleberries. The difference in size averages about 30 per cent, and there is no overlap. In some states, e.g. Maine, the "blueberry maggot" has been immemorially established, while the date of introduction of the "apple maggot" and the course of its subsequent spread are known. It is extremely hard to raise one form on the host-plant of the other. Crosses can be obtained artificially between the two forms, but only with difficulty, though the offspring are viable. There seems no question that the two forms are, reproductively speaking, good species, in spite of their morphological similarity. The original differentiation may have been into hawthorn and blueberry forms, the hawthorn type later becoming adapted to apples, but this is uncertain.

The two forms of the Homopteran *Psylla mali* provide a very similar case. Here again the adults of the two types differ morphologically only in size, but are exclusively confined to apple and hawthorn respectively. However, the differentiation has gone a little further than in *Rhagoletis*, for it has so far proved impossible to make the one race lay eggs on the other's food-plant, or to obtain cross-breeding. In addition, slight morphological differences have developed between the two types in the nymphal stage. An interesting point is that the hawthorn race is parasitized by certain Chalcids and Proctotrypids, but the apple race is not. Such forms, though for museum purposes it is convenient to leave them in the category of "biological races", must be considered by the evolutionary biologist as distinct species.

A much smaller degree of divergence is shown by the biological races of the ermine moth *Hyponomeuta padella*, one being adapted to apples, the other to hawthorn and blackthorn. No structural features separate the two, although there are slight colour differences; the colour of the forewings in the species as a whole ranges from dark grey to pure white, and the dark forms are more abundant on hawthorn, the white form on apple. The apple form is usually a leaf-miner in its first larval instar, the other not; the pupae of the apple race are usually to be found in neat packets or rows, with a dense cocoon, while those of the hawthorn and blackthorn race are generally scattered, and the cocoon is very flimsy.

If the moths are given the choice of food-plants, they show a decided preference for their normal host (80 per cent in the case of the apple race, 90 per cent in that of the hawthorn one). Although the hawthorn and blackthorn "sub-races" are indistinguishable in most ways, they are actually separable on the basis of egg-laying preferences (80 per cent and 70 per cent for the hawthorn and blackthorn forms respectively).

The food-preferences of the larvae also, though marked, are not fixed; they can be induced by starvation to feed on the "wrong" food, though the resultant imagines are generally undersized and often infertile. Finally, the mating-preferences are only relative. Elaborate and large-scale experiments showed that the attraction between individuals of the same race was about twice as strong as that between those of different races.

Owing to these various preferences, the different races must keep themselves fairly distinct in nature, although occasional crossing probably occurs. The races are thus "biological subspecies", and deserve trinomial recognition.

Some remarkable results have been obtained on crickets. Thus in Oregon the snowy tree-cricket *Oecanthus nivalis* exists in two forms. The one race is a tree-dweller, and lays its eggs singly on the bark of apples and similar trees; the other lives in bushes, and lays its eggs in dense rows inside the pith of raspberries and similar shrubs. The two types show no visible differences, but are immediately distinguishable by ear, the shrub race uttering its repeated notes with a frequency only about half that characteristic of the other. The form found in the eastern United States resembles the tree race in its habits, but is characterized by a distinctive song of its own. It is always difficult and sometimes impossible to make the shrub form lay its eggs on trees, and *vice versa*.

Another cricket, *Nemobius fasciatus*, is in Iowa divided into several races readily distinguishable by song-frequency. Again, each race has its own ecological niche, but shows no or negligible morphological or colour differentiation. In various regions, the different races are found side by side. In this case crosses have been made between members of distinct races, and the results indicate that the song-difference is genetically determined, and is dependent on several interacting genes.

Since the song of crickets is an epigamic character, and since recent work (cf. Pumphrey and Rawdon-Smith, 1936) indicates that insects must rely specially upon differences in song-frequency (rather than pitch) for auditory discrimination, this seems a clear case of the evolution of a special barrier against intercrossing between ecologically-differentiated groups (pp. 287, 385). The different types are perhaps best regarded as well-marked subspecies, though well on the way to complete independence.

In wood-boring beetles of the family Cerambycidae, results were obtained very similar to those in *Hyponomeuta*. Various species are differentiated into "biological subspecies", normally confined to one or a few kinds of wood. In every case (e.g. the hickory and wild grape strains of *Cyllene pictus*) the larvae can be made to abandon their preferences and to live on and eventually even to prefer a different type of wood; but the difficulty of inducing altered habits, and the initial mortality, differed very greatly in different species. In one case at least moderate assortative mating preferences were exhibited.

In Hawaii, in the beetle *Plagithysmus*, the process of biological differentiation appears to have proceeded further, to the stage of good species. Three species, each confined to its own food-plant, and apparently never crossing, may occur together within the space of a few yards. Distinct morphological differences between them exist, but are so slight that one entomologist has written, "It is hardly conceivable that species can be more closely allied than these and yet remain distinct." Such a judgment reflects the natural preoccupation of the taxonomist with visible structural diagnostics: we now know that groups may remain perfectly distinct though morphologically indistinguishable.

Many forms of gall-producing insects (e.g. *Cynips*) are distinguishable solely or mainly by the type of gall to which they give rise. These will probably turn out to be adaptive "biological races".

Sometimes these biologically adapted forms are also geographically separated. Thorpe (1930) mentions the following illustration. In the Orient, the red scale *Chrysomphalus aurantii* is parasitized by a chalcid wasp, *Camperiella bifasciata*. But when this was introduced into California to cope with the scale pest there, it was found to be useless. Although *C. aurantii* in California is indistinguishable from *C. aurantii* in the Orient, it must be different physiologically, for though the chalcid parasite lays its eggs on it, the larvae are always destroyed by phagocytosis, instead of developing freely at its expense, as in the Orient.

It is interesting that the concept of biological races in wood-boring and phytophagous insects was advanced sixty-five years ago by Walsh, but that his conclusions remained virtually unnoticed until 1923.

Biological races of this type are not confined to insects, but are found also in many other groups, such as Arachnida, Nematoda, Protozoa, Bacteria, Fungi, and some higher plants. Among the latter, the different races of mistletoe may be mentioned, each characterized by ability to parasitize a particular host (p. 308).

In Arachnida, the evidence, though not fully conclusive, makes it very probable that the mange-mites of the species *Sarcoptes scaber* are split up into biological races each adapted to a particular host—goats, sheep, camels, dogs, horses, guinea-pigs, rabbits, men, etc.

In the free-living mites of the genus *Paratetranychus*, the process has continued to full speciation, *P. pilosus* attacking only fruits of deciduous trees, and *P. citri* only citrus fruits. Though cross-mating occurs readily, it is never fertile; there are very slight morphological differences (so slight that the two forms were long regarded as belonging to a single species), and also slight differences in habits, egg-laying and food preferences, and in distribution.

The "red spider" (*Tetranychus opuntiae*) introduced into Australia to combat the spread of prickly pear (*Opuntia*) is morphologically identical with the "red spider" of orchards and gardens, but is entirely confined to *Opuntia*, and appears always to starve to death on any other food-plant. Here we have complete biological separation, but no visible divergence.

Among Nematoda, *Tylenchus dipsaci* appears to be well-differentiated into biological races, e.g. the strawberry race and the narcissus race. In *Heterodera radicola*, on the other hand, the various biological races can be made to adapt themselves to new hosts without much difficulty.

Among Protozoa, the trypanosomes show well-marked "biological races" adapted to different hosts (see e.g. Duke, 1921), but in these unicellular forms it is not certain to what extent the phenomenon is due to *Dauermodifikationen* induced by the different conditions.

In Myxosporidia, similar physiological races also exist (Fantham, Porter and Richardson, 1939).

The phenomenon of biological differentiation seems to be of common occurrence in certain fungi. The few examples which follow are taken from the summary by Ramsbottom (1940). The changes known to mycologists as *saltation* seem probably to be akin to the so-called "mutations" of bacteria (p. 131), and in some cases at least to the *Dauermodifikationen* of Protozoa. In any case, in pathogenic forms they often result, as in bacteria, in changes of virulence towards particular host-strains. In the rusts (Uredineae), what appear to be true biological races are widespread. Sometimes the parasitism is so strict that host-species may be identified by its means, as when, in the difficult group of willows, one species was identified by its reaction to the rust *Melampsora ribesii-purpurea*. Similarly some rusts occurring on separate but related hosts, and with specific life-histories, often show close morphological resemblances. In such cases we are clearly dealing with biological differentiation which has passed the species-level.

The *Puccinia* of grasses show the same phenomenon at the level of "biological races", but pushed to an extraordinary degree of diversification. Thus from one originally recognized "species" *P. graminis*, a second, *P. phlei-pratensis*, parasitizing *Phleum*, was divided off some thirty years ago. The restricted *P. graminis*, it was then found, could be divided into six "forms", according as the host-plant was wheat, oats, rye, or various grasses. Each of these has now been shown to consist of numerous minor biological races, varying in regard to their infective specificity for various strains of the host-plant; thus some seventy "physiologic forms" have already been detected within the main wheat form. Ramsbottom considers that the "species" *P. graminis* includes at least a thousand separate biological strains, each conserving its physiological peculiarities with "remarkable constancy" (see also below, p. 308).

It is of great biological interest to find that this veritable army of biological races, which in one phase of its life-history is specifically adapted to several genera and a great many full species of grasses and cereals, is restricted during its other phase to quite a few species of the two genera, *Berberis* and *Mahonia*. Two strains which cannot live on the same grass can and do live on the same barberry. This unequal specialization is doubtless due to the unequal taxonomic differentiation of the two types of host-plant, and must assuredly have been accentuated by the artificial production by man of new strains for the grass phase to invade. It is an excellent example of adaptation localized in time to a particular part of the life-history (cf. p. 424).

Of biological differentiation in bacteria we shall not speak, since it is not certain, owing to the absence of sexual reproduction in members of this group and their consequent different type of evolution, whether it really represents the same phenomenon as in higher organisms (p. 131). This at least can be said—that strains differing in virulence and in various important biological and biochemical properties do exist within types that appear homogeneous by ordinary criteria, and that the phenomenon in bacteria and higher organisms must rest on a common and fundamental capacity for physiological adaptation of strains within a group.

It remains to discuss the evolutionary origin of biological differentiation in animals. For a considerable time it was supposed that this was a lamarckian phenomenon, and various experiments apparently supporting this view were adduced. To take but one instance, J. W. H. Harrison (1927) studied a sawfly, *Pontania salicis*, whose larvae produce galls on willows. This "species" contains a number of distinct biological races, each normally confined to a particular species of willow, and each with specific egg-laying preferences. However, he was able to convert the biological race normally confined to *Salix andersoniana* into one adapted to *S. rubra*, by restricting specimens for four years to plants of the latter species. The experiment was continued for three further years, during which a choice of both species of willow was provided, but the strain remained true to its new host. It is to be noted that the mortality in the first generation was very high, and that only gradually was a race established which could be said to be adapted to *S. rubra*.

Thorpe cites numerous similar cases, but this appears to be the most thorough of what we may call the preliminary researches on this point. Lately, however, Thorpe himself has carried out beautiful experiments which demonstrate that the lamarckian interpretation is neither necessary nor tenable. He first of all (Thorpe and Jones, 1937) reared the ichneumonid *Nemeritis canescens*, which normally parasitizes only the larvae of the meal-moth *Ephestia kuhniella*, on those of the wax-moth *Achroia grisella*. This resulted in a significant change .in the responses of the adult females. All female imagines of the species possess a genetically-determined response to the smell of *Ephestia*; but those which have been reared as larvae on *Achroia*, or have been brought into close contact with it immediately after emergence, show in addition an attraction to *Achroia* which those from normal hosts altogether lack. Later work showed that this result of larval conditioning depends on a general tendency to be attracted by any olfactory stimulus characteristic of a favourable environment (Thorpe, 1938).

Further work with *Drosophila melanogaster* (Thorpe, 1939) has extended these results and shown their general applicability to non-parasitic as well as parasitic insects. Whereas adult fruit-flies are normally repelled by the smell of peppermint, those which have been reared on a synthetic food medium to which peppermint essence has been added, are markedly attracted by the smell of peppermint when tested in an olfactometer. Further, this response is not abolished (though it is somewhat reduced) by washing the fully-fed larvae or newly-formed puparia free of all traces of the medium and of the peppermint essence, thus proving that influences operative only during the larval phase can influence adult behaviour. If not reinforced, the influence gradually disappears and becomes extinct after about a week. Finally, in *Drosophila* as in *Nemeritis*, it was found that exposure of the adult insects only, immediately after emergence, to the smell of peppermint brings about positive conditioning even if the smell is not associated with any favourable aspect of the environment—the mere fact of the occurrence of the stimulus at this time brings about subsequent attraction to media containing the same substance.*

To use Thorpe's own words, "the theoretical importance of such a conditioning effect is that it will tend to split a population

---

* As Thorpe (1939) suggests, these results may also explain the interesting results obtained by Sladden and Hewer (1938) on the food-preferences of stick insects, for which, prior to Thorpe's work, a lamarckian interpretation seemed almost inevitable (see p. 459). It will be of the greater interest to test Sladden's results in the light of Thorpe's methods, and with a species capable of sexual reproduction.

into groups attached to a particular host or food-plant, and thus will of itself tend to prevent cross-breeding. It will, in other words, provide a non-hereditary barrier which may serve as the first stage in evolutionary divergence". We have here a beautiful case of the principle of organic selection (p. 523), as enunciated by Baldwin (1896, 1902) and Lloyd Morgan (1900), according to which modifications repeated for a number of generations may serve as the first step in evolutionary change, not by becoming impressed upon the germ-plasm, but by holding the strain in an environment where mutations tending in the same direction will be selected and incorporated into the constitution. The process simulates lamarckism but actually consists in the replacement of modifications by mutations (see also Osborn, 1897).

That such a replacement has actually occurred in the formation of biological races in insects is strongly indicated by the high mortality that, in Harrison's experiments with *Pontania* and many other cases, often attends transference to a new host. Harrison was able to transfer his sawflies to a new host-plant by means of their olfactory conditioning mechanism, but only at the expense of eliminating those that were genetically best adapted to the old host. Had previous genetic adaptation gone further, olfactory conditioning, while it might still have induced oviposition on the strange host, could not have given rise to a viable strain upon it.

Once genetic adaptation to a particular host has begun, selection will step in to prevent the biological waste which would be caused by the desposition of eggs on other hosts. The mechanism of olfactory conditioning provides a certain reserve of plasticity; but this plasticity will become hedged about by genetic safeguards. Genetically-determined attractions to the normal host will become established, and also specific assortative mating reactions to prevent cross-mating. Thus ecobiotic isolation here has the same general effects as geographical or ecotopic isolation, but operates by rather a different mechanism, and follows a somewhat different course as regards the degree of divergence in morphological, physiological, and reproductive characters respectively.

Organic selection, but of a quite different type, appears probably to be operative in lice (*Pediculus*; summary in Thorpe, 1930). As is now well known, though the human body-louse and head-louse are so distinct morphologically that they have received different names, yet head-lice can be transformed into the body-louse type by being kept on the body for four generations. Unfortunately no data exist as to the initial mortality, though the change seems to have been readily effected. The two types also exhibit biological differences. Head-lice feed more frequently but take smaller meals, are more active at lower temperatures, climb more actively, and exhibit egg-laying preferences for hair as against cloth. The two types must be constantly exchanging members by migration. It would seem that we are here witnessing the incipient phase of a process of organic selection, in which most of the quite well-marked differences between the two forms still depend on modification. However, anything which intensifies selection for closer adaptation would, we may prophesy, speedily bring about genetic and reproductive divergence. Nuttall suggests that, if man becomes progressively more hairless, body-lice alone will survive. If so, many of their adaptive peculiarities should become genetically fixed by selection (but see also Buxton, 1940; Parasitol: **32**: 303).

Organic selection may also operate in song-birds. Some basis for song is certainly fixed genetically in all birds, and in some species this is the whole story. In others, however, there is considerable plasticity, and much of the song is learnt by the young birds from their parents or other adults. Thus Baltimore orioles (*Icterus galbula*) reared in isolation developed a song totally unlike the normal, and retained it throughout their lives. Other Baltimore orioles reared with them learned this song and sang it exclusively, even after their foster-parents' death (W. E. Scott, 1901–2). By isolating young canaries and allowing them to hear only the song of the nightingale (on gramophone records) it has been possible to produce a strain with a song intermediate between the canary and nightingale type.*

Numerous data on the subject are scattered through the

* A brief reference to this experiment is made in *J. Orn.* **75**: 248 (1927). Dr. E. Mayr tells me that it was carried out by a fancier named Reich, but that complete proof was not supplied.

Heinroths' monumental work (1924-6); see also O. Heinroth (1924), Stadler (1929). In the blackbird (*Turdus merula*), the chiffchaff (*Phylloscopus collybita*), the grasshopper warbler (*Locustella naevia*) and the short-toed treecreeper (*Certhia brachydactyla*) song is innate, and is quite normal even in males reared without hearing others of their own species sing, whether in isolation or exposed to the songs of other species.

On the other hand, the whitethroat (*Sylvia communis*), the tree and meadow pipits (*Anthus trivialis* and *A. pratensis*), the greenfinch (*Chloris chloris*), and the chaffinch (*Fringilla coelebs*) have to learn their songs. Young males if kept in isolation produce a quite abnormal song, e.g. those of the untaught tree pipit and meadow pipit resemble the natural songs of grasshopper warbler and serin finch (*Serinus canarius*) respectively, while that of the untaught chaffinch is not unlike that of a lesser whitethroat (*Sylvia curruca*).

It is not easy to discover on how many cases the Heinroths' conclusions are based, and possibly the reality is not quite so clear-cut. However, the general conclusion that some species have to learn their song seems inescapable.

Forms in which song is not innate will, if kept with other species, learn from them. Thus a whitethroat and a linnet (*Carduelis cannabina*) reared together both had an identical song, resembling a mixture of a robin's and a skylark's.

There seems to be a predisposition to learn the normal song; thus a nightingale which mimicked the songs of various species with which it had been reared, very rapidly learnt its normal song on hearing it next year.

Other species if kept isolated will produce an imperfect version of the normal song, and will learn more or less thoroughly from other species. Thus the untaught yellowhammer (*Emberiza citrinella*) never develops the complete natural "phrasing": one kept with a normal linnet developed a song extremely like a linnet's! The robin (*Erithacus rubecula*) and blackcap (*Sylvia atricapilla*) fall into this category. The song of the song-thrush (*Turdus ericetorum*) is almost wholly innate, but can be slightly modified by "learning"; the skylark (*Alauda arvensis*) has a song which must be almost wholly learnt.

It would be expected that simple songs would be innate, elaborate songs learnt. But while this is true for simple songs like the chiffchaff's and for more elaborate songs like the whitethroat's, the elaborate song of the blackbird is innate, and the relatively simple song of the chaffinch has less innate basis than the blackcap's very elaborate song.

Members of the same group may differ radically; thus the warblers (Sylviinae) include all three types, e.g. chiffchaff (innate), blackcap (partly innate) and whitethroat (wholly learnt).

In most Oscines the call-notes are genetically determined, but in the whinchat (*Saxicola rubetra*) and several finches some or all must be learnt. A goldfinch kept with a budgerigar developed call-notes entirely of budgerigar type. In all other groups of birds, the call-notes are wholly innate.

One might further expect that learnt songs would be more variable in nature than innate ones; but this does not seem to be the case (except possibly for the chaffinch).

The need for distinctiveness gives a possible clue to the origin of this extraordinary phenomenon. Granted the widespread capacity to imitate the notes of other species, which appears to be widespread among Oscines (though to a very varying degree), the character of a song could be much more rapidly altered modificationally, by learning from exceptional performers, than genetically; and this would be advantageous with two related species, originally with very similar songs, inhabiting the same area (cf. p. 289). The new learnt type of song might later be rendered partly or wholly innate by mutation (organic selection; pp. 304, 523).

Barking in dogs and its absence in wolves are both non-genetic (Iljin, 1941); in certain conditions dogs cease barking, in others captive wolves begin barking like dogs.

In fungi, no conditioning mechanism (p. 303) can operate, as it obviously depends on a high degree of nervous specialization. Recent research (T. Johnson and Newton, 1938) on the wheat form of *Puccinia graminis* (see p. 301) show that the inbreeding (by selfing) of biological races brings about the appearance of many new types, apparently by the bringing to light of mendelian recessives. Some of the new characters concern colour, others are semi-pathological, while still others cause a change in the life-cycle or an alteration in virulence. The authors point out that homozygosity in rusts like *Puccinia* must be rare. Thus the variety of biological races would here appear to be maintained through a wide range of variability for those properties concerned with adaptation to various hosts, coupled presumably with widespread mortality of the non-adaptive combinations. If so, then we have a close parallel to the method by which ecoclines are established in higher plants (p. 275), and another case of marked divergence between plants and animals as to the mechanisms underlying adaptive differentiation.

True physiological races do occur in parasitic higher plants, e.g. the common mistletoe *Viscum album* (see A. W. Hill, 1930). Here, however, the mechanism of differentiation seems to be similar to that in insects. This species comprises three main races or groups of races, one parasitizing deciduous trees, one firs (*Abies*) and one pines (*Pinus*). These are so strongly differentiated that the seeds of a fir mistletoe, for instance, will not grow on a pine or *vice versa*: visible differences between the races, however, are negligible.

5. PHYSIOLOGICAL AND REPRODUCTIVE DIFFERENTIATION

Biological races provide the best-analysed cases of evolutionary divergence which is wholly or primarily concentrated on physiological as opposed to morphological characters. However, there are numerous other examples. E.g. subspecies of rattlesnakes may show marked differences in toxicity of venom (Baily, 1941): see also p. 273. We have also referred to the preponderance of vocal divergence in ecologically differentiated species-pairs of birds with inconspicuous habits (p. 289). Geographical differentiation in song is, however, quite a general phenomenon in birds. For instance, Promptoff (1930) and Howard (1900, 1902) have studied the geographical variation in the song of the chaffinch (*Fringilla coelebs*), and find it quite marked. An interesting point stressed by Promptoff is that the characteristic differences in the song of chaffinches are in part learnt by the young birds (Heinroth considers them entirely learnt; p. 306). Thus the different geographical groups will tend to maintain their song-differences in spite of a considerable amount of exchange of populations through the wanderings of young birds—a rather special example of the principle of organic selection. Howard also noted geographical variation in the song of several other species. In general, he concludes that a more humid environment is correlated with a lower pitch. In some species, e.g. blackbird (*Turdus merula*), cuckoo (*Cuculus canorus*), great tit (*Parus major*) and sedge-warbler (*Acrocephalus schoenobaenus*), he found marked geographical variation, while in others, such as yellowhammer (*Emberiza citrinella*) and cole tit (*Parus ater*) it was slight, and in still others, e.g. willow warbler (*Phylloscopus trochilus*), he could detect no differences.

The Shetland subspecies of wren (*Troglodytes t. zetlandicus*) differs more obviously in song than in size or colour from the type subspecies, while the reverse is true for the St. Kilda form (*T. t. hirtensis*). We have mentioned the vocal divergence of crickets (p. 298). Without doubt similar phenomena await discovery in all groups in which sound is concerned with sexual recognition or stimulation.

The recent intensive field study of birds has also brought to light many interesting examples of biological differentiation in habits. Thus the common robin (*Erithacus rubecula*), which is proverbially tame and an associate of man in Britain, elsewhere in its range frequents quite other habitats and may exhibit a very different temperament. For instance, in many parts of central Europe it frequents pine woods, and is not specially tame. In fact Heinroth and Heinroth (1924-1926; vol. I, p. 10) are surprised at what they regard as the legend of its tameness, and say that robins in nature are almost invariably shy and suspicious. Mr. H. F. Witherby informs me that both in Spain and in Corsica it prefers woods remote from human habitation, but whereas even in these situations it is tame in Corsica, in Spain it is very shy.

Tameness may be genetically fixed in regions where normal

predators are absent. Thus in the Galapagos islands Mr. D. Lack tells me that a tyrannid flycatcher, *Myiarchus*, hopped all over him, endeavouring to remove hair from his head, beard, and armpits as nest-material; and Beebe (1924, p. 285) records that the local buzzard (*Buteo galapagensis*) can be approached to within two feet, and specimens have been captured in a butterfly-net!

Individual and local peculiarities in such habits as nest-building have been noted in many species of birds. As an example we may cite Herrick (1939) on the American robin (*Turdus migratorius*). Thus in New Hampshire and Ohio the species never uses leaves in the construction of its nest, in spite of their abundant availability. In New England, where leaves are employed, a particular individual showed a marked preference for those of the silver maple. While these differences appear to be genetically determined, others depend on the availability of particular materials. Thus in the northern part of its range, where the birds are confined to stunted spruce woods, they construct a dense large frame of spruce-twigs, moss, and lichens, and are driven to use grass-blades or moss as lining in place of the customary mud or clay. In northern Maine, twigs are employed for the frame in place of the customary grasses and weeds, and leaf-mould for the lining. Such differences in nest-construction, dependent on availability of material, provide yet another example of organic selection. Genetically determined preferences are likely to be selected for later, to accentuate and fix the differences imposed by the environment.

The choice of nest-site itself may be changed by the environment. Thus to take only a few from the wealth of possible examples, on the treeless island of Texel off the Dutch coast, kestrels (*Falco tinnunculus*) breed on the ground instead of in branches (Van Oordt, 1926), and stockdoves (*Columba oenas*) in holes in the ground instead of holes in trees. Cormorants normally breed on rocky ledges; but in various places they have taken to nesting in trees. All such differences in habit, while originally mere modifications, afford a basis for further genetically-determined divergence of an ecological type. J. Fisher (1939*a*,

Ch. 11) gives various examples of this plasticity both in regard to nest-site and nest-material. Instinctive habitat-selection tends to isolate bird species ecologically, but Lack (1940b) considers that it plays little part in primary speciation, though it may help to keep differentiated forms from meeting and inter-crossing (see p. 254).

Many birds occasionally lay eggs in the nests of other species. This aberration of reproductive instinct has without question formed the basis for the evolution of the various cases of repro-ductive parasitism seen in cowbirds, cuckoos, etc. Cuckoos may show further differentiation into strains adapted to different fosterer species (Jourdain, 1925). Among insects, the slave-making ants provide a parallel example of reproductive specialization.

In migratory species of birds, differentiation may be promoted by individuals remaining in their winter quarters to breed, and eventually establishing isolated breeding-groups. Among examples cited by Meinertzhagen (1919) are the breeding colonies of the bee-eater *Merops apiaster* in S. Africa, and of the sandpiper *Totanus hypoleucus* in E. Africa. The common European swallow, *Hirundo r. rustica*, is suspected of breeding in Uganda. However established in the first instance, such groups would be repro-ductively isolated and might readily come to show visible differentiation.

A remarkable combination of biological with geographical divergence is seen in *Trichogramma* (summarized in Thorpe, 1940). The American forms of this hymenopteran egg-parasite have been carefully studied, and prove to be characterized by bio-logically important differences in length of life-cycle (due to differences in temperature-optimum), accompanied by slight colour-differences. Though the various forms are primarily geographical, there is considerable overlap of distribution, proving the existence of some physiological or reproductive barrier to intercrossing.

The biological differences are highly modifiable by environ-ment; so that rearing under standard conditions is needed to demonstrate them. The differential diagnosis of natural forms is consequently a matter of extreme difficulty. One authority on the genus is reduced to describing a certain form as that "which has distinctly lemon-yellow females during the warm part of the active season"!

This, like most cases of true biological races, has not been brought to light by taxonomists, but by workers in applied biology. It is the economic importance of divergence in physiological characters in pests and counter-pests which has led to the discovery of this new type of taxonomic diversification.

An interesting physiological divergence occurs in the termite *Formenkreis Nasutitermes guayanae* (Emerson, 1935). This can be divided into two distinct groups (considered by Emerson as good species) according to whether the nests contain one or another set of staphylinid beetle species as nest-parasites. The distinction is absolute, and is correlated with slight differences in the soldiers' head-size, though the sexual forms are indistinguishable. Emerson (1934) also reviews cases where termite speciation is accompanied by speciation of the contained protozoan symbiotes.

An even more curious case is that of the leaf-hopper *Cicadulina mbile*, which is divisible into two races solely on ability or inability to transmit the virus of "streak disease" in maize (Storey, 1932). The difference in this case depends on a single gene (a sex-linked dominant), and is concerned with the penetrability of the gut-wall by the virus. Here we would seem to have an "accidental" character present for unknown reasons in dimorphic balance with another. It is easy to see how, through the effect of the virus on the food-plant, it might become the basis for adaptive biological differentiation. But the two forms cannot yet be regarded as true biological subspecies.

Numerous infra-specific groups differing in life-cycle and reproductive mechanism also exist. Thorpe (1940) gives examples of these. Thus the spurge hawk-moth comprises some individuals which are subject to an obligatory diapause in development, while others do not; some authorities maintain that the cockchafer is divisible into groups characterized by three-year and four-year life-cycles; and so on.

A peculiar type of differentiation has been analysed by de Larambergue (1939, 1941) in the pulmonate mollusc *Bulinus con-*

tortus. Here some specimens lack a penis, and are therefore obligatorily self-fertilizing. In certain localities such aphallic individuals constitute the vast majority of the population, in others they are almost absent. Aphallism has a genetic basis, but artificial selection in the laboratory has as yet been unable to produce stocks in which *all* individuals either lack or possess a penis. The condition may possibly be one of balanced selective advantage, comparable with that of gynodioecism in plants (p. 140; and see Mather, 1940).

Reproductive divergence as a cause of speciation is discussed by Hogben (1940). It may characterize related species. Thus in five species of the sea-anemone genus *Sagartia* five distinct methods of reproduction exist (Stephenson, 1929). It may also be of preadaptive advantage. Then we have the recent very rapid extension of range in the gastropod *Paludestrina* (*Potamopyrgus*) *jenkinsi* in the fresh waters of this country, while elsewhere it seems to be restricted to brackish waters (Robson, 1923). Later work (Sanderson, 1940) shows that both British and continental types are parthenogenetic. The British form, however, appears to be tetraploid, and this may be the cause of its greater ecological tolerance.

A somewhat similar case, but one in which the reproductive advantage seems to be causing the replacement of one type by another, not the extension of range of the species as a whole, is described by Crosby (1940) in the primrose, *Primula vulgaris*. In this normally heterostyled species, long homostyle plants (with pin style and thrum anthers) have been found in abundance in an area in Somerset, the abundance decreasing round a centre. If, as seems to be the case, these homostyle plants are normally self-fertilized, it can be calculated that, owing to the peculiarities of reproduction in heterostyle forms, the homostyles will increase at the expense of the two normal heterostyle types (see p. 222).*

* The problem remains as to why the homostyle condition has not everywhere become normal, since occasional homostyles are found, presumably as mutants, in numerous natural populations. Possibly the homostyle type which has become abundant is exceptionally fertile. In any case heterostyly has a long-term advantage in promoting out-crossing (see p. 167).

Various cases in insects are known in which geographical races differ in reproductive methods. Thus in *Diprion polytomum* S. G. Smith (1940, 1941) finds that, though all races are capable of parthenogenesis, in some the unfertilized eggs produce only males, in others females plus a few functionless males. In addition, the types differ in chromosome-number, so that the divergence is also a genetic one. There are some other physiological differences, but no morphological distinctions. Vandel (1939) finds that in a woodlouse of the genus *Trichoniscus*, the triploid parthenogenetic form is much more resistant to low temperature and aridity than the diploid sexual form, and has a correspondingly wider distribution.

The triploid and autotetraploid varieties of numerous plants and some animals also fall into this category. These often differ in consequential characters affecting size, vigour, temperature-resistance, etc., and often in the prevalence (obligatory in triploids) of non-sexual methods of reproduction (see p. 335).

We have already mentioned the primarily physiological differentiation of the forms of *Carabus nemoralis* (Krumbiegel, 1932), the physiological characters of the geographical races of *Lymantria* (p. 216), and the geographical differences of temperature-resistance in *Drosophila funebris* (p. 191). Similarly, on the species level, the North American grape *Vitis labrusca* is much more cold-resistant than the European grape, and crosses with it can be used to confer cold-resistance on wine-grapes to be grown in climates with low winter temperature (Wellington, 1932). Eloff (1936) has shown that local genetic differences occur in *Drosophila melanogaster* as regards the tropisms of pupating larvae, those from a certain area in S. Africa pupating on or in the wet culture medium instead of creeping up to a dry situation.

The differentiation of the genus *Gammarus* seems in many cases to have been primarily physiological, in relation to salinity. A salient example is *G. tigrinus*, recently described by Sexton (1939). Its morphological differentiae are quite slight, but it is characterized by an exceptionally high range of tolerance for salinity and dissolved substances in general, which results in its being restricted in nature to inland waters of peculiar composition.

The case of G. *zaddachi* (Spooner, 1941, and see *J. Mar. Biol. Ass.*, **24:** 444) is even more interesting. This is essentially a brackish-water species, which in short estuaries in the west of England exists only in a low-salinity form. In long estuaries, however, a high-salinity form also exists, nearer the sea, and exhibits visible differences in a few minor characters. Though the two types are so similar, and though their zones somewhat overlap, there is no intergradation in nature, and in captivity, though they will mate and occasionally produce eggs, they are intersterile. These are clearly incipient physiological species, but the origin of the genetic barrier between them is as yet obscure. It is possible that in Germany the ecological relation of the species, and its differentiation, may be somewhat different.

The non-migratory (land-locked) and migratory forms of salmon, as well as the non-migratory brook and lake forms and the migratory form of the trout (Tchernavin, 1939) provide us with another type of physiological differentiation. The distinction between the non-migratory and migratory forms seems in some cases to have been compulsorily imposed by geographical changes resulting in some types becoming land-locked, and further differentiation, some of it adaptive, to have occurred subsequently; in others, however, no such isolation can have taken place, and the behavioural divergence must be primary. As we have already seen (p. 282), a somewhat similar divergence has occurred in lampreys.

"Preadaptations" which might give rise to physiological differentiation are probably not uncommon. Thus Gause and Smaragdova (1939) find that the sinistral form of the snail *Fruticicola lantzi* loses weight more rapidly than dextrals when starved. A species of American salamander contains two types differing in the size of their red blood-corpuscles (Finn J. B., 1937; J. Hered., 28: 373). The frizzled fowl (p. 118) provides an excellent example occurring under domestication where the preadaptive mutation has actually been utilized. See Chap. 8, § 5, for further examples.

We may conclude with a very extraordinary example of reproductive divergence, described in detail by Meyer (1938) after discovery by Hubbs and Hubbs (1932). They found a cyprinodont fish (*Mollienisia formosa*) which was characterized first by being always associated with one or other of two closely-related species, *M. sphenops* and *M. latipinna*, and secondly by consisting solely of females. Investigation revealed that the eggs of this species were activated by the sperm of the males of the other species! The one species is thus a reproductive parasite on the others, and mating occurs normally between it and them, though there is no resultant true hybridization. *M. formosa* itself, however, appears to be itself a natural hybrid, formed where the other two species meet, and maintaining itself in this peculiar fashion.

These examples will suffice to show how widespread are various forms of essentially physiological (non-morphological) evolutionary divergence. Thorpe (1940) concludes that certainly in most phyla, and probably in all, "there exist . . . groups of individuals which are undoubtedly distinct species in every sense except the accepted morphological one". We have given numerous instances showing the phenomenon in its incipient stages. And a survey of any group will reveal many cases in which physiological and ecological divergence must have been primary, morphological distinctions having been added in the course of later evolution.

6. SPECIAL CASES

In this section we shall refer to certain peculiar types of taxonomic groups which do not seem to fit into any of the normal categories of evolutionary differentiation. The most interesting is that of certain mosquitoes and gnats. The existence of these groups, like that of biological races, was first detected owing to their practical importance—in this case, for human health.

The intensive study of malaria had led to two apparently opposed views as to the methods to be used in eradicating the disease. The one, basing itself on the indubitable fact that malaria is transmitted by mosquitoes, urged that the insect vector must be eliminated; the other, adducing the equally indubitable fact that improvements in housing, notably in separating stables from human dwelling-places, often resulted in a marked drop in malaria incidence, was all for concentrating on "bonification" and the general raising of standards of living. Both have now been proved right—and both wrong: each method applies only to certain forms of malarial mosquito.

The insect vector of human malaria in Europe is generally stated to be a single species of mosquito, *Anopheles maculipennis*. Recent work (see Hackett and Missiroli, 1935; Hackett, 1937; Swellengrebel and de Buck, 1938) has shown that this "species" in reality consists of at least eight distinct groups, each with their own characteristics. No structural or colour differences between the adults of the various forms have yet been detected, or in the pupae; the larvae show slight structural differences, which in any case are valid only when tested statistically. But each form can be immediately diagnosed by egg-characters, both its colour and pattern, and the size and structure of the egg-float, and these are completely correlated with striking differences in habits and ecological preferences. In addition, each form has its own characteristic distribution, though there may be considerable overlap. Thus, to take but four of the forms, race *typicus*, with light grey eggs barred with black and large rough floats, breeds in fresh, pure, and usually running water, shows complete hibernation, refuses to breed in captivity, and neglects man entirely if other sources of blood (e.g. cattle) are available. It is mainly an inhabitant of mountain ranges. Race *elutus*, on the other hand, has an unpatterned egg, without floats; it breeds in shallow stagnant waters, often brackish or quite salty, as it is the most tolerant to salt of all the races.* In its feeding habits it is the most strictly adapted to man, and prefers human blood even when animals are also present. Geographically it is a southern form, confined to the Mediterranean region. Thirdly, we have *atroparvus*, a northern form with dappled eggs, and small smooth floats. It breeds by preference in cool and slightly brackish waters, and mates readily in small cages; it is unique in that the males

* This race shows a further physiological subdivision, since in Palestine it appears to lack this high tolerance, and is there confined mainly to fresh water

do not assemble in swarms. It winters in rather warm places, showing only partial hibernation, and feeds at irregular intervals during this period. It tends to have rather short wings (averaging about 10 per cent less than in race *messeae*). It will bite both man and animals, and a considerable proportion may be attracted away from man to animals, notably pigs and horses. In Holland, which has been carefully investigated, it and *messeae* are the two races chiefly present (with *typicus* occasionally found in the east). Their distribution overlaps considerably, but in regions of more brackish water *messeae* is rare or absent, while in fresh water it is in the majority, though not preponderantly so.

Finally, race *labranchiae*, with pale, broad eggs and very small but rough floats, is an inhabitant of brackish and salt marshes in warm regions. Its hibernation is both short and very imperfect, and it will bite man as well as animals, with rather more preference for man than *atroparvus*.

As a result of these peculiarities, *elutus* is always associated with intense malaria, which can only be eradicated by destroying the mosquito or its breeding places, or preventing the insect's access to man. *Typicus*, on the other hand, is of very little importance as a malaria vector, and raising the standard of life, by increasing the number of domestic animals and providing separate accommodation for them, will deviate it almost entirely away from man. *Labranchiae* is a serious malaria vector, which can only be partially deviated to animals; while *atroparvus* is a source of mild endemic malaria, and can be to a considerable extent deviated away from man by improving conditions.

The different races are also separated by sterility barriers. These are in some cases complete, but the stage at which they operate varies. Thus in some cases no eggs are obtained, or the larvae all die soon after hatching; in the *atroparvus-elutus* and *atroparvus-messeae* crosses the larvae die, but at a later stage, while the *typicus-atroparvus* cross gives healthy but sterile adults. In other cases, the barrier is only partial; sometimes all males and some females are sterile, in others all females and some males are fertile. Thus biologically these forms are full species.

Swellengrebel and de Buck (1938, p. 90) have shown further

that even within a single race (*atroparvus*) considerable diversification may exist, different strains showing different ecological preferences and different resistance to salinity, and broods occasionally turning up with unusual characters of eggs or larval hairs. They consider that many other races will show similar intra-group variation.

The practical needs of human health having brought these facts to light, a similar differentiation into ecological races has been looked for and discovered in other forms, both of *Anopheles* and of the common gnat *Culex pipiens* (see summary in Thorpe, 1940).

Finally, it is of some interest to note that the malaria parasites, as well as their vectors, are differentiated into physiological races. Thus *Plasmodium vivax*, the tertian parasite, exists in at least two forms (see Swellengrebel and de Buck, 1938, pp. 227 seq.) differing in number of merozoites, incubation period, type and gravity of symptoms produced, latency, susceptibility to temperature and anti-malarial drugs, and in showing an incomplete reciprocal immunity. Different strains may in some cases be capable of hybridization within the insect vector (Manwell, 1936).

This case has been dealt with at some length because of its numerous points of interest. From the evolutionary standpoint, the type of differentiation is unique in that the races, while well-defined ecologically and physiologically, and to a considerable extent geographically, yet show much overlapping, and are only kept distinct by genetic (reproductive) barriers. It is for the present extremely difficult to understand what has been the actual cause and mechanism of their evolutionary differentiation.

Equally puzzling, though in quite a different way, is the case of the common limpets (*Patella*) of Europe and North Africa, investigated by Fischer-Piette (1935). Here, again, two apparently contradictory opinions were prevalent, one that they constituted but a single species, the other that they should be divided into at least three species. Again, both views were partially right. Fischer-Piette, on the basis of extensive collections over a large area, has been able to show that in certain regions the assemblage of limpets falls into three discontinuous groups, characterized both structurally (differences in radula-teeth, etc.) and ecologically, each having a preferred zone of the intertidal area. In other regions, however, no such separation is possible, and the assemblage of limpets forms a continuous whole, the different types intergrading completely with each other. Dr. Fischer-Piette has, however, informed me verbally that the distribution will probably turn out to be trimodal, the three modes of the curve coinciding with the modes of the three separate types of other regions. These general conclusions have been confirmed by Eslick (1940) at Port St. Mary (Isle of Man), where, however, only two types can be distinguished.

Here we would seem to have an ecological divergence, which in some regions has led to complete speciation, in others only to a partial separation of adaptive types. But whether the condition of a single continuous trimodal group is primary and constitutes a step towards complete separation, or whether it is secondary, resulting from hybridization of three previously differentiated types, it is at present impossible to say, and both interpretations present obvious difficulties. So far, no experimental work has been undertaken on the very interesting problems raised.

Examples somewhat recalling the state of affairs in mosquitoes are provided by various insects, notably Hymenoptera. Here we may find "races" differing slightly in visible characters, in just the same way as do typical geographical subspecies, and showing no intergradation or other signs of interbreeding, yet overlapping geographically to a greater or less extent. In the overlap area they may be found quite close to each other, so that their distinctness cannot be brought about by spatial separation as occurs in some cases of ecotopic divergence.

Thus Bequaert (1918) describes "races" of the wasp *Eumenes maxillosus*, characterized solely by colour-characters, which, while possessing characteristic geographical ranges, are none of them mutually exclusive (see map in Robson and Richards, 1936, p. 68). A few appear to have an ecological basis, e.g. one is confined to deserts and subdeserts, another to tropical rain-forest and its neighbourhood, still another to typical savannahs. One might be regarded as a geographical race in that it is confined to Madagascar; but this region is shared by another form which extends there from the African continent. Intermediates are sporadic, and not confined to the zones where two ranges meet. An interesting feature is the recurrence of a number of the colour-patterns (some of them very striking) in related species. There is a possibility that this may be due to synaposematism (Mullerian mimicry); on the other hand, it also recalls the "homologous series" of parallel colour-variations found in various grasshoppers (p. 516), where genetic analysis has been possible and has revealed the existence of a selective balance as primary cause of the polymorphism (p. 99). Interestingly, in another African wasp, *Synagris cornuta*, the equally striking colour variations are connected by more frequent intermediates, and several may occur in a single colony.

The careful studies of Richards (1934) on another genus of wasp (*Trypoxylon*) have shed new light on the subject. To take but one set of three "species", *T. salti*, *T. spinosum*, and *T. armatum*: the first two are extremely similar, and intergrading forms occur. Their ranges overlap in Central America, though *T. salti* extends much further south. The third form, *armatum*, is more readily distinguishable, and less closely resembles *salti*, with which it overlaps, than *spinosum*, with which it does not. As Richards says (p. 243), "the present resources of entomological nomenclature are insufficient to deal with a group of forms such as these". *Salti* and *spinosum* intergrade, so cannot be regarded as full species; their ranges overlap and intermediates occur over a considerable part of the joint range, so they are not geographical subspecies; nor are they mere varieties (aberrations) or examples of simple dimorphism, since "in a large part of their range each form seems to maintain a homogeneous population".

Richards reaches the interesting conclusion that "geographical segregation in insects is often of a different nature to the more familiar process observable in birds and mammals". He suggests that non-geographical—i.e. ecological or physiological—forms of isolation can be much more effective in insects—a conclusion borne out by the abundance of "biological races" in the group, as contrasted with their total absence, in any strict sense, in higher vertebrates. Experimental analysis of such cases is urgently needed.

If this is correct, a special type of ecobiotic divergence, combined with considerable geographical differentiation, is frequent in insects. Richards cites other examples, e.g. in hornets, which seem to fit in with this idea, and the case of *Eumenes* just cited may depend in part on this. He informs me that the same phenomenon, of "non-geographical speciation", also occurs in various beetles.

These general conclusions seem to be borne out in other insects, e.g. in ants. The numerous forms (subspecies or species according to taste) of *Myrmica rubra* seem to conform quite closely to Richards' views, since they are very similar morphologically, have distinct ecological preferences, and do not normally cross in spite of extensive spatial overlap.

Particularly interesting is Diver's summary (1940, p. 317) of our knowledge concerning two forms of *Lasius niger*, *L. n. niger* and *L. n. alienus* (considered by a minority of authors as good species). Morphological distinctions between the two are very slight, being confined to the presence or absence of a few small hairs on antennae and tibiae. Differences in behaviour, however, are more definite, and usually permit identification in the field. The geographical range of *alienus* appears to be wholly confined within that of *niger*. Ecologically, the two forms show distinctive preferences. *Niger* has much the greater range of tolerance, from sand-dunes to wet sphagnum bog, from grass to dead trees, while *alienus* is (in the Dorset area investigated by Diver) almost confined to dry heath, with some overflow onto moist heath and turf. Even within the single type of habitat represented by dry heath there are differences, *alienus* preferring blown sand. Sometimes the two species nest only a few feet apart. In regard to swarming dates there is an extensive overlap, providing opportunities for crossing, though *niger* tends to be slightly later. Very occasionally forms are found which are intermediate between the two types, not only morphologically but in behaviour and ecological preferences. These, in the absence of evidence to the contrary, must be assumed to be produced by intercrossing, which must accordingly be rare.

We seem here to be dealing with fine ecotopic divergence which has just reached the stage of speciation; but it is extremely difficult to envisage by what means the distinctness of the two types was first brought about.

Diver gives other puzzling examples—e.g. three apparently distinct species of hoverfly (*Syrphus*) with extremely small morphological differences, with the geographical distributions of one species including that of the other two, and of the second including that of the third, with general similarity in ecological preferences, and extensive overlap in the periods in which adults are on the wing. Diver suggests that the two species with more restricted distributions have arisen by the segregation of small discontinuous groups, followed by accidental divergence and later expansion of range, but this is quite speculative.

We must also remember the remarkable case of the two 'races" of *Drosophila pseudoobscura* (p. 369). These differ in various physiological characters such as temperature-resistance, are intersterile, and are further characterized by sectional chromosome-rearrangements which could only have originated in isolation. They have different geographical distribution, but overlap considerably. It seems clear that the divergence leading to intersterility first occurred in an isolated local group, which later was able to invade the other's range. Within each race, "strong" and "weak" forms are found which differ in their sex-determining mechanism like those of *Lymantria*, and also resemble those of *Lymantria* in showing some gradation in their distribution (see p. 359, and Dobzhansky, 1937, p. 284).

In any case, the taxonomic differentiation of invertebrates clearly provides a vast and almost virgin field for experimental analysis. A number of general principles have emerged as a result of intensive work on various organisms, plant and animal, vertebrate and invertebrate; but their relative share in causing differentiation may differ markedly from group to group.

7. DIVERGENCE WITH LOW COMPETITION; OCEANIC FAUNAS

Decreased selection-pressure permits increased variation. This is true not only for species or subspecies but for entire groups. In the former case the result is higher variability, in the latter more extensive evolutionary divergence and radiation. An excellent example comes from the Cichlid fish fauna of the African lakes (Worthington, 1937, 1940; summary in Huxley 1941a). In some of the lakes, their chief predators (the large fish *Lates* and *Hydrocyon*) are wholly absent. Where this is so, the Cichlid radiation, as measured by the number of endemic species, and as shown by the greater variety of ecological niches occupied, is far greater. Thus of the lakes isolated during the second pluvial or later, Victoria-Kioga and Edward-George are without large predators, and contain 58 and 18 endemic species respectively, while Albert and Rudolf, where the predators are present, contain but 4 and 3; the larger number of endemics in Victoria-Kioga is due to greater environmental diversity. Nyasa and Tanganyika were isolated during the early Cenozoic; the former lacks predators and contains 171 endemic species, while the latter, where predators are present, contains only about 90 endemics in spite of its greater environmental diversity.

The principle can be generalized in relation to competitor-pressure as well as to predator-pressure. This is well shown by the Australian marsupials. These also illustrate the fact that the total radiation of the fauna is normally not increased: among them some of the chief placental types are missing, and various adaptive characters, notably intelligence, are below placental standard. However, the best examples are found on oceanic islands. Here, the number of types which have established themselves is much restricted, and under these conditions of biological low pressure, the few favoured groups may differentiate into a surprising variety of forms.

Perhaps the most remarkable example of oceanic radiation is afforded by the sicklebills (*Drepanididae*) of the Hawaii archipelago. General accounts are given by Gulick (1932) and Mordvilko (1937). The *Drepanididae* are passerine birds, according to Gulick derived from a tropical American honey-creeper, according to Mordvilko from a finch related to the goldfinches (*Carduelis*). In any case, they are now restricted to Hawaii and to Laysan Island, 800 miles further west, and have produced a quite astonishing variety of types, meriting division into no less than 18 genera. There are small insect-eaters and finchlike seed-eaters, some with small and some with heavy bills; a very large-billed nut-eater; a peculiar woodpecker type (*Heterorhynchus*) with long upper mandible for prying away bark, and short lower mandible for probing out wood-boring grubs; nectar-suckers (with special tongues); forms which combine nectar-eating with searching for insects in flowers; and others. No other bird family shows such adaptive diversification; at first sight one would say that half a dozen distinct families were represented.

A characteristic of many genera is the curvature of the beak, from which the family name of sicklebill is taken. In connection with this, the bird-pollinated plants of Hawaii have curved corolla tubes, while those of their mainland relatives are straight.

Mordvilko stresses the analogy of the evolution of a group like the sicklebills with the excessive radiation of domesticated animals. Gulick points out that the bill and habits of a form like *Heterorhynchus* are true evolutionary novelties, which have not been evolved elsewhere. A similar example is afforded by the freshwater gobies of the same area, which have evolved unique sucker-like fins for clinging to the rocks in rushing torrents.

The ancestral sicklebill must have been the first bird immigrant to the archipelago. The remaining passerine fauna belongs to four families only—crows, thrushes, flycatchers, and honeyeaters. Differentiation here is not nearly so marked, though endemic genera have in some cases been evolved: presumably these were all later arrivals.

A very similar case is that of the groundfinches (Geospizidae) of the Galapagos. Here, again, we have a family confined to an oceanic archipelago and an outlying island (one monotypic genus, on Cocos Island). This family is highly differentiated (five well-marked genera on the Galapagos); the remaining passerine birds are much less distinctive, though endemic genera have been produced, and must have arrived later than the ancestral geospizid, when there was not only less time available, but many niches had been filled. In most archipelagoes, however, many endemic forms are differentiated, they do not usually overlap geographically. However, in the Geospizidae (like the sicklebills) several distinct species (up to 10 in the groundfinches) may coexist on one island.

The Geospizidae have been subjected to an exhaustive taxonomic analysis by Swarth (1934), while Lack (1940a) has been able to draw important general conclusions from his study of the group in the field. Most *Geospiza* species are large-billed and eat seeds, some having the most powerful bills of any passerine birds.* *Platyspiza* is mainly a leaf-eater, *Camarhynchus* mainly insectivorous, while *Cactospiza* has evolved from *Camarhynchus* in the direction of a woodpecker: it also has the unique habit of using a twig as a tool to pry out insects, thus making up for the incomplete specialization of its beak. Finally *Certhidea* resembles a warbler both in beak and habits.

In addition to this "minor adaptive radiation", as Lack calls it, numerous non-adaptive specific differences exist, presumably due to the Sewall Wright effect (p. 58). In addition, some of the beak differences are concerned not with adaptation to mode of life, but with specific recognition for mating purposes. Lack concludes that the virtual absence both of competitors and of predators has permitted this remarkable radiation. Elsewhere an island has been colonized by two closely-related species which will not interbreed (p. 255). Apparently the rapid differentiation of the Geospizids in peculiar conditions has permitted this phenomenon to be intensified. Large-scale hybridization does not seem to have contributed (see p. 356).

He also draws attention to the partial or total loss by many

* The interesting point may here be mentioned that insular land birds tend to have larger bills (either longer or more robust) than their nearest continental relatives (Murphy, 1938). This applies to non-oceanic as well as to oceanic islands. Murphy has checked this statistically for North American passerine species and finds that it holds for all insular full species, and for 78 per cent of the insular subspecies. Chapman (1940) confirms the fact for central and South American subspecies of the sparrow *Zonotrichia capensis*. The enormous bills of some *Geospiza* species on the Galapagos may illustrate the same phenomenon. Its significance is at present quite unknown.

of the species of the typical male plumage, the juvenile plumage type being prolonged into the adult phase. This is a common tendency in the land birds of oceanic islands. As another example we may cite the hen-feathered subspecies of bullfinch (*Pyrrhula p. murina*) found on the Azores (Murphy and Chapin, 1929). This Lack suggests to be due to the absence of related forms with which a female might hybridize: the need for specific distinctiveness, which is such a feature of secondary sexual characters, then disappears. In the Geospizidae, as differentiation has proceeded, distinctiveness has been reacquired in respect of the non-sexual beak characters. The converse of this process, as D. Lack suggests, in an unpublished paper which he kindly allows me to cite, may be seen in such forms as the ducks and some pheasants, in which, owing to the looseness of the bond between the mated pair, there is an unusual tendency to natural hybridization. Here, the females of related species are often very similar, demonstrating close relationship, but the males show strikingly distinctive characters.

Other groups, too, show increased radiation on oceanic islands. As Buxton (1935) says, "one characteristic of the [insect] fauna of such an archipelago as Hawaii is the development of complex groups, many of them containing a very large number of closely related species". Other areas with a less lengthy history, such as Samoa, show the same phenomenon, but to a lesser degree.

As Gulick points out, the difficulties of immigration make the land faunas of oceanic islands "disharmonic", in the sense that they lack the normal balanced ecological diversification of types, being restricted to types pre-adapted to long-range dispersal across salt water, and to a chance assortment of these. But the longer the fauna persists, the greater will be the tendency for it to become secondarily harmonic, through adaptive radiation of the earlier immigrant stocks. Thus oceanic faunas represent very peculiar special cases, but at the same time they conform to the general rules of evolutionary divergence.

As we should expect, precisely similar phenomena may occur in lakes which have been long isolated. The most striking example is Baikal, the zoogeography of which is discussed by Berg (1935). Here the Gammarids show excessive radiation; e.g. the one genus *Echinogammarus* is represented by some 40 species, and the three species found elsewhere are probably examples of convergence and should not be placed in this genus, which then would be endemic to the lake. In the fresh-water oligochaete genus *Lamprodilus*, 12 of the 16 species are found only in Baikal.

8. GENETIC DIVERGENCE

Next we come to a group of several methods of species-formation which have this in common, that the primary separation of the new type is not spatial but genetic. A further common feature is that our knowledge of all of them is quite recent.

First we may take genic separation. In maize, two strains have been found, differing only in a single gene-pair, which will not cross. This shows that a single mutation may effect the separation of one interfertile group into two. Such occurrences appear to be very uncommon; and for the moment the evolutionary bearings of this fact are not clear. We can only say that single gene-mutations, if they affected either mating-reactions or the delicate machinery of meiosis, might be of importance in breaking up animal species also. Dobzhansky (1937, p. 263) has a discussion of genic effects on reproduction; see also Stern (1936).

We mention elsewhere how the randomness of mutation will lead to intersterility in isolated groups (pp. 186, 360): but here the genetic differentiation is secondary. A similar example is given by Wolf (1909; and see discussion in Jennings, 1920) for Myxobacteria, where non-sexual fusion of colonies from a single strain occurs. But after prolonged culture, substrains incapable of colonial fusion may be produced.

Most genetic separations, however, may be called chromosomal, as they are concerned with alterations not in genes, but in their chromosomal vehicles (see Darlington, 1931, 1940).*

---

* See Darlington and Upcott (1941b) for a discussion of variation in types of breakage and reunion of chromosomes to be found in different forms.

First come those cases in which the barrier to crossing, whether more or less complete, does not produce any visible differentiation, so that any taxonomic divergence follows later, as with geographical isolation.

We may begin with segmental interchange (reciprocal translocation) between different chromosomes, as described on p. 90. Here the same gene-complex is merely rearranged. The various "prime types" thus produced can cross with each other, but owing to peculiarities of the chromosomal mechanism tend to maintain themselves; for the heterozygotes are less fertile than the homozygous types, and further, crossing-over between chromosomes which have interchanged segments is restricted so that recombination is almost abolished. Further differentiation and separation of the prime types into subspecies or species could then occur by the accumulation of different mutations in different types, and by the development of other barriers to crossing, which would be advantageous (as preventing waste) if two or more types occurred together.

In *Datura*, only the first stage has been reached; different prime types occur in different regions, but are not visibly distinct. This, it is probable, is due to *D. stramonium* having in recent times spread rapidly as a weed of civilization, so that insufficient time has elapsed for differentiation.

A quite different development, however, may occur if recessive lethal mutations occur in both interchange chromosome-groups. In that case, the homozygotes will be inviable and only the hybrid will survive. This is the condition of *balanced lethals*. Since lethal mutations are common, and since the heterozygote will enjoy increased advantage in various ways as soon as one homozygote has become inviable, we may expect this condition to develop out of segmental interchange at least as readily as that of differentiated prime types.

The classical case is that of the evening primroses (*Oenothera*). Here abundant genetic and cytological evidence converge to show that almost all the species are balanced-lethal heterozygotes, the original pure types having disappeared. Elaborate subsidiary mechanisms ensure the production of the heterozygotes with the minimum of wastage. This type of speciation has probably occurred in other plants, e.g. *Hypericum* and *Rhoeo* (see Darlington, 1937). Sokolov and Dubinin (1941) have discovered a wild *Drosophila* species with balanced-lethal heterozygosity based on inversions.

Although probably not widespread or of great evolutionary importance, the balanced-lethal heterozygote type of species-formation has great historical interest, since it was de Vries' investigations on *Oenothera* that led him to propound his mutation theory of evolution. We now know that most of the "mutations" which he described were not mutations at all, in the strict sense of substantive changes in the germ-plasm, but merely recombinations of a peculiar sort, to be expected only in balanced-lethal heterozygotes, and due to occasional crossing-over. Gene-mutations of this order of magnitude do not seem to occur.

Blakeslee and his school have been able to produce various interchange types artificially by X-rays, and then, in certain cases, by means of crossing to synthesize quite new strains which possess certain sections of the gene-complex in duplicate as compared with the normal. These show numerous character-differences from the type, and can be regarded as artificial incipient species (Blakeslee, Bergner, and Avery, 1936).

Translocations, both reciprocal and non-reciprocal, also occur quite frequently in *Drosophila*, and will normally produce some reduction of fertility in the F1 hybrid (see Stern, 1936, for a discussion of the different possible types of translocation). This may be the first step towards speciation, though it is apparently much less important than inversion in this respect (Dobzhansky and Tan, 1936).

The next method of chromosomal separation is inversion (p. 91). Here, too, a mere rearrangement of parts of the chromosome outfit has occurred, but in this case by a reversal of a portion of one chromosome, so that the order of the genes is here inverted. Affairs are here slightly complicated by the fact that such inversions often produce a visible "position-effect" (p. 85). This is presumably due to genes exerting some of their effects in virtue of a special type of interaction with their immediate neighbours: the genes at either end of an inverted section will of course be interacting with new neighbours.

Inversions were first inferred from genetic analysis. Later they were detected cytologically at the prophase of meiosis in maize. To-day, thanks to the discovery of the giant chromosomes in the salivary glands of *Drosophila*, they need not wait to be detected by their abnormal behaviour at crossing-over and its results, but can be directly observed; for chromosome-segments can be seen in which the normal band and line pattern is reversed, and these are then found to cause abnormalities of pairing and crossing-over at meiosis when opposite a non-inverted segment.

Among the properties of inversions is that they interfere (of course in the heterozygous condition only) with chromosome-pairing and crossing-over, and it is in virtue of this fact that they exert their effect on breaking up species. But this effect will be quite different according to the magnitude of the inverted segment. When it is very small, the disturbance will be small; and crossing-over between genes one or two units apart is in any case of very rare occurrence. Thus the main effect of very small inversions will be viâ their visible position-effects, which will be similar in magnitude and nature to the effects of small true gene-mutations. Small inversions will thus merely add to the internal variability of a species, and will not tend to break it up into separate groups.

Large inversions, on the other hand, will have two important effects. They will reduce the fertility of heterozygotes, so that the pure types—that with two normal chromosomes, and that with two chromosomes both with an inverted section—will be at an advantage: and the impossibility of crossing-over between an inverted and a non-inverted section will effectively isolate these two regions of the gene-complex from each other. Recombination can no longer take place between them, so that any mutation taking place in an inverted section cannot be transferred to its non-inverted homologue, or vice versa. Darlington (1937) was the first to grasp the full implications of this fact, and to point out that such "chromosomal isolation" was of equal importance with other more obvious kinds of isolation, such as that due to geographical separation (*v. infra*; and p. 362).

Single inversions may thus cause a certain reduction of hybrid fertility between types. Fertility would be still further reduced by further inversions in other kinds of chromosomes, while two or more inversions in each of two or more chromosomes would produce very considerable sterility (Stern, 1936).

A large inversion may thus pave the way for the separation of a species into two non-interbreeding groups. For one thing its isolating effect may be accentuated by further inversions; and in addition, once any degree of hybrid sterility has occurred, natural selection will operate to produce other sterility barriers, in the shape of different mating reactions, so as to prevent the waste caused by crossing, with its production of relatively infertile individuals. Still further genetic sterility-barriers are also likely to arise by gene-mutation of various kinds. Inversions may also lead to the production of visible diversity by the accumulation of different mutations in homologous inverted and non-inverted sections.

If several favourable mutations occur in an inverted section, and are therefore prevented from crossing-over and recombination with the homologous non-inverted section, the spread of chromosomes with the inverted section will be favoured by selection. The two homologous sections, inverted and non-inverted, will in fact each become an isolated partial genetic system; within this there will operate the same phenomenon of mutual genic adjustment discussed for total genetic systems in Chap. 3 (see also Malinovsky, 1941). These segmental harmoni-ously-stabilized gene-complexes will continue to evolve within the less thoroughly stabilized total gene-complex. Something of this sort has undoubtedly occurred in the divergence of *Avena sativa* from *A. fatua* and *Triticum vulgare* from *T. spelta*: in either case the two members of the pair differ essentially in a group of characters all located in a region of one chromosome, which in one species has suffered inversion (Huskins, 1927, 1928).

In general, it appears that sectional rearrangements are rarely if ever the sole cause of evolutionary divergence (cf. Muller, 1940). For one thing they have a negligible prospect of becoming established, except by chance in a small and relatively well-isolated group. And in the second place their presence in non-interbreeding groups is normally accompanied by numerous single-gene differences, which are often responsible for much of the group-incompatibility. They can therefore only be regarded as secondary agents in bringing out speciation, though their role may be quite important in species which are normally broken up into small isolated population-units, and still more in those (among which various species of *Drosophila* are to be included) which are subject to violent fluctuations in numbers with small, isolated groups at the low point of the cycle.

It is, for instance, probable that inversion has had a good deal to say in the separation of *Drosophila melanogaster* and *D. simulans*, though the single-gene effects must have played the major role, since important effects on the sterility of the hybrids are determined by them (Stern, 1936; and p. 359).

Whenever inversion has played an important part in species-formation, the two species may be expected to remain very similar in appearance, since they will overlap in their ranges, and will both possess almost the same genetic constitution, well-adapted to a common environment. A gradual ecological divergence may occur later. The same will apply to cases of divergence initiated by translocation. Thus the two "races" (incipient species) of *Drosophila pseudoobscura* can only be distinguished by statistical analysis, which brings out, in males only, certain differences in wing and leg measurements, and in the numbers of the teeth on the sex-combs (Mather and Dobzhansky, 1939).

Such species will only be detected by refined and detailed systematic methods, and will often not be recognized by systematists who are not alive to the implications of genetics. It will be of great interest to discover whether species-pairs of this type occur in higher vertebrates.

A peculiar method of forming new types is that of asexual

segregation in certain parthenogenetic plant species of hybrid origin. Parthenogenesis in such cases is due to a suppression of the reduction of the chromosomes. But even in the absence of reduction, any corresponding chromosomes from the two original parents which are able to pair will be subject to crossing-over, since we now know that crossing-over takes place by two stages, and not only as an accompaniment to reduction. And such crossing-over will produce new types, which will maintain themselves, subject to selection, save for further cross-overs (see also pp. 352-3).

Such a process should lead to the formation of numerous closely-related true-breeding types. Some of these will doubtless be at a disadvantage and will disappear, while others will maintain themselves. Further divergence between the types may occur, though slowly, by gene-mutation. It is probable that some of the numerous species of hawkweed (*Hieracium*) and blackberry (*Rubus*) owe their origin to such asexual segregation. Apparent mutations due to this process have been detected in both forms (Darlington, 1937, pp. 296, 475, for *Hieracium*; Crane and Thomas, 1939, for *Rubus*; and p. 352 of this volume).

Next we have the various phenomena of polyploidy in which a multiplication of whole chromosome-sets occurs (see p. 143). As already mentioned, polyploidy is of two fundamentally distinct types: autopolyploidy in which the chromosome sets are all of the same kind, derived from the same species, and initial allopolyploidy, in which they are of different kind, derived from two distinct species. The actual doubling is in both cases due to the suppression of division of a cell after division of the chromosomes has taken place, but whereas this is the primary event in autopolyploidy, in allopolyploidy it is subsequent to hybridization.

As previously mentioned, polyploidy is widespread in plants, but very rare in animals (pp. 140 seq.). We there pointed out the *a priori* reason for its non-existence in bisexual forms. M. J. D. White (1940) points out that this might be expected not to apply in hermaphrodite animal groups. However, his investigations of chromosome-number show that in one such group (pulmonate molluscs) it appears not to occur at all, in another (Rhabdocoela) it occurs to a moderate extent, and in two others (Hirudinea and Oligochaeta) the meagre data suggest its possibility as a rare phenomenon. His conclusion is that polyploidy has not occurred in the hermaphrodite groups of animals to anything like the same extent as in higher plants. This may be due to the rarity of self-fertilization in hermaphrodite animals, or to some as yet unknown cause. Polyploidy may possibly occur in Hemiptera (p. 370).

In this section, only autopolyploidy concerns us, as allopolyploidy connotes convergence, not divergence. Chromosome-doubling will usually occur through failure of cell-division but not of chromosome division. If the tetraploid cell forms all or part of a growing point, a totally or partially tetraploid shoot will result. Such a shoot will not be fully fertile, since at meiosis there will be four of each kind of chromosome instead of two, so that in addition to pairs, groups of three and four chromosomes will be formed. Many gametes will, therefore, not possess two entire genomes, but will be unbalanced, with some chromosomes represented in triplicate or only in single dose; and such gametes will often be inviable.

The continuance of the species can be ensured either by concentrating on asexual reproduction, or, if fertility is not much reduced, by means of a differentiation of the chromosomes, presumably through mutation, so that instead of four similar members of each kind, two slightly dissimilar pairs are found. Instead of AAAA,BBBB, etc., we would have A_1A_1, A_2A_2, B_1B_1, B_2B_2, etc. So long as the dissimilarity is sufficient to prevent pairing between members of different pairs (e.g. A_1 and A_2, or B_1 and B_2) complete fertility will be restored. In this case the initial autopolyploidy will have been converted into a secondary functional allopolyploidy (p. 143; Darlington, 1937, his pp. 183, 226).

Doubling can of course be repeated, leading from tetraploid to octoploid and higher forms. This is likely to occur especially in types which have specialized in parthenogenetic reproduction, leading to the establishment of series with 2n, 4n, 8n, 16n chromosomes.

Autotriploid (3n) forms may arise from diploids by fertilization between a diploid (unreduced) and a haploid (normal reduced) gamete. Triploids are sexually sterile and can only reproduce by non-sexual methods. Hexaploids (6n) may arise in similar fashion from 4n plants. They may also originate by doubling in a triploid form, and then of course reacquire sexual fertility. An interesting case of this sort is given by Perlova (1939). The wild triploid and sterile potato species *Solanum vallis-mexici* was grown at high altitudes, and there, presumably as a result of the low temperature, produced a fertile hexaploid form. As this species is more resistant to frost and drought and certain diseases than other potato species, this result should be of considerable importance.

Darlington (1937, p. 216) gives a table of autopolyploid species and mutants. Various wild triploid species are known, all reproducing vegetatively, e.g. in tulips and narcissi. Extremely few cases are known in animals; e.g. the land crustacean *Trichoniscus*: here reproduction is parthenogenetic (p. 314; Vandel, 1937).

Other triploid types have been experimentally produced by crossing 2n and 4n forms. Of great interest is the fact that autopolyploidy may give rise to forms which are not associated with any systematic visible differences. For instance, *Anemone montana* occurs in diploid (2n), tetraploid (4n), and hexaploid (6n) forms, *Silene ciliata* in 2n, 4n, and 16n forms, all similar.*

In other cases, the polyploid forms differ slightly in visible characters, but are still classified within the limits of a single species. There are, for instance, five such forms of *Viola kitaibeliana* (some of them aneuploid) and of *Prunus spinosa*, and three of *Erophila (Draba) verna*. Such forms were at one time included under the term "elementary species".

The most interesting evolutionary fact concerning autopolyploids, however, is that different members of a series may and often do have different geographical distributions. In general, tetraploid forms seem better adapted to difficult environmental conditions. Many are more cold-resistant than their diploid

---

* On the other hand, Müntzing (1936), who has studied autopolyploidy very extensively, has stated that members of a polyploid series always show *some* visible distinguishing characters, though these may admittedly be slight.

relatives. Accordingly we find many tetraploid forms in the far north and in mountain regions. Almost all the grasses in Spitsbergen are polyploids (see Haldane, 1938). The sharper climatic zoning produced by the glacial period must have encouraged the survival of tetraploids and promoted the formation of tetraploid subspecies. Others are adapted to the extreme temperatures and great aridity of deserts—e.g. various forms of *Enagrostis* in the Sahara (Hagerup, 1932). Tetraploid forms are also in many cases more generally vigorous, a fact reflected in their distribution, which is frequently wider (often considerably so) than that of the diploid variety. Many widespread weeds of cultivation and waste land are also tetraploid forms, the diploid types having quite restricted distribution. (For general discussion see Müntzing, 1936, Tischler, 1941.)

In experimental tetraploids in tomatoes, Fabergé (1936) finds that the tetraploid is less variable phenotypically than the diploid. This cannot be due to diminished segregation of recessives; Fabergé suggests that it is due to the greater effectiveness, in certain cases, of four as against two homologous genes, resulting in greater stability of early developmental processes. In colchicine-induced tetraploidy, Badenhuizen (1941) finds that long chromosomes diminish fertility and viability. It is also more likely to be of economic value for quantitative than subtle qualitative characters.

A few examples will serve to illustrate these general points. In the difficult genus *Potentilla*, numerous "species" are apomictic. Some of these are allopolyploid (see below), others autopolyploid (Müntzing, 1931). For instance, *P. argentea* (n = 7) exists in 2n, 6n, and 8n forms. Doubtless 4n types will also be discovered. In general the high polyploids were more vigorous. One diploid type was very small and prostrate, while one hexaploid, growing only a dozen miles away, was tall and erect.

In the Central European crucifer *Biscutella laevigata* (Manton, 1934), the distribution of the diploid forms is restricted and discontinuous, of the tetraploids continuous and much more extensive. The diploids seem to be relict forms, confined to areas which were not covered by the ice during the glacial period.

On the other hand, most of the area now inhabited by the 4n types was under ice during the periods of maximum glaciation. Thus we can safely conclude that the tetraploid races were evolved in response to the onset of colder conditions, and have been, in virtue of their greater vigour and cold-resistance, able to colonize large areas either unavailable *per se* to the diploids, or where the diploids cannot compete successfully with the tetraploids to which they have given rise. An almost precisely similar state of affairs is found in the North American genus *Tradescantia*, but here in several species (Anderson, 1937; and see Dobzhansky, 1937, p. 196). In many cases, it seems clear that the advantages enjoyed by autopolyploids have enabled them to supplant their diploid progenitors entirely.

Thus autopolyploidy, regarded from the evolutionary standpoint, in general seems to provide a method by which a type may become adapted to new and especially to less favourable conditions. Once the polyploid forms have become established and have undergone the necessary internal genetic adaptation (p. 145) as well as further external adaptation, they will often extend their range far beyond the original diploid distribution, and may frequently restrict the range of their diploid ancestors through competition. In other cases the formation of an extended autopolyploid series may enable a type to occupy a greater variety of ecological niches. Crossing sometimes takes place between members of a series, producing new polyploid types, which then may be preadapted to still other conditions. Long-term plasticity, however, is reduced by polyploidy (pp. 143, 374).

In one sense, the different members of close autopolyploid series should be regarded as species, since they are kept quite distinct by genetic barriers. The morphological differences between them, however, are usually very slight, so that for taxonomic purposes it is undesirable to give them separate specific names, and the totality of the forms may be named as one "polyploid species". From what has been said above, it is probable that the majority of 4n and higher autopolyploid forms of such polyploid species are of geologically very recent origin. With the passage of time, we may prophesy that the morphological differences between them and their 2n ancestors will become more marked, until they merit specific naming. It is presumably by such means that some of the polyploid series of obviously good species in various plant genera have been evolved. (See also pp. 347–8).

In general we may say that divergence based primarily on genetic isolation has been of less evolutionary importance than other types of divergence, its only major achievement being the autopolyploid series of various plant groups. It has often been of the greatest secondary importance, however. Once geographical or ecological isolation has separated groups, it is largely the accident of genetic divergence, genic or chromosomal, which eventually render the two types intersterile.*

9. CONVERGENT SPECIES-FORMATION

The most important type of diversification produced primarily by genetic isolation is the origin of new true-breeding forms,

* A peculiar condition has recently been described in the wild millet *Sorghum purpureo-sericeum* (Janaki-Ammal, 1940). This is a diploid (2n = 10), but 40 per cent of wild plants have from 1 to 6 (mostly 2 or 1) extra so-called "B-chromosomes" in their floral parts; these are, however, absent from the roots.

The B-chromosomes do not pair at meiosis, and have a marked effect in reducing pollen-fertility. To offset this reproductive disadvantage, there must clearly be some considerable somatic advantage accruing from their presence in the floral tissues. But how it operates, why they are absent in the roots, and what the origin of the condition may have been—these points all remain obscure.

Darlington and Upcott (1941a), investigating a somewhat similar state of affairs in maize, have come to some more general conclusions as to the function of these so-called inert or B-chromosomes. These, though variable in number, exist with a definite mean size and frequency in various strains. Since various agencies involved in the mechanics of mitosis and meiosis are constantly operating to reduce both their size and the numbers present, some counter-selection must operate in the opposite direction. Darlington and Upcott conclude that this counter-selection is concerned with their special activities in nucleic acid metabolism.

In the domestication of maize, the B-chromosomes appear to have taken over and enlarged the metabolic function originally carried on by the heterochromatic knobs which form part of some of the normal chromosomes. They appear to provide a more elastic means of adjusting the plant's nucleic acid metabolism to the increased demands made on it by agriculturists in selecting for higher yield.

Similar arguments seem to apply in other cases, both in plants (e.g. *Fritillaria, Ranunculus,* and *Secale*) and in animals (various Heteroptera).

sufficiently distinct both morphologically as well as reproductively to be styled good species, by hybridization between two
pre-existing species.

When polyploid forms arise after hybridization, they will
be allopolyploid from the start, so that we here speak of initial
as against secondary allopolyploidy. In addition, new forms are
here produced by convergence, not by divergence. Summaries
of the evolutionary effects of polyploidy are given by Darlington
(1937) and Tischler (1941).

The classical case of species-formation by allopolyploidy is
that of Primula kewensis. This arose from a spontaneous cross at
Kew between two well-known species, P. verticillata and P.
floribunda, both with 2n = 18 chromosomes. The hybrid was
originally entirely sterile. The chromosomes of the two parental
species were able to pair and segregate in spite of their dissimilarity, but the resulting combinations of genes were so
abnormal that all the offspring were inviable.*

The hybrid was cultivated vegetatively for some years, until
a shoot appeared which was fertile. On cytological examination
this was shown to possess thirty-six chromosomes. The sterile
hybrid possessed one set from each parent—A^v, A^f, B^v, B^f, . . .
R^v, R^f. The fertile shoot possessed two sets: A^vA^v, A^fA^f, . . .
R^vR^v, R^fR^f. Pairing could now occur between identical chromosomes. Every gamete thus possessed a complete set of chromosomes from both original parents, and viable offspring were
accordingly formed. Reproduction is not entirely normal, since
sometimes groups of four chromosomes instead of pairs are
formed at meiosis, leading to reduced fertility. In the course
of time we may expect selection to operate to reduce such super-
numerary association, and so to increase fertility. In any case,
however, the tetraploid is not only capable of maintaining itself,
but is sterile when crossed with either parent species, so that it
must be regarded as a new species. Species-formation is here
abrupt, and is also convergent.

* In other cases the chromosomes of the two forms are so dissimilar that
meiosis is interfered with. For further discussion of sterility due to gene-interaction
causing abnormality of reproductive processes, see Patterson, Stone and
Griffen (1940).

In this case, the sterile hybrid would probably not have maintained itself until the chromosome-doubling occurred, without human interference. However, that new species can be formed by this method in nature is shown by the striking example of the rice-grass *Spartina townsendii* (Huskins, 1931). There seems to be no doubt that this is an allopolyploid derived from the crossing of the European *S. stricta* with the imported *S. alterniflora*. The basic haploid number (x) of the genus is 7. *S. stricta* itself appears to be an octoploid (2n = 56) and *S. alterniflora* a decaploid (2n = 70). *S. townsendii* has 2n = 126 = 18x. Most interesting from the evolutionary standpoint is the fact that the new species is in some as yet obscure way better equipped than either of its parents; it not only kills them out in competition, but is extending its range beyond theirs. It is now being employed by the Dutch for reclaiming land from the sea. This favourable result of the interaction of two gene-complexes is the reverse of that described on p. 66. It also demonstrates the role of range-changes in this type of speciation (p. 348).

Two species of horse-chestnut are known to have originated by hybridization. It is interesting that one of them is a parent of the other. From the two tetraploid species, the European *Aesculus hippocastanum* (the common horse-chestnut) and the American *A. pavia* (the red buck-eye) the pink-flowered octoploid garden species *A. carnea* has arisen. This, on crossing with *A. hippocastanum*, gave rise to *A. plantierensis*. In this latter case, a hexaploid was produced, which at once bred true without further doubling. These and other examples are enumerated by Darlington (1937, p. 234).

A very pretty example is the experimental synthesis of a wild species of hemp-nettle, *Galeopsis tetrahit*. On various grounds this tetraploid species was presumed to be the result of a cross between *G. pubescens* and *G. speciosa*, both ordinary diploids. After crossing these, an allotetraploid was produced, which is almost identical with the wild form (Müntzing, 1932, 1937). Undoubtedly, the wild species did originate from this cross, but has since its origin undergone slight further differentiation by mutation and selection.

Occasionally what merits the title of a new true-breeding species is formed by hybridization *without* subsequent chromosome-doubling. This may happen when, as in the *Aesculus* case just mentioned, an isopolyploid is produced between two other isopolyploids of different chromosome number. E.g. 4x × 8x; gametes 2x + 4x = 6x zygote. Otherwise, the process can only occur when both parents have the same chromosome number, and when the hybrid enjoys certain advantages over the parents. If capable of sexual reproduction, the hybrid will of course be exceedingly variable, as independent assortment between the members of the two parental genomes will occur.

The best case is that of the hybrid between two species of *Medicago*, the imported purple-flowered lucerne (*M. sativa*), and the yellow-flowered sickle medick (*M. falcata*) of Europe (see Gilmour, 1932). The hybrid, originally described as a distinct species under the name of *M. sylvestris*, has strange greenish-black flowers, is exceedingly variable, and is both more vigorous and more fertile than either parent. In Britain this hybrid may be dated back with reasonable certainty to the seventeenth century, when lucerne was first introduced. One would conjecture that its initial variability would have been somewhat reduced by selection, but there is no direct evidence for this. In one region of France, where lucerne has not been reintroduced for some time, the hybrid appears to have ousted both parent forms entirely.

Ledingham has recently shown (1940) that *M. falcata* exists both in a diploid and tetraploid form (2n = 16 and 32), while *M. sativa* always has 2n = 32, and is thus presumably tetraploid. "*M. sylvestris*" involves the tetraploid form of *M. falcata*. Homologous chromosomes of the two species pair and segregate freely in the hybrid. Ledingham wishes on this account to classify *M. falcata* and *M. sativa* as "varieties of one highly polymorphic species", but Mr. J. Gilmour assures me that no plant taxonomists hold this view. The two types have different distribution, and differ in numerous characters, both morphological and physiological. If one makes interfertility the sole criterion of species, then the diploid *M. falcata* would have to be put in a distinct species from its almost identical tetraploid, while this latter would be classed specifically with the quite distinct *M. sativa*!

"*M. sylvestris*" is in one sense a hybrid swarm, on account of its high segregating variability, but a hybrid swarm which is capable of permanent existence as a group-unit apart from either parent, and thus a new species, albeit one with peculiar properties (see pp. 147, 355).

We may also cite the case of *Phaseolus vulgaris* and *P. multiflorus*. These are two well-defined species, crosses between which have recently been investigated by Lamprecht (1941). Both species have n = 17 chromosomes. The cross only succeeds with *vulgaris* as female parent, and the F1 is almost sterile. However, by breeding from the few seeds produced, a number of constant lines were obtained in F5–F9, some very close to one or other pure parent species, others intermediate, showing all possible combinations of the parents' characters. Fertility was originally low, but could gradually be raised to a high level. Here is an excellent example of species-differences depending solely or mainly on gene-differences. Further, the gene-complexes of the two forms have gradually become largely, but not quite, incompatible, so that selection is still able to restore viability and fertility in the hybrid. Some of the hybrid lines can properly be regarded as artificial species, since they are wholly or largely sterile with pure *P. vulgaris*.

Allopolyploidy has undoubtedly played an important role in the evolution of many plant genera. The careful analysis that has been made in *Nicotiana* will serve as a good example. Kostoff (1938) has experimentally produced a new allopolyploid by hybridizing *N. glauca* (n = 12) and *N. langsdorffii* (n = 9). An allotetraploid (n = 21) arose by parthogenesis. This showed rather poor fertility, but fertility rose gradually in successive generations, until it approximated to normal. The allotetraploid, though possessing unique characters, was by no means constant, throwing forms that differed in numerous characters, both morphological and physiological. This was due to the relative frequency of heterogenetic pairing—i.e. pairing and consequent segregation of chromosomes belonging to the two parental species, though homogenetic pairing was naturally the rule. This inconstancy also decreased in the course of generations, but not to any great extent.

Kostoff also produced an allotetraploid (2n = 80) between N. multivalens (n = 24) and N. suaveolens (n = 16). In this case the new species was remarkably constant, owing to the absence of heterogenetic pairing.

Another synthetic species, N. digluta, was manufactured ten years previously by Goodspeed and Clausen, by crossing N. tabacum (n = 24) with N. glutinosa (n = 12); the hybrid became tetraploid, with 72 as its somatic chromosome-number. Still another was produced in 1933, N. diglutosa, between N. glutinosa and another 12-chromosome species (references and discussion in Goodspeed, 1934; Babcock, 1939).

This experimental production of new allopolyploid species by hybridization is only the human continuation of a natural process in this genus (Goodspeed, 1934; summary in Dobzhansky, 1937; p. 214). Cytogenetic analysis has made it certain that the 24-chromosome American species are allotetraploids resulting from the hybridization between members of the 12-chromosome group. N. tabacum in particular, the source of tobacco, can be demonstrated, on the basis of the pairing attraction of its chromosomes in species-hybrids, to be the product of a cross between a form similar to N. sylvestris and one in the N. tomentosa group.

N. tabacum is highly polymorphic, like the artificial species glauca × langsdorffii mentioned above, and apparently for the same reason. During the time since its first origin, its chromosomes and those of its progenitors have altered their genic composition somewhat, but not enough to disguise their ancestral affinities.

Similarly N. rustica, another highly variable 24-chromosome species, can be shown to be derived from the crossing of two members of the N. paniculata group, though here the subsequent genetic divergence of the original progenitors and the new species has been greater. And one progenitor of N. nudicaulis must be sought in a form related to *N. trigonophylla*. Nothing is known as to the reason for the widespread occurrence of allopolyploidy in *Nicotiana*, but we may safely suggest that the opportunity for the necessary species-crosses was provided by extensive range-changes in relation to alterations of climate and land-level.

The wheats provide an equally striking example, with certain different features (summarized by Dobzhansky, 1937, pp. 215 seq.). Wheats fall into three groups with n = 7, 14, and 21 respectively. Broadly speaking, the 21-chromosome forms (*vulgare* group) have three distinct genomes, A, B, and D, of which the 14-chromosome form (*emmer* group) have two (A and B), and the 7-chromosome forms (*einkorn* group) the A-genome only. Allopolyploidy appears to have occurred twice, once with an unknown form providing the B-genome, and subsequently with an *Aegilops*-like form introducing the D-genome.

Complications have been introduced by the genetic divergence of various types. Thus one of the emmers, *T. timopheevi*, has a B-genome which differs considerably from the normal. This may mean that its B-ancestor was not identical with that of other emmers, but a related species;* or possibly the differentiation may have occurred subsequently. Again, heterogenetic pairing between members of the different genomes takes place to a different extent in different cases. Obviously, a twice-repeated allopolyploidy such as has here occurred provides the opportunity for great diversification.

In willows (*Salix*), Nilsson has been able to build up artificial species of an amazingly synthetic nature. One artificial species (Nilsson, 1936) contained genetic elements from no less than eight wild forms. Similar cases are known in orchids. The hybrid "genera" *Potinara* and *Burrageara* have been built up artificially from four different species belonging to four distinct natural genera (Sander, 1931).

Recently, the discovery that polyploidy may be artificially

---

* That allotetraploidy has occurred in more than one way is made probable by recent Russian work; e.g. *T. persicum* (n × 28) seems to be an allotetraploid derived from a cross between *T. dicoccoides* and *Aegilops triuncialis*, both with n = 14 (see Waddington, 1939, p. 323).

produced by colchicine has opened up new possibilities in this field, since sterile hybrids can often be immediately converted into more or less fertile allopolyploids by this means, instead of waiting for the lucky chance of natural chromosome-doubling. As an instance, we may take the recent work of Harland (1940) on cotton. For example, he has synthesized an allotetraploid between the Old World *Gossypium arboreum* and the New World *G. thurberi* (both n = 13). This can then be crossed with commercial tetraploid forms (which themselves appear to be the product of allotetraploidy between Old and New World diploids), and the immunity to pink bollworm carried by *G. thurberi* can thus be introduced into cultivation.

Again, he has synthesized allohexaploid forms between the commercial *G. barbadense* (n = 26) and various New World diploids (n = 13). The addition of the wild genome confers increased resistance to drought and to various pests, as well as great vigour and sometimes high quality of lint.*

Allopolyploids, like autopolyploids, often differ in physiological and ecological peculiarities from their diploid ancestors, and therefore come to occupy different ranges; and, again as with autoplyploids, their ranges are usually more extensive. To take but one example, G. H. Shull (1937) has summarized our knowledge of the species of the crucifer genus *Capsella*. Here the basic chromosome-number (x) is 8. The diploid species with 2n = 16 are, with few exceptions, found in the Mediterranean area, which appears to be the original centre of distribution of the genus. This region is also inhabited by various tetraploid forms; but these, taken together, are world-wide in their extension. Although Shull has not been able to detect any differences in vigour between the 2x and 4x forms, he is convinced that some such differences must exist, together probably with differences in adaptability, to account for the observed distributional difference. While autopolyploidy may have occurred, Shull is convinced that hybridization and allotetra-

* The use of colchicine has of course other application. It permits the building up of autopolyploids. These may themselves show valuable new characteristics, or they may sometimes give fertile crosses with other polyploid species of the same chromosome-number, and so produce new recombinations.

ploidy has been the chief source of 4x forms. In one area of Texas, two 4x forms, *C. occidentalis* and *C. bursa-pastoris*, which are restricted to the region west and east of the Rockies respectively, have met and crossed, producing a more or less stable new type; Shull does not give cytological data for this form. The genus *Potentilla* is one in which both auto- and allopolyploidy have occurred. We have already referred to the autopolyploid series in *P. argentea* (p. 337). In *P. collina* and *P. crantzii* on the other hand, Müntzing (1931) finds strong evidence for allotetraploidy, in the shape of anisoploid (5x and 7x) forms, Apomictic reproduction has enabled these heterozygous forms to remain in permanency. Most *collina* biotypes, however, are hexaploid. Müntzing considers that the very variable "collective species" *P. collina* arose through a cross between *P. argentea* and a form close to *P. tabernaemontani*. In general, the species of *Potentilla* "which are regarded as old and primitive . . . are characterized by low chromosome numbers and a relatively limited and decreasing geographical distribution", whereas the dominant and aggressive types have a high chromosome number (up to 12x), mainly due to allopolyploidy. See also Christoff (1941).

A curious case is cited by Tischler (1941), where a *gigas*-form of the normally hexaploid *Aloe ciliaris* turns out to be pentaploid.

One final case deserves to be mentioned, since it shows that new species can arise by this means even after intergeneric hybridization. This is the radish-cabbage hybrid *Raphano-Brassica* (Karpechenko, 1928). This is the product of a cross between the radish (*Raphanus sativus*) and the cabbage (*Brassica oleracea*), both with 2n = 18 chromosomes. The 18-chromosome hybrid was at first sterile, as with *Primula kewensis*, but became fully fertile on achieving allotetraploidy.

That allopolyploidy after species-hybridization has been an important agency in evolution in giving rise to new species in nature is shown by the large number of cases in which allied species within a genus or group of genera show chromosome numbers which are all multiples of some basic number. For instance, the basic haploid number (x) in the genus *Chrysanthemum* is 9, and 2x, 4x, 6x, 8x, and 10x species are known. In wheat and oats x = 7, and 2x, 4x and 6x types occur. Similar series occur in every large genus of flowering plants as yet investigated, with the exception of *Ribes* and *Antirrhinum*.

The evidence goes to show that while some of these series may be due to the occurrence of autopolyploidy (p. 335), the great majority, notably of sexually reproducing types, are due to initial allopolyploidy.

Kinsey (1936) suggests that species-hybridization (presumably followed by allotetraploidy) has played a considerable role in the evolution of the gall-wasp family Cynipidae, but his conclusions are unsupported by experimental evidence. In general it appears unlikely that this mode of speciation has occurred to any extent in any animal group. It has been suggested that polyploidy might be commoner among hermaphrodite animals on account of the absence of the X-Y sex-determining mechanism, but M. J. D. White (1940) has shown that even here it is much rarer than in plants. In moths, Federley has shown that allotetraploid hybrids may arise through non-reduction of the chromosomes in gametogenesis. But new species do not appear to arise in this way, partly because mating preferences keep normal species apart, partly because the hybrids are not fully fertile (see Federley, 1932). Species-hybridization occurs in fish, but we do not know the cytological phenomena. Hubbs (1940) has described cases in which desiccation in the American desert has brought together in one pool two species originally differentiated in relation to lake and stream life. E.g. with chub, two pure species and many hybrids were found in a single section of creek. Such cases would repay further investigation.

Considering the general role of allopolyploidy in plant evolution, we may conclude that it is likely to occur when changes of climate bring about range-changes, these then providing opportunities for hybridization between plant species which have developed in isolation and between which no reproductive barriers have therefore been evolved, such as different flowering seasons or adaptation to different insect pollinators. But, once induced, allopolyploidy often provides the opportunity for taking advantage of the new conditions. This is partly due, as with autopolyploidy, to increased vigour and resistance, partly to the fact that quite new types, some of which are pre-adapted to various ecological conditions, are produced (pp. 336, 351), and finally to the plasticity conferred by a certain degree of heterogenetic chromosome-pairing.

This plasticity is due to the fact that heterogenetic chromosome-pairing produces a unique type of variation. The mechanism of meiosis produces segregation and recombination. The characters segregated and recombined are in the vast majority of organisms dependent on single-gene mutations which form part of the general constitution of the species. However, in allopolyploids with some degree of heterogenetic pairing, what are segregated and recombined are not single genes, but groups of genes which have evolved for long periods, often millions of years, in isolation from each other, so that such species possess a new kind of recombinational variation in their genetic stock-in-trade.

We must finally consider the cases of so-called aneuploidy or secondary polyploidy, in which some kinds of chromosomes are represented more often than others in the total complement (polysomy). Different strains within *Viola kitaibeliana* include not only polyploids, and polyploids lacking one chromosome (monosomics), but polyploids with some chromosomes polysomic (Clausen, 1927). The analysis here is not, however, so clear-cut as in the species of dahlia, *D. merckii*. All species of the genus *Dahlia* save this one have $n = 8$ or some multiple of 8; *D. merckii*, however, has $n = 18$. Cytological evidence proves that this must be interpreted as a tetraploid in which two kinds of chromosomes are represented by three pairs instead of two; i.e. whereas most kinds of chromosomes will exist in the form F^1F^1, F^2F^2; G^1G^1, G^2G^2, two kinds will exist as A^1A^1, A^2A^2, A^3A^3; B^1B^1, B^2B^2, B^3B^3. The species is thus mainly tetraploid, but partly hexaploid. It is noteworthy that this species shows more striking differences from the rest of the genus than does any other. This is to be expected, since the balance between the genes contained in different chromosomes is upset. Such cases must have originated suddenly by duplication of whole chromosomes, those forms surviving which have a proper genetic balance. They are not known for certainty in diploids: the reason here is presumably that the upset of balance would be more considerable (2 : 1 instead of 3 : 2).* Collins, Hollingshead and Avery (1929) produced a secondarily balanced "species" of *Crepis*, *C. artificialis*, by crossing the tetraploid *C. biennis* (2n = 4x = 40) and the diploid *C. setosa* (2n = 8). In the F1, the 20 *biennis* chromosomes formed 10 pairs by autosyndesis, but the 4 *setosa* chromosomes segregated at random. However, after some generations of selfing, a true-breeding strain was produced in which two of these had been completely lost, while the other two had become paired. Here, then, the secondary polyploid has been produced by loss of chromosomes. According to Sikka (1940) secondary polyploidy has played a considerable role in the cabbages (*Brassica*). The basic chromosome number is x = 5. Straightforward tetraploids (2n = 20) exist, together with both *plus* and *minus* secondary tetraploids (2n =20+4; 2n=20—2; 2n=20—4). From these various forms allopolyploidy has produced new species, with 2n = 34, 36, 38, and 48 chromosomes respectively.

Darlington (1937) has given cogent reasons for believing that the whole Pomoideae section of the Rose order, comprising the apples, pears, medlars, etc., are of similar constitution, derived from a basic number of x = 7, by tetraploidy followed by extra representation (six times instead of four) of three chromosomes. They then have 2n = 34, four of the original seven chromosomes being represented by two pairs each, the remaining three by three pairs. It is probable, though by no means certain, that this condition has been reached by the loss rather than the addition of chromosomes after a cross. On paleontological grounds, this condition must have originated not later than the early Tertiary period.

* An aneuploid form with extra representation of one kind of chromosome has been experimentally produced in tobacco (*Nicotiana*) by Webber (1930); the result here followed five generations of in-breeding after a cross, and involved various complex processes which need not concern us here. Lammarts (1932) has, by similar methods, produced another "species" of this type.

Thus in addition to the various evolutionary implications of polyploidy already mentioned, we see that it permits a new type of initial variation, in the shape of alterations in the numerical balance between different kinds of chromosomes.

10. RETICULATE DIFFERENTIATION

We must now briefly consider the extremely complicated state of affairs to be found in certain plant groups like the roses (*Rosa*), brambles (*Rubus*), willows (*Salix*), and hawthorns (*Crataegus*), resulting in a network of forms (reticulate evolution).

In all these groups, matters are complicated by a combination of polyploidy and various methods of non-sexual reproduction. In the *Caninae* section of the genus *Rosa*, what has been called *subsexual reproduction* occurs. The species of this group typically possess 35 chromosomes, 7 being the basic number for all roses. In the formation of ova, 14 of these normally pair at meiosis, while the remaining 21 all go to one pole of the spindle. This results in cells with 7 and with 28 chromosomes respectively, and from the latter the ova are formed. In the formation of pollen, on the other hand, no such differential behaviour of the unpaired chromosomes is observed, but most of them are eliminated from the nuclei by lagging during division. The result is that the majority of the viable pollen-grains have the complete single set of 7, together with 0, 1, or 2 others. The 21 unpaired chromosomes are thus generally handed down asexually, while the few that appear in viable pollen grains provide a certain amount of excess variability. The *Caninae* group has undoubtedly arisen through hybridization—either by repeated crosses between different types of diploid species or by a cross between hexaploid species—after which the special peculiarities of the system must have arisen adaptively. It is noteworthy that whereas self-pollination leads to sexual reproduction, cross-pollination normally acts as a stimulus to parthenogenetic development.

In other sections of the genus, all the even-multiple polyploids (and even certain of the diploids) appear to have arisen as species-hybrids. In some cases these hybrids are interchange heterozygotes, with the result that segregation produces forms resembling the presumed original parents. Crosses between different species often occur, and may be viable and capable of reproduction (Darlington, 1937, pp. 460 seq.).

It will thus be seen that hybridization is not uncommon in the genus *Rosa*, and that as the result of it, in addition to true-breeding polyploid species, a certain amount of segregation, either of single chromosomes or genomes, takes place. The group thus forms a network, in which convergent species-formation has not merely led to new species, but also to their partial or total dissociation; and some of the new types produced by this dissociation will maintain themselves. The course of events can be represented as a network, so that we can speak of the evolution of the group as *reticulate* (Turrill, 1936).

The same absence of sterility-barriers between related species as is shown by *Rosa* occurs also in *Rubus*, though here the position is complicated by the fact that whereas crosses between closely-related species usually yield true hybrids, those between more distantly related forms yield "false hybrids". These are produced entirely apomictically, although the stimulus of the foreign pollen appears to be necessary. A remarkable fact is that in New Zealand, though reticulate evolution is frequent in the flora, it does not occur in *Rubus* (Allan, 1940).

Some hybrid *Rubus* forms breed true as new polyploid species (this is also true of the loganberry, a species artificially produced by allopolyploidy after a cross between raspberry and blackberry). In nature, species occur with 2x, 3x, 4x, 5x, 6x, and 8x chromosomes (x = 7, as in *Rosa*), and apparently divergent segregants as well as convergent hybrid forms are produced.

Crane and Thomas (1939) have shown that reproduction in the polyploid species may be entirely sexual, entirely apomictic, or partly sexual and partly non-sexual. In addition segregation may occur even in apomictic reproduction by means of crossing-over, the apomictic embryo presumably arising *after* the first meiotic division. Some of the distinctive types thus produced breed true and maintain themselves in nature (and see p. 334). Thus "many of the species and micro-species of *Rubus* are evidently clones and subclones, produced by segregation and maintained by apomixis".

The willows (*Salix*) show the same bewildering multiplicity of "species" in nature as do *Rubus* and *Rosa*, and almost certainly for the same general reasons (see e.g. Nilsson, 1930), and synthetic species have been artificially created (p. 345). Bewildering hybrid swarms are found in New Zealand (e.g. in *Aleuosmia*, etc. p. 355; Allan, 1940), but cytogenetic investigation is needed before we can say if they are of the true reticulate type, or merely show mendelian gene-recombination. Similar but less extreme "reticulation" appears to occur in one section of the genus *Viola*.

As a result of these processes, the classification of such groups according to ordinary criteria is rendered all but impossible. We may quote what an experienced plant systematist has to say on the matter (Turrill, 1936): "The taxonomy of the British genus *Rubus* is in such a state that specialists sometimes cannot agree in more than one determination in ten. It is probable that in such genera a totally different scheme from that of species and varieties will have to be evolved before stability of expression is reached."

The case of the hawkweeds (*Crepis*) is dealt with elsewhere (p. 372). Babcock and Stebbins (see Stebbins, 1940*a*) propose the term *polyploid complex* for groups in which self-perpetuating secondary hybrids between auto- and allopolyploid forms are produced, so that "there arises a complex network of interrelated forms, which defies classification according to the usual concepts of the species"—i.e. which shows reticulate evolution. Reticulate polyploid complexes of this sort occur not only in *Crepis*, *Rosa* and *Rubus*, but in scores of other plant genera.

This "convergent-divergent" type of reticulate evolution may be contrasted with the "recombinational" type found in man. Here, a reticulate result has been achieved by quite other means. Instead of the initial crossing being between distinct species, and the divergent variability being due to segregation of whole chromosomes or genomes, the crossing appears to have taken place between well-marked geographical subspecies,* and the divergent variability is thus due to ordinary gene recombination. So far as we know, no polyploidy and no formation of specially stable types has occurred, but the progressive increase of migration and crossing has led to a progressive increase of general variability (see general discussion in Huxley and Haddon, 1935; Huxley, 1940).

Man is the only organism to have exploited this method of evolution and variation to an extreme degree, so that a new dominant type in evolution has come to be represented by a single world-wide species instead of showing an adaptive radiation into many intersterile species. Doubtless this is due to his great tendency to individual, group, and mass migration of an irregular nature, coupled with his mental adaptability which enables him to effect cross-mating quite readily in face of differences of colour, appearance, and behaviour which would act as efficient barriers in the case of more instinctive organisms.

Keith and McCown (1937) refer to the extraordinary variability of Palestine man some sixty thousand years ago. As a "neanderthaloid type can be distinguished in this population, it may be suggested that the variability is partly dependent on crosses with *H. neanderthalensis*.

It is interesting that in the animal group with the largest powers of irregular dispersal, the birds, adumbrations of the same process occur. We have already spoken of the hybridization of the two species of flickers (p. 250), but in addition to the "mixed zone" where the two species have come into contact by extending their ranges, obviously hybrid birds are found sporadically in the areas of the pure species, the frequency of such forms naturally diminishing with distance from the mixed zone (Taverner, 1934).

We have also (p. 252) mentioned the somewhat similar picture

---

* Some authors, such as Gates (1930), prefer to call them distinct species: the difference is here largely a matter of convenience, but since they are clearly of geographical origin and completely or reasonably interfertile, so that the resultant largely hybrid group constitutes a single interbreeding unit, it seems better, and more in accord with modern practice, to style them subspecies of a single large species or *Rassenkreis* (p. 163).

presented by the red-tailed hawks of the genus *Buteo* in Canada. Here the number of sporadic hybrids occurring within the areas of the various normally pure types appears to be more considerable (Taverner, 1936). Taverner points out that the occurrence of sporadic individuals of the general type of one subspecies or species within the range of another occurs in a fair number of birds.

A slightly different effect is shown by the water-thrush (*Seiurus noveboracensis*), a migratory species. McCabe and Miller (1933) find that this species shows "incipient geographic differentiation" into three statistically separable subspecies, but "even in the geographic centres of one of these races individuals may appear that show a considerable approach to the other race. Geographic segregation and correlation of characters . . . are incomplete not only at the borders or zones of intergradation, but to some extent throughout each race".

We have already referred to the hybrid swarms produced by the crossing of plant species in nature (pp. 147, 353). These may be so extensive and so successful that they constitute a definite element in the flora of a country. Evolution in such cases is also reticulate, though the meshes of the biological network will not be so large as in *Rubus* or *Rosa*, and the result is more like that obtaining in man. The best-investigated cases come from New Zealand, where no fewer than 491 hybrid groups have been recorded (Allan, 1940). Allan refers to "colonies of *Hebe* that present a multitude of forms none of which can at present be separated out as belonging to a 'good species' ". The same sort of thing occurs in *Leptospermum* and *Senecio*. In *Aleuosmia* there is an extraordinary multiplicity of forms, many of them hybrids, in the northern part of North Island, N.Z.; the complexity diminishes with increasing latitude, until in the southern part of the island only a single well-characterized species is found.* As Allan says, new methods of nomenclature must be devised to deal with such situations.

In many cases the hybrid swarm arises as a result of human

---

* We have here a very unusual form of cline—in degree of interspecific crossing.

interference (see p. 258). This probably applies to the kidney vetch, *Anthyllis vulneraria* (Marsden-Jones and Turrill, 1933), where what seem originally to have been well-marked geographical varieties (subspecies) have hybridized in numerous areas to give rise to complex hybrid swarms, each with its own characteristics (see also pp. 247, 291).

It has been suggested (Lowe, 1936) that the state of affairs to be found in the ground-finches of the Galapagos and the sicklebills of Hawaii is to be explained as the result of large-scale crossing and reticulation. However, we have seen (p. 327) that this is not supported by more careful analysis. Hybridization does seem to occur occasionally, however. Lack (1940a) mentions *Geospiza cinerostris darwini*, which occurs on a single island and appears to have arisen as a hybrid between *G. c. propinqua* and *G. magnirostris*: as would be expected it is exceedingly variable. One other such case is also known in the Geospizids.

It will be seen that reticulate evolution, though uncommon, is not so uncommon as was until very recently supposed. There is a natural reluctance among systematists to recognize its existence and its implications, since these run counter to the generally-accepted basis of taxonomic practice. The fact that this basis is largely unconscious merely enhances the reluctance to change. It may be that once the necessity of admitting the existence of reticulate differentiation has been recognized in principle, it will be detected, in large or small degree, in a much greater number of instances, especially among plants, but also among animals. In the latter case, it is likely to be of the small-meshed or recombinational type only, while in plants both this type and that of the polyploid complex are to be expected.

II. ILLUSTRATIVE EXAMPLES

To illustrate how different the methods of speciation may be in higher animals and higher plants, two concrete examples are here presented of genera which have recently been subjected to the fullest analysis—the fruitflies (*Drosophila*) and the hawkweeds (*Crepis*).

Drosophila is unique in being the only genus among either plants or animals in which we have at our disposal not only the results of intensive taxonomic study of the usual type and of work on ecology and population-structure, but of an astonishingly complete genetic analysis and of what we may call ultra-cytology (of salivary gland chromosomes). Furthermore, it has a very wide range, and comprises a large number of species. In what follows, the accounts of Muller (1940) and Spencer (1940) have been mainly drawn upon, while Dobzhansky's book (1937) has also proved a mine of information, and M. J. D. White (1937) gives a brief but useful summary.

A recent careful taxonomic study by Sturtevant (1939) has been undertaken in forty-two species of the genus available for detailed examination. Twenty-seven characters were selected which could not be regarded as due either to similarity of developmental processes, or to selective (adaptive) agencies, and their correlations tabulated. Further work is in progress, but on the basis of the results to date it was found that the accepted taxonomy should be modified, and the genus should be divided into three subgenera, one so far containing only a single species (*D. duncani*), one (subgenus *Drosophila*) containing such species as *funebris*, *hydei*, *repleta*, and *virilis*, and the third (subgenus *Sophophora*) containing other well-analysed species such as *melanogaster*, *simulans*, *athabasca*, *azteca*, *ananassae*, *miranda*, *obscura*, *pseudoobscura*, and *subobscura*.

The two main subgenera differ in such points as the fusion or separation of the posterior pair of Malpighian tubes, the number of filaments on the egg, and the shape of the dark posterior bands on the abdominal segments.

A considerable time ago Sturtevant in his monograph (1921) showed that many of the specific characters in the genus could be matched among the mutant characters which appeared in experimental cultures.

The conclusions reached on the basis of cytogenetic work are as follows. Firstly, *Drosophila* is as yet the only organism in which sufficiently detailed tests can be carried out to decide whether, in addition to obviously mendelizing characters, the vague types of variation, more fluid and more continuous in their phenotypic variation and their inheritance, also mendelize and are therefore dependent on chromosomal and particulate inheritance, or are due to some quite different type of process (cytoplasmic inheritance, organismal relations, etc.). The answer is decisive; with one possible exception, perhaps due to a virus (L'Héritier and Teissier, 1938), all heritable differences in *Drosophila* are chromosomal. The further important conclusion can be drawn that "small" mutations, with slight effects, many of them often affecting the same character, are more frequent than large ones, and much more important in evolution (Muller, 1940).

Another important general result (p. 75; Dobzhansky, 1939*b*) is that wild populations are full of gene-differences, mostly recessives in single dose, to an extent much greater than originally thought possible. These gene-differences must be presumed to have originated by mutation of the same type as has been studied in the laboratory, though recent work (p. 55; Zuitin, 1941) indicates that, owing to the rapid changes in temperature, etc., in the wild, the mutation rate in nature may be considerably higher than in standard laboratory conditions.

Detailed population analysis has also revealed the important fact that populations from different areas, though superficially alike, often differ in regard to their content of recessive genes and also of chromosome rearrangements. Further, different species of the genus show different degrees of this local differentiation, doubtless owing to differences in behaviour and ecology (see Dobzhansky, 1939*b*, N.W. and E. A. Timoféeff-Ressovsky, 1940).

Quite recently Spencer (cited by Muller, 1940) has shown that a limited fertility exists in crosses between two species of the genus—*D. virilis* and *D. americana.** The genetic analysis thus made possible revealed that all the character-differences investigated were due to multiple genes, each having a small effect.

---

* The latter is sometimes referred to as a subspecies of *D. virilis*, but the differences between the two in ordinary taxonomic characters, in polyploidy, and in chromosome morphology are, according to Spencer, as great as those between various pairs of forms within the genus, which are universally recognized as "good species": but see below, p. 367.

Although the hybrids between *D. melanogaster* and *D. simulans* are wholly sterile, Muller, by an ingenious method (Muller and Pontecorvo, 1940), has recently been able to obtain flies with combinations of the chromosomes of the two species which are equivalent to the results of a back-cross between a hybrid F_1 and the *melanogaster* parent. The results show that in both species each major chromosome (X, II and III) contains interacting genes affecting viability and another interacting system affecting fertility. The small IVth chromosome of *simulans*, when transferred into an otherwise pure *melanogaster* genotype, produces various new genetic effects. Again, the abnormality of abdominal banding and bristles shown in the normal F_1 turns out to be due to interaction between a sex-linked *simulans* gene and one or more autosomal *melanogaster* genes, a result reminding us of the melanotic tumours produced by species-hybridization in certain cyprinodont fish (p. 66).

In general the results thus support the view that once groups become isolated they start to diverge in respect of a number of genes, and that these are interlocked in a harmoniously-stabilized system or systems. After a certain time, apparently not of great duration, the specific systems become mutually inharmonious or even incompatible through the sheer accumulation of difference.

It has sometimes been suggested that sterility between species depends on special factors. Here, again, the evidence from *Drosophila* is to the contrary. The two "races" (well-differentiated genetic subspecies) of *D. pseudoobscura* show a marked lowering of fertility on crossing, the F_1 males being wholly sterile, the females very slightly fertile. By an ingenious method (only possible in a genetically well-analysed form), Dobzhansky has shown that, in later generations from back-crosses of the hybrid females to either pure species, the fertility of the males depends wholly on the particular combination of "fertility genes" (or, if the term be preferred, "sterility genes") which they happen to receive. These genes are distributed through all the chromosomes, and furthermore (as was also noted for the *virilis-americana* cross) different strains of each parent type differ in their cross-ability, owing to their containing different complements of fertility genes. Thus the special criterion of most animal species, their mutual infertility, appears in *Drosophila* to depend largely on gene-mutations (together with sectional chromosomal mutations, as mentioned later).

In addition, the intensive genetic work carried out on single species of the genus, notably *D. melanogaster*, has shown that they all contain the genetic potentiality for developing strains with reduced interfertility if evolutionary occasion should offer. The most interesting and relevant cases are those in which a combination of genes exerts an effect on fertility which is not exerted by any of the genes singly. Thus *curly wing* and *moiré eye* when in combination give males with almost complete infertility. An opposite effect is found in relation to *deltex*, which in most stocks thickens the wing-veins and also produces complete male sterility. However, Bridges has found three separate "deltex-suppressor" genes, two autosomal and one sex-linked, which almost wholly suppress both the morphological and the sterility effects of deltex.

Similar effects are known for viability (see Chapter 3). Muller points out that such effects, of reduced fertility and viability after crossing, are bound to arise sooner or later in strains that are in any way reproductively isolated from each other. "For, given enough mutational differences, some at least of the genes, in recombination, will give non-additive effects on viability or fertility, and, as is always the case with effects not yet subjected to the sieve of selection, these effects will far oftener be adverse than beneficial." Thus any partial genetic isolation will automatically tend to become more complete with time. Furthermore, natural selection will also operate to reduce the wastage caused by any degree of lowered fertility after crossing. F_1 sterility will be favoured as against F_2 sterility, F_1 inviability as against F_1 sterility, and mutations preventing P_1 crossing at all (psychological and reproductive barriers) as against those concerned with effects on F_1.

The same general principles apply to viability, to normality of development, and to normality of chromosome-conjugation in meiosis. Genetically isolated groups are bound to develop their own characteristic systems of genes adapted to harmonious development and function, but these gene-systems are equally bound to become more or less disharmonious *vis-à-vis* each other, so that crossing will produce some reduction of harmonious functioning in F1 or later generations. In particular, certain genes which on their first incorporation were merely advantageous deviations will become converted into necessary bases for later stages of the genetic system.

It is extremely unlikely that hybrid sterility in higher animals can ever be brought about by a single gene-mutation or a single sectional rearrangement. On the other hand, reduction of crossability might be brought about in this way, and would then lay the foundation for the development of intersterility.

The existence of a highly differentiated sex-determining mechanism, as in *Drosophila*, provides an extra cause of hybrid sterility. In the first place, the X-chromosome (in *Drosophila*) contains a disproportionately large number of fertility genes; and secondly, sex-linked genes must have especially strong expression, since in the heterogametic sex one dose of these genes must be balanced against a double dose of any complementary autosomal genes. Thus in crosses between incipient or full species, sex-linked genes in the male F1 are especially likely to be in imbalance with their autosomal complements, resulting in lowered fertility of this sex. This is the basis for Haldane's rule of the reduced F1 fertility of the heterogametic sex in wide crosses; as Muller points out, similar or even larger effects may be exerted in later generations. Here again the species of higher animals may be regarded as being more highly differentiated, and more sharply delimited genetically, than those of plants.

Drosophila, owing to its giant salivary gland chromosomes, is especially favourable material for studying sectional chromosome-rearrangements. Recent work has made it possible to evaluate the degree of their importance in speciation with some degree of assurance. The first point to notice is that sectional rearrangements tend to impede crossing-over. Wherever crossing-over is thus interfered with, and the sectional rearrangement is fairly widespread within the species, the genes in the rearranged section are effectively isolated from those in the corresponding "normal" section. Thus, as Darlington especially has stressed, there are produced within the species two isolated partial genetic systems which may diverge from each other like two distinct species, by the accumulation of different mutants (see p. 332; also 67, 139).

It was at first thought that large rearrangements were common causes of speciation in *Drosophila*, but Muller points out that in this regard they must be quite secondary to gene-mutation. This is shown by the fact that the types of rearrangement which most commonly characterize related species also exist commonly within species.

In any case, they are much rarer than gene-mutations, and can hardly ever recur identically, as happens with numerous of these latter. Furthermore, the above-noted fact of the genetic isolation of the rearranged section from its normal homologue will mean that, so long as the rearrangement remains rare, it will not have the same evolutionary plasticity, so that its possessors will be handicapped if adaptive change is demanded. Thus rearrangements are only likely to become established through the accidental process that Sewall Wright calls "drift", which will be favoured by the existence of small more or less isolated populations. Their maintenance may also be favoured by their heterosis effect, in the heterozygous condition, on vigour and productivity.

Finally, individuals heterozygous for sectional rearrangements are destined, owing to their peculiar behaviour at meiosis, to give rise to a certain proportion of gametes with an unbalanced gene-complement (included by Muller under the term *aneuploid*), which give rise to inviable offspring. The resultant reduction of productivity is especially marked with translocations, increasing with the size of the translocated section; within this type of rearrangement, mutual translocations of practically entire chromosome-arms suffer least. It also occurs with pericentric inversions, which include regions on either side of the centromere, and then is more or less proportional to the length of the inversion.

On the other hand, paracentric inversions, which do not include the centromere and lie wholly within one chromosome-arm, do not suffer this reduction of productivity. Sturtevant and Beadle (1938) have shown that this depends on the fact that in *Drosophila* the polar bodies are all formed in a straight line extending radially outwards, and that this causes the aneuploid chromosome-sets to remain in the two central polar bodies, the egg nucleus and the outer polar body receiving normal gene-complements.

Small "repeats" (including "shifts" of the repeated section into another part of the same individual chromosome) will not cause any serious loss of productivity.

The changes that lead to the resolution of a V-shaped chromosome into two rods, or to the reverse process, also occasion little or no loss of productivity. It was originally supposed that such alterations were readily brought about, but a proper understanding of the chromosomal mechanism has shown that they require a combination of several relatively rare events, and must themselves thus be much rarer than ordinary sectional rearrangements (pp. 365–6).

The analysis of sectional rearrangements as found in nature, both within species and as characteristics of closely allied species, confirms the expectations derived from what we have just set forth. In many thousands of chromosomes from wild populations of several *Drosophila* species Dubinin and his associates (1934, 1936) found only thirty-five sectional rearrangements. Thirty-three of these were paracentric inversions (many of them widespread), one was a small shift, and one a small translocation. This emphasizes both the difficulty of other types of rearrangement becoming established, and the rarity of rearrangements in nature as compared with gene-mutations.

Again, *D. simulans* and *D. melanogaster* differ sectionally in respect of one large and one very small inversion; but they are characterized by a large number of visible character-differences which must be ascribed to gene-mutations. A large number of gene-differences have been shown to exist between *D. virilis* and *D. americana*, while sectionally they differ only in two inversions and probably one shift.

A very interesting point, however, is that in some species of the genus sectional rearrangements are much more numerous. This is so in *D. pseudoobscura*, which has yielded twenty-five sectional differences (almost all intra-arm inversions), as against seven discovered in *D. melanogaster*. In this case, different combinations of sectional differences are found in different regional populations, and each such population shows the same degree of prevalence of sectional rearrangement as characterizes the entire population of species such as *D. melanogaster*. The local groups also differ in regard to numerous gene-mutations. It is thus probable that *D. pseudoobscura* differs biologically from other species of the genus in being split up, owing to some ecological peculiarity, into relatively isolated local groups, which will facilitate the local accumulation of sectional rearrangements through Sewall Wright's "drift". The same cause has doubtless operated to divide it into the two more or less intersterile subspecies, "races" A and B. *D. montium* is also divisible into similar "races"—at least two and probably more. In its race B one arm of one of the V-shaped large chromosomes is absent; possibly it is genetically inert in the other race (Kikkawa, 1936).

So far, only very closely-related species have been considered. When a greater degree of divergence has occurred, many more sectional rearrangements have accumulated. Thus, although *D. pseudoobscura* is quite closely related to *D. miranda*, Dobzhansky and Tan (1936) have shown that at least forty-nine chromosome-breaks, and probably more like one hundred, must have occurred in the course of their differentiation from a common ancestor. Patterson and Crow (1940) point out that the small size of the breeding-units of *D. miranda* would allow a large number of rearrangements to become irreversibly fixed, whereas the larger and less isolated groups of *D. pseudoobscura* will promote a smaller number of rearrangements floating through the population, and fluctuating in frequency. *D. athabasca* and *D. azteca* differ in a still greater number of rearrangements, and, though they are not widely remote systematically from *D. pseudoobscura* and *D. miranda*, show no recognizable homology with either of these in the banding of their salivary gland chromosomes. It is thus probable that all these four species share the biological peculiarities of *D. pseudoobscura*, whereby sectional rearrangements are accumulated with greater frequency than in forms like *D. melanogaster*. There is again no recognizable similarity in chromosome-banding between *D. melanogaster* and *D. pseudoobscura*.

One interesting bearing of sectional rearrangements on taxonomy results from their relative rarity, and from the fact that most of those occurring in a single chromosome-arm, especially if they involve sections of the chromosome-map which overlap, cannot undergo recombination with each other by crossing-over. It is accordingly possible in certain cases to deduce with certainty or high probability the phylogenetic course of events by which two related species showing a number of differences in sectional arrangements diverged. The only restriction on the method is that the seriation of steps can be read in either direction: to decide which is the origin and which the terminus, we must rely on other data, such as morphological resemblances and geographical distribution.

As an example we may take the rearrangements found in the third chromosome of *D. pseudoobscura*. It is found that all the rearrangements of race A must have a common origin, and so must all those of race B. These two original types are both removed by one step only from a configuration which no longer appears to exist, but which was presumably ancestral. In addition, from this presumed ancestral type, the rearrangements found in the related *D. miranda* can also be derived. Corresponding studies on other chromosomes, together with data on the geographical distribution of the various rearrangements, should add considerably to the accuracy of the results (Sturtevant and Dobzhansky, 1936; and see Muller, 1940, p. 233).

It is well known that the different species of *Drosophila* differ in the gross morphology of their chromosomes. Thus the haploid *melanogaster* has 2 V's, 1 rod (X), and 1 dot (microchromosome); *willistoni* has no microchromosome, 2 V's and 1 rod, but the X is here a V; *virilis* has 5 rods and a microchromosome; *immigrans* 1 V and 3 rods; etc.

It was at one time thought that this would throw light on the taxonomic relationships of the genus. Later research, however, has made it clear that this is not so. As Muller (1940) puts it, "Evidently the species wander back and forth between one metaphase picture and another, so that quite closely related species may show very different chromosomal pictures. Even such close forms as D. *virilis* and D. *americana* differ in such an important respect as whether the X is a V or a rod."

The chief processes at work in changing the metaphase picture are: (1) fusion or separation of whole arms—union of two rods to form a V or *vice versa*. This is more readily accomplished between autosomes than between the X and an autosome. (2) The acquisition or loss of microchromosomes (dots). This may occur comparatively readily because of certain technical reasons, whereas the formation or loss of a new chromosome of considerable dimensions would be impossible. (3) Marked change in the size of a given arm. This is the least frequent of the three. All these changes are likely to be much rarer than ordinary rearrangements, but not so rare as not to occur and become established with some frequency when geological time is considered.

Certain of the changes have consequential genetic effects. Thus when an X-rod becomes attached to a previously autosomal rod, the dosage relations of the genes in the new X-system must undergo alteration, implying a modification of the whole gene-complex. Incorporation of autosomal material in the Y will lead to its gradual genetic degeneration to the status of inert material.

Recently Stone and Griffen (1940) have experimentally altered the chromosome pattern in D. *melanogaster* by translocation. In one stock, the chromosome-number was reduced. The dot-like IVth chromosome was translocated (possibly apart from a very small residual portion) to the X-chromosome and thus became hemizygous in the male sex. Three different sub-types have been produced. In one, IV was transferred to one end of the X, resulting in a J-shaped chromosome, in another to its other end, and in a third it was inserted into the body of the X.

In another stock, an additional small chromosome-pair was produced by an elaborate process, resulting in part of the X-chromosome now being represented in excess (sectional hyperploidy) as a new small autosome.

These and other conversions were all at a disadvantage against the normal as regards viability, but the disadvantage was not very great and Stone and Griffen anticipate that full viability may be fairly soon restored by selection for modifiers, mutational or recombinational.

Other recent studies from the University of Texas are of interest in throwing light on the various modes of speciation in the genus.

Patterson, Stone, and Griffen (1940) have studied the forms allocated to *D. virilis*. The species falls into two groups, (*a*) forms with red pupae, pupating at the edge of the food, and with adults highly susceptible to ether, (*b*) forms with grey pupae, pupating on the side of the container above the food, and with adults more resistant to ether. The "red" group includes two subspecies, *D. v. americana* (regarded as a full species by Spencer: see p. 358), and *D. v. texana*; the "grey" group includes but one subspecies, *D. v. virilis*, but this shows some differentiation even within the U.S.A., and its Asiatic form is also somewhat distinct. The species is rare and local in America, but abundant in eastern Asia. *D. virilis* is unusual in showing marked chromosomal differences between its subspecies. *D. v. virilis* possesses 5 rods and a dot as its haploid complement; in *D. v. texana* Nos. 3 and 4 of *D. v. virilis* are fused to form a V; and *D. v. americana* has Nos. 2 and 3 and also X and 4 fused to form 2 V's (in the female; in the male there is no Y-4 fusion). There are also some inversions as between the different subspecies. But the main causes of isolation between the forms are sexual (behaviour) isolation, low viability of F1 eggs, and complicated fertility relations. Thus in male hybrids between "red" and "grey" forms, those containing a "red" Y-chromosome must also contain 2nd and 5th chromosomes from the same parent strain if it is to be fertile. This relationship causes high sterility in the subspecific crosses that go easily, namely with "red" males, whereas the reciprocal cross, though it can only be made with difficulty, is fertile. This applies only when "grey" forms from northern

U.S.A. are used; the south-western and Asiatic types will not cross at all with "red" forms.

The net effect is that in some regions a certain amount of gene-transfer is likely to occur between the two subspecies, or, as we had better call them, semispecies. And this, as Sewall Wright has shown for ordinary subspecies (p. 229), will be beneficial in conferring greater plasticity in evolution, though the loss of productivity due to crossing will act as an immediate offset against this long-term advantage. A curious fact is the high degree of sterility found in pure cultures of both "red" subspecies.

The home of the species (or supraspecies) appears to be eastern Asia, and the forms of the "red" group we may conjecture have differentiated owing to "drift" in the sparse populations found in less favourable areas.

The case of D. mulleri and its relations (Patterson and Crow, 1940) is equally interesting, but quite different.

The group consists of D. mulleri, with the two subspecies D. m. mulleri from Mexico and Texas and D. m. mojavensis, a pale desert form from the desert area of California, and D. aldrichi, also from Texas (but probably from Mexico as well), but with a rather more restricted distribution than D. m. mulleri.

The mulleri-aldrichi pair are very similar to the melanogaster-simulans pair, in resembling each other closely (there are a few minor but diagnostic character-differences), and in overlapping considerably in their distribution. In both cases there is complete genetic isolation between the members of the pairs in nature, but the isolation has proceeded a stage further in the mulleri group, since the cross between the two can only be made one way. Ecobiotically there is more differentiation, aldrichi taking considerably longer for its development than mulleri. A few F1 male hybrids (all hybrids are sterile) have been discovered in nature, showing that some reproductive waste still occurs. The gross chromosome-structure is similar and there are few if any large sectional rearrangements. It would appear that the ancestor of D. aldrichi developed genetic incompatibility with D. mulleri while isolated, that the incompatibility was due in the first instance to the progressive accumulation of gene-mutations (though it may have been strengthened later by selection: see p. 287), and that, once present, it permitted *aldrichi* to spread and to exist side by side with *mulleri*.

D. *m. mojavensis* appears to be a true geographical subspecies. The distributional centre of the species appears to be Mexico, and it is a warm-climate form unable to tolerate low winter temperatures. Its spread northwards into U.S.A. was thus restricted to the warm plains on either side of the Mexican-Rockies mountain system, and the western group, reaching the Californian desert, there evolved into a markedly distinct subspecies, D. *m. mojavensis*. This shows several large sectional rearrangements which were able to establish themselves owing to isolation; but it still produces fertile offspring with D. *m. mulleri*, at least in one of the reciprocal crosses.

Patterson and Crow compare the *mulleri* to the *pseudoobscura* group (*D. pseudoobscura* A and B and *D. miranda*). In each case there are three forms, one of which behaves as a good species while the other two are best regarded as highly differentiated subspecies. There are some differences. Thus the *miranda-pseudoobscura* cross is almost but not quite sterile. Further, the ranges of *pseudoobscura* A and B overlap, and probably still exchange genes in nature; and the visible ecoclimatic differentiation of D. *m. mojavensis* (pale colour) is not found in D. *pseudoobscura*. The chief difference is in regard to sectional rearrangements, of which there are many between *pseudoobscura* A and B and still more between either of these and *miranda*. This appears to be correlated in part with the abundance of the *mulleri* forms and the greater size of their breeding populations. Patterson and Crow suggest further that sectional rearrangement in the *mulleri* forms may be accompanied, as in D. *melanogaster*, by breakage effects, in the shape of visible and lethal pseudo-mutations. This would tend to keep rearrangements down to a minimum. Such effects must be negligible or absent in the *pseudoobscura* group. These examples illustrate vividly the unexpected modes of taxonomic differentiation to be found in insects.

Interspecific grafting (Stubbe and Vogt, 1940*b*) has revealed that different *Drosophila* species differ both quantitatively and qualitatively in regard to the precursor substances involved in eye-colour differentiation.

An interesting point for which no adequate explanation has yet been found is that, whereas in most *Drosophila* species, many clear-cut characters with sharp dominance are found, in *D. virilis* most characters are determined by multiple factors, often with incomplete dominance. It was a lucky chance that *D. melanogaster* and not this species was first chosen for genetic work.

Muller is careful to point out that other groups of animals (let alone plants) may have genetic mechanisms which do not favour the same kinds of evolutionary change as in *Drosophila*. We have already mentioned the fact that having the polar bodies all in one line, while no crossing-over occurs in the male, permits *Drosophila* to accumulate intra-arm inversions with comparative ease. This would not be the case either where the polar bodies were not formed in line, or where, as in mammals, crossing-over occurs in both sexes. Where crossing-over is absent in certain regions, other types of inversions could easily become established. On the other hand, translocations would be much more readily established in any animals whose chromosomes behaved like that of *Oenothera* and *Datura*.

The amount of inert material near the centromeres will also have its influence, an increase favouring the detachment or attachment of whole arms and *vice versa*.

There is also evidence (Slack, unpublished, cited in Muller, 1940) that polyploidy may occur in some animal groups, e.g. Hemiptera-Heteroptera. This will wholly alter the evolutionary possibilities of a group.

In conclusion, Muller draws attention to the fact that in closely-related well-analysed pairs of forms different characters may show different degrees of divergence. Thus serological differences, though usually agreeing with morphological ones, occasionally give quite aberrant results—e.g. in regard to the relationships of *D. hydei*. Again, *Drosophila simulans* and *melanogaster* are the least alike of five pairs of closely related forms in regard to morphological characters, but most alike in regard to sectional rearrangements. In the same study it was found that

Drosophila virilis and *americana* were least alike as regards metaphase chromosome-picture, but most alike in respect to their fertility on crossing. It seems clear that the element of accident is considerable. On the other hand, while complete parallelism in regard to divergence in 'different characters is not to be found, evaluation of the average divergence of numerous characters of several different kinds does give a reasonable measure of the relationship between related types.

Summing up, we may say that speciation in *Drosophila* appears to have been brought about mainly by the accumulation of gene-mutations as a result of some sort of isolation. The isolation operative appears to have been mainly geographical. Once in existence, it will favour the origin of sterility barriers, which in their turn will both permit and favour the increase of morphological divergence.

Certain types of sectional chromosomal rearrangements are also favoured by the genetic mechanism of the genus. Although these have played some part in speciation, it appears to have been essentially a secondary one, the consequence rather than the cause of primary divergence.

On the other hand, the extent to which such rearrangements have proceeded (often rendering it impossible to trace any resemblance between the salivary chromosome-structure of morphologically not very remote species) shows what a large number of such differences accumulate within even a somewhat uniform genus like *Drosophila*; while the known fact of their rarity compared with gene-mutation proves that the single-gene differences between species must be enormously numerous. Gone is any notion of species in higher animals arising by a single mutation, or even by a few steps. Even closely-related species will differ in scores, possibly hundreds of genes, and the longer they remain in existence the greater are the number of genic and sectional differences that are likely to arise between them. Evolution consists in the accumulation and integration of very numerous and mostly small genetic changes (p. 360).

In *Drosophila* as elsewhere, mode of life appears to modify evolution. *Drosophila pseudoobscura* is more differentiated geographically (both as regards sterility-barriers and sectional re-arrangements) than most species of the genus, which is almost certainly to be ascribed to greater isolation between its local groups (see pp. 60, 61). In the production of its "races" A and B, isolation appears to have been the first step, genically-determined sterility the second, and sectional rearrangements the final step in evolutionary divergence.

Even in *Drosophila*, where the species originally seemed exceptionally well delimited, careful analysis has revealed the existence of all grades in speciation, both as regards geographical sub-speciation and the formation of sterility barriers.

All its species so far investigated carry large numbers of recessive mutants in nature, and are thus provided with an adequate reservoir of variability for future adaptive change and possible further speciation.

It seems probable that speciation in most large genera of higher animals is essentially similar to that in *Drosophila*, though with minor differences connected with consequential effects of their chromosomal mechanism and mode of life.

* * * * *

The genus *Crepis* (hawkweeds) has differentiated in an entirely different manner (see the monograph by Babcock and Stebbins, 1938; also Stebbins, 1940; Jenkins, 1939). Here various repro-ductive peculiarities are at work which are available only in higher plants, and we are given a very interesting picture of the varying roles of selection, environment, and polyploidy in a facultatively apomictic plant genus belonging to one of the most advanced groups, the Compositae.

The old-world species of *Crepis* have basic haploid chromo-some-numbers ranging from 3 to 7, together with polyploid forms. Two of the American forms belong to this group, with $x = 7$, one a circumpolar form found also in the old world, *C. nana*, the other a closely-related type, *C. elegans*, which appears to have diverged from *C. nana* in America, and to have become adapted to less extreme climatic conditions.

All the other American forms have the basic chromosome-number $x = 11$. There are seven distinct diploid forms ($2n = 22$)

together with a large number of polyploids, all apomictic (though often with slight facultative sexual reproduction), with diploid chromosome-numbers ranging from 33 to 88, 44 being the commonest. In addition, a few aneuploids are found with chromosome-numbers differing by 1 or at most 2 from a eupolyploid number.

The evolution of this group of forms is deduced to have been as follows. The original ancestors were produced by hybridization between 4-chromosome and 7-chromosome old-world types in the Siberian portion of the land-bridge which once existed between Siberia and Alaska. This can be deduced from the resemblance of the American forms to old-world species with these chromosome-numbers. The hybrids underwent chromosome-doubling to become fertile allopolyploids with $2n = 22$ chromosomes. They did not spread westwards into the old world, partly because they were there confronted with the competition of the original and already established types, while the area to the eastward had not yet been occupied by *Crepis*; and partly because the prevailing winds are westerly, and this, in forms like *Crepis* with air-borne fruits, would encourage easterly spread.

From a consideration of the morphological divergence of the various American 22-chromosome species from old-world species and from their present climatic and geological ranges, it can further be deduced that different species were evolved at different times—the two earliest during the Miocene, the next set (two species) in the early Pliocene, the last (four species) in late Pliocene or early Pleistocene times.

These eight fertile species, though allopolyploids in origin, have acted functionally as the diploid basis for later polyploidy in America. We can call them the American diploids. They seem first to have become specialized to particular climatic conditions, and the ranges of the earlier species were much restricted by the climatic changes that followed.

As regards their later history, those forms fall into two groups. The first consists of a single species, *C. runcinata*. This is the only American *Crepis* adapted to moist stream-bank habitats. It thus tends to follow valleys rather than mountain ranges. Accordingly it has spread more widely to the east of the Rockies, where the drainage basins are more continuous. Also, being ecologically isolated from the other species with their preference for more arid habitats, it has not hybridized with them to form allo-polyploids. Instead, it has differentiated to form a polytypic species or *Rassenkreis*, with well-marked geographical subspecies in certain regions, and considerable variability in others. For some as yet unexplained reason, it has not produced any auto-polyploid varieties.

All the other diploids appear to have hybridized to form allopolyploids, sometimes with three or more components, and in addition also to have produced autopolyploids. In some cases, diploid geographical subspecies have also been differentiated. All the polyploid forms are apomictic, some entirely, others preponderantly so. The ancestry of the polyploids can in general be inferred by the degree of their resemblance to the various diploids.

The formation of allopolyploid apomicts is favoured by climatic and physiographic changes, which bring originally separate species into contact. Once in existence, however, the apomicts have less evolutionary plasticity, on account of their total or considerable lack of recombination. Thus it is highly probable that the intense environmental changes during the glacial period will have encouraged the formation of many new apomicts, while causing the extinction of the majority of those produced in earlier periods.

The effect has been to produce what Babcock and Stebbins call a largely agamic *polyploid complex*, in which all the original and qualitatively differentiated diploid types are connected by an enormous array of intergrading forms. These differ from the original diploids either in purely quantitative ways (e.g. effect of polyploidy on size), or by combining their characteristics. The divergent evolution of the group, which had given rise to the ecologically specialized and morphologically distinct diploids, came practically to a standstill, to be replaced by *gigas* phenomena, recombination of characters, and the segregation of innumerable apomict "microspecies".

The number of apomict types is very large near the main centres of distribution, but much reduced in outlying areas. New types are doubtless being constantly produced near the distribution centres, and are still in process of being "tried out", so that many of them are likely to disappear. The outlying forms are those which have survived and spread after earlier origin, and therefore tend to have larger areas of distribution.

The production of polyploids has undoubtedly enlarged the range of the group as a whole, while the ranges of the original diploids have in general been reduced by competition with closely similar polyploids equipped with greater vigour.

Babcock and Stebbins also discuss the taxonomic treatment of the group. They come to the conclusion that, while any such agamic complex is in reality of a wholly different nature from a group of non-interbreeding true species, yet for practical reasons it is best to continue to employ the classical nomenclature. They accordingly recognize a series of "species", each corresponding to each of the original diploid groups together with its geographical subspecies and its autopolyploid derivatives, and attach to each such species those apomicts which show a preponderant resemblance to its diploid form. The Latin names of the apomicts, however, are not regarded as forming part of the nomenclature subject to the international rules; following Turesson, they are preceded by the abbreviation *apm.*, for *forma apomictica*. In addition, two other "species" are recognized, consisting wholly of apomicts which are of such complex origin as not to be attachable closely to any diploid type.

This procedure is purely pragmatic and artificial, and, as subsidiary terminology is evolved, may perhaps be superseded (see also Turrill, 1938c, for *Taraxacum*).

One or two special points may be noted. In the American agamic complex of *Crepis*, the pure autopolyploids are much less widespread than the partially or wholly allopolyploid types, contrary to the general rule in plants (see Müntzing, 1936), and their range as compared with that of the diploids is not nearly as great as in such genera as *Tradescantia* or *Galium*. This is to be ascribed to an ecological reason—namely the preference of *Crepis* for arid habitats. The greater vigour of most auto-polyploids might thus cause the plants to demand more water than is normally available, while the frequent prolongation of their flowering would, in regions of summer drought, also often be a disadvantage. Thus in *Crepis* the chief advantage of polyploidy has come from allopolyploidy, which provides new combinations of characters, permitting their owners to invade new habitats.

In general Babcock and Stebbins regard the production of numerous polyploid forms as an evolutionary short cut by which a genus may adapt itself more rapidly than by gene-mutation and recombination to a rapidly changing environment. On the other hand, in the long run, both polyploidy and apomixis constitute a barrier to the more important evolutionary process of divergent specialization, the former because the duplication of gene-pairs makes it more difficult for recessive characters to come into action, the latter because sexual recombination is impossible.

Furthermore, the immediate plasticity conferred by allopolyploidy will only continue so long as the sexually reproducing forms of a complex continue to be present and to cross. Thus in western America, where *Antennaria* exists in a polyploid complex still containing sexual as well as apomictic polyploid forms, it is an aggressive and dominant form. In Newfoundland, on the other hand, the genus is represented only by obligatory apomicts. These are all relict forms, not at all aggressive, and often very localized in their distribution (Fernald, 1933). Eventually, groups of apomicts separated from their sexual ancestors will be doomed to extinction as they can no longer meet changing conditions.

One effect of polyploidy is to spread the polyploids at the expense of the diploids. Thus, while the bringing together of diploids by climatic change will encourage an outburst of allopolyploid forms, the very success of the polyploids will, if conditions later become stabilized, gradually remove the conditions in which the continuance of their new formation is possible.

Babcock and Stebbins consider, first, that the present high

incidence of polyploidy in higher plants is a consequence of the extremely large and rapid climatic changes of the Pleistocene and Recent periods, which have not only promoted allopolyploidy by bringing diploids together, but have enhanced the evolutionary value of polyploidy as a short cut to meet rapidly changing conditions. Secondly, that the prevalence of apomixis in such groups as Gramineae, Rosaceae, and Compositae is not due to any peculiarity of their germ-plasm, but to the fact that they happen to be groups which in geologically recent times were rapidly evolving in such a way as to produce numerous young and vigorous agamic complexes.* And thirdly, that all such agamic complexes are destined eventually to decay until they are extinct or are represented by a few relic types only, while new agamic complexes may be formed later by those groups which are at the right evolutionary stage when the next rapid change of climatic conditions takes place.

In a later paper Stebbins (1940b) discusses the taxonomy of some forms related to *Crepis* in the tribe Cichorieae, notably the somewhat primitive genera *Soroseris*, *Dubyaea*, and *Prenanthes*. Both the first two appear to have 2n = 16 as their diploid chromosome-number, though one probable tetraploid is known. Apparently in primitive members of the tribe, quite large changes in general structure and macroscopic characters are accompanied by comparatively slight changes in chromosomal morphology and structure, while the reverse is usually the case in the more specialized forms. *Dubyaea* probably dates from the Cretaceous and later became restricted to a "refuge" in the Sino-Himalayan area, having been exterminated elsewhere in competition with its more aggressive descendants. This confirms Matthew's view (1915) that primitive types tend to be preserved near the margins of the range of a group.

One section of the genus appear to have given rise to *Prenanthes* (probably as far back as the early Tertiary), *Lactuca*, *Hieracium* and *Crepis* itself. *Soroseris* must also have been derived from

---

* The fact that *Crepis runcinata* has, owing to its ecological peculiarities, escaped from the agamic complex and undergone a more normal type of evolution, is another proof of this.

Dubyaea, but probably from a section now extinct, and perhaps polyphyletically. It also is restricted to the Sino-Himalayan area. It appears to have originated in Tibet, at a time of desiccation, presumably in the later Middle Tertiary. During the Pleistocene, glaciation isolated various groups, thus providing the basis for the differentiation of the numerous closely related species and subspecies now found in the genus. It is interesting to find how different the mode of evolution has been in these primitive genera from that in *Crepis*.

The state of affairs in *Crepis* may be briefly contrasted with that in *Tulipa*, recently monographed by A. D. Hall (1940). In this genus there appears to have been considerable divergence, not associated with polyploidy, into a number of main sections. Within the sections, however, autopolyploidy has been frequent, giving 3n, 4n and occasional 5n forms, the anisoploids showing vegetative reproduction. In some types, tetraploids have originated separately in different parts of the range, giving forms which show slight quantitative differences as well as size-differences associated with the chromosome-doubling. In some types there is considerable geographical differentiation, giving rise to forms which zoologists would certainly recognize as subspecies. There is no evidence of allopolyploidy or reticulate evolution. In the garden tulips polyploidy is unknown, apparently owing to their large chromosomes (Darlington, 1937, p. 84).

Similarly, the state of affairs in *Drosophila* may be profitably contrasted with that in the bird genus *Zonotrichia*, one of the New World finches or "sparrows (see Chapman, 1940b). It comprises only five species. Four are North American, one confined (in the breeding season) to a central region of northern Canada, another to western and southern Alaska and neighbouring islands. A third (*Z. albicollis*) is essentially an eastern species, breeding as far south as Wisconsin and Pennsylvania, but reaching almost to the Arctic and the Pacific oceans in the N.W. None of these three species, not even the last-named with its large range, shows any subspeciation. The fourth, however, with a larger (and rather more westerly) range, from Greenland and the St. Lawrence to the Pacific, and from the northern tree-limit to southern California, has differentiated into 4 well-marked subspecies.

Finally *Z. capensis*, a Central and South American form, boasts no fewer than 22 subspecies. Chapman considers that it was the southernmost representative of this originally northern genus, was forced southwards across Central America by the onset of glacial conditions, and then continued to spread wherever the climate was cool enough, until finally it colonized all suitable habitats in South America, down to Cape Horn. Its distribution now covers 4,000 miles from N. to S., 3,000 miles from E. to W., and 15,000 feet of altitude—a much larger range than that of any other member of the genus.

Once it reached South America, its further spread must have been due not to climatic influences, but solely to natural increase, which appears to have been rapid in the new territory thus made available to a hardy form differentiated in the more rigorous conditions of the northern hemisphere.

The original migration through Central America must have been at sea level, but with the post-glacial amelioration of climate it moved up to higher altitudes, thus becoming restricted to discontinuous upland areas in various more tropical parts of its range. There are two exceptions: certain groups early colonized some islands on the Pacific coast of Central America and others off the north coast of South America, and thus could not move to higher altitudes when the climate grew warmer. The forms on the South American islands overlap with those of the adjacent mainland in character, but are paler, and distinct enough to merit subspecific naming; but the Central American insular populations show no visible distinctions from the neighbouring mainland forms, though separated from them by a minimum of 2,500 feet of altitude. It would, however, be of great interest to see whether they show special physiological adaptations to the unusual climate of their enforced habitat.

Some further points of interest are as follows. All forms of the species appear to be residents, except for the southernmost subspecies. which is definitely migratory. Here is a good example of local adaptation, which must be of recent origin, since this subspecies must clearly have been the last to differentiate. It also possesses the longest and the most pointed wing of any of the subspecies. Though this must in part be regarded as adaptive, Chapman points out that it is in part the culmination of a cline in wing-size, which increases more or less steadily southwards through the continent, and is presumably a "correlated character", non-adaptive *per se*. Adaptive change would here have been superposed on non-adaptive in the migratory subspecies.

There is also a general N.–S. intergroup size-cline within South America, but there are exceptions to it, and there is considerable independence in the variation of the size of different parts. The different subspecies show a good deal of geographical variation in song.

An interesting barrier is found at one spot in the mountainous interior of Venezuela. Here isolation has allowed a subspecies to differentiate from the main Venezuelan form; but the table-land at the summit of Mt. Roraima is separated from the area below by a 1,400-ft. vertical cliff, and this in turn has permitted the summit population to differentiate into a darker form just distinct enough for subspecific recognition.

Accidental "drift" in isolated populations has also clearly contributed to differentiation. One curious feature is that, whereas all the North American species have some yellow on the bend of the wing, this is present in only four of the subspecies of *capensis* —one form from the Antilles, and three adjacent subspecies from the centre of the east coast of the continent. In the central of these latter the yellow is all but universal, but in the subspecies to N. and S. it is sporadic, and in one of them only faint. In the distant Antilles race it is universal but faint. Here, as Chapman points out, we appear to have the partial resuscitation (or less probably the preservation) of an original generic character which has been lost in the main body of the species.

In this genus, differentiation thus seems to have been brought about *via* geographical isolation followed by adaptive and accidental character-divergence. We have the somewhat puzzling fact of the absence of subspeciation in one wide-ranging North American form, a moderate degree in another, and a high degree in the one South American species. This last fact is probably due to the very large range of habitats thrown open to the species once it had been pushed through the Central American bottleneck by the onset of a glacial climate. *Zonotrichia* shows no obvious trace of the genetic isolation to be seen in *Drosophila*; and though genetic analysis (if it were possible) might possibly reveal that it had occurred, it cannot well have played more than a very minor role in this genus.

As a parallel illustration from plants, of the principle that differentiation may vary considerably with local conditions (see also the case of *Crepis*), we may take the peonies, *Paeonia* (Barber, 1941). The pre-glacial species appear to have been diploids. In Europe and the Caucasus, the majority of modern species are tetraploids, but in China and Japan there are only a few tetraploids. The reason appears to be as follows. In the former area, the diploids were for geographical reasons unable to retreat far to the south before the advance of the ice, and they were exterminated except in a few "refuges". Any tetraploids which arose then had a field almost free of competition, in addition to any advantages due to extra hardiness (p. 337). In the Far East, however, the original diploids simply retreated southwards before the ice, and advanced again in mass on its retreat,* so that there was much greater competitor-pressure against any tetraploid forms (cf. the case of *Crepis*, p. 373). Finally in California, for reasons unknown, structural hybrids of the *Oenothera* type, based on segmental interchange and balanced lethals (pp. 90. 329) are found.

Postscript—Since first printing E. Mayr has published his valuable *Systematics and the Origin of Species* (New York 1942). Reference must be made to his important conclusion that, in higher animals at least, with the exception of "biological" differentiation (my p. 295), the only factor permitting group divergence is geographical isolation; neither ecological nor genetic isolation is ever primary. I am bound to say that Mayr has convinced me on this point.

---

* A similar mass retreat and advance was possible for the pre-glacial forests in North America, but not in Europe, leading to a great impoverishment of the European forest tree flora as compared with that of the U.S.A.

CHAPTER 7

SPECIATION, EVOLUTION, AND TAXONOMY

1. DIFFERENT TYPES OF SPECIATION AND THEIR RESULTS

So far, we have been considering the different methods by which species may originate. It should be remembered that the type of origin may have effects upon the subsequent type of variation shown by the species. Thus in vegetatively reproducing polyploids, variation will be much restricted since no recombination of mutations can occur. In parthenogenetically reproducing allopolyploids, on the other hand, crossing-over may give rise to pure-breeding segregants (p. 334), so that we may expect a number of sharply defined but closely related pure-breeding types. In balanced-lethal heterozygote species, crossing-over will also operate to give large apparent mutations. Sexually-reproducing polyploids will show a different type of variation from diploids, since each gene will be represented in four or more identical or closely similar forms instead of two. This will give a greater supply of similar mutations and thus a greater evolutionary flexibility, but less opportunity for single mutations to exert any considerable effect. Darlington (1933), looking at the matter from the comparative, not the evolutionary, point of view, distinguishes six kinds of species according to their genetic-reproductive mechanism: (1) the habitually self-fertilized diploid; (2) the habitually cross-fertilized diploid; (3) the sexually-reproducing fertile polyploid; (4) the mixed species containing both diploid and polyploid forms; (5) the complex-heterozygote species (balanced lethal type), as in *Oenothera*; (6) the clonal species not reproducing sexually at all. This last category could be divided further into the parthenogenetic forms showing asexual segregation, and the rest which do not. To this list we may add (7) the subsexual species like *Rosa canina* (p. 351); and (8) those animals such as Hymenoptera (and certain beetles: A. C. Scott, 1936) with diploid females but haploid males. Still further types might be added, e.g. those with close linkage promoting polymorphism (p. 99). Darlington concludes his paper: "Genetics leaves no doubt that each of these types will have certain characteristic properties of variation. It is for the taxonomist, armed with the cytological information, to find out what these are."

Apart from this, selection may be expected to act in quite different ways and with quite different intensities according to the method of speciation. Our analysis has enabled us to distinguish in principle between the causes of their isolation and those of their divergence—between the factors making for isolation between groups within an original single species, and those making for difference in the structural and functional characters separating new species from their parents or nearest relatives.* Groups separated by geographical isolation are originally species only *in posse*. Their separation into good species is a subsequent process, accompanying the process of character-divergence. This divergence is normally slow, but occasionally, as on oceanic islands and other places where the intensity of selection is relaxed, it may be much more rapid and more extensive than usual.

Elsewhere, as apparently in the case of *Drosophila simulans* and *D. melanogaster*, the isolation is of such a nature that the two groups must be regarded as separate species even when still almost indistinguishable in any characters save those which isolate them. Indeed it is conceivable that in such species, character-divergence may not subsequently occur: in *Drosophila simulans* it has at least been minimal. At the opposite extreme are those cases in which the factor inducing isolation simultaneously produces character-difference, of an order which will—or at least may—be accepted as of specific magnitude by the systematist.

---

* Plate's (1913) chapter on isolation is still very well worth reading in this connection.

This is so in *Spartina townsendii*, and most cases of convergent and reticulate species-formation. Further character-divergence may, of course, occur later, as with *Galeopsis tetrahit* (p. 341), but this is irrelevant to our argument.

From the standpoint of the mode of action of natural selection, species will then fall into two contrasted categories. On the one hand, we have those in which natural selection can have had nothing to do with the evolution of the basic specific characters, but merely acts upon the species as given, in competition with its relatives. These include all species in which character-divergence is abrupt and initial. On the other hand, we have those forms in which character-modification is gradual. Here natural selection may, and on both deductive and inductive grounds often does, play a part in producing the characters of the species (and by characters we, of course, mean not only those which are employed by the systematist, but all those which do in point of fact distinguish it from its nearest relatives). These include not only all forms in which the separation of groups occurs by geographical, physiological, or ecological isolation, but also those in which the initial separation is genetic but involves no visible differentiation.

From the point of view of the intensity of selection, the successional evolution of species will, *ex hypothesi*, be directed by selection wherever the trend of evolution is towards some adaptive specialization (p. 494). Then it is clear that groups separated ecologically will be exposed to a considerable intensity of selection to adapt them fully to their different modes of life When they overlap spatially with closely-related groups, selection may also be expected to act upon them to produce barriers to mating (p. 287). This latter mode of selection will not operate in the case of geographically separated groups, but selection towards divergent general adaptation will occur if the environmental conditions in the two areas are different. When, however, the two areas are similar in the environment they provide, there will be reduced scope for selection, and if divergence occurs, it will be primarily of an accidental and often of a biologically non-significant nature. This will also apply to species which overlap spatially, but owe their origin to a genetical mode of separation which does not cause visible differentiation, such as large inversions or asexual segregations: in the former case, however, selection should operate, as with overlapping ecologically divergent species, to produce barriers to interbreeding.

We may present the chief results of the two previous chapters in tabular form (see p. 386).

In the first column we distinguish between the four major types of species-formation—successional transformation, divergence, convergence as a consequence of species-crossing, and reticulate evolution.

In the second column we distinguish the main factors leading to the separation of two species. In successional transformation, time is the factor at work. In geographical, ecological, and physiological divergence there is always some topographical isolation. We may call this type of separation spatial, contrasting it both with the temporal and the genetic; but the scale of the spatial factor is different in the three sub-types. If we preferred, we could equally well call it environmental, since it is concerned with something outside the organism, in contrast with constitutional separation, depending on genetic factors.

Genetic separation operates in the remainder of the divergent and in all the convergent types.

In the third column we note whether the actual formation of species, regarded as distinctive or intersterile groups, is gradual or abrupt; and in the fourth we consider the same distinction with regard to their visible differentiation. It should be noted that the two do not always run parallel. In column 4, the phrase *initially abrupt* means that some visible difference occurs with the first abrupt origin of the species, but that further gradual divergence may supervene later.

Finally, in the last column we consider the actual barriers to fertility, including under these barriers to cross-mating between the pairs of species. *Consequential* implies that these barriers are, in some way (p. 359; Muller, 1940), the consequence of the differences that have gradually arisen between the two species. *Initial* implies that the new species is automatically, by its genetic constitution, unable to cross with its nearest relatives, or that

MODE OF SPECIATION	ISOLATION OF GROUPS	SEPARATION OF NEW SPECIES	VISIBLE DIFFERENTIATION	BARRIERS TO FERTILITY
I. Successional	1. Temporal	gradual.	gradual.	
II. Divergent	2. Spatial			
	(a) large-scale: geographical.	gradual.	gradual.	consequential.
	(b) medium-scale: ecological.	gradual.	gradual; distinctive characters frequent.	largely selective.
	(c) small-scale: biological (biological races).	gradual.	gradual, slight.	
	3. Genetic			
	(a) genic.	abrupt.	gradual.	initial.
	(b) asexual segregation.	abrupt.	abrupt.	initial.
	(c) segmental interchange.	gradual.	gradual, slight.	partly initial.
	(d) inversion.	gradual.	gradual, slight.	initial.
	(e) autopolyploidy.	gradual or abrupt.	mainly gradual.	
III. Convergent	(f) allopolyploidy.	abrupt.	initially abrupt.	initial.
	(g) aneuploidy (secondary polyploidy).	abrupt.	initially abrupt.	initial.
IV. Reticulate				
(i) Convergent-divergent (polyploid complexes)	(genetic, various).	abrupt.	abrupt.	partly absent.
(ii) recombinational	(geographical, reduced by migration).	not found.	(increased variability).	absent.

the offspring of such a cross are either infertile or of reduced fertility. *Selective* implies that selection will operate to erect special barriers to cross-mating or cross-fertility.

2. SPECIES-FORMATION AND EVOLUTION

Since the origin of species has occupied the centre of the biological stage since the time of Linnaeus, it is to this problem that we have devoted the bulk of the two previous chapters. One point at least emerges clearly: if Darwin were writing to-day he would call his great book *The Origins*, not *The Origin, of Species*.

But we may conclude by looking at the matter from a still broader point of view, in the perspective of evolution in general. Evolution may be regarded as the process by which the utilization of the earth's resources by living matter is rendered progressively more efficient. Early in the process, living matter became organized into cells, evolved a particulate hereditary constitution arranged in chromosomes, and developed the sexual process. The reason why the sexual process (which in its inception was not connected in any way with reproduction) occurs in the great majority of animal and plant types alike, is that it confers a greater potential variability on its possessors, and therefore a greater plasticity in evolution. It does this by being able to combine mutations which have occurred in different strains, and which in an asexual form would have to remain separate.

The exploitation of the earth's natural resources progressed in two complementary ways—by improvements in basic mechanisms of exploitation, and by adapting a given basic mechanism to every possible kind of environment. We shall discuss the former more in detail in our chapter on Evolutionary Progress: here we may give as illustrative examples the colonization of the land by plants, and the evolution of considerable size and of rapid locomotion by means of limbs in animals.

We then come to the second method. The green plant exploits light and air and water in every conceivable habitat, appearing here as floating diatoms in the surface layer of the sea, there as giant forest trees, here as prairie grasses, there as duckweed in a pond. Again, in animals the fish type exists in the deep sea, in its surface layers, on sandy and rocky shores, in rivers, in lakes, in caves. There is operative a selection-pressure forcing life to occupy every geographical area and every ecological niche within each area. (See also Chapter 8).

Now it is clear that, living matter being what it is, mere difference will quite soon make breeding impossible between diverging groups. Chromosomes will not pair at meiosis unless reasonably similar, and unless they pair at meiosis, sexual reproduction cannot occur; and see p. 359. With still further divergence, the two sets of chromosomes are unable to combine in the work of building up a new organism: hardly any case is known of offspring resulting from a cross wider than intergeneric.* Living matter thus inevitably becomes broken up into a large number of non-interbreeding groups, the majority of which coincide with taxonomic species.

On the other hand, there would seem to be no *a priori* reason why a single species should not range over a very wide geographical area, varying somewhat from region to region, but with all such varieties forming, actually or potentially, part of one interfertile group, nor any *a priori* reason why more than one species of the same family or genus should occur in the same ecological habitat.

However, we find that in neither case is our expectation justified: very large numbers of species occur for whose existence there seems at first sight no reason or meaning. On looking further into the matter, we see that this depends on two sets of facts, one connected with the relation of the organisms with their environment, the other with their genetic basis. The environment is subjected to changes which create barriers between one region and another, and thus isolate groups belonging originally to the same species. And complete isolation permits differences, both of an adaptive and of a chance non-utilitarian character, to accumulate relatively fast in the two groups, until in many cases they become new species.

Then the chromosomal basis of heredity is subject to accidents, such as inversion, segmental interchange, hybridity, and poly-

---

* Dr. W. B. Turrill in a letter states that the widest cross he knows is between the rushes *Cyperus dentatus* and *Rhynchospora capitellata*, which are placed in different sub-families of the Cyperaceae. The hybrid is entirely sterile.

ploidy, which sooner or later will reduce or abolish fertile mating between the new and the old type. In this way large numbers of new species essentially similar to those from which they arose are brought into being, and the new and the old come to compete with each other in identical or (often as the result of subsequent migration) in overlapping habitats.

The formation of many geographically isolated and most genetically isolated species is thus without any bearing upon the main processes of evolution. These latter, as we shall see in later chapters, consist in the development of new types endowed with mechanisms of higher all-round biological efficiency; in the adaptive radiation of these types to take advantage of all available types of environment and modes of life; in the colonizing of new regions of the globe's surface; in the tapping of new resources for exploitation; and in a more rapid turnover of the resources tapped.

These major processes in evolution thus consist essentially in a greater extension of life's activities into new areas and into new substances; in a greater intensity of exploitation; and in a progressive increase of life's control over and independence of the environment. Superimposed upon these processes, and having little or no bearing upon them, are the processes of species-formation we have just described which are the consequences of accidents in the environment or in the genetic machinery of life. Much of the minor systematic diversity to be observed in nature is irrelevant to the main course of evolution, a mere frill of variety superimposed upon its broad pattern. We may thus say that, while it is inevitable that life should be divided up into species, and that the broad processes of evolution should operate with species as units of organization, the number thus necessitated is far less than the number which actually exist. Species-formation constitutes one aspect of evolution; but a large fraction of it is in a sense an accident, a biological luxury, without bearing upon the major and continuing trends of the evolutionary process.

3. MODES OF SPECIATION AND SYSTEMATIC METHOD

Having now discussed modern work dealing with the different modes of speciation, we must now consider its bearings upon taxonomy and systematic method. Historically, we may distinguish three main phases in the history of modern taxonomy, each with a different principle serving as its main philosophic basis (see Turrill, 1936; Gilmour, 1937). In the first or Linnaean period, the underlying principle was the separate creation of species. In the second or Darwinian phase, it was the doctrine of descent with modification. And in the third, the Mendelian period upon which we are now entering, it is selection based on the cytogenetic theory of particulate inheritance and mutation.

Let us amplify these points a little further. Linnaeus, in the latter part of his career, was a firm upholder of the immutability of species: "Species tot sunt, quot formae ab initio creatae sunt." This doctrine of the fixity of species was in one aspect the rationalization, or at least the reflection, of the practical need for identifying plants for medicinal purposes (see p. 263). Once accepted, it lent itself to the furtherance of easy identification.

If species are immutable and distinct entities, the chief aim of systematics becomes that of distinguishing between them. This naturally led to the codification of artificial "laws" and "systems", of which that of Linnaeus for higher plants is the classical example. This was really no more than a key to the identification of larger entities, based on arbitrary and for the most part biologically almost non-significant features such as the number of stamens and pistils.*

The artificiality of such unnatural systems was in part corrected by an instinctive logic which led man to search for a basis of classification that should take into account both the number of the points of resemblance between groups, and the intrinsic importance of the points of resemblance chosen as diagnostic. We can accordingly trace the abandonment of purely artificial systems for those based on general likeness. Still later, as it was

* On lower taxonomic levels, such as the generic and specific, Linnaeus's common-sense and natural intuition led him to remarkably modern groupings.

realized that superficial resemblance (as between a porpoise and a true fish) may mask basic difference, we may see the substitution of likeness in fundamental structural plan as chief criterion, in place of mere superficial likeness. Pre-Darwinian nineteenth-century classification, as practised by Goethe, Cuvier, Oken, Owen, T. H. Huxley, etc., worked on this assumption.

But although this method, at least for larger groups, was identical with that practised in the latter half of the century, it lacked any real theoretical basis grounded in biological justification. The analytic but less speculatively-minded, like Huxley (e.g. 1853, 1854), simply *assumed* that structural homology (or common archetypal plan) was the right key to unlock classificatory secrets: the idea that it was right because it implied genetic relationship did not enter their minds, or at least was not allowed to enter their conscious minds, until after the publication of Darwin's *Origin* in 1859. The more theoretically-inclined, such as Goethe and Oken, regarded the existence of structural plans common to a large number of animals as evidence of some form of planning in the act of creation. In extreme form, this theoretical view found the basis of homology in the existence of a limited number of archetypal ideas in the mind of the Creator.

With the coming of the Darwinian epoch, however, all this was changed. Homology, instead of being essentially a descriptive term implying nothing more than the sharing of a common archetypal plan, became an explanatory term implying the sharing of a common plan on account of descent from a common ancestor. The basis of classification became, in theory at least, phylogenetic. Degree of resemblance was taken as index of closeness of relationship, and taxonomic categories were defined on the assumption that each represented a branch of higher or lower order on a phylogenetic tree.

This way of looking at the facts provided what was on the whole a very satisfactory basis for the delimination and arrangement of larger classificatory groups down to orders, sub-orders, and even families: but it was not always easy to apply it to the minor systematics of genera and species.

In practice, minor systematics was still ruled by an outlook which in some respects remained Linnaean. In spite of the theoretical belief that species were mutable, they were usually defined by the aid of criteria which tacitly assumed immutability, or by arbitrary characters frankly based on mere convenience. This point of view is still employed by many taxonomists to-day, and the result is often an arbitrary compromise between practical convenience and the desire to give a specific name to every recognizably distinct form. This is perhaps less so in zoology, where subspecific naming in accordance with the principle of geographical replacement is now the practice in most well-worked groups. Even here, however, as mentioned in the section on clines (p. 206), subspecific names are often allotted on the basis of an arbitrary degree of difference in a continuous series, not on that of the existence of natural self-perpetuating groups with relatively uniform characters.

In botany, however, procedure is often still quite arbitrary. To take one recent example, Cowan (1940) divides the rhododendrons of the *sanguineum* series into eight species and thirty-eight subspecies. This is done on certain arbitrary diagnostic characters. "It must now be decided whether each of these eight groups is to be regarded as a single variable species or as a section including a number of specific units." . . . "It must be understood that the species vary within the widest limits in characters not taken as diagnostic. The same argument applies with even greater force to the subspecies." No attempt is made to employ geographical distribution as a taxonomic character. Although there is "abundant evidence of the distribution of these (diagnostic) characters upon mendelian lines", and "many of the possible combinations do occur in nature", there is no discussion as to whether this state of affairs may not be due to hybridization and reticulate evolution; the only criteria used are morphological separability and practical convenience: "Even if all these variants can rightly be regarded as species, the multiplication of specific names to this extent is so obviously undesirable that one turns at once to the alternative course of modifying the standard. It is equally undesirable to regard all the plants within this group as forms of a single very variable species, a not unreasonable view, but they differ too widely." In other words, taxonomy in cases like these makes no pretence of describing the facts of nature concerning the distribution and relationships of natural groups, but is concerned solely with the arbitrary distinction of forms.

It is clear that distinguishable forms should receive some designation; but this should not be a specific or subspecific Latin name unless there is some ground for supposing that the distinguishable form is also a natural group-unit. Other forms should be distinguished by some type of subsidiary nomenclature, as Turrill (1938a) proposes.

Botany also lags behind zoology in another point of taxonomic practice, which, though small, makes for convenience. I refer to the convention by which all specific names are spelt with a small initial letter. This is now universal in zoology, and I have deliberately adopted it in this volume. The elaborate conventions of botanical practice occasionally make for confusion and have nothing to recommend them save historical tradition.

The value of employing every possible type of character in taxonomy is illustrated by recent work on the related plant genera *Hebe* and *Veronica*. The two genera were separated according to the mode of dehiscence of their capsules, and on this basis a number of New Zealand species were assigned to *Veronica*. However, they have now been found (Frankel, 1941) to have the same basic chromosome-numbers as *Hebe* (two polyploid series, with $x = 20$ and $x = 21$), in this differing from all typical *Veronica* species. Re-examination of the capsule then showed that the mode of dehiscence is much more similar to that of typical *Hebe*. The species have accordingly been transferred to *Hebe*. Similar corrections of faulty taxonomic observation by new methods, in this case the utilization of chemical data on pigments, have been made by Ford (1941) in Lepidoptera. Metcalf (1929) has pointed out the value of parasites for taxonomic purposes.

In spite of all efforts to draw the taxonomic consequences of the geographical replacement of forms, efforts dating from Gloger's pioneer work in the second quarter of the nineteenth century and continued by such men as Allen and Gulick in the '70's, Eimer in the '80's, and Kleinschmidt and the Sarasins in the '90's, the determination of species down to the beginning of the present century was usually undertaken on the assumption that they were all well differentiated by a series of diagnostic characters, and separated from their nearest relatives by sharp gaps.

Determination was made almost exclusively, and often rather arbitrarily, on the basis of morphological characters of structure and appearance. As research brought to light more and more geographical or other forms, populations which could be clearly distinguished from the populations of other areas were generally accorded specific rank.

The last decades of the period of phylogenetic classification, roughly from the beginning of the present century onwards, may be distinguished as a definite sub-period, characterized by the use of geographical distribution as a taxonomic criterion, in addition to morphological characters. From what we have just said, it should be clear that this also meant the abandonment of the last traces of a subconscious "Linnaeism", and the adoption of a thoroughgoing phylogenetic outlook, in minor as well as in major systematics. In the battle between the "splitters" and the "lumpers", the "splitters" represented the last survival of the Linnaean outlook, the "lumpers" the geographical phase of the Darwinian.

The first result of the refinement of detailed systematic methods was thus to force the geographical criterion into prominence and to introduce the Darwinian idea of plasticity into the taxonomics of species.

To-day, however, the discoveries of cytology and genetics, together with the mass of detailed systematic data which they are illuminating from a new angle, have shown us that we must adopt additional and in a sense other criteria.

A classification based on the idea of phylogenetic descent must at best remain highly speculative, for, save in a few fossil lineages, we do not and cannot know the actual course of events in the evolution of a group. In most groups, the only data we possess on which to base our classificatory scheme, are those concerning the species, subspecies, and genotypic variants as they exist at the present time, for these are the only groups with concrete biological existence. These obviously represent the *results* of evolution, but often tell us little about its past course. From what we now know with regard to the different methods by which new species are produced, and the genetical and cytological mechanisms underlying their production and maintenance, we can see the problem in a new light. We are beginning to realize that a new basis for classification will be necessary for dealing with minor systematic diversity, although the phylogenetic method will remain applicable to major groups.

Let us see in what main ways a scheme with such a genetic basis for taxonomy will differ from one with a phylogenetic basis. In the first place, we have the undoubted existence of parallel mutations (see p. 510). When these occur and are preserved in stocks which are already specifically distinct, the Darwinian concept of homology breaks down. For the homology, though perfectly real, no longer implies descent from a common ancestor showing the common feature. Two white-eyed mutant strains in two species of *Drosophila* are not descended from any common white-eyed ancestral strain; and the same doubtless holds for various wild-type characters of related species. It is true that where a number of separate characters are involved, as in the plan of construction of the body as a whole or of any complex organ, the phylogenetic concept of homology will still hold. It is impossible to maintain the independent evolution, on more than one separate occasion, of such structures as the pentadactyle limb of land vertebrates, or the crustacean appendage, or the chordate notochord. Phylogenetic classification based on the idea that the possession of such organs by a number of organisms implies their descent by modification from a common ancestor remains as valid to-day as it did when the principle was applied by Kovalevsky to prove the vertebrate affinities of the Tunicates. In plants, on the other hand, the organization of the body is on the whole so much simpler that structural plans of such complexity as to rule out close parallel evolution are rare; it is for this reason that the phylogeny of plants is much more uncertain than that of higher animals, and botanists as a whole correspondingly more pessimistic than zoologists as to the possibility of phylogenetic classification in general.

In certain long-range evolutionary trends in animals, parallel changes appear to have played a greater part than was earlier supposed. It is for instance probable on *a priori* grounds, and certain on the basis of fossil evidence, that many adaptive features in a type undergoing specialization are due to the selection of parallel but independent mutations. This is brought out clearly in the case of the horses (Matthew, 1926). Here, quite distinct lines, including some which eventually become extinct, show the same general changes, though some may be in advance of the average in one specialization (e.g. teeth), and behind it in another (e.g. feet). Something similar occurs in the more finely-documented evolution of *Micraster* (p. 32). Presumably the general direction in which selection-pressure is being exerted on the group remains constant, and thus all mutations and recombinations favouring change in this direction are selected. It is not necessary (and indeed highly improbable) that the parallel mutations should be strictly homologous, in the sense of being changes in the same gene; the parallelism of evolution and consequent upset of the classical concept of homology will occur just the same, if they merely exert similar effects.

It is possible that parallel specializations or parallel progress of this sort occurs also in larger groups. W. E. Le Gros Clark, for instance (1934), believes that it has played a large role in the evolution of the Primates as a whole.

It is, however, in minor systematics that the greatest difficulties occur. In the first place, we have the fact that parallel mutations, including a number that are fully (genically) homologous, occur in related species of *Drosophila* and other organisms. They are conspicuous where fixed in domesticated forms (see Haldane, 1927a, on mammals), but occur also in wild populations. This makes natural the presumption that certain characters actually found established in some of the species owe their origin to parallel mutation and not to common descent. It is clear that the distribution, among a group of related species, of characters due to parallel mutation might be quite different from a distribution dependent on phylogeny. Similarity of mode of life, with consequent preservation of similar mutations, would be more influential than common ancestry (though parallel mutation is only likely to occur ih closely related forms). Sturtevant (1939), for the Drosophilinae, is probably the only taxonomist who has consciously endeavoured to discount this possibility (p. 357).

Quite frequently characters will form a mosaic pattern. Character A will in one species be combined with B and C, in another with B and D, in yet another with C and E, and so on (e.g. in *Drosophila*; p. 370). In such cases we must be content to let the phylogeny of species elude us.

In general, taxonomic "relationship" will in many cases be quite different from relationship in human affairs, as between members of a large family. In the first place, the one is essentially an affair of groups, the other of individuals. In the second place, the facts concerning mutation, such as its recurrent nature, and indeed the necessity (if we are to account for the variance actually found in nature) for some recurrence to balance the wastage due to random loss of mutant genes from the germ-plasm, make it clear that while human relationship is based on physical continuity by reproduction, taxonomy is essentially concerned with the number of characters or genes shared in common.

Let us amplify these points a little. The taxonomist is not concerned, or is concerned only in a very minor degree, with rare individual variants. These may, in certain cases, constitute the raw material out of which taxonomic units are shaped, as with dominant melanism in moths (p. 93), but in themselves deserve notice, if at all, merely as "aberrations" from the type of the group. It is only when a group is involved, whether in the form of a single localized unit, multiple localized units, or a distinct and common type scattered through the population (as with genetic polymorphism: p. 96) that taxonomy is involved. In human relationships, on the other hand, we deal primarily with individuals: A.B. is the son of C.D., the nephew of M.N., the cousin of X.Y.

And the basis of these human relationships is reproductive

descent. First-cousinship implies common grandparents, second-cousinship common great-grandparents, and so on. But in taxonomic group-relationships, descent may play a blurred or incomplete part, or even no part at all. To take an obvious example, numerous wild plants have white-flowered varieties in nature; but all the members of "*var. alba*" in bluebells no more constitute a single group with common descent than do all the albinos in human beings. Wherever we find sporadic groups of variants differing from the type in a single main character, the same will apply. Many such examples are known, both from plants and animals.

Where, however, a group is characterized geographically as well as genetically, as, for instance, with most animal subspecies, the hypothesis of descent from a common ancestral group is usually tenable, especially when numerous separate genes enter into the characterization. But even here it is not necessary. With changed climatic or other ecological conditions, only certain types and combinations within a highly variable population may be able to spread into new areas. They will then constitute a single geographical and genetic group, but will not have a single common origin. This has been postulated by Turrill for the origin of *Ajuga chamaepitys* from *A. chia* (p. 267), and doubtless will be found to hold for many other cases as investigators bear this possibility in mind.

Even in the commoner case of the differentiation of a local group *in situ*, the picture will be complicated by migration and intercrossing with members of other groups. This may be frequent, as with many continental subspecies, or infrequent and sporadic, as with many island subspecies; but only rarely, as on oceanic islands, is it likely to be wholly absent. In any case, with biological groups "common ancestry" does not imply descent from a single ancestral pair, as in human relationships; it means the gradual modification of a more or less sharply delimited group by the progressive substitution of some genes for others.

The parallel with individual human relationships is particularly misleading in the case of human groups, for the obvious reason that migration, reticulate crossing, and consequent recombination are more widespread in man than in any other organism. So-called "racial types" may be mere recombinational segregants, thrown up from a highly mixed population, without any continuity of descent through the same phenotype or genotype from the original stock which they are held to represent; the most abundant types in a mixed group may well be new recombinations, different from any found in any of the parent stocks from whose crossings the group arose, and so forth. The question has been discussed in more detail by Huxley and Haddon (1935, Chapters 3-5).

Recently, a dispute has arisen between the adherents of a phylogenetic classification and those who maintain that the only possible basis for taxonomy is a purely logical one, based on a maximum correlation of attributes (see Gilmour, 1940, Calman, 1940, and discussion in *Proc. Linn. Soc. London.*, **152**: 234). However, the believers both in a completely logical and in a completely phylogenetic taxonomy would appear to be aiming at ideals which are quite unattainable in practice; in addition, both systems are in some cases not consonant with fact. For instance, taxonomic practice, at any rate in larger groups among animals, appears to base itself on the co-ordination of characters in an organizational plan, rather than on the totality of attributes, while a phylogenetic classification simply will not fit certain facts of nature, such as those produced by reticulate evolution.

In practice, however, the two concepts largely coincide. They coincide because the processes of mutation and selection distribute characters among taxonomic groups in such a way as to fulfil approximately the postulate of a maximum correlation of attributes demanded by the upholders of a logical classification. The more characters there are available, the greater in general the approximation (cf. p. 371). Geographical distribution and paleontological history are to be included among characters in this sense. In fossil material, however (e.g. molluscan shells), the number of characters may be very much limited compared with the range available to the student of living forms; it is probably this which accounts for many of the cases of apparent parallel evolution to be found in the paleontology of e.g. molluscs and brachiopods.

When divergent groups have evolved separately for long periods, the co-ordination of character-distribution with taxonomic grouping will be very close. It need not be so close, however, when the divergence is of recent date; in this case, the chance of parallel mutations upsetting the co-ordination is much greater.

In one respect taxonomy would appear definitely to have a phylogenetic basis, in that named categories are in general monophyletic groups. Wherever the distribution of characters contradicts the hypothesis of monophyly for a group, the taxonomy demands revision; here the phylogenetic outlook can play a constructive part in taxonomy. This generalization may break down in regard to certain subspecies (p. 215) and species, which in e.g. apomictic and in reticulate evolution must be delimited purely on the basis of convenience. It also breaks down in the case of "horizontal" groups (e.g. genera) in paleontology, which may be merely stages run through independently by several lineages, and yet necessary categories for the sake of taxonomic convenience (see also p. 409). But in regard to higher categories the principle certainly holds.

When it comes to detailed taxonomic *arrangement*, however, as opposed to taxonomic naming, it is difficult to see how a phylogenetic basis, or even a phylogenetic background, can be found for this. As various workers have shown, the elaborate trees and other diagrams of arrangement (relationship) proposed, e.g. for the groups of higher plants, are largely contradictory *inter se*, and must be regarded as highly speculative. Whenever there is reasonable certainty as to arrangement—e.g. when one set of families or orders can be deduced to have a common origin separate from that of others—this can and should be represented by means of named categories, such as superfamily, suborder, subclass, etc. Where this is not possible, the arrangement (e.g. the order in which groups of a certain taxonomic category are enumerated) should not be presumed to have any phylogenetic meaning.

Even if we had a full knowledge of the phylogeny of, say,

all genera and families within an order, the diagrammatic representation of this would be exceedingly complex, and must be held to be a "subsidiary classification" in Turrill's sense rather than falling within the province of taxonomy *sensu stricto* (Turrill's "alpha or orthodox taxonomy").

Gilmour has pointed out that taxonomic practice was actually little altered by the introduction of the idea of evolution and phylogeny into biology. We must remember, however, that the more philosophically-minded pre-Darwinian taxonomists thought in terms of an "ideal plan" or archetype which was modified in detail in various subgroups of a major group (see p. 391), and that this is in point of fact a symbolic representation of phylogeny.

Thus, while taxonomic practice inevitably rests upon the evaluation of characters, and while phylogenetic relationship must always (in the absence of full paleontological data) remain a deduction, the phylogenetic idea, whether directly, or symbolically in the form of a modifiable archetype, may and often does aid the taxonomist in evaluating his characters and in framing his categories. In general, it is more correct to speak of a phylogenetic background for taxonomy than of a phylogenetic basis. And we must constantly beware of arguing in a circle and giving independent existential value to the phylogenetic groupings which we have merely deduced from the distribution of characters and structural plans in existing groups.

The possibility that the initial separation of groups, capable of leading on to species-formation, may in some cases be genetic instead of ecological or geographical also introduces complications into minor systematics. Two genetically isolated species in the same area and habitat may remain closely similar, both physiologically and morphologically, for long periods, whereas two ecologically divergent species might differentiate markedly in a much shorter period.

Again, as we have previously seen, the physiological divergence found in "biological races" may become quite extensive without being accompanied by more than minimal differentiation in visible characters. It may be argued that taxonomy cannot and should not take account of time, only of divergence. But should it not take as much account of physiological as of morphological divergence?

We have, next, the existence of polyploidy. Autopolyploids provide one not inconsiderable difficulty; they are well isolated as reproductive groups, but differ extremely little in visible characters from other members of the series (though often markedly in physiological characters and consequently in area of distribution). But allopolyploid species arising as the result of a cross simply do not fit into the classical framework. New methods of denoting relationship are needed when we have to take into account the convergence and union of branches as well as their divergence. This difficulty is accentuated in the case of reticulate groups (p. 353) where, as we have noted, ordinary taxonomic methods have already partially or completely broken down.

Another point, of purely practical but none the less real importance, concerns the modern tendency to push the geographical-Darwinian method of classification to a conclusion so logical that its application becomes harmful. The battle of the "splitters" and the "lumpers" still continues, though now in respect of subspecies instead of species. The "splitters" wish to distinguish as a separate subspecies, with its own trinomial designation subject to the international rules of zoological nomenclature, every population which can be distinguished, by however slight a criterion, from other populations. As an example of the lengths to which this process is already being carried, let us take a case recently adjudicated on by the British Ornithologists' Union. It appears that British-breeding specimens of the common redshank, *Tringa totanus*, can be distinguished from their continental relatives by a slightly darker coloration. There are no structural or size differences, and the colour distinction, in addition to being slight, exists only in summer plumage. In winter plumage members of the two populations are admittedly indistinguishable. Yet the British form has been solemnly allotted subspecific rank. In consequence, the continental subspecies must now, it is ruled, be banned from the British list, since any birds shot in winter on our shores cannot be ascribed to this form, even if we know perfectly well that most of them will be migrants from Europe! The subspecies cannot reacquire its British status before a European-ringed specimen is shot in Britain. Such decisions tend to reduce systematics *ad absurdum*. This holds also for the erection of new subspecies on the basis of being slightly darker (e.g. Clancey, 1938, for west Scottish birds, which are anyhow more likely to be on a cline).

Difficulties arise in other cases where forms regarded by the "lumpers" as subspecies vary locally. We have met with such a case in the crows (p. 248). Hoodie and carrion crows are both divisible into local groups with considerably better differentiation than that of the redshanks just discussed. But if the conclusion of the adherents of the *Rassenkreis* idea be sound, that hoodie and carrion crows are themselves merely well-marked subspecies, then we must allot "sub-subspecific" names to their local forms. Apart from the practical inconvenience of any such multi-nomial system, we should then be giving a lower systematic rank to the local forms of crows than to those of titmice or wrens distinguished by approximately the same amount of divergence. The difficulty is real, however, and not artificial. It may perhaps be avoided by using the term *semispecies*. This has been proposed by Mayr (1940) for forms which "can be deduced to be geographical representatives of some other species, but have during isolation developed morphological differences of the order of magnitude to be seen between undoubted species"; and under the term he includes forms like the flickers (p. 250), which hybridize in a manner precisely similar to the crows. Taxonomically it will perhaps be best to give binomial names to such semispecies, while uniting them and their geographical vicariants in a supraspecies, to which some name may be given compounded from two of the binomials of the group.

Zuckerman (1940), discussing some of the defects of the present classification of the Hominidae, points out that the desire to ascribe the utmost possible importance to any new find of fossil man has led to the erection of several quite unjustified genera. He pleads for the setting up of empirical criteria of difference for species and genera, in the absence of that abundance of material which alone could make a phylogenetic classification really possible.

The Sabbath was made for man, not man for the Sabbath. Similarly systematics exist for human convenience, not in the interest of some Platonic *eidos* stored up in Heaven. The time has come when we must make a decision as to the implications of recent research for nomenclatorial practice.

A quadrinomial system, by which genera, subgenera, species, and subspecies are given formal names, is a useful invention for the purposes of detailed pigeonholing. Practical convenience, however, dictates that for the ordinary purposes of general biology, binomialism should remain. This can be achieved if large species of the nature of *Rassenkreise*, and large genera containing numerous *Artenkreise* and other types of subgenera, are used for the normal designation of different kinds of animals and plants, reserving the subgenus and the subspecies for the use of systematists or for various special purposes. The subspecies should be more widely used than the subgenus, since different subspecies of a species are concrete biological groups, differing often in quite important points of physiology and behaviour as well as in size or other visible characters. The common habit of splitting old-established genera into a number of new genera, often monotypic, is frequently an abuse of systematic method, because an unnecessary denial of the principle of taxonomic convenience.

Modern systematics, in so far as it is coping with geographical divergence, must in fact recognize various fruits of its own activities. The principle of geographical replacement has for its taxonomic corollary not merely the degradation of many groups from specific to subspecific rank and their grouping within major (polytypic) species or *Rassenkreise*, but also the disallowance of many genera and their degradation to the status of *Artenkreise* or (geographical) subgenera.

In the second place, the same principle, carried to its logical extreme, implies that we must frequently expect the population of one geographical area to differ from that of another by very small though constant differences. This does not, however, imply the desirability of each such form receiving a Latin name. For one thing the principle of practical taxonomic utility forbids subdivision being carried too far: this is especially true of names which are subject to the rules of systematic nomenclature, and thus enshrined for ever in an official position. For another, the principle of character-gradients (clines) must be taken into account. Such geographical forms may prove to be merely points on a cline. If so, then, unless a discontinuity, or at any rate a much steepened portion of the gradient intervenes between them, they assuredly do not deserve separate subspecific names, but the cline as a whole should be named (p. 226).

The fact that two or more clines may be operative in different directions across the range of a species introduces yet another complication.

It seems certain that systematics will have to invent subsidiary terminologies to cope with the complexity of its data (see Turrill, 1938a). Genus, subgenus, species, and subspecies will doubtless remain more or less universally as main categories. The definition of genera and subgenera is often largely a matter of convenience. Besides geographical subgenera we may also expect other types—e.g. those of an ecological and perhaps those of a cytological nature. The definition of species we have discussed at length (p. 157). It is essential that, if the term is to be retained, it should be used in a broad sense, with due regard to practical systematic convenience.

Subspecies have usually been defined on a geographical basis. This, however, is largely due to the historical reason that the refinements of taxonomy were most readily worked out in vertebrates, where ecogeographical divergence is the main factor in minor systematic diversity below the level of the species. Rensch, indeed, has maintained that geographical forms alone are admissible as named subspecies. There would, however, appear to be every reason for employing other categories where they apply—e.g. the physiological or biological, the ecological, and the cytological, notably as regards polyploid forms; genetic divergents like those of *Drosophila pseudoobscura* should also be included. In this case it might, however, be desirable to indicate the nature of the divergence whenever it could be certainly assigned. Perhaps some such method as the prefixing to the subspecific name of the letters "G", "E", and "C" for geographical, ecological (including physiological and biological), and cytological divergence respectively would serve. In some cases considerable geographical differentiation may occur within genetic or biological subspecies. Here, presumably, two subspecific names will be required.

For specifying character-gradients (clines) it is hard to see any fully satisfactory solution save the marking of them on a map. However, a useful first approximation would be a statement of the character they concerned and their approximate direction. For instance, after the description of a polytypic species which showed considerable geographical variation, one might add such phrases as "Size S-N; melanin E-W from desert belt to sea, then SW-NE", the increases in the character being in the geographical directions named. But the complexity of the data might often stultify such an attempt.

When dealing with differences characterizing a regional population, especially when this is geographically discontinuous from neighbouring populations, regard must be had to practical convenience. We must not erect subspecies whose diagnostic differences are smaller than those of mere local groups of other subspecies: the term subspecies should connote a moderate degree of difference, not mere difference, however minute (p. 402). Practical convenience, on the other hand, makes it extremely undesirable to introduce a new nomenclatorial category, though the existence of such microsubspecies or microraces (Dobzhansky) is indubitable. It would seem best for systematists in such cases to confine themselves to descriptive statements, such as that minor geographical forms (microsubspecies), characterized in such-and-such a way, and perhaps denoted by a letter or number, occur in such-and-such regions.

Another method is that suggested by Turrill for designating varieties by combinations of letters according to the combinations of characters which they exhibit. This will not be of much service when variation chiefly takes the form of clines, but will be useful wherever sharply-contrasting characters are involved, and especially so where hybridization has been at work. It will thus be more applicable to plants than to animals. Within its sphere, however, it should often be of value as a subsidiary method of taxonomic description not involving formal nomenclature; and may prove to be the only method for dealing with the bewildering confusion of reticulate groups.

The main kinds of taxonomic units with concrete existence as natural groups are thus as follows. Those to be named in accordance with the international rules are in italics.

1. *a.* Geographical genus   (Rensch's *Artenkreis*).
   b. Geographical sub-   Consisting of species showing
      genus   geographical (or ecological) replacement.

2. Supraspecies   Consisting partly of subspecies, partly of semispecies or full species, all showing geographical (or ecological) replacement.

So far geographical replacement is the only basis known for categories 1 and 2, but we may prophesy that ecological replacement will be detected as a basis for such categories, in insects at least.

3. *Species.*
   a. Polymorphic   Differentiated into numerous spatially co-existent ecotypes or other sharply contrasted forms.

   b. Polytypic   Differentiated into subspecies showing geographical or ecological replacement, or into forms with different chromosome - number; the subspecies may fall into clines.

   c. Monotypic (mono-   Not differentiated into subspecies
      morphic)   (or into an array of well-marked and co-existent ecotypes).

4. *Semispecies*   On the borderline between subspecies and species.

5. *Clines* — To be given Latin names when they are considerable and continuous and not differentiated into subspecies.

6. Chromosome-races — Differing in chromosome-number, usually by whole genomes; to be designated by the ploidy (3n; 4n — 2; etc.) after the specific name.

7. *Subspecies*

8. Microsubspecies

9. Apomict strains (clones).

Natural groups, in the sense here employed, have a geographical distribution *qua* groups and are either self-perpetuating or have clearly been recently derived from a self-perpetuating group. Phases, forms, and sporadic mutants are not natural groups in this sense, nor are ecotypes. If a phase or an ecotype becomes the only form in a given area, and persists there, it *ipso facto* merits subspecific rank. The word *variety* has been used in so many senses that it should be dropped. If a general term is required for any variant form, *paramorph* may serve. The nomenclature of hybrids is discussed by Allan (1940), and the taxonomy of cultivated plants by Vavilov (1940).

In paleontology, many difficulties arise. A technical difficulty arises from the fact that the paleontological taxonomist is confined to fewer characters, since soft parts are not available. This becomes acute, e.g. in many molluscs, though it is not serious in such forms as mammals. Some paleontologists arrive at conclusions which do not square with the experience of taxonomists who have the advantage of dealing with living material. Thus Macfadyen (1940), describing Liassic Foraminifera, writes of the Lagenidae: "in this family there appears to be wide variation within some of the groups, where neither 'species' nor even 'genera' are sharply defined." In view of what we have previously said as to the biological reality of species, it is probable that such conclusions derive from the inevitable difficulties of the material (see also Macfadyen, 1941).

A more fundamental difficulty is the fact that he must consider the dimension of time as well as of space. Parallel evolution is a real phenomenon, but in many fossil groups its apparent extent is exaggerated by this paucity of taxonomic characters. Wherever parallel evolution occurs in a group, two types of classification are possible—by vertical lineages, along the time-dimension, and by stages run through by several lineages, cutting across the time-dimension (see e.g. Arkell, 1933; W. D. Lang, 1938). It is often advisable to give generic names to such horizontal stages. It has been maintained that such "horizontal" genera are purely artificial; but as E. I. White pointed out in a recent discussion (unpublished) at the Zoological Society, this is not the case; granted the ocurrence of parallel evolution, horizontal stages are inevitable facts of nature. It thus becomes necessary to introduce a double terminology, vertical as well as horizontal. The simplest convention would be to apply generic names to horizontal stages and to introduce a subsidiary terminology for lineages; but the details must clearly be left to the paleontologists themselves—with the one proviso that they work out a simple and agreed system. (See Arkell and Moy-Thomas, 1940.)

Many paleontologists (see e.g. discussion in Swinnerton, 1940) give binomial names to so-called "morphological species" which are without doubt only extreme variant types arbitrarily selected from the assemblage provided by a variable true species. This is an unfortunate misuse of taxonomic terminology: some other method of naming such forms should certainly be devised.

Undoubtedly the most important result of modern research in and bearing upon systematics is that species may originate by numerous and quite different methods, which fall under three main heads: the geographical, the ecological (in the broad sense), and the genetic (cytogenetic). The degrees of morphological divergence and intersterility between related forms vary greatly according to the method of divergence which has been pursued.

Faced with the abundance of new facts, we must acknowledge that some new step in taxonomic practice is due. Two major improvements in the methodology of systematics have been effected in the past. The first was the substitution of the Linnaean system of binomial nomenclature for the earlier method in which nomenclature was confused with description. The second was the introduction of trinomialism to cope with the data of geographical distribution. It is safe to prophesy that the next decade or so will see a third phase of major improvement. This will involve the introduction of some method, concerned largely with subsidiary terminologies, by which, while the principle of taxonomic convenience is still given due weight in the main terminology, the cytogenetic and ecological data of systematics, and the facts concerning actual or potential interfertility, can be adequately described and discussed. It will also involve the reduction of taxonomic differences to metrical form. The importance of this has been ably urged by Richards (1938), who also makes numerous practical suggestions. A few decades hence it will, we may prophesy, be regarded as necessary taxonomic routine to give the mean measurements, with their standard deviations, of at least five or six standard characters, as part of the description of a new form. The characters would vary from group to group, but could readily be standardized for each group. Leitch (1940) stresses the importance of such methods in paleontology, and points out that certain assemblages can be characterized by their degree and type of variability. Equally important are accurate methods for the quantitative study of the numbers and properties of populations; see references in Timoféeff-Ressovsky (1940), Dowdeswell, Fisher and Ford (1940), Spencer (1940), and Dobzhansky (1940).

It has been customary to distinguish sharply between artificial and natural classification. But the "natural classification" at which post-Darwinian biology has aimed is itself in certain ways artificial. For one thing it represents an unattainable ideal. And for another it assumes—what we now can perceive to be erroneous— that the only natural method of classification is one based on naïve and pre-mendelian ideas of relationship taken over from human genealogy and applied to groups instead of to individuals. Furthermore, it has unconsciously accepted certain implications of the Aristotelian method of classifying things into genus and species, implications which are of philosophical rather than scientific import and based on *a priori* logic rather than on empirical fact. The most important of such implications is a tendency to accept the discreteness and fixity of separate species (and subspecies) at more than their face value.

The new classificatory systems that are destined to arise will be more natural, in the sense of more truly reflecting nature. They will provide us with a picture of the diversification of life as it actually exists, and sometimes as it has actually occurred. They will give due weight to gradients of change, their different directions, and their variations in steepness. They will help us to think in terms of genes and their distribution as well as in those of individuals. As regards the units of the taxonomist, we shall cease to regard them as so absolute or so necessarily distinct. We shall begin by thinking of life as a unity, into whose continuum discontinuities have been introduced. Some of these are partial, of various degrees of completeness, while the complete gaps are of various widths. Further, the discontinuities are of various origins. Some are imposed by geographical causes which are, biologically speaking, accidents. Others are the outcome of ecological specialization, and are then often accentuated by selection. Still others are the by-products of the working of the physical machinery of heredity, the chromosomes, their division and meiotic reduction. Some discontinuities arise gradually, others abruptly. Some are the accidental outcome of isolation, others the consequence of mere divergence, while still others have been selectively involved so that related groups may be more effectively kept from interbreeding.

The new taxonomy, with the aid of its subsidiary terminologies and its quantitative measurements, will seek to portray this many-sided reality. The picture will inevitably be less simple, but it will be more true to nature. The origin of species is largely irrelevant to the large-scale movements of evolution. But, through taxonomy, it will be perceived as a complex and multiple process, responsible for much of that amazing variety of life which at one and the same time attracts and bewilders the biologist.

CHAPTER 8

ADAPTATION AND SELECTION

I. THE OMNIPRESENCE OF ADAPTATION

We next come to the origin of adaptations. It has been for some years the fashion among certain schools of biological thought to decry the study or even to deny the fact of adaptation. Its alleged teleological flavour is supposed to debar it from orthodox scientific consideration, and its study is assumed to prevent the biologist from paying attention to his proper business of mechanistic analysis. Both these strictures are unjustified. It was one of the great merits of Darwin himself to show that the purposiveness of organic structure and function was apparent only. The teleology of adaptation is a pseudo-teleology, capable of being accounted for on good mechanistic principles, without the intervention of purpose, conscious or subconscious, either on the part of the organism or of any outside power. And to the second objection, the answer is that since adaptations are facts, it is the business of biologists to study them. If a biologist thinks that he has exhausted the study of a structure or a function merely by showing its adaptive advantage, he is a bad biologist; but so is he who thinks he has done so merely by giving a mechanistic account of its present condition and its embryological development. The truth is of course that every biological problem has its evolutionary as well as its immediate aspect, its functional meaning as well as its mechanistic basis; and both need to be studied.

Adaptation, in point of fact, is omnipresent. The field worker rightly laughs at the disbelievers in the adaptive significance of mimetic or protective coloration or of threat behaviour. I have been deceived in Africa by the resemblance of a mimetic spider to the ants with which it associates *; have spent vain hours on a Surrey common searching for a nightjar's nest, so perfect was the bird's cryptic coloration, before stumbling accidentally upon it; have nearly fallen out of a tree when a wryneck on its eggs simulated a hissing snake. That the examples of protective coloration, afforded by the leaf-insect, the woodcock, the dab, or the twig-like larvae of geometrid moths, should be hackneyed is no argument against their biological validity. Nor does the disbelief of certain laboratory mechanists in warning coloration and other aposematic characters prevent chicks from associating the black and yellow of cinnabar caterpillars with nauseousness, or hinder human beings from paying attention to the rattle of a rattlesnake. The biologist who discovers by comparative study that the metabolism and respiratory pigments of animals are closely adjusted to their mode of life is not likely to imagine that the correspondence is fortuitous. The physiologist who unravels the postural reflexes of a bird or investigates the chemical regulation of respiration-rate is not likely to dismiss organic function as non-adaptive; the naturalist who notes the constant correspondence between structure and inborn behaviour on the one hand and environment and way of life on the other—one has only to think of sloth and owl, anteater and flamingo, angler fish and whalebone whale—must believe either in purposive creation or in adaptive evolution; the evolutionary biologist who finds that the rise of each new dominant group in turn is associated with some basic improvement in organic mechanism, be it in the shelled egg, or warm blood, or placental reproduction, will have to admit that adaptation has been all-important in evolutionary progress.

It is perhaps unfortunate that the study of adaptations has

* For a coloured figure of a spider mimicking an ant, see Donisthorpe (1940).

been so closely associated with highly specialized and striking cases of the "wonders of nature" type, such as the resemblance of a butterfly to a dead leaf complete with mould-spots and imitation holes, or the almost fantastic contrivances of certain orchids which secure insect-pollination. For this tends to distract attention from the bedrock fact that some degree of adaptation is omnipresent in life, and that this fact demands an evolutionary explanation.

However, in his recent very striking book Cott (1940) has shown that concealing and revealing coloration, when properly investigated, remain the paradigm of adaptive studies, and has thoroughly turned the tables on captious objectors. Such critics of the theories of protective coloration and mimicry have been in the habit of dismissing them as pure fantasies or armchair speculations. A. F. Shull (1936), for instance, goes so far as to state that the theories of aggressive and alluring resemblance "must probably be set down as products of fancy belonging to uncritical times" (p. 175), and concludes (p. 212) that "if the doctrine [of natural selection] can emerge minus its sexual selection, its warning colours, its mimicry, and its signal colours, the reaction over the end of the century will have been a distinct advantage"! The array of facts presented by Cott shows that it is these objections which deserve the designation of "armchair": it is the field naturalist and the experimental biologist who provide the facts from which the theories are educed. Cott (and see Carpenter, 1939) also summarizes the numerous experiments and observations which demonstrate the reality of selection operating in nature in favour of cryptic or aposematic coloration. He also points out the irrelevance of the criticisms of McAtee (1932).

In addition, Cott analyses the features of pattern by which illusions of various sorts, whether for decrease or increase of conspicuousness, can be created, and then demonstrates their existence in nature. The particular method employed will be related to the type of habitat occupied. Thus inconspicuousness of the flat wing of a butterfly in low rough herbage is generally obtained by a false illusion of relief; the obliteration of sharp outline in a tangle of vegetation tends to be achieved by countershading together with ruptive markings, whereas with forms which must expose themselves on bark it involves arrangements for preventing marginal shadows, often coupled with an actual irregularity of the outline itself, achieved by irregular outgrowths. Most convincing are special correlations of pattern with unusual positions: an excellent example is the reversed countershading of sphingid caterpillars which feed at night, but rest in an inverted position by day, and of the peculiar Nile catfish *Synodontis batensoda*, which swims upside-down (see Norman, 1931, pp. 29, 227).

It is interesting that Süffert (1932, 1935), as the result of intensive studies pursued without knowledge of Cott's work, arrived at similar conclusions. Three recent independent observers may also be quoted. Cornes (1937) cites the moth *Venusia veniculata*, which lives on a particular tree-lily. Its wings are marked with lines running at right angles to the body; and at night it invariably orientates itself across a dead leaf, so that its markings coincide with the conspicuous longitudinal lines on the leaf. Its antennae, which would destroy the resemblance if visible, are tucked out of sight under the fore-wings. When disturbed it settles down again, "after a few compass-like vacillations", in a similar position.

Again, W. W. A. Phillips (1940) describes the nest of *Hemipus picatus leggei*, a shrike from Ceylon. The bird nests on bare limbs of trees. The nest is not only camouflaged with lichens and bark flakes, but its sides are built down flush with the branch so as to resemble a knot. Finally, the fledgling young, so long as the parents are away, sit motionless facing each other with eyes half-closed and beaks pointing upwards and nearly touching in the centre. Their coloration is a mottled drab and blackish grey, so that they are almost invisible, even when nearly fledged. From a distance of little more than 12 feet the nest with the young bears a most remarkable likeness to a snag left on the upper side of a branch through the breaking off short of a smaller branch just beyond its junction with the major stem. The upward-pointing beaks help to heighten this similarity; they represent the sharp-angled fracture left at the top of the stump. This example may be compared with the protective coloration-*cum*-attitude of the brooding nightjar *Nyctibius griseus* (see Cott, 1940, Fig. 74), but is almost more remarkable as involving a co-operative attitude on the part of several birds.

Finally, Holmes (1940) describes the unique case of the common cuttlefish, *Sepia officinalis*, which can change its colour and pattern within the space of a second. By this means, it can draw on an amazingly varied repertoire of protective devices, including concealment by means of obliterative shading, close environmental resemblance, striking ruptive patterns, and flash patterns which bewilder an enemy by their extremely rapid sequence and great difference from each other, and also the scaring of enemies away by conspicuous threat patterns. Any particular one of these will be adopted according to circumstances. In addition, it employs special epigamic. stimulative patterns in courtship. Related cephalopods do not show this multiform adaptation, which can be related to the particular habits of the species.

In regard to mimicry, the detailed following by the mimic of the pattern of the model, as the latter changes geographically from subspecies to subspecies, constitutes a beautiful case of detailed adaptation (see e.g. Poulton, 1925, Pl. D). This phenomenon is not due to any direct or indirect effect of climate. (See also p. 102; Carpenter and Ford, 1933).

As Cott rightly says, physiologists and anatomists do not dispute as to whether a wing is or is not adapted to flying: they set themselves to discover the extent to which, and the precise method by which, it is adapted to that function. Colour and pattern in this respect fall into line with any other functional attribute of organisms.

Actually, in view of the remarkable studies of particular kinds of adaptations made in the latter half of the nineteenth century, the incredulity shown by a certain school of modern biologists appears very remarkable. Thus, to take only one example—the various adaptations concerned with cross- and self-pollination in higher plants—we have the intensive work of Darwin (1877) on orchids, and the exhaustive survey, largely original, by Kerner (Kerner and Oliver, 1902). After reading Kerner's account of the devices for securing cross-pollination, and those equally remarkable ones for securing self-pollination, the two often co-existent in the same flower as what the Germans call *doppelte Sicherung*, there would seem to be no room left for scepticism on this point. And if on one point, why on others? However, Cott's book deserves special attention, since it takes account of all the objections, theoretical, factual, and methodological, raised by the sceptics of the early twentieth century.

T. H. Morgan (1932, p. 115), in reviewing the subject, makes the following pertinent remarks. "A fact of some interest becomes apparent at once, namely, that what are usually cited as adaptations are instances in which a species shows some unusual type of structure, i.e. one in which it departs from most of the other species in the group. In other words, it is the exceptional that is often referred to as a typical case of adaptation. The reason for this is apparent. The exceptions stand out conspicuously as specialties for some particular situation. Nevertheless, a moment's thought should show that the general problem of adaptation is not to be found so much in these particular occasional departures as in the totality of the relations of the organism to its environment, which makes the perpetuation of the individual and of the species possible. The extreme cases catch our attention, and their special relation is sometimes more easily seen, or guessed at, than the more subtle physiological processes that make all life possible."

2. ADAPTATION AND FUNCTION; TYPES AND EXAMPLES OF ADAPTATION

Adaptation and function are two aspects of one problem. We may amplify this statement by reminding ourselves that the problem of adaptation is merely the problem of functional efficiency seen from a slightly different angle. There are certain basic functions, such as assimilation, reproduction, and reactivity, which are inherent in the nature of living matter, and can thus hardly be called adaptations. But any of them can be specialized or improved in various ways during evolution to meet the needs of the organism. The fact, for instance, that our gastric glands begin to secrete when our nose or eyes are stimulated by the smell or sight of food, is an adaptation concerned with assimilation, just as is the elaborate structural ruminating mechanism of the oxen and their allies.

The distinction between basic property and superposed adaptation may be well brought out by a historical example. Weismann considered the property of regeneration to be a special adaptation, acquired during the course of evolution by such animals as were especially exposed to loss of limbs or other damage. Experiment, however, failed to confirm this conclusion: for instance, Morgan found that the abdominal appendages of hermit-crabs, though normally protected by the hard molluscan shell inhabited by the animal, regenerate just as readily as the exposed big claws or walking legs. Further, on general grounds it became more and more obvious that regeneration depended essentially on the basic capacity of living matter for reproduction and growth. Regeneration is to-day universally looked upon as one aspect of an inherent quality of life, and the chief problem set by it to biology is not how to account for its presence in lower forms, but how to explain its restriction and absence in higher types.

Frequently associated with regeneration, however, is the faculty of autotomy or self-mutilation, whereby an animal detaches a limb, like a lobster, or a tail, like a lizard, sacrificing a part rather than risk the whole. In most cases autotomy takes place at definite spots. The higher crustacea have special breaking-joints which enable them to throw off their claws and legs easily and with hardly any loss of blood; similar but less rigidly-predetermined breaking-joints occur in lizards' tails. It appears quite clear that whereas the regeneration of a lobster's claw is a survival of a basic property of life, its autotomy mechanism is a more special adaptation—to the risk of the animal being unable to escape if it is seized by the claw, and to the dangers of loss of blood if the exposed claw is damaged.

In addition to the basic functions, others may arise in the course of evolution to meet the needs of the particular type. Thus active locomotion is absent in most plants; and colour and pattern can only play an adaptive role in relation to higher animals with their elaborate sense-organs.

From the point of view of selection, adaptations fall into two categories—those of preadaptations fitting an organism for a different environment or mode of life from the outset (p. 449), and adaptations in the ordinary sense, gradually evolved within the normal environment, whether stable or changing.

A biological classification shows that adaptations fall into a few main groups. In the first place there are adaptations to the inorganic environment. Some of these, like the temperature-adaptation of local races in *Drosophila* (p. 191), or in frogs as described by Witschi (p. 235), or of tropical as against arctic organisms, may be of a general physiological nature, unrevealed in any structural peculiarity. Others, like the climbing and para-chuting habits of animals in tropical forests, or the black or red colour and the luminosity of deep-sea animals, are more special-ized. Hesse and others (1937) in their *Ecological Animal Geography* have produced an imposing array of the general types or regu-larities of adaptation imposed upon various types of fauna by the peculiarities of their inorganic environment. Frequently we can deduce an animal's mode of life and habitat from the struc-tural adaptation which it possesses. Occasionally we may be puzzled, but find that fuller knowledge solves the puzzle. Thus the association of prehensile tails, indicating arboreal life, and fossorial forefeet indicating burrowing habits, in some of the South American anteaters, appears a paradox, until we remember that the fossorial claws are needed to open up the nests of tree-termites (see Emerson, 1939, p. 293).

Next we may take adaptations concerning the organic environ-ment—covering the functions of protection against enemies, the pursuit of prey, reaction against infectious disease and parasites, and the like. These are essentially interspecific. We also find intraspecific adaptations, concerned with competition or co-operation between individuals of the same species, e.g. the rapid growth of many plant seedlings, and the recognition marks of gregarious mammals and birds.

Finally there are adaptations of a more internal nature, concerned with improvement in functions such as digestion or excretion; or with general co-ordination, whether by nervous or endocrine means; or with the regulation of the internal environment. Reproduction may also be considered in this category. As examples of these various internal adaptations we may take the adaptation of the form of the digestive tract and the kinds and quantities of enzymes produced by it to the type of food normally eaten; in nervous co-ordination, we need only think of the inborn mechanism whereby every time a limb-muscle is stimulated to action, its normal antagonist is inhibited and relaxed, enabling the contraction of the other to be more effective; in internal regulation we may take the astonishingly delicate mechanism whereby the acidity of the blood is kept constant in higher mammals; in reproduction we need go no further than the human species and reflect on the mutual reaction between early embryo and uterus by which the elaborately-organized placenta is produced.

These various classes of adaptations of course overlap and intergrade. None the less, an enumeration of them is useful in reminding ourselves that adaptations are nothing else than arrangements subserving specialized functions, adjusted to the needs and the mode of life of the species or type. Most adaptations belonging to our first two categories subserve functions usually called ecological, while the functions of most of those in the last group are physiological. The concept of function has for so long been the preserve of physiology in the restricted sense that we are apt to forget that ecological function is of equal importance to the species.

Our enumeration will also serve as a reminder of the omnipresence of adaptation. Adaptation cannot but be universal among organisms, and every organism cannot be other than a bundle of adaptations, more or less detailed and efficient, co-ordinated in greater or lesser degree.

On the other hand, adaptations subserving different functions may be mutually destructive, e.g. high specialization for sexual display is antagonistic to cryptic resemblance. In such cases, the balance between the opposing tendencies will vary in a very instructive way according to the ecology of the species (see p. 426). Artificial selection, as so often, provides valuable parallels. Thus some breeds of dogs, such as bulldogs and St. Bernards, owe their appearance to genes which are on the verge of inducing lethality, and can only be retained by selection of compensatory modifiers (see p. 71). Again, very high milk-producing capacity, rapidity of growth, or extreme conformation for meat purposes in cattle, pigs, etc., may be close to the limit of physiological possibilities; in inferior environments (backward tropical regions) animals of this type cannot maintain themselves, so strong is counter-selection.

From the inexhaustible array of possible examples, we may select a few which have been subjected to quantitative analysis, which are unfamiliar or striking, or are of particular importance for evolutionary theory.

A. H. Miller (1937) has analysed in detail the structural peculiarities of the Hawaiian goose (*Nesochen sandvicensis*). This is an endemic of the Sandwich Islands, and exhibits specialization towards a non-aquatic running and climbing habit, with restriction of flying power and absence of migration. Its habitat is arid, and not only does it appear never to enter water, in the wild state, but never to drink it except in the form of dew. In correlation with its specialized habits, the webs of the feet are reduced, the legs increased markedly in relative size; a number of muscle and tendon characters (quite different from those prominent in forms specialized for swimming) promote walking and running ability, while the long and flexible toes, with the large plantar pads, help it to climb among the steep irregular lava-flows; the wings and sternum, on the other hand, are definitely reduced. This example is of course much less striking than many classical cases, such as that of the giraffe or the mole, but it illustrates the general adaptive correlation of structure with habit, so clearly set forth by Böker (1924). Similarly the thrashers (*Toxostoma*) are adapted to digging (Engels, 1940).

From a rather different point of view the exhaustive work of Sick (1937) is worth mentioning. His detailed analysis of feather-structure in flying birds demonstrates that feathers exhibit adaptations for efficiency in flight down to the smallest and most unexpected details of structure and intercorrelation.

Desert animals show interesting behavioural adaptations against high winds (Buxton, 1923, p. 110). Thus various desert butterflies spend most of their active life flying about inside quite small bushes, in order to avoid being blown away; and various desert birds, like Clot-bey's lark (*Rhamphocorys clot-bey*), fortify the rim of their nest with ramparts of pebbles.

Our next set of examples concerns adaptations for the performance of a function overlooked by most biologists, that of toilet in mammals, on which Wood-Jones (1939b) has just published a valuable essay.

The most interesting cases are concerned with the care of the coat. Ungulates lack special structural adaptations for this function, and substitute the crude method of the rubbing-post, combined with a very restricted application of the tongue, and in some instances with the almost equally crude use of horns or antlers. In Equidae the subcutaneous muscle-sheet is highly developed so as to be capable of strong twitching; this, while mainly directed against flies, has a subsidiary toilet function.

In various mammals the tongue is the chief toilet organ. Its greatest specialization for this function is seen in the Felidae, among which it is much rougher than in other mammals. Wood-Jones seems to be correct in maintaining that this roughness has been evolved primarily as a brush-and-comb. In regard to behavioural toilet adaptations also the cats are specialized: they are the only animals to lick their paws and use them to reach parts of the head not accessible to the tongue. Other organs that may show special toilet adaptations are the teeth and the feet. The most remarkable of these are the procumbent lower incisors and canines of the lemurs. These have all become strangely modified both in shape and position, so that they constitute a most efficient six-toothed comb, the downward strokes of which are well suited for dealing with the animals' thick woolly fur. Further, just as combs need cleaning, so do these teeth: this secondary toilet function is carried out by an abnormally developed sublingua. It should be noted that the development of teeth as toilet adaptations in lemurs is correlated with the almost complete substitution of nails for claws on their digits.

The unrelated "flying lemur", *Galeopithecus*, and the bats are also precluded, though in another way, from the full use of their feet as toilet organs; and Wood-Jones points out that they, too, have lower front teeth which appear to be adapted as combs, though in a different way from the lemurs'. In *Galeopithecus* there is also a secondary toilet organ, in the shape of the serrated front edge of the tongue, which acts as a tooth-brush for the pectinated teeth. The toilet function of the special teeth has not been observed here as it has in the lemurs, but may with reasonable certainty be deduced.

In marsupials, Wood-Jones has observed that the polyprotodonts use their incisors as combs, so that the small size, large number, structure (and in some cases position) of these may be regarded as toilet adaptations, though the hind feet are also employed (as we employ both brush and comb). The few large incisors of the diprotodonts, on the other hand, are ill-suited for this purpose, and not employed in the toilet, Here, the united but much reduced syndactylous digits of the hind feet appear to be of use solely as toilet instruments. As with the teeth of the polyprotodonts, their size and shape are correlated with the length and type of fur with which they have to deal. The bandicoots (Peramelidae) appear to be an exception, since they are polyprotodont but syndactylous. But observation shows that the shape of their teeth is not adapted to acting as a comb, so that the exception proves the rule.

Dusting instincts are among the important toilet adaptations, and may restrict habitat (e.g. in *Dipodomys*: Dale, 1939).

Among the other cases cited by Wood-Jones we may mention the special bristly brushes on the feet of certain bats.* But enough

---

* Actually the most elaborate of all structural toilet adaptations are found in higher insects, such as ants and bees.

has been said to show the common characteristic of a particular type of adaptation. It is concerned with a function: the function may be carried out by different organs or combinations of organs in different forms: and the organs concerned show different degrees of structural modification correlated with efficiency in carrying out the function.

A word may here be devoted to the nest sanitation of birds, as this is a good illustration of an adaptation with two points of special interest—it is transitory, but unlike other transitory adaptations such as the foetal membranes of amniotes, the egg-tooth of birds, or the larval structure of echinoderms, it is wholly or mainly a matter of behaviour. In almost all birds, the nest-cup shows a degree of cleanliness which is astonishing until one reflects on the impossibility of rearing a brood of nestlings in their own filth. This cleanliness is secured in various ways. In some forms, such as birds of prey in the later nestling stage, the young defecate only after backing up to the nest-rim; in these, specially developed muscles ensure that the faeces are projected well clear of the nest. In most passerines (and some other forms), the droppings are encased in a gelatinous sac secreted by the nestling's intestine. This makes it easy for the parent bird to handle the droppings, which are either eaten or carried away to a distance. In some cases they are eaten while the nestlings are small, but removed when they grow larger, and in still other cases (e.g. starling, wren, swallow) a third stage is added in which the young evacuate backwards, clear of the nest. In some woodpeckers, the parents mix the nestlings' excreta with sawdust to facilitate handling. Young kingfishers appear to use the innermost part of the nest-tunnel as a latrine. In various species with domed nests, such as the willow warbler (*Phylloscopus trochilus*), the nestlings eject their faecal sacs on to the outer rim of the nest, outside the entrance hole and to the side of it, whence they are removed by the parents. But perhaps the most interesting fact is that in many species the nestlings will not defecate until the parent taps the cloaca with its beak, often awaiting relief for long periods with upturned posterior! All these adaptations cease to operate, whether in parents or nestlings, as soon as the young birds leave the nest (Blair and Tucker, 1941).

The delicacy of transitory adaptation is shown by the larval jaws of the parasitoid *Glypta haesitator* (Cameron, 1938). These are feebly developed in the second and third instars, when only fluid food is taken, but are powerful in the first, when they are needed for eclosion, and the fourth, when they are required for feeding on solid food and for eating a way out of the host.

In conclusion, we may mention some cases of adaptation for display among birds. Stonor (1936, 1938, 1940), gives a detailed analysis for the birds of paradise (Paradiseidae) and shows conclusively that the remarkable variety of display structures and the equally remarkable variety of display attitudes found in the family are invariably combined to produce the maximum of visual effect. Two examples must suffice. The rifle-bird, *Epimachus (Ptilorhis) paradisea*, has a display quite unlike that of any other member of the family, in which the wings are spread in butterfly fashion; and the effect is enhanced by the broadening of some of the wing-feathers, resulting in a broader and more conspicuous wing. Again, the lesser superb bird of paradise (*Lophorina superba*), has two small patches of specially iridescent feathers on the head. For display, these are erected in such a way as to catch the light and appear as brilliant false eyes.

Stonor (1940) gives an equally illuminating functional analysis of the displays of the pheasants and their allies (Phasianidae). We may cite one little-known example. In Bulwer's pheasant (*Lobiophasis bulweri*), the hinder feathers of the compressed tail are stiff and project downwards. In display, they are rapidly drawn through the dead leaves of the forest floor, and enhance the striking visual effect by means of sound (Heinroth, 1938).

Among the herons, I have myself studied the display of the Louisiana heron (*Hydranassa tricolor*) and the lesser egret (*Egretta thule*). Both have a crest, somewhat lengthened neck-feathers and special feathery aigrette plumes on the back. However, the latter are much more highly developed in the egret, the crest and neck-feathers in the heron. And in correlation with this, the egret in display bends down so as to render the fan of filmy aigrettes conspicuous, while the heron erects its head and neck, and the visual effect of the display depends mainly on the crest and much-bristled neck-plumes (Huxley, 1923*b*).

Conspicuousness is an essential of display: but this function runs counter to the need for concealment. The reconciliation of these opposing selective tendencies is effected in various interesting ways (see Huxley, 1938*c*). Where the need for visual concealment is least, as in dense forest, selection for conspicuousness can have full play. It is certainly no coincidence that the most brilliant secondary sexual characters are found in forest forms such as birds of paradise, peacock, most pheasants, trogons, many humming-birds, etc. (Stonor, 1940). Where the need for more concealment is greatest, as in defenceless birds of open or relatively open country, display-coloration may be wholly absent, as in the skylark (*Alauda arvensis*), and visual stimulation must be effected solely by striking behaviour. In other cases, as with the prairie chicken (*Tympanuchus cupido*) of the American prairies, a compromise is effected by which the display characters are normally invisible and the bird is markedly cryptic, but become strikingly conspicuous (in this case by expanding of concealed patches of bare yellow skin on either side of the neck, until they look like half-oranges) during the display itself. The great bustard (*Otis tarda*) of the European plains is another striking example, which, by inflating an enormous throat-pouch and everting the wings to show normally concealed white feathers, transforms itself from an inconspicuous to a highly conspicuous object during its display.

Finally, the difference in reproductive habits in birds makes it possible to calculate the differing selective advantage that accrues from success in mating (Huxley, 1938*a* and *b*). We may distinguish fractional, unitary, and multiple reproductive advantage. Fractional reproductive advantage is provided by stimulative characters whose effect is merely to raise the reproductive efficiency of a single mate. Unitary reproductive advantage accrues to monogamous forms from characters adapted to securing a mate in the first instance: the male bird either secures a mate and reproduces, or does not do so and fails to reproduce. And multiple reproductive advantage accrues in polygamous forms from characters adapted to securing mates and in promiscuous forms from those adapted to securing coition: success here means transmitting successful characters to the offspring of many mates instead of only one. In correlation with these differences in selective value, characters with a fractional advantage, like display-characters in monogamous territorial passerine birds, in which display occurs only after a mate has been secured, are never very strongly developed. But in such forms a number of males regularly fail to secure a territory and a mate; and the characters concerned with securing this reproductive advantage, such as song, are striking and may appear exaggerated or "hypertelic". Finally, where multiple reproductive advantage exists, display characters and display behaviour normally reach an extraordinary pitch of exaggeration, as in ruff (*Machetes*), peacock (*Pavo cristatus*), various pheasants and grouse, birds of paradise, etc., and the display-characters may even be clearly disadvantageous to the individual in all aspects of existence other than the reproductive, as in the train of the peacock, the wings of the argus pheasant (Huxley and Bond, 1942, Proc. Zool. Soc. A.3: 277), or the plumes of some birds of paradise (and see p. 484).

The giant panda (*Ailuropoda melanoleuca*) has recently been shown to possess an unexpected structural adaptation to its special feeding habits (Wood-Jones, 1939a). As is well known, this aberrant carnivore lives almost exclusively on bamboo-shoots. In order to hold these properly while feeding, the sesamoid bone on the radial side of the hand has been much enlarged and furnished with a regular articulation with the scaphoid bone, and a muscle which normally runs to the base of the pollex has become diverted to it. The sesamoid with its overlying horny pad has thus become modified into an organ functioning as an opposable thumb. The actual pollex was apparently too specialized to be modified in this direction. Through this remarkable adaptation the giant panda has become endowed with delicate grasping capacity far beyond that of any other member of the order, though the common panda (*Ailurus fulgens*) shows some modification in this direction.

As one more example of this type of adaptation we may take

the external ears of the nocturnal bush-babies (*Galago*). These are very much enlarged, to catch and concentrate sound-vibrations. They are also mobile, like the enlarged pinnae of many other mammals, thus ensuring a considerable degree of directional hearing. Finally they (together with the ears of other lorisoids, but to a greater degree) are unique in having transverse discontinuities in the cartilages which enable them to be rapidly folded up, thus obviating damage to the delicate pinnae from contact with branches, etc. (Osman Hill, 1940). Here we have three sets of modifications all subserving one adaptive function.

A recent study by Thorpe (1936) on the life-history of the chalcid *Encyrtus infelix*, parasitic on a scale insect, will serve as an example of an unusual adaptation. On reaching its fourth instar, the parasitic larva changes its position and becomes invested with a membranous sheath produced by the host. The sheath then becomes attached in an extraordinary manner to the main lateral tracheal trunks of the host, in four (or six) separate places close above the larval spiracles, in such a way that air can pass through, and the parasite from then on respires at the expense of its host. "The conclusion that the whole structure is an adaptation for the respiration of the parasite seems inescapable."

Such "induced adaptation", utilizing the tissues of a host organism, is of course also found in gall-producing animals; the galls they produce may be highly elaborate structures, clearly adaptive in protecting and sheltering the parasite. To quote from Went (1940), "The complexity of the structures induced by the gall insects is often astounding. The central part of the gall with the insect in it may become detached after it is full grown. Then the insect will be released from this box through opening of a pre-formed lid. . . . The inside of the larval chamber is often lined with cells very rich in proteins."

Adaptation is as normal in instinct as in structure. The host-selective instincts of parasitoids hardly ever miscarry (W. R. Thompson, 1939); the specificity of such instincts is secured by utilizing a distinctive combination of a few sensory clues (Russell, 1941). The curious roosting instincts of the hornbill *Lophoceros melanoleucos* (Ranger, 1941) are adaptations to secure its nocturnal safety.

Adaptation is just as often manifest internally as externally, in improvement of some physiological function as in better adjustment of some obvious external character like colour or pattern to the environment. Thus, to take a recently investigated example, the giant nerve-fibres of various cephalopods constitute an adaptation for quick and simultaneous contraction of the mantle to expel a jet of water (Pumphrey and Young, 1938). In *Loligo*, the size of the fibres is graded, larger fibres being found in longer nerves; "this is apparently a further device for securing more nearly simultaneous contraction".

The adaptation of parasites to their hosts comprises a wide range of physiological features, among which the degree of virulence may be singled out here. As is well known, many parasites are only mildly or not at all pathogenic to their natural hosts, though extremely virulent when given the opportunity of attacking "virgin" hosts, e.g. the trypanosomes of wild game when they obtain a footing in domestic cattle. While this is in part due to an adaptive increase of resistance on the part of the hosts (cf. the resistance to measles, etc., of human populations which have been long exposed to the disease, while unadapted populations exhibit a high mortality), it may be in part due to the parasite developing an adaptive lower degree of virulence. For it is obviously a disadvantage, from a survival standpoint, for a parasite to kill its host, so that strains of too high virulence will tend to eliminate themselves.

Adaptations to symbiosis are sometimes very striking. Thus numerous animals are enabled to exist in wood by utilizing fungi which break down the wood and probably also act as a source of food for the animal. Special pockets are often produced by the animal, in which a supply of the fungus is carried. This occurs for instance in the larvae (probably only the females) of the wood-wasp *Sirex* (Parkin, 1941); for numerous other examples, see Buchner's book (1928). That the special organs are definite adaptations for ensuring a constant supply of the symbionts cannot be questioned. *Tridacna* has remarkable adaptations for exploiting algae (Yonge, 1936), including lenses for increasing photosynthesis.

Again, the comparative study of respiratory pigments and respiratory behaviour in animals has revealed a series of respiratory adaptations to way of life (see p. 435). Recent work on animals with ciliary feeding has similarly revealed the existence of diverse and elaborate adaptations adjusting the ciliary mechanism to different modes of life (cf. Yonge, 1938b).

The total range of these functional devices is very large, and (once the hypothesis of special creation is ruled out) can only be ascribed to accurate selective adaptation. We need not continue the list: it would be almost coterminous with the data of comparative physiology and physiological ecology.

3. REGULARITIES OF ADAPTATION

The perusal of such a work as Hesse, Allee, and Schmidt's *Ecological Animal Geography* (1937) shows that the study of faunas and floras confined to particular habitats will invariably reveal certain recurrent peculiarities. Sometimes these recurrent characters are obviously, or at least *prima facie*, adaptive, like the coloration of desert or pelagic forms, the prevalence of special touch-organs and of luminescence in the deep sea, webbed feet in aquatic birds and mammals, or prehensile tails in forest-living vertebrates. In other cases they are correlated characters in Darwin's sense: this applies, for instance, to some (though not all) of the reduction in relative size of exposed parts like ears or limbs, in subspecies or closely related species of mammals from high latitudes (p. 213). In still other cases, their significance is doubtful, but even then the fact of their correlation with a particular habitat must be of some significance, and points the way to further analysis.

We have already mentioned certain regularities of variation in discussing clines (pp. 211 seq.), and given reasons for believing that most of them were genetic and adaptive, though the visible characters concerned might often be only correlates of the invisible physiological adaptations.

In other cases, we cannot be sure whether the regularities are genetic or purely modificational. Among these we may mention the parallel variation seen in many related species of fish with decreasing salinity (see e.g. Möbius and Heincke, 1883), the tendency of fresh-water mussels to be more globose in larger waters (Ball, 1922), or the increase in thickness and spinosity of shell in the river snails of the genus *Io* as one proceeds downstream (Adams, 1915). One must therefore suspend judgment as to the adaptive nature of such regularities pending experimental analysis.

As illustrating genetic regularities, we may take those of desert grasshoppers (Acrididae), as described by Uvarov (1938). This example is perhaps specially pertinent, since Uvarov is an opponent of all adaptational interpretations. He distinguishes four main faunas within the major climatic habitat afforded by desert—the deserticolous proper, inhabiting bare open ground; the saxicolous, inhabiting the rougher habitat provided by the rocky slopes of low eroded desert mountains; the arbusticolous, inhabiting the xerophilous shrubs of many deserts; and the graminicolous, inhabiting the perennial grasses of certain desert plains. These four types differ markedly in body-shape. The deserticolous forms have a depressed body (measured on the metathorax) with width-height ratio from $1 \cdot 0$ to $2 \cdot 0$. In saxicolous forms the ratio is from $0 \cdot 7$ to $1 \cdot 0$, much of the height being due to a prominent narrow dorsal crest. Arbusticolous forms have a similar ratio, though without the crest; and the graminicolous forms have the most compressed bodies of all.

In addition, deserticolous forms tend to be hairy, with punctured, wrinkled, or otherwise sculptured surface, and close resemblance in colour to the soil, often coupled with flash coloration in the hind wings and legs. Most of them are good fliers. In saxicolous forms, the sculpturing is much coarser (the above-mentioned dorsal crest being itself an example of this), and there is a considerably higher percentage of flightless forms. Coloration is similar to that of the first group. Arbusticolous forms possess "climbing legs", which differ in their proportions from the jumping legs of the first two types; they also exhibit concealing coloration, which here, however, tends to be greyish-green. Finally, in the graminicolous forms hairiness and surface sculpture are usually negligible, flash coloration is absent, and general coloration is that of green or dry grass, frequently with the sharply-defined light longitudinal stripes that Cott (1940) has shown to be obliterative in grassy habitats.

In spite of Uvarov's anti-adaptional bias, it would seem clear that in these various faunas coloration, both general and flash, body form, and body sculpture are all adaptive. If the form of the legs in the arbusticolous forms can be designated by the functional term of "climbing", it would seem natural to designate the coloration as "concealing". The high pilosity of the open desert forms merits further study.

Another excellent recent example, the result of careful field study of a fauna inhabiting a region with well-marked ecological characteristics, is the work of Linsdale (1938) on the avifauna of the Great Basin in the western U.S.A. The region is arid, the climate severe, with prevalence of strong winds and somewhat scanty and usually low vegetation; the distribution of most birds therefore tends to be more scattered than in more luxuriant surroundings. The preponderating characters of the passerine birds correlated with those environmental features are as follows: a great development of flight-songs, in relation to the scarcity of high perches; a high percentage of protectively-coloured adults; a tendency for both nestling plumage and nest-lining to be pale-coloured, in order to reflect excessive light;* strong powers of flight, to cope with the wind; a high proportion of species are migratory, in relation to the severity of the climate; songs and calls are unusually loud, to compensate for the scattered distribution of individuals; long-range vision is unusually acute, partly for the same reason, partly in correlation with the lack of obstruction by vegetation; a high proportion of forms nest on or close to the ground.

Dice (1940b) calls attention to adaptive regularities among the subspecies of the single genus *Peromyscus*, and we mention else-

---

* Linsdale (1936) has also shown that the opposite conditions are correlated with dark nest-lining and nestling plumage, thus facilitating the maximum absorption of heat.

where (p. 214) the similar regularities in the Australian bird *Acanthiza*.

We have already referred to the frequent correlation of general tint with climate (Gloger's rule, p. 273). Meinertzhagen (1934) gives a good example of this, in the darker plumage of a number of bird species in the Outer Hebrides. He concludes that reduced sunshine and increased atmospheric humidity, rather than higher rainfall, are the meteorological factors responsible.

Meinertzhagen (1919) also points out that in migratory species these regularities are correlated only with the climate of the breeding-quarters, not at all with that of the winter-quarters. This may be due to the greater intensity of selection during the breeding-season (cf. p. 212).

Buxton (1923, ch. 7) gives a valuable summary of the coloration of desert animals; but his rejection of their cryptic selective value is much too sweeping. Though doubtless many instances of sandy pallor in deserts are examples of Gloger's rule, and correlated primarily with climate, many others are certainly cryptic. His objection that normally invisible areas, such as the soles of the feet in mice, are of the same colour as the visible parts may be accounted for by "correlated variation", the entire colour being affected except where selective counter-reasons exist. In general, pigmented chitin is tougher, more heat-absorptive, and less permeable to water-vapour. This accounts for various regularities of insect distribution (Kalmus, 1941*b*), e.g. the frequency of black desert species (p. 451), and the increase of pigmentation with altitude and latitude.

It should be mentioned here that some bird species have been experimentally darkened by exposure to humid conditions. The most interesting case for our purpose is *Munia flaviprymna*, a desert form of weaver from Australia (Seth-Smith, 1907). The dark experimental modification of this form, though rather variable, is somewhat similar to a dark form found in nature in a more humid region of Australia. It was at first concluded that the dark colour of this latter form (which was treated by Seth-Smith as a distinct species, but is to-day regarded as subspecific) was itself only modificational. It is much more likely, however, especially in view of its greater variability, that the experimentally darkened desert form was what Goldschmidt (e.g. 1940) calls a *phenocopy* of the genetic darkening of the subspecies from the humid region. If so, the two contrasted forms may have arisen by organic selection (p. 304), genetic adaptation having replaced an original adaptive modification. In any case it is worth noting that other climatic colour-forms are not modifiable in this way. Thus Sumner (1932, p. 26) could obtain no darkening of pale forms of desert *Peromyscus* in more humid conditions, or lightening of dark humid forms in drier conditions.

When adaptive regularities exist, any exceptions to them immediately attract attention and call for analysis. For instance, the correlation of some sort of webbing on the feet with markedly aquatic habits is all but universal in birds. Ducks, geese, swans, gulls, terns, petrels, frigate birds, pelicans, cormorants, gannets, and the like have either three or all four toes joined by a web; coots, moorhens, grebes, and phalaropes have lateral lobes on each toe. But the dippers (*Cinclus*) exhibit not a trace of webbing or any other aquatic adaptation, although they are restricted to streams, obtain much of their food below the surface of the water, and can swim on the surface. Structurally, they appear as terrestrial as a thrush or a wren. Can there be a reason for this exception to the rule, or are they still in the early stages of adaptation to a new habitat? Their wide distribution seems to negative the latter explanation. The suggestion may be made that they have adopted a unique type of aquatic food-seeking. Many birds that frequent stream-edges walk some way into the water in order to find food: the dippers have extended this habit and walk on until they are wholly submerged. They search for food by subaqueous walking, and in this they not only do not require webbing but can get a better grip of submerged water-plants and rough surfaces if their toes are free. The exception is a clue to exceptional habits.

Determination of metabolism, temperature-resistance, etc., when combined with accurate anatomico-physiological study of respiration and directed by ecological knowledge, often reveal regularities in the close adaptation of forms to their habitat.

As an example we may take the work of Wingfield (1939*a*, *b*) on mayfly nymphs belonging to various genera. Thus in *Baëtis* from swift streams, the tracheal gills do not aid oxygen-consumption; in the pond-dwelling *Chloeon dipterum* they act as an accessory respiratory mechanism by promoting ventilation, but at low oxygen concentrations only; while in the burrowing *Ephemera vulgata* they aid oxygen-consumption in all circumstances, apparently as true respiratory organs as well as by providing ventilation. Similarly, forms from swift streams have a lower thermal tolerance than those from slow streams, while those from ponds are most resistant. This is in accordance with the temperature extremes expected in nature (see also Whitney, 1939).

Fox and his co-workers (see H. M. Fox, 1939) have studied the activity and metabolism of poikilothermal animals of very various kinds from different latitudes. Among closely-related species, the one living in higher latitudes is generally, but by no means always, adapted in some way to the lower temperatures of its normal habitat: at a given temperature, its heart-beat, respiratory movements, or other activity, is greater than that of its relative from warmer regions. The same phenomenon may also be found as between high-latitude and low-latitude populations of the same species. Differential heat-resistance also exists in many cases. As Fox points out, it is difficult to be sure whether the undoubted adaptation thus shown, enabling cold-water types to carry on the business of living at a reasonable rate, is modificational, genetic, or a mixture of the two. We are probably safe in assuming that, when the difference is one between different species and is of considerable extent, it is mainly genetic, although the recent work of Mellanby (1940) shows how rapid and extensive modificational adaptation may be. A critical analysis of the problem is highly desirable. (Cf. calcicole plants, p. 273.) J. A. Moore (1941) has demonstrated a similar and undoubtedly genetic adaptation in different species of frogs, those from colder breeding habitats having a lower temperature-tolerance, and faster-developing eggs. Even the jelly-membranes and the form of the egg-mass are climatically adapted (Moore, 1940). Again, the field-mouse *Apodemus flavicollis*, in correlation with its distribution, prefers rather lower temperatures than the closely related *A. sylvaticus* (Kalabuchov, 1939); furthermore, within the species, individuals from higher latitudes preferred lower temperatures than those from warmer regions. (See p. 271.)

That the adaptation between geographical varieties or sub-species of a single species may also be mainly genetic is shown by various researches, such as Timoféeff-Ressovsky's previously cited work on local variation of temperature-resistance in *Drosophila funebris* (p. 191), but most exhaustively by the studies of Goldschmidt (1934, 1938*b*) on the gipsy moth *Lymantria dispar*. Here the genetic peculiarities of the geographic race, to use Goldschmidt's own words, "harmonize the life-cycle of the animal, especially the feeding season and the diapause, with the seasonal cycle of the inhabited region".

In many cases, notably in Japan, the lines of genetic demarcation between major groups of races are quite sharp. Originally it had been found impossible to correlate these lines with corresponding sharp changes in any single meteorological factor. Recently, however, as Goldschmidt (1938*b*) points out, it has been shown that they correspond with extreme accuracy with changes in soil type, and that the soil types in their turn depend upon the interrelation of several meteorological factors. This is a reminder of the fact that climate cannot be properly measured by variations in single meteorological phenomena, such as temperature or day-length, since it inevitably represents a complex summation of numerous factors; and further, that physical factors like soil or biological features such as geographical distribution may often prove the best indicators of such summations. In this instance, the discovery of physiological adaptations between subspecies of moths proved to be the first (and very accurate) indication of climatic regional differences. It should, however, be noted that though the subspeciation of the gipsy moth is thus delicately adjusted to climate, adaptation to food plants may act as a limiting factor (see later for cases of climatic limiting adaptations). For instance, in the U.S.S.R., the area of periodic mass outbreaks of rapid reproduction of *L. dispar* coincides with the distribution of its optimal food, the oak plant.

Plants, too, may show delicate climatic adaptation of geographical (ecoclimatic) subspecies. Thus according to Clausen, Keck, and Hiesey (1937) the coastal subspecies (which they call ecotypes) of most Californian plants have a constitution genetically harmonized with a climate providing mild winters and a long growing period. Transplanted to an alpine station, although their development is hastened through dwarfing, they can seldom or never mature any seed, and are often unable to flower on resuming growth in the summer. The alpine subspecies ("ecotypes") of the same plant have a cycle related to a climate of long cold winters and a short growing period. Transplanted to a coastal station, they flower poorly or not at all, and show a generally weak appearance in spring. "The adaptive capacity (modificational plasticity) of coastal and alpine ecotypes is therefore insufficient to allow either to live and to compete in the habitat of the other. It is the difference in inheritance that enables them to succeed in their respective regions."

The exhaustive experimental studies of Turesson (see summary in Barton-Wright, 1932) have independently led him to similar conclusions. In different regions, adaptations arise which are jointly related to climate and life-cycle. He investigated both summer-flowering (aestival) and spring-flowering types. In aestival forms, the more southerly populations showed a considerable (genetic) increase in height combined with lateness, while alpine populations showed earliness and reduced height as compared with lowland ones. In spring-flowering forms, on the other hand, it is the more northerly populations that show lateness, up to the latitude of southern Sweden; further north than this, earliness is again favoured. The low-latitude earliness appears to be related to the general earliness of trees in the region, for it is advantageous for the spring herbs to produce their leaves and flowers before the leafy canopy cuts off the sunlight; in very high-latitude spring forms, earliness is doubtless correlated with the shortness of the vegetation period. All the regional peculiarities of the plants investigated are thus adaptive.

Similar though less exact conclusions are reached by O. E. White (1926). For instance, black walnuts (*Juglans nigra*) from

Minnesota are much winter-hardier than those from Alabama or Texas, though morphologically indistinguishable. Again, a high mountain ecotype of the Cedar of Lebanon (*Cedrus libani*) is perfectly hardy in Massachusetts, where the normal form of this species shows poor cold-resistance. In support of adaptive climatic differentiation within the species, White cites the common practice of gardeners and foresters to use seed from the northern limit of a species' range when winter-hardiness is desired.

4. ADAPTATION AS A RELATIVE CONCEPT

In cases like these, the physiological characters of the local groups must clearly have been adjusted during evolution to the climatic characters of their environments, and are thus in the strictest sense adaptive. But there are many examples where the evolutionary relation between physiology and climate is not so obvious. As illustration we may take some of the cases of plant distribution in Britain so interestingly discussed by Salisbury (1939). In the Scots pine (*Pinus sylvestris*), pollination occurs normally in May, but fertilization not for another thirteen months. Unless the temperature in both summers reaches a certain minimum combination the pollen-tubes will not reach the ovules. This provides quite a different set of meteorological conditions for fulfilment than does the attainment of a minimum level of temperature during one season, as would be the case for the fertilization of most species, and there is some evidence to show that it is a limiting factor for the northern distribution of the species.

In many cases it is the temperature obtaining during the time of fruit-formation, not flower-formation, which is decisive. This is so, for instance, with many species of the southern element in the British flora, such as the common milkwort, *Polygala calcarea*, or the fluellin, *Linaria spuria*. The form of the life-history may be of importance in various ways. For instance, the time at which flower-buds are laid down varies in different plants. In daffodils it is May, and the optimum is about 9° C., while in hyacinths it is August and the optimum about 25°. Thus in daffodils either too high or too low May temperatures would inhibit flower production, while they would have no influence on the process in hyacinths. Again, the two British species of *Arum* differ in their winter habits, the common cuckoo-pint, *A. maculatum*, over-wintering as a deep-situated corm, immune from most frosts, while *A. neglectum* produces its new foliage in December. The latter is thus readily killed by frost, but where it can survive, its winter photosynthesis gives it an early start in spring before the trees above it have developed their leaves. The British range of *A. maculatum* extends far into Scotland, whereas that of *A. neglectum* is restricted to our southern and south-western coasts. We may say that *A. neglectum* shows an adaptation to woodland life—but only in mild temperate climates. A somewhat similar difference, with similar results on distribution, is seen between *Scilla verna* and *S. autumnalis*.

Numerous similar cases may be found in textbooks of plant ecology. We may add a recent example from animals. Nash (1937) has been able to study the ecology of the tsetse-fly *Glossina morsitans* both in East and West Africa (Tanganyika and Northern Nigeria).* Both races appear to demand the same or very similar optimum conditions—a temperature of about 23° C. and a saturation deficiency of about 6 millibars. These conditions are much more nearly reproduced in the *Berlinia-Brachystegia* woodlands of Tanganyika than in the rather different habitat provided by the small residual forest islands of North Nigeria. In both regions these forest areas constitute the "true habitat" of the species. In the dry season, as evaporation rises the flies become restricted to this true habitat; but in the wet season they show a much wider dispersal. Distribution is definitely controlled by climatic factors, not by abundance of game for feeding.

In Tanganyika, the species breeds mainly under fallen trees; in the rainy season dispersal is very extensive, and the comparative mildness of the dry seasons may allow it to consolidate some of its wet season advances and to form new fly-belts. In North Nigeria, on the other hand, the species breeds promiscuously on

---

* The West African form is often distinguished as a separate species, *G. submorsitans*; but is better regarded as a geographical subspecies.

the forest floor (so that the logtraps so valuable in East Africa are useless); the wet season dispersal is much less in extent, and the severity of the dry season is such that no new colonization can occur; the concentration of fly during the dry season is much more pronounced; the heat and aridity of the dry season is so great that certain habitats (small meadow-pans) are never available, and mid-day inactivity (never observed in East Africa) occurs.

Nash considers that the West African form has remained essentially similar to the East African in its physiological requirements. "Having failed to adapt its constitution to the climate, it has perforce adapted its habits; had it evolved a constitution which preferred a higher degree of evaporation and temperature, the greater frequency of optimum conditions would have enabled it to become as widespread a pest as its East African representative."

In a later paper Nash (1940) has applied these theoretical considerations in practice. Dealing with the three species of *Glossina* found in Nigeria, *G. tachinoides*, *G. palpalis*, and *G. morsitans*, he first established their basic ecological relations, and then introduced experimental clearing designed to accentuate the severity of pessimum conditions. With *G. tachinoides*, partial clearing on a small scale leads to local extermination, but this is followed by recolonization. With large-scale clearing, however, total extermination is obtained. With *G. palpalis*, this method appears to be of value only in the drier parts of the species' range. Finally, with *G. morsitans*, which has rather different ecological requirements, very extensive and ruthless total clearing is needed to effect extermination, and is not recommended "unless warranted by a large [human] population and abundant funds". The case is interesting as illustrating the practical applicability of an ecological viewpoint which thinks in terms of adaptation to environment.

These examples from tsetse-flies are illuminating in various ways. They illustrate, like the plant examples previously adduced, the importance of inherent physiological requirements, but also well demonstrate the role of modificational plasticity in ensuring adaptation.

As would be expected, plasticity in this sense is more widespread among plants than among animals. Following up the pioneer work of Bonnier (1895), its extent has been investigated by various authors. Many forms have an astonishing degree of plasticity. Thus Clements (1929) was able to demonstrate marked alpine dwarfing in lowland types of many species transplanted into alpine conditions. He was at first inclined to minimize the existence of genetic differences between types. Later, however, (e.g. Clements, 1932) he admits that species differ in their plasticity. Thus in the genus *Mertensia*, *M. sibirica* has no plasticity, while *M. pratensis* and *M. lanceolata* can be made to resemble each other very closely.

Clausen and his associates (see e.g. Clausen, Keck, and Hiesey, 1938, 1940) have shown how complex is the interrelation of genetic and modificational factors in such cases. For instance, four major ecotypes (ecoclimatic subspecies) are differentiated in the majority of plants in the U.S. Pacific slope—a coast range, a lower mountain, a subalpine, and an alpine form. Yet corresponding ecotypes of different species may react quite differently when transplanted. Thus the alpine race of *Potentilla diversifolia* is relatively stunted when transplanted to a mid-altitude station (though near sea-level it again becomes larger); but the alpine races of *P. glandulosa* and *P. gracilis* become largest at the mid-altitude station and are most dwarfed in their natural habitat: the alpine races of *Achillea millefolium* and *Aster occidentalis*, on the other hand, while tallest at the mid-altitude station, are more dwarfed in lowland than in alpine conditions.

Meanwhile Marsden-Jones and Turrill (1938, etc.), though failing to corroborate some of the more sweeping claims of Bonnier and of Clements (see discussion in Turrill, 1940), have demonstrated how different is the range of modificational plasticity in different species. Thus the knapweed *Centaurea nemoralis* and the kidney-vetch *Anthyllis vulneraria* are little modifiable by different soil conditions, while the plantain *Plantago major* is extremely plastic. In higher animals, behavioural adaptation seems to take the place of modificational plasticity in plants.

In some of these cases, the modification can hardly be regarded as adaptive. This applies, for instance, to the stunting of organisms by unfavourable conditions as the limit of the range of the species is approached. This is of course common in plants, but may also occur in higher animals. Thus the American freshwater fish *Xenotis megalotis* is markedly smaller in the northern part of its range, in correlation with the mean temperature and the length of the warm season (Hubbs and Cooper, 1935). Fully-grown forms from northern Michigan are 20 per cent smaller than those from the south of the state. Though such modification appears to be wholly non-genetic, it must alter the ecological relations of the species.

These examples of correlation between organic constitution and climate or habitat begin to shed light on the problem of adaptation as a whole. Some climatic adaptations show high specialization—for instance, the run-off mechanisms of plants exposed to constant moisture, or contrariwise the water-storage mechanisms of certain desert plants; some of these latter from the Arizona desert can store enough water to last for more than one rainless year—in certain cases (e.g. *Ibervillea sonorae*) up to ten or more! (see MacDougal, 1912). Other correlations with climate are more general, though clearly adaptive in the narrow sense of having been accumulated by selection over a long period. Here we may reckon the various adaptations of plants to cold winters—deciduousness in broad-leaved trees; restriction of transpiration in needle-leaved trees; over-wintering as bulbs, corms, or seeds, etc., in herbs; general resistance to low temperature. Adaptations of mammals in cold climates to hibernation, to the reduction of heat-loss, or to adjust the breeding season to the needs of the growing young, fall under the same head. For example, in the roedeer fertilization occurs in autumn as with other north temperate Cervidae, but the embryo does not develop beyond the early segmentation stage until spring, thus ensuring birth in the favourable period of early summer (see F. H. A. Marshall, 1910, p. 32). Similar definite climatic adaptations, but of a much more delicate nature, are to be found between closely related species, or, as we have seen in *Lymantria*, between races of a single species.

At the other extreme there are organisms with ranges limited by climatic factors, rather than closely adjusted to them. We have just seen excellent examples in *Glossina morsitans* and in various plants. Such forms of course show some climatic adaptation—no tsetse-fly could exist in the arctic, for instance, or in a full desert—but it is of a very general nature. The correlation between the organism and its environment is in this respect neither delicate nor exact: there is an absence of the lock-and-key correspondence to be seen, for instance, in some colour-adaptations, or in various devices for securing cross-pollination in plants—and apparently in the climatic relations of *Lymantria*. Similarly, many higher animals are found in a number of different habitats. Adaptation is then to a range of habitat-types, not to a single habitat. Certain features in the environment (here often in the plants rather than in physical characters) act as limits to the distribution of the species, but adaptation is not close or detailed (see Diver, 1938, 1940).

The common heron (*Ardea cinerea*) shows a marked ecobiotic adaptation to securing food from shallow waters. In addition, it is restricted, and presumably adapted, to a certain climatic range. But the environment also acts selectively in yet another way. During exceptionally severe winters, herons may starve through the freezing of the waters which they frequent. The careful records compiled annually by the British Trust for Ornithology (Alexander, 1941) show that herons from colonies within easy range of salt water were least affected by the very severe winter of 1939–40. In 1940, the heron population of the British Isles showed a general decrease in number of occupied nests, compared with the average for the previous three years. But whereas for inland heronries (more than 25 miles from tidal waters) the decrease was 31 per cent and for those between 2 and 25 miles from tidal waters it was 26 per cent, for coastal heronries (less than 2 miles from tidal waters) it was only 13 per cent. Thus low winter temperatures and distance from the sea, sometimes separately, sometimes jointly, are bound to be factors limiting the northern distribution of the species. This is borne out by the facts. The heron breeds up to 70° N. in Norway but only to 66° in Sweden and to about 60° in the U.S.S.R. (Witherby, 1938–41).

We find further that organisms may be adapted to climatic (and other environmental) factors either narrowly or broadly. Stenothermic species, for instance, have a narrow range of temperature-tolerance, eurythermic forms a wide one; Moore (1940, *Amer. Nat.* **74**: 188) points out that eurythermy is very rare in aquatic animals, and is itself an adaptation to the fluctuating temperature of land life. Stenohaline and euryhaline forms may be similarly distinguished. We may extend the concept to individual plasticity by distinguishing "stenoplastic" and "euryplastic" forms (p. 519). Euryplasty may grade over into general high viability, which is itself an adaptation, though internal or intrinsic rather than related to particular external conditions. Range of ecological habitat may also be broad or narrow.

We must also remember that adaptations may be very close and detailed, and yet, like mimicry in Lepidoptera, of no or negligible value to the species as a whole, since they have arisen entirely by intra-specific selection (§ 8), and are thus biologically subsidiary to adaptations affecting general viability, resistance to parasitoids, etc. (see A. J. Nicholson, 1927).

This is perhaps the place to mention some interesting cases which suggest that evolutionary adaptation to recent climatic change may now be active. I refer to the numerous well-authenticated cases of steady and considerable extension of range which cannot apparently be put down directly or indirectly to human interference. Timoféeff-Ressovsky (1940) cites several cases, of which we may mention the serin finch (*Serinus canarius serinus*) and the yellow-breasted bunting (*Emberiza aureola*). The former has since 1800 extended its range northwards from southern France almost to the English Channel, and from the eastern Alps almost to the Baltic. The latter since 1825 has extended its range westwards from the Urals to west of Leningrad. Similarly the roller (*Coracias garrulus*) has shown a northern range-extension in eastern Europe, and the warbler *Acanthopneuste viridana* a westward extension very similar to that of *Emberiza aureola*; while the black redstart (*Phoenicurus ochrurus*) has more or less paralleled the serin, and the greater spotted woodpecker (*Dryobates major*) has within fifty years extended its British range from south of the Tweed to the northernmost woodlands in southern Caithness (Witherby and others, 1938–41, J. Fisher, 1940c). The last two cases are not cited by Timoféeff-Ressovsky.

Meinertzhagen (1919) cites other cases, such as the shore-lark, *Eremophila flava*, which has not only expanded its breeding-range westwards, but about 1847 established a new migration route, in this differing from other species which have extended their range in a similar way. He also mentions the crested lark, *Galerida cristata*, as an example of the same phenomenon on a more extended time-scale, and accompanied by subspeciation. The fulmar petrel (*Fulmarus g. glacialis*) has shown a marked southern extension of range within the last sixty years along the coasts of Britain. The old supposition that the spread was initiated by a reduction of human depredations seems to be erroneous (J. Fisher, 1940a, b; Fisher and Waterston, 1941).

Among Lepidoptera, the moth *Plusia moneta*, first recorded in S. England in 1890, is now common there, and has reached Scotland (South, 1939). The comma butterfly, *Polygonia c-album*, hardly known in Britain outside Gloucestershire, Monmouth-shire, and Herefordshire before 1920, has since markedly extended its range E., S., and N. (numerous reports in *The Entomologist*).

It may be suggested that, whenever the effects of human interference can be shown not to have been operative, such range-changes will generally be the result of a changed ecological adaptation. The ranges of forms like the fulmar would be much restricted by the amelioration of climate since the last ice-age, and any genetic changes in temperature-tolerance or nest-site selection which enabled the species to regain some of the lost ground would be subject to positive selection. The other species mentioned are extending into milder climates: here presumably a climatic preadaptation was already present, which changes in habitat-preference or nest-site selection have finally enabled the species to utilize. The matter is a complex one, however, and needs thorough investigation before we can conclude that the range-changes are the result of adaptive change.

It must not be forgotten that, in the long perspective, dynamic evolutionary trends are as important as are static interrelations at any given moment. The worsening of the climate at the end of the Mesozoic reduced the general adaptiveness of the dinosaurs, pterosaurs, and other reptilian groups, while increasing that of the early mammals and birds. The recent glacial period enabled the cold-climate preadaptation of many tetraploid plants to become dominant over the other adaptive features of the corresponding diploids in higher latitudes, leading to extensive spread of the former. The spread of man favoured that of organisms preadapted to be commensal or semi-parasitic on him or his crops, like house-sparrow, rat, house-martin, or "weeds" in general.

Adaptation is thus seen, not as a hard-and-fast category, but as something relative. It is not an all-or-nothing phenomenon, but takes many forms and exists in all degrees. Like other biological categories, it can only be properly understood by detailed and where possible quantitative analysis. Furthermore, the mistake must never be made of thinking of adaptational adjustment solely or primarily in relation to the physical environment: the biological environment is just as important. In some cases plants are restricted to special habitats not because of special climatic adaptations but because they possess a wide range of tolerance towards climatic conditions, with a low degree of what we may call biological or competitive vigour. Thus competition prevents their establishment in most habitats; only where their extra margin of tolerance removes them from the swamping effect of their biological competitors can they flourish. Salisbury (1929) cites various cases of this phenomenon. Thus *Ranunculus parviflorus* is in Britain restricted to very unfavourable habitats, e.g. dry shallow soil overlying rock. In cultivated ground (unmanured) it not only grows well, but much better than in nature, and produces ten to twenty times as many fruits. Again, the sorrel *Rumex acetosa* is notorious as a plant of acid soils. In cultivation, however, it shows an increased growth on limed soils, proving that its restricted distribution in nature is due to the competition of plants which are less tolerant of acid conditions.

Such examples "sufficiently illustrate the fact that plants grow not where they would, but rather where they must". The same sort of thing is probably true of many plants characteristic of marginal conditions, e.g. alpine habitats (see p. 274).

In a letter (5. iv. 1940) Professor Salisbury has kindly furnished me with some further striking examples. One concerns the rosette plants of open grazing land. For instance, *Senecio campestris* and *Filipendula hexapetala* "are confined, as wild plants, to our chalk pastures, but their vigorous growth in other types of soil, when they are protected from competition by cultivation, indicates that their restriction in nature is due to the competition factor". The continual grazing prevents other plants from growing high enough to affect the rosette plants' growth, whereas their peculiar growth-habit flattens their own leaves down in such a way that they cannot readily be eaten.

Another example, involving quite different factors, is that of the hellebore (*Helleborus foetidus*), which in Britain is almost entirely confined to ash woods on calcareous soils. Here again in cultivation this species grows and reproduces well in non-woodland and non-calcareous situations. Its peculiar restriction appears to be due to a combination of two factors. In the first place, it seems susceptible to competition, and any woodland habitat suppresses competitors which are vegetatively active only in summer, whereas it, being evergreen, can assimilate also in winter. On the other hand, most woodlands are too shady in summer; but the unshaded phase of ashwoods, which lasts for seven months out of the twelve, is sufficient for the hellebore. As Salisbury (1929) well says, "dominance may be the consequence of unfavourable conditions acting by *selective depression*, or to favourable conditions acting as a *selective stimulus*, but in either case the dominance is determined by the *relative* vigour of the species and its competitors".

The perfection of adaptation is also correlated with the degree of competition and other forms of selection-pressure. We discuss this phenomenon more at length elsewhere (pp. 426, 469 seq.) of this chapter. Here we will merely recall the well-known fact that the intensity of life in the tropics is correlated with a greater prevalence and a greater perfection of various adaptations, of which mimicry is perhaps the best studied. Similarly arboreal adaptations such as prehensile tails are most fully developed where the arboreal habitat is developed in most extreme fashion —in South America. Conversely, where selection-pressure is lower, adaptation tends to be less perfect. We have seen a small-scale example of this in the cichlid fish of African lakes (p. 324). A large-scale example is provided by the marsupials of the Australian region. Tree-kangaroos, for instance, show an adaptation to arboreal life so incomplete that one cannot imagine their survival in the tropical forests of Malaya or the Amazon. And in general, the Australian marsupials seem unable to compete successfully with introduced forms from other regions, whether predators or direct competitors.

This brings us back to what has already been said about adaptation and function (p. 417). Adaptation, we there said, "is merely the problem of efficient function seen from a slightly different angle". But it is a commonplace that all grades of efficiency of every function coexist in nature. The function of vision ranges from mere response to high light-intensities up to binocular colour-vision. Aquatic locomotion is at a low level in *Amoeba*, at a high pitch in a dolphin or mackerel. Thus we find in nature, not merely every possible type of adaptation, but every grade within each type. Efficiency of function at its most general consists in all-round viability, and this is largely a matter of harmonious adjustment of parts and part-functions. Thus whereas specialized adaptation may push its possessors close to the limits of biological possibility, extremes of all sorts will be discouraged in what we may call generalized adaptation. This is illustrated by the classical work of Bumpus (1899) who picked up a number of sparrows (*Passer domesticus*) found helpless in a storm, and compared those which died with those which revived. The survivors were in general more uniform, while those which died showed greater variability. What is possibly the result of a similar selection of a central type was found by Weldon (1901) and by Cesnola (1907) in two types of land-snail (but not in a second species of *Clausilia*). The inner whorls of adult shells were found to be considerably less variable than young shells of the same size, though the mean was the same. This appears to indicate selective elimination of extreme types.*

This is what we would expect on a selectionist view. Organisms are selected, not on the basis of conformity to an ideal plan, not in relation to complete functional efficiency, but on the basis of survival. The forms that exist are those that have managed to survive; and survival may be and often is achieved by means of curiously makeshift devices. Not only that, but a high degree of adaptation in one character or function may be a measure of low efficiency in some other respect. It seems, for instance, to be no chance that the most elaborate devices for cross-pollination occur in somewhat rare species of orchids; and Batesian mimicry can only develop in types which are much rarer than their models. Again, specialization which brings success in one set of conditions may involve a loss of plasticity, and so be a real disadvantage if conditions change (see p. 377).

Thus the study of adaptation seems destined to take a new turn. The first stage concerned itself with the fact of adaptation —is such-and-such character an adaptation, or is it not? In the next stage biologists were interested in the mechanism of adaptation—do adaptations arise through natural selection, by Lamarckian means, or in what other way? To-day the emphasis is on the analysis of adaptation itself, and the bearing of that analysis on other branches of biology—how well-developed are the different types of adaptations shown by a particular organism, and what light does its particular adaptive complex throw on its ecology and on the direction and the strength of the selection to which it has been exposed? The significance of adaptation can only be understood in relation to the total biology of the species.

5. PREADAPTATION

The subject of preadaptation demands a section to itself. By preadaptation (sometimes styled passive adaptation) we mean

* The criticisms of Robson and Richards (1936, p. 211) do not appear to be pertinent. If, as they suggest, the young shells are more plastic, this should have been revealed in the inner whorls of old shells also. It is also difficult to see why environmental agencies should always reduce adult variability as compared with juvenile.

either that an existing species (or subspecies) is by its peculiarities predisposed to take advantage of a certain type of environment, or that a particular mutant or natural variety is from the outset adapted to particular conditions, whether those in which it originates, or others into which it might be thrown by chance. We may distinguish the two as constitutional and mutational preadaptation respectively. Let us take this latter category first. Lamoreux and Hutt (1939) find that White Leghorn fowls are markedly more resistant to vitamin B deficiency than other breeds, such as Rhode Island Reds or, still more, Barred Plymouth Rocks. On normal diet, this characteristic is without any effect on survival, but on a somewhat deficient diet it could be decisive.

A somewhat similar type of variation in a physiological (and therefore potentially adaptive) character is seen in the response of the crop-sac of pigeons to the pituitary hormone known as prolactin (R. W. Bates, Riddle, and Lahr, 1939). Some breeds proved no less than eight times as responsive as others. Similarly, among plants different strains of the same species may differ markedly, e.g. in water-requirements.

We have already drawn attention (p. 118) to the marked preadaptation of certain mutants in fowls to warm climates, a preadaptation which has been taken advantage of by man. Hutt (1938) has shown that other breeds show minor differences in genetic heat-resisting capacity, which could well serve as preadaptive features.

An interesting case was found by Strohl and Köhler (1934) in the meal-moth *Ephestia kühniella*. Here a mutation to brown colour, though accompanied by certain unfavourable properties —reduction in egg-number and length of life—also involved a markedly higher heat-tolerance. This differs from the thermal preadaptation of the cladoceran mutant previously described (p. 52) in the complex of characters involved, one of them a visible colour-mutation. What appears to be an example of mutational preadaptation is the replacement of normal by melanic forms in various warm-blooded vertebrates in certain areas (p. 104). As pointed out, the dark forms appear to be preadapted to a moister and cooler climate.

Polyploidy in plants is frequently a thermal preadaptation, but in this case usually towards cold-resistance (p. 337). An excellent example of preadaptation in a hybrid is the rice-grass *Spartina townsendii*, which has proved better adapted than either of its parent species to their own habitat of saline marsh and mud-flats (p. 341). In general, it is clear that any form arising by a sudden large change, as by autopolyploidy, or still more by hybridization and allopolyploidy, must be preadapted in some way if it is to survive (p. 349).

Another possible case of preadaptation, here as regards coloration, is that of the lapwing *Lobipluvia malabarica*, which on a belt of brick-red soil along the Malabar coast lays highly cryptic red eggs in place of the "earthy-coloured" ones seen elsewhere (Baker, 1931). As suggested in *Nature* (February 13, 1932, p. 247), this may be due to local selection of types laying the erythrystic eggs found sporadically in so many species. However, the facts concerning egg-mimicry in cuckoos cannot be explained on the basis of preadaptation, and show that elaborate true adaptations may be brought about in egg-colour, so that further analysis of this case is required.

Kalmus (1941*a* and *b*) finds that various body-colour mutations in *Drosophila* are potential preadaptations to changes in humidity. Thus yellow flies are less resistant to desiccation than wild-type, but ebony and black flies are more so. This appears to depend on the fact that darkening of the cuticle is associated with a tanning process which renders it less pervious (p. 433; Pryor, 1940), a fact probably to be connected with the frequency of black insects in deserts.

It is of course true that many such preadapted and markedly distinct new forms are later modified by the selection of small gene-mutations; and it is equally obvious that even the most triflingly beneficial gene-mutation to be found in the constitution of a wild species, must in one sense have been preadapted at its first occurrence. But there is a real and important distinction between the two types of occurrence. For one thing, many (or most) gene-mutations appear to be of necessity carried on in the recessive state until such time as they can be made part

452 EVOLUTION: THE MODERN SYNTHESIS

of some especially favourable combination: when this is so, they were not preadapted as regards their original phenotypic effect. The truth, as so often in biology, is that a continuous series exists, but that the two ends of it are very distinct. In general, when the origin of a successful new form is due solely or mainly to a single large step (or at least to one that is readily perceived as large by the biologist) we speak of mutational preadaptation, but when a new form arises by a series of small and in general imperceptible stages, we speak of adaptation in the accepted Darwinian sense.

We next come to constitutional preadaptation, where the existing constitution of a stock predisposes it to certain modes of life rather than to others. Salisbury (1929) points out that annual plant species are preadapted to desert conditions. Another example is afforded by the adhesive digital pads or discs of various frogs, which are best developed in the arboreal tree-frogs, though also present in fully functional form in various non-arboreal types (Noble and Jaeckle, 1928). Adaptation to tree-life here seems to have been secured by enlarging these pre-existing structures relatively to body-size.* Engels (1940) shows that the digging habit of the thrashers (*Toxostoma*) depends on pre-adaptive peculiarities of musculature—an interesting case of structure preceding function in birds.

In other cases, the preadaptation is less immediate, an organ subserving one function being readily modified for another. The classical example is the evolution of the lungs of land verte-brates from the air-bladders of certain fish, but there are of course numerous other cases of *Funktionswechsel* which illustrate this long-range type of constitutional preadaptation. In all these, however, a great deal of adaptation in the ordinary sense is also necessary, so that it could be better to exclude them from the category of preàdaptation proper, and style them predisposition.

General predisposition is shown in the ease with which second-ary aquatic life is resumed by terrestrial types. Terrestrial life

* It is fair to state that some authors would not exclude the hypothesis that the non-arboreal disc-possessing forms are secondarily derived from arboreal forms.

involves numerous progressive advances (Chap. 10, pp. 563-4) in general physiology: the possession of these predisposes such forms to be able to compete successfully with aquatic types in their own environment. Predisposition in the endocrine field is found where an organism which lacks a certain hormone, yet contains tissues capable of responding to that hormone. An example is the response of bird oviducts to progesterone, which appears to be produced only by mammals (Riddle, Bates, and others, 1938).

Returning to true constitutional preadaptation, we have the well-worn example of flightlessness in the insects of small oceanic islands. Although very numerous groups may be represented among them, a disproportionate number belong to groups which are not in general good fliers, or are characterized by reduced wings. Flightlessness is here thus the accentuation of a pre-existing tendency. We may here mention the interesting experimental results of L'Héritier, Neefs, and Teissier (1937) on *vestigial*, the wingless mutant of *Drosophila*. When a mixed population of winged (wild type) and functionally wingless (vestigial) individuals was reared in the open air in such a way that they were moderately exposed to the wind, the result after thirty-eight days was an increase in the percentage of homozygous vestigials from 12·5 to 67 per cent, through the wind carrying away more of the winged flies. When the culture was transferred to a large room, the wind could no longer act as a selective agent, and in fifteen further days the percentage of pure vestigials was halved.

A less familiar example is cited by Eigenmann (1909), who maintains that modern fresh-water fish must have been recruited from ancestors preadapted to fresh-water existence by possessing non-pelagic types of eggs. But the *locus classicus* of discussion concerning preadaptation is the blind cave fauna. The out-and-out Darwinians believe that their sightlessness is due to selection gradually ridding the stock of useless organs, while some out-and-out preadaptionists have gone so far as to maintain that mutational blindness came first, and that the sightless type then found a favourable environment ready-made in caves. The truth would appear to be between these two views. No proof has ever been given of full mutational preadaptation in this case, and it is in any event most unlikely. But it is a fact that the cave fauna is drawn preponderantly from types that normally shun light and therefore live in holes and corners. Such forms are constitutionally preadapted to enter caves, and will frequently be visually under-equipped. Their later evolution will consist in their further adaptation to a completely cavernicolous existence, accompanied by further reduction of eyes.

Thus Eigenmann (1909) points out that the fish fauna of the Kentucky caves must have been sifted out by this type of preadaptation from a normal riverine fish fauna when a certain stretch of river became subterranean. The types that were negatively heliotropic, nocturnal, or stereotropic remained subterranean, and then developed further adaptations to cave life; while other ecological types moved out into a connecting river which remained in the open. "The major adaptation to cave existence, the power of finding their food and mates without the use of light, they [the ancestors of the existing cave-fish] possessed before the formation of the caves, and it is responsible for their present habitat." The same general view, with certain modifications, is taken by more recent workers in this field. Hubbs (1938), for instance, after presenting an analysis of the characters and relationship of the thirty-five or so known cave-fish, concludes that this "confirms the theory that cave animals have arisen from species moderately preadapted to cave life". To take an example, the "weak-eyed, long-barbelled, nocturnal catfishes" have given rise to an undue percentage of cave-fish.

There is one notable exception to the general rule, namely the Mexican characid cave-fish, *Anoptichthys jordani*. Although this, as its name implies, is blind, it must have been derived from a form very similar to *Astyanax fasciatus*, which is a large-eyed open-water form, without any obvious preadaptation to caves. Hubbs suggests that the lack of competition, as evidenced by the absence of other cave-fish in this region, facilitated its colonization of caves, sightlessness evolving later.

Hubbs concludes by pointing out that preadaptation has constituted but the first step in the evolution of cave-fishes: later changes, such as further degeneration of skin pigmentation and eyes, and further specialization of sensory barbels and the like, must have been produced by progressive adaptation after the cave habit had been established.

It may be pointed out that, in general, the preponderance of degenerative (loss) mutation will result in degeneration of an organ when it becomes useless and selection is accordingly no longer acting on it to keep it up to the mark (p. 476; Muller, 1939). In other cases, as in the hind limbs of Cetacea, degeneration may be actively promoted by selection, as the organ's presence externally is disadvantageous (for vestiges, see Huxley, 1932).

Thus, while normal Darwinian adaptation adjusts a species to a constant or a changing environment *in situ*, constitutional preadaptation acts as a preliminary sifting device, restricting the inhabitants of specialized habitats in the main to forms with some definite predisposition to the peculiar mode of life involved. Mutational preadaptation is intermediate in the nature of its action, providing a preliminary sifting of lesser extent and shorter range.

Some writers, e.g. O. E. White (1926), consider that a constitutional preadaptation towards cold-resistance has led to certain natural orders of plants being able to survive in higher latitudes when the uniform warm conditions of the earlier cenozoic later give place to a sharply-zoned climate, while other groups, not similarly preadapted, became restricted to the tropics. Among the former, he cites the willows (Salicaceae) and horsetails (Equisetaceae), among the latter the palms (Palmaceae) and the Artocarpaceae.

A somewhat different constitutional preadaptation to temperature is found in Crustacea (Panikkar, 1940). The osmoregulatory mechanism of various marine Crustacea is such that they are able to tolerate waters of low salinity much more readily at high than at low temperatures. This fact is reflected in the natural distribution of fresh- and brackish-water Crustacea, and very possibly of other invertebrate groups.

Goldschmidt in various of his writings (see 1940, p. 390) has suggested that preadaptation may play a rather different role by means of large mutations giving what he styles "hopeful monsters", which then can serve as the starting-point for quite new evolutionary trends. As one example of where he thinks this must have occurred he cites the flatfishes, since he considers it impossible for their asymmetry to have arisen gradually. He then extends the principle to other less cogent cases. Mr. J. R. Norman, of the British Museum (Natural History), however, tells me that there exist a few less extreme forms of flatfish, which must be similar to earlier evolutionary stages, and that there seems to be no reason against assuming a gradual evolution of the group from the beginning. Many fish occasionally rest on the bottom, some on their bellies, others on their sides. If benthic existence for any reason were advantageous, selection would set in to improve the type in this respect—with the belly-resting forms by dorso-ventral flattening and lateral extension (as has happened in sharks and rays), with the sideways-resting forms by behavioural and structural asymmetry of the eyes and head.

However, Goldschmidt goes further than this. In his latest book (1940) he maintains that there is a fundamental distinction between micro- and macro-evolution. The former, depending on gene mutation and recombination, may lead to subspecific and other diversification within the species, but cannot produce new species, or, *a fortiori*, higher categories. These come into being through macro-evolutionary change, which, according to him, demands a radical change in the primary chromosomal pattern or reaction-system. Such a change in reaction-system he calls a *systemic mutation*, though he states that it may have to be accomplished in several steps. Only after the repatterning has reached a certain threshold value does the new species-type emerge. He considers (1940, p. 207) that in some cases at least the initial stages arise only in the absence of selection-pressure against the heterozygote and under certain conditions of inbreeding. But once a new stable pattern, viable as a homozygote, is produced, "selection acts only upon the new system as a whole". In other words, if it survives, it survives as a preadaptation in viability. In other cases he considers that the early steps, too, may be favoured by selection on account of viability effects on development, and that the change will be much quicker than any micro-evolutionary effect dependent on single genes; this process could be regarded as halfway between normal adaptation and preadaptation.

I do not propose to discuss these rather revolutionary views. What has been said elsewhere shows that I disagree with them in general. There is a great deal of evidence that gene-mutations *are* involved in specific differences, and that subspecies may evolve into full species. Many of Goldschmidt's analogies between "monstrous" forms found in nature and large mutational steps observed in the laboratory (e.g. partial or total wing-rudimentation) are valueless until we know that the natural forms have arisen at a single bound; they may well be merely phenotypically similar to the mutants, but be due to the accumulation of small gene-mutations. Such accumulations may evolve into "gene-patterns" characteristic of species (Silow, 1941); and the association of gene-mutations with sectional rearrangements may produce relatively large effects (p. 93): but these are not systemic changes. When he states that the evolution of the *Drepanididae* (see p. 325) "by a series of micromutations controlled by selection is simply unimaginable", one can only reply that his imagination differs from that of many other biologists. He rightly insists on the importance for evolution of mutations with consequential developmental effects (p. 525); but these are presumably gene-mutations (see also Waddington, 1941b).

However, even if we dismiss Goldschmidt's views as unproven or unnecessary, preadaptation of various kinds has clearly played a not inconsiderable role in evolution.

6. THE ORIGIN OF ADAPTATIONS: THE INADEQUACY OF LAMARCKISM

How has adaptation been brought about? Modern science must rule out special creation or divine guidance. It cannot well avoid frowning upon entelechies and purposive vital urges. Bergson's *élan vital* can serve as a symbolic description of the thrust of life during its evolution, but not as a scientific explanation. To read *L'Evolution Créatice* is to realize that Bergson was a writer of great vision but with little biological understanding, a good poet but a bad scientist. To say that an adaptive trend towards a particular specialization or towards all-round biological efficiency is explained by an *élan vital* is like saying that the movement of a railway train is "explained" by an *élan locomotif* of the engine. Molière poured ridicule on the similar pseudo-explanations in vogue in the official medical thought of his day.

Modern biology, taken by and large, also repudiates lamarckism. I need not refer to the lamarckian views of literary men such as Samuel Butler and Bernard Shaw. They are based not on scientific fact and method, but upon wish-fulfilment. Shaw, in his preface to *Back to Methuselah*, says in effect that he dislikes the idea of a blind mechanism such as Natural Selection underlying evolutionary change—*ergo*, such a blind mechanism cannot (I had almost written "must not!") be operative. *Pace* Mr. Shaw, this reasoning does not commend itself to scientists. One of the main achievements of science has been to reveal that the facts of nature frequently fail to accord either with the wishes or with the apparently logical preconceptions of human beings. *Per contra*, we may remind ourselves that, as was pointed out nearly half a century ago by Ray Lankester (summarized by Poulton, 1937), lamarckism is self-contradictory, since it maintains that "a past of indefinite duration is powerless to control the present, while the brief history of the present can readily control the future".

Nor need I go in detail through the wearisome discussion of the various scientific "proofs" of lamarckian inheritance that have been advanced. I would merely say that subsequent work has either disproved or failed to confirm the great majority of them. An unfortunate suspicion rests on Kammerer's work, and his results on salamanders have not been confirmed by Herbst (1924). Heslop Harrison's adaptive induction of melanic mutations in moths could not be re-obtained by McKenny Hughes (1932) or by Thomsen and Lemcke (1933). Repetition of Guyer's work on induced inheritance of immunity by other investigators has yielded entirely negative results (Huxley and Carr-Saunders,

1924). Pavlov himself withdrew his claim to have demonstrated the inheritance of experience in mice. Recently Crew (1936) has repeated the elaborate researches of McDougall on the hereditary transmission of the effects of training in rats: his results entirely contradict McDougall's lamarckian claims, and he is inclined to ascribe the discrepancy to an insufficiency of controls and an inadequate attention to genetic method on McDougall's part.

Other work, such as that of Heslop Harrison on the feeding habits of insects, is capable of alternative explanation, and is therefore not crucial. Indeed, the researches of Thorpe (see p. 303) have made the alternative explanation the more likely, by demonstrating the role of larval conditioning to food in determining the egg-laying reactions of the adults. The researches of Dürken (1923) on the colours of butterfly pupae are also capable of alternative explanations, here in terms of unconscious selection of predispositions, and/or of *Dauermodifikationen*.

There remain one or two results, such as that of Metalnikov (1924) on immunity in waxmoths, and of Sladden and Hewer (1938) on food-preferences in stick insects which seem *prima facie* to demand a lamarckian explanation (but see p. 303 n.). However, in view of the fate of other claims, and of the theoretical difficulties we shall discuss below, too much weight must not be attached to such isolated cases.

Nor need we pay attention to the view advanced by certain lamarckians, that the inherited effects of function or environmental modification are so slight that they cannot be detected experimentally but require cumulative action through thousands of generations to become obvious. Exceedingly minute differences can be detected by proper technique. The total failure of sixty-nine generations of disuse to affect the eyes or the phototropic responses of *Drosophila*, as shown by Payne (1911), is a good example of the failure of disuse to produce lamarckian effects.

To plead the impossibility of detection is a counsel of despair. It is also unscientific: the only scientific procedure would be to refine technical methods until the postulated effects were capable of detection. The experiment has nothing impossible about it with pure-bred stocks and in a rapidly-breeding species.

It is, however, necessary to realize that important indirect objections can be made to any lamarckian view. In the first place there is the fact of mendelian recessivity. A recessive character can be rendered latent indefinitely by keeping the gene concerned in the heterozygous condition; yet when the recessive gene is allowed to unite with another like itself, the resultant character is identical with that of pure-bred recessives in which it has been manifested, and therefore exposed to environmental stimuli, throughout.

An equally fundamental difficulty concerns all those almost innumerable cases in which the two sexes differ in adaptive characters of structure or behaviour. For we know with certainty that the genetic constitution, in the shape of the chromosomes, is distributed irrespective of sex. The chromosomes of a sire will be distributed among his descendants of the second and later generations according to the laws of chance, in a purely random way, and equally among his male and female descendants (a quantitative exception, but one irrelevant to our present purpose, is provided by the distribution of the sex-chromosomes). What lamarckian mechanism could ensure that the hereditary effects of functions confined to males are transmitted to male descendants only? The situation can just possibly be saved by subsidiary hypotheses, but only at the cost of much superfluous complexity, as the geocentric hypothesis was formally saved by the doctrine of epicycles.

Apart from this, we find numerous cases where lamarckian inheritance, even if it existed elsewhere, must be either impossible or exceedingly restricted. Let us first take the case of the higher mammals. These have their internal environment regulated to an extraordinary degree of constancy. The temperature of the blood and to a still higher degree its salt composition and its acidity, are kept constant by elaborate special mechanisms. The reproductive cells, like all other cells in the body, are exposed to the internal environment supplied by the blood-stream. How then can changes in the external environment be transmitted to them? The regulation of the internal environment provides an effective shock-absorber for all the more obvious alterations which could occur in the external environment. Yet higher mammals have evolved as rapidly and in as obviously adaptive ways as any lower types in which this buffering does not exist.

The social Hymenoptera provide another natural experiment of great interest. In them, as is well known, the bulk of the work of the colonies is carried on by neuter females, while reproduction is entrusted to the much less abundant full females and the males. How is it possible on any lamarckian view to discover a mechanism by which the special instincts and structures of the workers have been evolved? They cannot transmit them in reproduction, for they do not reproduce; and the males and females do not practise the instincts nor possess the structures. Attempts have been made to obviate the difficulty by pointing to the fact that occasionally neuter females will lay unfertilized eggs, so producing males. If, however, such occasional abnormalities of reproduction suffice to generate the elaborate special characters of neuter ants and bees, then lamarckian transmission operating through normal reproductive channels should have such strong effects as to be detectable by the crudest experiment; and this is certainly not the case.

Insects, indeed, provide a number of hard nuts for lamarckian cracking. All higher insects emerge from the pupa into an adult or imago stage, during which they never moult, and so are incapable either of total or local growth (save by mechanical stretching of membranous parts of the exoskeleton), or of alteration in the form of hard parts. Here again it seems all but impossible to imagine any mechanism by which any modification involving structural change in hard parts could be transmitted. Indeed, such modifications cannot very well be produced at all in the individual: thus the only lamarckian mechanism conceivable is one by which a tendency or an attempt to alter the structure of hard parts would have its first visible effects in the next or later generations! Yet adaptations of hard parts are striking in insects.

A very similar objection applies to mammalian teeth. These, as is well known, exhibit remarkable adaptations to the type of food on which they are normally used. Yet the only effect of use upon them is mechanical abrasion, tending to wear away the structure which has been built up in the plastic stage when the tooth is not used at all.

The origin of the general cryptic resemblance of animals to the prevailing colour of their habitats, whether desert, open sea, green foliage, tundra, or snow, has often been ascribed to a direct effect of the environment. If this rather vague statement means anything, it must imply that the characters in question are either pure modifications, or have been genetically induced by some form of lamarckism. Granted that there exist, notably in insects, some cases of modification, we can now safely assert that most of these characters are genetic. Some of these in their turn may be merely correlated with physiological adaptations; but there are some examples where we can show that selection in favour of cryptic resemblance must have been the agency at work.

In an earlier chapter we mentioned the case of dark subspecies of *Peromyscus* inhabiting local lava-flows. Precisely similar examples are known in birds, e.g. in the desert lark, *Ammomanes deserti*, of which the darkest and the palest subspecies live close together in North Arabia, the one on black lava-desert, the other on pale sand-deserts. This is cited by Meinertzhagen (1934), who makes the pertinent comment that such cases of protective resemblance to soil are largely confined to ground-loving birds. Thus in the black Ahaggar desert, the *Ammomanes* are very dark, while the local babbler (*Argya fulvus buchanani*) is even paler than on the sand of the Sahara—presumably in relation to climate. An even more striking case has recently been described for other mice of another genus, *Perognathus* (J. E. Hill. 1939). In a valley of southern New Mexico a black lava area of between 100 and 200 square miles exists quite close to an area of gleaming white gypsum. *P. intermedius* exists on the lava beds in an almost black form, while the representatives of *P. apache* on the gypsum area are nearly white. Both species have normal "mouse-coloured" forms on neighbouring rocky areas. Other mammals, reptiles, and insects from the two special areas show corresponding but less extreme colour modifications. Here again no climatic or other influences capable of bringing about the colour-differences can be detected, and we are driven to conclude that the colour is a protective adaptation originated by selection. If selection can be effective in such cases, there is no reason to postulate any lamarckian effect for any examples of general cryptic resemblance.

Hovanitz (1940) cites a similar and very striking case from the butterfly *Oeneis chryxus*, which in the Sierra Nevada exists in two sharply-contrasted dark and pale subspecies or forms, restricted to dark volcanic and pale granitic rocks respectively, the two pure forms connected by clines extending over 10 to 40 miles, where the rock-types are intermingled. Dark rock outcrops in the granitic area below a certain size are inhabited by light forms, being apparently too small to support a dark population that can maintain itself against swamping by crossing. Hovanitz is forced to the view that the two forms owe their origin or at least their maintenance to selection, but rejects the idea that this is exercised viâ predators in relation to concealing coloration. His objections may be profitably analysed. In the first place, since the upper surface resembles the environmental background much more closely than the lower, he states that visual selection by predators could only occur when the upper surface is exposed, namely, in flight. However, his own photographs show a certain degree of difference in the lower surface. Secondly, he states that when not in flight, they rest in "relative darkness" between rocks, among herbage, etc., "where colour is of no value". This last statement is a mere assertion, as no evidence is given as to possible predators in such situations. (In other habitats, Lepidoptera are frequently captured when at rest.) Finally, he states that almost the only possible predators are two species of birds which only occasionally take insects, and therefore cannot act selectively. In the first place, because his search for predators has not been successful, that is no reason for concluding that they do not exist. Cases must indeed be rare where a small butterfly has no enemies. But further, he appears to disregard the quantitative findings of students of the mathematics of selection, such as Haldane (1932*a*) and R. A. Fisher (1930*a*). A 1 per cent advantage—i.e. the average survival of

101 members of one form as against 100 of another—would be almost impossible to detect, yet it would promote an evolutionary change of considerable rapidity, markedly modifying the stock within a few hundred generations (p. 56).

Hovanitz also makes the general objection to the theory of protective coloration that "the animals getting along best in nature are those which are not 'protected'"—a fallacy so hoary that it hardly needs serious discussion (but see the general analysis, pp. 466 seq.; and on hypertely, p. 484). Most naturalists will prefer to regard such a case as this as *prima facie* one of concealing coloration until definite evidence to the contrary is produced.

Finally we may mention various special examples of protective resemblance and mimicry. The resemblance of certain moths to birds' droppings or of a stick insect to a stick cannot very well be put down to the inheritance of environmental modifications or the effects of use! In mimicry, the resemblance of model to mimic is often achieved by way of a trick—a similar effect is produced by quite a different mechanism. The "painting in" of a waist on various beetles or bug mimics of ants is a good example: numerous others may be found in Carpenter's little book on mimicry (Carpenter and Ford, 1933), or in the more general work of Cott (1940).

These are some of the most striking cases in which a lamarckian explanation cannot, it seems, apply. We have already seen (p. 38), that, merely from the standpoint of logic and theory, most adaptations or functional evolutionary changes could be interpreted equally readily on the basis of indirect control by selection as on that of direct control by environment and use. We are therefore driven to ask why, when numerous adaptations like those just cited are shown to be incapable of lamarckian explanation, we should postulate lamarckism to account for the others, which are no different *quâ* adaptations. To do so would be to sin against the economy of hypothesis and demand the application of William of Occam's razor.

Thus we are driven back on to direct experimental proof, and that, as we have already set forth, is meagre and confusing. It is for these reasons that the majority of biologists, including the very great majority of those who have experience of actual genetic work, repudiate lamarckism, or, at best, assign to it a subsidiary and unimportant role in evolution. Even if lamarckism be operative at all, it seems clear that some other mechanism must be invoked to account for the major part of evolution.

Most biologists also look askance at orthogenesis, in its strict sense, as implying an inevitable grinding out of results predetermined by some internal germinal clockwork. This is too much akin to vitalism and mysticism for their liking: it removes evolution out of the field of analysable phenomena; and it, too, goes contrary to Occam's razor in introducing a new and unexplained mechanism when known agencies would suffice. Furthermore, as R. A. Fisher has cogently pointed out, the implications of orthogenesis, like those of lamarckism, run directly counter to the observed fact that the great majority of mutations are deleterious. In any event, as we shall see in a later chapter (p. 506), the cases in which a true orthogenetic hypothesis is demanded in preference to a selectionist one are very few, and even in these few it may turn out that it is our ignorance which is responsible for the lack of alternative explanations. As set forth elsewhere (p. 516), numerous cases exist where evolutionary potentiality is restricted; but these are quite distinct from orthogenesis in the strict sense of a primary directive agency in evolution.

Selection itself often produces an apparent orthogenetic effect. This was realized by H. W. Bates over three-quarters of a century ago in his classical paper on mimicry (1862), where he wrote "the operation of selective agents gradually and steadily bringing about the deceptive resemblance of a species to some other definite object, produces the impression of their being some innate principle in species which causes an advance of organization in a special direction. It seems as though the proper variation always arose in the species, and the mimicry were a predestined goal". However, these and the similar examples drawn from paleontology (pp. 416, 515; 494) on analysis turn out to be much better explicable on selectionist principles. Just as the apparent purpose of adaptation is only a pseudo-teleology, so its apparent inner direction is only a pseudo-orthogenesis.

7. THE ORIGIN OF ADAPTATIONS: NATURAL SELECTION

There remains natural selection. Before discussing some concrete examples of selection at work to produce adaptation and of adaptations illustrating the work of natural selection, a few general points deserve to be made. In the first place there is the aged yet apparently perennial fallacy that such-and-such an arrangement cannot be adaptive, since related organisms can and do exist without it. This is, quite frankly, nonsense. It is on a par with saying that electric refrigerators are not useful, because many people, even among those who can afford the expense, manage to get on happily without them, or even that alphabets and wheeled vehicles are useless luxuries or accidents because the negro and other human stocks never invented them.

There are in fact numerous possible explanations of such a state of affairs. It may be that mutations in that direction did not crop up, or were not available before mutations in some other direction set the stock specializing along other lines; it may be that there are differences in the genetic make-up or the environment of the two forms, as yet undetected by us, which make such an adaptation less advantageous to one than to the other.

All that natural selection can ensure is survival. It does not ensure progress, or maximum advantage, or any other ideal state of affairs. Its results, in point of fact, are closely akin to those of commercial business. In business, what gets across— i.e. is sold—is what can be sold at a profit, not by any means necessarily what is best fitted to meet the real needs of individuals or of the community. The reason for the failure of a commodity to be sold may be lack of purchasing power in the community as much as poor quality, or lack of persuasive (and not necessarily truthful) advertising as much as inefficient production methods.

In the same way a species or a type may survive by deceiving its enemies with a fraudulent imitation of a nauseous form just as well as by some improvement in digestion or reproduction, by degenerate and destructive parasitism as much as by increased intelligence. There still exist those who, even while rejecting the view of Paley and his school that adaptation is a proof of divine design, continue to approach evolution in a rather reverential attitude and to attach some sort of moral flavour to natural selection. They should be reminded of adaptations such as those by which the ant-parasite *Lomechusa* obtains its food, or the orchid *Cryptostilis* ensures its reproduction. *Lomechusa* produces a substance which the ants so dote upon that they not only feed the adult beetle in return, but allow its grub to devour their own larvae—a sacrifice to a gin-producing moloch (Wheeler, 1910); *Cryptostilis* practises an ingenious variety of prostitution: by resembling the females of a fly both in form and in odour, it induces the males to attempt copulation with its flowers, thus securing its own pollination (Coleman, 1927).

We should finally remember that the incidence of selection is different for rare and for abundant species, and that an adaptation forcibly promoted by intraspecific selection in an abundant species might have little or no biological value when worked upon by interspecific selection in its rarer relatives.

It is another fallacy to imagine that because the major elimination of individuals occurs, say, in early life, that therefore selection cannot act with any intensity on a phase of minimum numbers, say the adult stage. It has, for instance, been argued that because the main elimination of butterflies takes place by parasitization or enemy attack during the larval stage, therefore elimination of the imagines by birds or other enemies can have no appreciable selective effect, and therefore any protective or warning or mimetic colouring which they exhibit cannot have any adaptive significance. But selection need not act with equal intensity at all stages of the life-cycle: even if it should be more intense in early life (and much early mortality appears to be accidental), it could still produce effects on adult characters (see A. J. Nicholson, 1927).

The same argument applies to adaptive colouring shown in the larval stage. Even if this has no effect in protecting the larvae from parasitization, it will have selective value if it protects from attack by other enemies. Granted that on the average 90 per cent of larvae will in any case succumb to parasites, selection can clearly act in other ways on the remaining 10 per cent, just because they are the survivors. In general, selection may promote highly specialized adaptations not only in any particular organ or function, but at any particular phase of the life-history. The elaborate pelagic specializations of many invertebrate larvae at once come to mind, or the adaptations of seeds. Salisbury (1929) cites an interesting case of juvenile adaptation: most plant species, even if light-demanding forms, show greater shade-tolerance in early life, which militates against suppression by shading in the crowded conditions soon after germination.

However, as Professor Salisbury points out in a letter, since the adult phase follows the juvenile in time, many adult characters may well be non-selective *quâ* adult characters, but merely consequential results of juvenile adaptations. Some cases of this sort are discussed later (p. 525).

It is, after all, the adults which reproduce, and a 1 per cent advantage of one adult type over another will have precisely the same selective effect whether the adults represent ten, one, or one-tenth of 1 per cent of the number of fertilized eggs originally produced. The same applies to those plants in which the main elimination occurs during the seedling stage. Selection, in fact, can and does operate equally effectively at any stage of the life-cycle, though it will operate in entirely different ways at one time and another. Further, elimination is far from being the only tool with which selection operates. Differential fertility of the survivors is also important, and in man and many plants is probably the more influential.

There is finally the experimental demonstration of selection. We have referred to this on p. 120; see also p. 414 for the summary of such work on adaptive coloration given by Cott (1940). Here we may cite a further piece of work.

Popham (1941) has made a careful investigation of the biological significance of the variation in colour (measured in terms of shade of grey) in various water-boatmen (Corixidae). The animals tend to resemble the backgrounds of the ponds where they are found. This is due partly to habitat-selection: animals confined in surroundings markedly different in background from their own shade become restless and leave to seek other waters. Secondly, it is due to developmental colour-adaptation, the nymphal and adult shade approximating to that of the surroundings in which they have lived in the previous instar (though during a given instar there is no power of colour-adjustment). And finally, it is due to selection, predators (rudd, *Scardinius erythrophthalmus*, were used) taking a heavier toll of "unprotected" animals, i.e. those which are least like their backgrounds.

In regard to selection, a number of interesting results were obtained. For one thing, two fairly similar colour-varieties for which there was marked differential predation when one of them closely resembled the background, were equally attacked when the background was markedly different from both. It is thus, as would be expected, the relative difference of the two forms from the background, not the absolute difference between them, which acts selectively. Again as expected, a decrease in the population-density of the prey increased the advantage of the protected form. This of course implies a self-regulatory mechanism as regards predator-prey balance, protection conferring maximum benefit when most necessary to the species. A decrease in the predators' population-density also increased the selective advantage of protective colour, presumably on the purely mathematical basis of a reduction in the number of encounters.

Quantitatively, the selection in certain circumstances was very intense. E.g. in one experiment, in which there were employed equal numbers of insects of the same shade as the background ("protected") and differing from it by one colour-standard ("unprotected"), the relevant results were as follows:

Insects eaten		Selective advantage
Unprotected per cent	Protected per cent	(Protected ÷ Unprotected)
75·5	24·5	3·08

In another set of experiments, three types of insects were used, differing from each other by one colour-standard, and used against backgrounds of various standards. The results show the variation in intensity of selection with change in the relative difference of coloration between insects and background.

Differences from background (in colour-standard units)	Per cent eaten of insects, of colour-standards:—			Selective advantage		
	x	(x + 1)	(x + 2)	$\dfrac{(x+1)}{x}$	$\dfrac{(x+2)}{x}$	$\dfrac{(x+2)}{(x+1)}$
4, 5, 6	34	33	33	All approximately equal		
3, 4, 5	28	36	36	1·29	1·29	1·00
2, 3, 4	27	32	41	1·19	1·32	1·28
1, 2, 3	11	36	53	3·27	4·82	1·47

A further set of experiments was carried out with species of water-boatmen of different sizes. It was found that the predator used, the rudd, is almost entirely restricted to those of a certain intermediate size. Large forms were difficult to capture (14 per cent taken as against 86 per cent of a medium-sized species) while small species were apparently not noticed at all. This illustrates the point made on p. 280, that a predator must be adapted to its prey in size as in other respects.

Selective advantage is here, in certain conditions, very large. But we must remember that an advantage which it would be extremely difficult to demonstrate experimentally, say of 1 per cent, would have an effect which, biologically speaking, would be rapid (see p. 56).

Various cases where a selective balance is involved show as forcibly as any laboratory experiment the strength of selection-pressure. We have referred to some of these in the section on polymorphism (p. 96). The best of all (see p. 93), is probably that of industrial melanism. Ford (1940b) has recently shown that in unfavourable conditions (feeding only on alternate days) the dominant melanic form of the moth *Boarmia repandata* has a selective advantage of nearly 2 to 1 (52 blacks : 31 normals surviving to the imago stage where equality was expected).

Even where optimum food-conditions were provided, the ratio was 101 : 91. Yet in spite of this enormous constitutional advantage of the melanics, the selective advantage conferred by cryptic colouring on the non-melanics has prevented their replacement by melanics in all non-industrial areas. Mr. Ford informs me that in another case (not yet fully analysed), the melanic form is more cold-resistant. Yet it has not managed to oust the cryptic form, even in the extreme north of Scotland, far to the north of the industrial regions where it has become the type.

An elaborate and large-scale demonstration of selection in action has been given by the work of Quayle (1938) on the gradual development, by various scale-insect pests of citrus fruits, of a high degree of genetic resistance to the hydrocyanic acid used to try to kill them. As long ago as 1914 Quayle's attention was drawn to the unsatisfactory results from tent fumigation of lemon trees against red scale (*Aonidiella aurantii*) in the Corona district of California. In most localities it was not then necessary to repeat fumigation for two, three, or even four years. At Corona, however, neither increased dosage nor repetition of fumigation every year or even every six months was effective.

Controlled experiments were later carried out in which the scales from different areas were grown on the same tree and exposed to different concentrations of gas in the same chamber. The results showed that whereas in insects from many localities the normal dosage was reasonably effective, and no scales survived a 50 per cent increase of dosage, in those from the resistant areas, about five times as many survived normal dosage and almost as many survived the increased dosage as survived the normal one in the case of non-resistant strains.

In 1915 evidence turned up of a resistant local strain of the black scale (*Saissetia oleae*), and since then the area of resistance has spread and the degree of resistance has been increased. In 1925 a resistant strain of the citricola scale, *Coccus pseudomagnoliarum*, was first observed. Prior to this date, fumigators had guaranteed their work with this pest and offered a second fumigation free if the first proved unsatisfactory. In the next few years, the area of resistance spread rapidly, and the highest dosages compatible with the health of the trees failed to give satisfactory results, with the result that fumigation could not be guaranteed, and was eventually abandoned in favour of spraying. Controlled experiments showed that a dose four times the "danger dose" for trees was needed to kill all the resistant insects. In another experiment all insects of a non-resistant strain were killed by sixty minutes' exposure to 0.05 per cent HCN. But after sixty minutes' exposure to a sixfold increase of gas (0.3 per cent), many insects of a resistant strain were alive and a few survived ninety minutes. In general the resistant strain, in concentrations which killed 60 to 100 per cent of non-resistant strains, proved from two to four times more resistant.

Scale insects are not the only forms to show this phenomenon. Hough (e.g. 1934) experimentally proved not only that strains of codling moth (*Cydia pomonella*) from different areas differ markedly in the capacity of their larvae to enter apples sprayed with lead arsenate, but that, when the strain is raised on freshly sprayed fruit in the laboratory, the percentage of larvae capable of this increases from generation to generation.

Resistance in red scale is genetic (see Dickson, 1941) and it remain unaltered after many generations in the laboratory. An interesting fact is that the resistant strain of red scale has shown itself more resistant to various other toxic substances, to which it has not been exposed in the orchards, e.g. to the fumigants methyl bromide and ethylene oxide, and to oil sprays. It is also probable that it shows greater ability to withstand desiccation. Thus its newly evolved resistance appears to be a general rather than a specific one: the same is true of the codling moth.

Quayle concludes that the resistant strains have developed locally, as a result of intense selection due to the fumigation methods in vogue. When, as appears usual, they have developed earlier in some localities than in others, this is presumably due to the availability of actual or potential variance of the right type, or of new mutations in the right direction. In all cases the area inhabited by resistant strains has rapidly increased. Quayle gives reasons for thinking that this is in the main due to the rapid spread of local resistant types, as soon as these are available through mutation or recombination, rather than to immigration of the resistant forms from the localities where they first appeared. Quayle further points out that the standard fumigation dosage in California, in non-resistant as well as resistant areas, is now much higher than originally. "The schedules have been revised several times and always upwards. It is interesting to note that in Australia, South Africa, and Palestine, countries much younger than California in fumigation practice, the dosage used against the same insect is much lower than in California."

This large-scale experiment with its laboratory controls is of great interest in showing that intense selection may be very effective in bringing about important changes, and in giving indications as to the rate at which the process can operate.

As regards the intensity of selection operating in nature, R. A. Fisher (1939) has been able to calculate the selection operating against (a) homozygosity as against heterozygosity of the various single dominants giving the numerous colour-patterns other than the normal or basic one, (b) combinations of two of these dominants, in the grasshopper *Paratettix texanus* (cf. p. 99).

The selection against homozygous single dominants varies from about a 7 per cent to a 14 per cent disadvantage, while the elimination of double dominants is estimated to be not less than 40 per cent in each generation. This Fisher considers points to "powerful and variable ecological causes of elimination", whereas the selection in favour of single-gene heterozygotes is probably to be accounted for solely in terms of viability differences.

In any case, if we repudiate creationism, divine or vitalistic guidance, and the extremer forms of orthogenesis, as originators of adaptation, we must (unless we confess total ignorance and abandon for the time any attempts at explanation) invoke natural selection—or at any rate must do so whenever an adaptive structure obviously involves a number of separate characters, and therefore demands a number of separate steps for its origin. A one-character, single-step adaptation might clearly be the result of mutation; once the mutation had taken place, it would be preserved by natural selection, but selection would have played no part in its origin. But when two or more step are necessary, it becomes inconceivable that they shall have origi ated simultaneously. The first mutation must have been spread through the population by selection before the second could be combined with it, the combination of the first two in turn selected before the third could be added, and so on with each successive step. The improbability of an origin in which selection has not played a part becomes larger with each new step.

Most adaptations clearly involve many separate steps or characters: one need only think of the detailed resemblance of a close mimic to its model, the flying qualities of a bird's wing, the streamlining of secondary aquatics like ichthyosaurs or whales. When we can study actual adaptive evolution with the aid of fossils, as with the hooves of horses or the molar teeth of elephants, we find that it is steadily directional over tens of millions of years, and must therefore have involved a very large number of steps. The improbability is therefore enormous that such progressive adaptations can have arisen without the operation of some agency which can gradually accumulate and combine a number of contributory changes: and natural selection is the only such agency that we know. In such cases it is especially evident that what is selected is not a particular gene, but a whole complex of genes in regard to their combined interacting effect (see Sewall Wright, 1939, who has an interesting discussion of the systems of mating, breeding, and selection best suited to obtaining results with various types of genes and gene-combinations affecting a given character).

R. A. Fisher has aptly said that natural selection is a mechanism for generating a high degree of improbability. This is in a sense a paradox, since in nature adaptations are the rule, and therefore probable. But the phrase expresses epigrammatically the important fact that natural selection achieves its results by giving probability to otherwise highly improbable combinations—and "in the teeth of a storm of adverse mutations" (R. A. Fisher, 1932).

This is an important principle, not only for the conclusion that adaptations as seen in nature demand natural selection to explain their origin, but also for its bearing on the "argument from improbability", used by many anti-Darwinians against Darwinism in general. Bergson has employed this with regard to the origin of the eye. Haldane (1932a) and others, however, have pointed out that a gradual improvement of the visual mechanism from pigment-spot to fully-developed eye is to be expected, and that the parallel development in vertebrates and cephalopods of eyes with lenses is, on the basis of the laws of optics, not in the least unlikely. Indeed, on more general grounds, the properties of natural selection entirely nullify the argument from improbability in this and other cases.

Thus T. H. Morgan and Hogben have asserted that natural selection is seen, in the light of modern genetics, to be essentially destructive: in the absence of natural selection, all the known forms of life would exist, and in addition a vast assemblage of other types which have been destroyed by selection. Though both have now adopted a much more selectionist standpoint, these past views must be refuted as anti-selectionists still often cite them.

T. H. Morgan (1932, p. 130) writes: "If all the new mutant types that have ever appeared had survived and left offspring like themselves, we should find all the kinds of animals and plants now present, and countless others." The catch here is in the *if*; and the answer, of course, is that every type immediately ancestral to a mutant has been brought into existence only with the aid of selection (see also Hogben, 1930, p. 181).

In point of fact the general thesis is entirely untrue. It is on a par with saying that we should expect the walls of a room to collapse on occasion owing to all the molecules of gas inside the room moving simultaneously in one direction. Both are of course only improbabilities—but they are improbabilities of such a fantastically high order as to be in fact entirely ruled out. Each single existing species is the product of a long series of selected mutations. To produce such adapted types by chance recombination in the absence of selection would require a total assemblage of organisms that would more than fill the universe, and overrun astronomical time.

It should further be remembered that the degree of adaptive specialization is correlated with intensity of selection-pressure.

Elsewhere (p. 426) we have noted how, in the balance between the opposed adaptive tendencies towards cryptic coloration and display coloration in birds, the degree of development of display (epigamic) adaptations is directly proportional to the reproductive advantage it confers upon an individual male. The greater abundance and development of cryptic and aposematic adaptations to be found in the tropics, where selection-pressure is highest, is also to be noted (see p. 448).

The converse of this positive correlation is the tendency of originally adaptive structures or functions to degenerate in the absence of further selection-pressure in their favour. We have spoken of this in relation to the eyes and pigmentation of cave animals (p. 453), but the fact is one of the commonplaces of evolutionary biology, e.g. in parasites. The vestigial wings of ratite birds provide an excellent example. These are in all cases degenerate as regards the adaptations needed for flight. Where, however, they are employed in epigamic display as in the ostriches (*Struthio*) or the rheas (*Rhea*), they remain of considerable size; but where this further function is absent, as in the emus (*Dromaeus*) and cassowaries (*Casuarius*), they are reduced to vestiges. This tendency towards degeneration of useless structures—i.e. those on which selection-pressure is no longer maintained—is, as we have seen (p. 455), automatic in most organisms, owing to the accumulation of small degenerative mutations that throw the delicate mechanism of adaptation out of gear. This may be further generalized in terms of gene-effects (Wright, 1929). Most genes have multiple effects. Organs under direct selection will be modified by a system of genes; but the genes of such a polygenic system will also have secondary effects on "indifferent" organs, and most of these secondary effects will tend to promote degeneration in size or function. Further, when two linked polygenic systems (p. 67) are lodged in the same chromosome or chromosomes, and selection is acting to alter the main character controlled by one system, while that controlled by the other is useless, the resultant recombination will "break up" the useless character; in virtue of the tendency of random change to be towards decreased efficiency, this also will promote degeneration.

None of this reasoning, however, should apply in the case of organisms which do not practise outcrossing. Here, the recombination of "loss" mutations is impossible, and thus degeneration should be exceedingly slow. Furthermore, since many loss mutations need recombinational buffering (p. 67) to survive, they will be automatically eliminated where recombination is impossible. The result should be the persistence of originally adaptive but now functionless structures. The natural place to look for such "relict adaptations" is the floral mechanisms of plant species which have wholly abandoned outcrossing.

At first sight there would appear to be numerous examples of this. For instance, in various Compositae, such as dandelions (*Taraxacum*) and hawkweeds (*Hieracium*) there exist a number of forms which, in spite of producing all their seed by obligatory apomixis, continue to form showy flower-heads, obviously adapted to attract insects. However, the persistence of these erstwhile adaptations may be due to the short time elapsed since the change to apomixis. On the other hand, in *Taraxacum* Dr. Turrill informs me that apomixis very probably dates back at least 10,000 years.

A more serious objection is the existence of numerous "correlated characters" of the capitulum which still have functional significance. Various parts of the mechanism provide the developmental scaffolding for the adaptive pappus; the ray florets still play a protective role during the night closure of the head, though this protection itself is perhaps a relict adaptation as it probably concerns the pollen. However, such considerations would not apply to obligate apomicts in grasses, where the relict floral mechanism was adapted to anemophilous cross-pollination, nor to the vegetatively reproducing coral-root, *Dentaria bulbifera*, which still makes the unnecessary gesture of producing obviously entomophilous flowers without any apparent subsidiary function.

Obligatory self-pollination should produce the same result. Here the difficulty is to find satisfactory examples, since in most cases some outcrossing still occurs. Thus the orchis *Epipactis leptochila* is normally self-pollinating, but cross-pollination can occur during a brief period. The closely allied *E. latifolia* is exclusively cross-pollinated (Godfery, M. J., 1933, Monograph of British

Orchidaceae, Cambridge). However, Dr. Mather informs me that, in Britain at least, the tomato (*Solanum lysopersicum*) shows no cross-pollination (save in one anomalous variety); yet its obviously entomophilous flowers persist. In some cereal strains, the frequency of cross-pollination is so low (only 2 per cent) that it should enormously reduce the speed of degeneration.

There is thus a prima facie case for the persistence of "relict adaptations" whenever cross-breeding is absent (and perhaps when markedly reduced), but more investigation is required for full confirmation (See Huxley, 1942, Nature *149*: 687).

8. ADAPTATION AND SELECTION NOT NECESSARILY BENEFICIAL TO THE SPECIES

So far, we have been discussing adaptation more or less *in vacuo*. We must now draw attention to the important fact that it will have different effects according to the type of selection operating.

This is best illustrated by the distinction between interspecific and intraspecific selection. In one sense, almost all selection is intraspecific, in that it operates by favouring certain types within the species at the expense of other types. The only exceptions would be when species spread or become extinct as wholes. The former occurs with such species as are produced abruptly, e.g. by allopolyploidy after hybridization. The latter occurs when no strains within a species are capable of adjusting themselves to a change of climate or to the arrival of new competitors or enemies. Selection in such cases no longer operates by any differential action between different strains, and the whole species spreads or disappears in competition with other species.

The term intraspecific selection can, however, properly be used in a more restricted sense, to denote selection concerned only with the relations of members of one species. On the same basis, interspecific selection is then selection which is ultimately concerned with the environment or with other species. Thus selection for speed in an ungulate will *operate* intraspecifically in the broad sense, but is *directed* interspecifically in being concerned with escape from predators. Similarly selection for cold-resistance in a period of decreasing temperature is directed environmentally, and may favour the entire species in competition with others. But selection for striking epigamic plumage in male birds is directed intraspecifically, in being concerned with the advantage of one male over another in reproduction. It would thus be more correct to speak of selection concerned with intra- or interspecific adaptation; however, it is more convenient to use the terms in the sense I have just outlined.

We have already discussed intraspecific selection briefly in relation to the numerical abundance of species (p. 34). In scarce species, competition will be more with other species and selection will be related more directly to the environment, while in abundant species there will be more competition between individuals of the species itself. Of course inter- and intraspecific selection will often overlap and be combined; but the intensity of one or the other component may vary very greatly.

An interesting type of selection which is in a certain sense intermediate between interspecific and intraspecific, may occur in forms which exist in numerous and relatively isolated local populations, particularly if the local populations are subject to large fluctuations in numbers. In such cases (Wright, 1940*b*) a local population may "arrive at adaptations that turn out to have general, instead of merely local, value, and which thus may tend to displace all other local strains by . . . excess migration". Wright calls this *intergroup selection*. When this operates, groups compete *quâ* groups, on the basis of elaborate gene-combinations restricted to the separate groups. It is probable that this type of evolution has played a considerable role in some kinds of species: cf. Sumner (1932, p. 84) for *Peromyscus*.

Intergroup selection, however, may operate between groups with a functional basis as well as between those with a regional basis (local populations). Intergroup selection of this sort we may perhaps call social selection, since it will encourage the gregarious instinct and social organization of all kinds. As Allee (1938) has recently stressed with the aid of a wealth of examples, the bases for social life in animals are deep and widespread. There exist numerous cases where it has been experimentally shown that aggregations of a certain size enjoy various physiological advantages over single individuals. Once that occurs, selection will encourage behaviour making for aggregation and the aggregation itself will become a target for selection.

In a later paper (1940) Allee develops this theme further. He shows that when degree of crowding is plotted against efficiency for a large number of functions, the resultant curves are of two sharply distinct types. In the first type (which I suggest might be distinguished as unit-selective, since selection falls on the unit individual), the performance has optimum efficiency of lowest population density (e.g. a single pair for maximum fertility per pair in various insects). But in the second (which perhaps could be called group-selective, not because there are more selective factors, but because the group of many individuals becomes a target for selection), there is a phase of "undercrowding", during which the efficiency of the function increases with population density, finally reaching a peak and then descending in a phase of overcrowding. A special case is the reproductive advantage conferred by size of colony in colonial-nesting birds (Darling, 1939; Vesey-Fitzgerald, 1941, p. 525; J. Fisher and Waterston, 1941; and cf. p. 103).

Processes of this type will of course give curves differing in shape, slope, and so forth, and will have correspondingly different results. Wherever such a curve occurs, it means that an aggregation near the peak value will constitute "a supraindividual unity on which natural selection can act. . . . Such low or feeble social units may be poorly integrated, but still possess demonstrable survival value"; and out of such primitive groupings, intergroup social selection can evolve such specialized group-units as the ant or termite colony.

Finally, since processes giving curves of the multiselective type have been discovered in every major group of animals, it becomes clear that social selection will be widespread, and that "sociality is seen to be a phenomenon whose potentialities are as inherent in living protoplasm as are the potentialities of destructive competition".

In general, the intraspecific type of selection is much commoner than is generally supposed. Thus to think of natural selection as first and foremost a direct struggle with enemies or with the elusive qualities of prey is a fallacy. An equally important feature of the struggle for existence is the competition of members of the same species for the means of subsistence and for reproduction. Surprise has been expressed by some biologists at the fact that in New Zealand, domestic pigs which have become feral have, in spite of the absence of predatory enemies, reverted to something like the wild type; but in competition for food and reproduction the leaner and more active wild type must clearly have a strong relative advantage over the fatter and more sluggish domestic forms, so that reverse mutations or reversionary recombinations will be favoured by selection.

Elsewhere (p. 426) we consider other examples of intraspecific selection. Sometimes the competition is restricted to individuals of one sex, as in intrasexual selection; sometimes to individuals of a single litter, as in the intrauterine selection of mammals (p. 525). Again it may be especially intense at a certain period of life, as is the competition for light and space between the seedlings of many higher plants. Another example from plants concerns the competition between the haploid male plants produced by the pollen-grains. Genetic research has shown that these may be affected in various ways, including the rapidity of their growth down the style, by the genes they bear. As a result of this, *certation*, or a "struggle for fertilization" between genetically different types of pollen-grain, may and often does occur, and genes which induce rapid growth of pollen-tubes will often be at a premium. Nothing of the sort, however, appears to take place in higher animals. The only known exception is the gene described by Gershenson (1928) in *Drosophila*, with lethal effects only on Y-bearing sperms. There is also the alleged differential activity of the two types of sperms in forms with male heterogamety; if this be a fact, it is probably due to some effect of differential size, the male-determining appearing to have in many cases a smaller head.

Even in most of the relations between a species with its enemies, competition is intraspecific. Normally, a certain number of individuals are bound to be killed: when so, the main pressure of selection is directed to keeping an individual out of the category of the relatively unprotected, where it will be an almost certain victim, into that of the well-protected where at least it has an even chance of survival. Any improvement in the protection of some individuals will lead to the bulk of the population being placed at a disadvantage, so that they will once more come under selection-pressure. Such considerations will apply to speed in escape, cryptic and mimetic resemblance, and many other adaptations against predators.

In a different sphere, most competition within civilized human societies is between individuals. The difference of course is that success in this competition is not biological, measured by increased survival to later generations, but social, consisting of monetary and other satisfactions; in fact social and biological success are usually inversely correlated.

Artificial selection is clearly intragroup in its methods. Thus racehorses are selected for reproduction almost entirely on the basis of their individual performances. In most domestic forms, however, once marked breed characteristics have been established, intergroup (interbreed) competition may operate, and reduce or wholly eliminate certain types.

The dependence of the results of selection on the type of competition prevailing is well seen in the case of the social hymenoptera, such as honey-bees, wasps, and ants, where reproductive specialization prevails, and therefore the extinction of individual neuters can have no effect on the constitution of later generations, provided that the community survives (see p. 480).*

Haldane (1932a) has demonstrated that only in such a society, which practises reproductive specialization, so that most of the individuals are neuters, can very pronounced altruistic instincts be evolved, of a type which "are valuable to society, but shorten the lives of their individual possessors". Thus unless we drastically alter the ordering of our own reproduction, there is no hope of making the human species much more innately altruistic than it is at present.

* As Weismann early pointed out (see discussion in Emerson, 1939), selection of this type will become more effective as the number of reproductives in a colony is reduced—hence the single-queen condition in most termites and social hymenoptera.

The existence of intraspecific selection, i.e. selection between genetically different types within a species, enables us to expose another widespread fallacy—namely, that natural selection and the adaptations that it promotes must be for the good of the species as a whole, for the good of the evolving type pursuing a long-range trend, for the good of the group undergoing adaptive radiation, or even that it must promote constant evolutionary progress. In actual fact we find that intraspecific selection frequently leads to results which are mainly or wholly useless to the species or type as a whole. Thus the protection afforded by a cryptic or a mimetic resemblance of moderate accuracy might speedily approach the limit so far as its value to the species is concerned, if there were any way in which selection could be restricted to effects on the species as a species. But as a matter of fact selection acts viâ individuals, and this intraspecific competition between individuals will often lead to the process of adaptation being continued until almost incredibly detailed resemblances are reached. The perfection of the resemblance of *Kallima* to a dead leaf is one of the marvels of nature; not the least marvellous aspect of it is that it is of no value to the species as a whole (see p. 427).

A. J. Nicholson (1933) has pointed out how advantages operating at one stage of the life-history may be compensated for by increased mortality in other stages, so that the species does not benefit as a whole. Thus in most Lepidoptera a cryptic pattern favouring survival of adults will result in more larvae, which in turn will permit a disproportionate increase in parasitoid infection, thus bringing down the number of adults again. Wherever this balance of elimination as between stages is approximately self-regulating, factors affecting it will be over-riding as regards interspecific selection, while selection for other characters must be intraspecific. (In very unfavourable conditions with much reduced adult numbers, the cryptic pattern might become valuable for the species as a whole.)

In such examples, the adaptation is at least not deleterious. In other cases, however, it may lead to deleterious results. This is perhaps especially true of selection which is not only intraspecific

—confined to competition between members of the same species —but also intrasexual—confined to competition between members of the same sex of the same species. When polygamy or promisiscuity prevails, the selective advantage conferred by characters promoting success in mating will be extremely high (p. 427): accordingly in such forms we meet with male epigamic characters of the most bizarre sort which, while advantaging their possessor in the struggle for reproduction, must be a real handicap in the struggle for individual existence. The train of the peacock, the tail of the argus pheasant, the plumes of certain birds of paradise, the horns and antlers of certain ungulates, are obvious examples. In such cases of course a balance will eventually be struck at which the favourable effects slightly outweigh the unfavourable; but here again extinction may be the fate of such precariously-balanced organisms if the conditions change too rapidly (see Huxley, 1938a and b).

We may, however, go further and suggest with Haldane (1932a) that intraspecific selection is on the whole a biological evil. The effects of competition between adults of the same species probably, in his words, "render the species as a whole less successful in coping with its environment. No doubt weaklings are weeded out, but so they would be in competition with the environment. And the special adaptations favoured by intraspecific competitions divert a certain amount of energy from other functions, just as armaments, subsidies and tariffs, the organs of international competition, absorb a proportion of the national wealth which many believe might be better employed".

Intraspecific competition among anemophilous plants has led, it seems, to a real overproduction of pollen; among male mammals to unwieldy size as in sea-elephants, or to overdeveloped weapons and threat-organs as in deer and various horned groups; among parasites to their often monstrous exaggerations of fertility and complications of reproductive cycle.

There can be little doubt that the apparent orthogenesis which pushes groups ever further along their line of evolution until, as with size in some mesozoic reptiles and armour in others, they are balanced precariously upon the edge of extinction (p. 506), is due, especially in its later stages, to the hypertely induced by intraspecific competition.

This conclusion is of far-reaching importance. It disposes of the notion, so assiduously rationalized by the militarists in one way and by the *laisser-faire* economists in another, that all man need to do to achieve further progressive evolution is to adopt the most thoroughgoing competition: the more ruthless the competition, the more efficacious the selection, and accordingly the better the results. . . . But we now realize that the results of selection are by no means necessarily "good", from the point of view either of the species or of the progressive evolution of life. They may be neutral, they may be a dangerous balance of useful and harmful, or they may be definitely deleterious.

Natural selection, in fact, though like the mills of God in grinding slowly and grinding small, has few other attributes that a civilized religion would call Divine. It is efficient in its way—at the price of extreme slowness and extreme cruelty. But it is blind and mechanical; and accordingly its products are just as likely to be aesthetically, morally, or intellectually repulsive to us as they are to be attractive. We need only think of the ugliness of *Sacculina* or a bladder-worm, the stupidity of a rhinoceros or a stegosaur, the horror of a female mantis devouring its mate or a brood of ichneumon-flies slowly eating out a caterpillar.

Both specialized and progressive improvements are mere by-products of its action, and are the exceptions rather than the rule. For the statesman or the eugenist to copy its methods is both foolish and wicked. As well might the electrical engineer copy the methods of the lightning or the heating-engineer those of the volcano. It indubitably behoves us to study the methods of natural selection, but this will be to discover how to modify and control them in new ways and, very definitely, to see what to avoid. Not only is natural selection not the instrument of a God's sublime purpose; it is not even the best mechanism for achieving evolutionary progress. An important step towards a rational applied biology will be the full analysis of the various modes of operation of selection with a view to its eventual control and its intensification for our own purposes.

EVOLUTIONARY TRENDS

I. TRENDS IN ADAPTIVE RADIATION

We have now to consider long-range evolutionary trends. The primary evidence on these comes from continuous fossil series, but incomplete or even fragmentary series may often be satisfactorily completed by the use of indirect evidence from comparative anatomy and embryology, and the indirect evidence may supplement the direct by showing us, to a considerable degree of probability, with what physiology and what behaviour to cloak the fossil bones.

Later in this chapter, we shall discuss those trends for which no adaptive meaning has as yet been discovered. But it seems clear that the considerable majority are definitely adaptive. So obvious is this conclusion that it has found expression in the current phrase *adaptive radiation* (first employed as a generalization by H. F. Osborn; see e.g. Osborn, 1910). This is employed to cover the well-known fact that large systematic groups usually contain representatives adapted to a number of mutually exclusive ways of life. The converse principle is that of the parallel physiological or structural adaptation shown by the most diverse kinds of animals confined to a single type of habitat (pp. 430 ff.; and examples in Hesse, Allee, and Schmidt, 1937). Adaptive radiation is most obvious in the case of classes and sub-classes, but may be traced both in higher and lower systematic units: however, in phyla and other units of high rank, the phenomenon is manifested only on very broad lines, while in small groups such as families the type is in general so much restricted that the radiation is neither so many-sided nor so obvious.

Thus classes and sub-classes provide the optimum size of group in which the phenomenon may be studied: and in such cases, whenever paleontological evidence is available (as it is notably in the placental mammals, but also in the reptiles and other groups) the adaptive radiation is seen to be the result of a number of gradual evolutionary trends, each tending to greater specialization—in other words to greater adaptive efficiency in various mechanisms subservient to some particular mode of life. As we have already pointed out, adaptive radiation is ecological divergence in the grand manner. It is the large-scale group manifestation of the process whose details in minor systematics we have discussed under the head of ecological speciation; and each single adaptive trend also shows the phenomenon of successional speciation.

In typical cases of adaptive radiation, a number of lines take their origin in a generalized early group. There has been some dispute among paleontologists as to the degree of generalization to be expected in an ancestral form (see Gregory, 1936). For instance, Henry Fairfield Osborn and his school wished to extend considerably the principle of parallelism in (mammalian) evolution, by assuming that in each group numerous separate lines of descent run parallel far back into geological time, before divergence from a common ancestor can be postulated (even for the orders of modern placental mammals, common ancestry is, by authors of this way of thinking, frequently assumed to date back to the Upper Cretaceous); in correlation with this view, the Osborn school further assumes that "even any remote ancestors of any type must, in order to be admitted as such, already exhibit unmistakable signs of the characters which are very evident in their descendants". Thus Miller and Gidley deny to the Eocene rodent *Paramys* any ancestral significance for modern rodents such as squirrels and beavers, because it exhibits no trace of the specialization which these modern forms possess. On the other hand, most paleontologists do not shrink from the idea of radical transformation and apparent new origin of characters within a line. Thus W. D. Matthew regards *Paramys* as ancestral at least to the squirrels and beavers. There would appear on general grounds no reason to accept the views of the Osborn school. At some time the specialized must certainly have arisen from the generalized. However, just because the ancestral type *is* so generalized, it is often, in view of the imperfections of the fossil record, very difficult to push the history of a given line back beyond the point at which the first obvious signs of its characteristic specialization appear. The stock at this stage of its evolution is often a variable one, and may show numerous combinations of characters not found in any of the later types derived from it. Specialization often consists partly in the restriction of the character-combinations found; and for the rest, chiefly in quantitative alterations in the relative development of this or that character. The process of specialization in all lines continues steadily, but with different intensity in different lines, for a considerable time, which in the higher mammals at least seems to last for between ten and forty million years; eventually change ceases, and the specialized type either rapidly becomes extinct or else continues unchanged for further geological periods.

A further feature of such trends as have abundant fossil documentation, such as that of the horses, is the amount of parallel evolution that occurs. Closely related stocks appear to develop along similar lines, although frequently one line will show acceleration in one adaptive trend, such as the specialization of the grinding mechanism of the teeth, with relatively slow development in another, such as the specialization of the hoofed foot (see Matthew, 1926, and Stirton, 1940, for horses; Osborn, 1929 and 1936, for titanotheres and for elephants; Swinnerton, 1921, for various invertebrates; and pp. 514 seq.).

Another feature of trends that are well-documented by fossils is the great amount of variability that often occurs at any one time, with consequent marked overlap at different levels. Thus

Trueman (1922) investigated the evolution of a curved *Gryphaea* type of shell from a flat *Ostrea* type. The curvature in the flattest shells from the lowest level investigated was only 10°, while in the most curved shells from the highest level it was 540°.* But the range of variation at five successive levels was as follows:

degrees

No. 1   10–130
No. 2   100–340
No. 3   180–400
No. 4   220–500
No. 5   270–540

In general, no sharp line can be drawn between long-range trends extending over scores of millions of years and short-range trends of under a million years (see Swinnerton, 1932).

Swinnerton (1940) has investigated the same evolutionary trend in more detail in another *Ostrea-Gryphaea* lineage. He finds the same great range of variability at any one time. He has further been able to prove, by interesting graphic methods, that in certain characters the later communities differ from the earlier merely in a restriction of the original variability, whereas in other characters they have moved partly or wholly beyond the limits found in the original community.

We will for the moment leave out of consideration those advances (though they too are adaptive) which concern higher all-round organic efficiency rather than greater efficiency in relation to a particular environment or mode of life, and which are better classified under the head of biological progress than under that of specialization: these will be discussed in Chap. 10.

The process of adaptive radiation may be illustrated by the group of placental mammals. From the small and generalized terrestrial forms of the end of the Cretaceous and the very beginning of the Cenozoic, lines radiated out to take possession of different environments.. Two quite separate lines became fully aquatic, one of flesh-eaters culminating in the whales and por-

* Measurements expressed in degrees of total coiling instead of in terms of the spiral angle, as given by Trueman.

poises, the other of herbivores leading to the sea-cows and manatees. Still another line, that of the seals and the sea-lions, branched off from the carnivore stock and became aquatic except for reproduction. The bats meanwhile specialized on aerial life, and the primates on life in trees. The main ground-living forms belong to five chief branches—the carnivores, the rodents, the elephants, the odd-toed and the even-toed ungulates. The rodents specialized for gnawing, the carnivores for the capture of large living prey; both ungulate groups, though quite separate in evolutionary origin, became highly adapted to a herbivorous diet of grass or leaves and, in the most advanced types, to rapid locomotion; the elephants concentrated on a different type of vegetarian specialization, with the aid of tusks, trunk, and large bulk.

Among other groups, the South American edentates or Xenarthra are instructive. They represent the surviving remnants of a primitive early mammalian stock, and are not characterized, as are the successful groups, by one predominant specialization. On the contrary, their affinities are revealed only by comparative anatomy, and they show remarkable divergent specializations—the armadillos to protection by heavy armour, the anteaters to an ant and termite diet, the sloths to an upside-down arboreal existence, and the recently extinct ground-sloths to a sluggish herbivorous life coupled with great bulk. It appears that they have only been able to survive through embarking on a secondary adaptive radiation of their own, superposing high ecological specialization on a primitive organizational ground-plan.*

Something of the same sort has occurred with the insectivores—we need only think of mole and hedgehog—though the members of this group have in large measure survived by remaining generalized and of small size and by occupying humble niches in the economy of life.

Other groups, however, have disappeared entirely, notably the higher creodonts among the carnivores, and among vegeta-

* A similar secondary radiation, but here correlated with more complete competition, is seen in marsupials in the Australian region: see pp. 324, 491.

rians, the amblypods, the titanotheres, the typotheres and their relatives, the chalicotheres and the baluchitheres. All these were specialized, and many of them of large bulk. In every case it appears that they were extinguished because with their primitive general organization, notably as regards the size and efficiency of their brain, they were unable to compete successfully with the later-evolving carnivorous and herbivorous lines.

Each successful line of course radiates further into sub-lines. Among bats, for instance, there are fruit-eaters, insect-eaters, fish-eaters, and blood-suckers. Among cetaceans there are the giant whalebone food-strainers, the big toothed whales specialized to feed on deep-sea cuttlefish, the carnivorous killer-whales attacking other marine mammals, and the porpoises and dolphins specialized for fish-eating. Even among seals there is marked adaptive-radiation, some eating fish, others cephalopods, others crabs, and still others penguins. Still finer adaptive specialization takes place within the sub-lines. Emerson (1938) gives a valuable summary of the adaptive radiation of termites, which is largely concerned with the type of nest-construction. We have given examples from birds in Chapter 6 (p. 325).

It is instructive to compare the adaptive radiation achieved by different groups. The marsupials, for instance, that were isolated in the Australian region underwent adaptive radiation quite separately from other mammals elsewhere, whether marsupials or placentals. The fact that they alone among marsupials were able to specialize to this extent is doubtless a large-scale example of the phenomenon noted in Chapter 6 (p. 324), of the greater degree of differentiation made possible by reduced competition from other types. However, the number of specializations achieved, and their efficiency, was not so high as in the placentals. This in all probability is to be ascribed to the lesser scope for variation and the lesser degree of selective pressure; this is due to the smaller size and less varied nature of the area, which in their turn restrict the total numbers of organisms in a species, and therefore the potential of variation, and also limit the numbers of different ecological niches. Some of the specialized trends are extremely similar to those found in placentals. For instance, the marsupial mole and wolf show a remarkable parallelism with their placental counterparts. In many cases, however, the same general type of specialization is achieved, but in a different way. The kangaroos are the outstanding example of this. They are well adapted to life on grassy plains; but nothing similar to them in detail has been evolved among placentals as dominant plains herbivore, and among marsupials nothing has been evolved similar to the placentals' main specializations for plains life—the horses on the one hand and the antelopes on the other.

Some lines are altogether lacking in the marsupial radiation: e.g. neither aquatic nor fully aerial forms were evolved. Others, such as carnivorous types, are relatively poorly developed; but still others, such as small arboreal types, are more extensively developed than in placentals. In general, however, adaptive radiation saw to it that the main ecological niches are occupied by the Australian marsupials, even though the methods of occupying them frequently differs from those adopted by the placentals in their radiation. There is little evidence that intrinsic variability or other inherent properties of the stock have much to do with the differences between the two sub-classes.

The evolution of the Australian marsupials demonstrates adaptive radiation on the part of a medium-sized taxonomic group restricted to a medium-sized area. Adaptive radiation may be seen in much smaller areas as well as in much smaller groups. Thus modern work (Yonge, 1938a, 1938b) indicates that the remarkable prosobranch molluscan fauna of Lake Tanganyika, which is unique in fresh waters both in abundance of species and in special types, is not (as was originally suggested) derived from a part of a Jurassic marine fauna cut off in the lake, but has evolved in situ from forms already adapted to fresh water. All fresh-water gastropods are herbivorous: this is proved for all the Tanganyika forms by their possession of a crystalline style. They have radiated into a variety of forms, adapted for living at different depths and in waters containing different amounts of sediment, and for securing their food in radically different ways. However, it is interesting to note that the radiation is limited in one important particular—no carnivorous types have been evolved.

Similar local radiation permitted by long isolation has been shown to occur in the gammarids and other forms of Lake Baikal, the cichlid fish of Tanganyika and other African lakes (p. 324), and certain birds of oceanic islands (p. 325). As we should expect, all degrees in amount of radiation appear to exist.

The adaptive radiation (or rather radiations, since several were superposed) of the reptiles during the Mesozoic Period is perhaps more comparable with that of placental mammals than is that of the Australian marsupials, since they affected a major group in the main land area of the globe. In this case all possible main lines were evolved, including the full aerial and a disproportionately large number of aquatic types. The excess of lines tending towards very great bulk is also prominent. This fact looms over-large in most discussions of the subject, and it is often forgotten, even by professional biologists, that small types adapted to erect as well as to quadrupedal running, to arboreal life, etc., were also evolved. Here again there is no evidence of any restriction of variability: the peculiarities of the reptilian radiation, while in part due to the inherent properties of the reptilian stock (scaly covering, small brain, etc.), appear to depend in the main on peculiarities of the physical and biological environment of the period.

The essence of adaptive radiation thus consists first in the invasion of different regions of the environment by different lines within a group, and secondly in their exploitation of different modes of life. In both cases progressive adaptation is at work. In the first case this may lead to wholly new parts of the environment being colonized: for instance the sea and the air formed no part of the environment of the original mammalian stock. In the second case it may lead to wholly new organic arrangements: for instance binocular and macular vision in higher primates, the baleen filter of whalebone whales, or the ruminant stomach in higher even-toed ungulates.

2. THE SELECTIVE DETERMINATION OF ADAPTIVE TRENDS

The trends seen in adaptive radiation would appear to present no difficulties to the selectionist, and it is hard to understand why they have been adduced as proof of non-adaptive and internally-determined orthogenesis. Whenever they are truly functional and lead to improvement in the mechanical or neural basis for some particular mode of life, they will confer advantage on their possessors and will come under the influence of selection; and a moment's reflection will show that such selection will continue to push the stock further and further along the line of development until a limit has been reached.

This limit is usually determined by quite simple biomechanical principles. A horse cannot reduce its digits below one per foot, nor can it, with a given body-size, increase the complexity of the grinding surface of its molars beyond a certain point without making the grinding ridges too small for the food to be ground. The selective advantages of mere size, which must often be great in early stages of a trend, will be later offset by reduction of speed, or difficulties of securing sufficiency of food, or, in the final limit in land animals, by the relative increase of skeleton necessitated.* There is a limit to the acuity of vision, to the streamlining of aquatic form, to the length of a browser's neck, which can be useful or indeed possible to hawk or vulture, to whale or porpoise, to gerenuk or giraffe.

When those biomechanical limits have been reached, the trend ceases, and the stock, if it is not extinguished through the increasing competition of other stocks which have not yet reached the limits of their trends, is merely held by selection to the point it has reached. Ants, in some ways the most successful of inverte-

---

* If the same proportions are retained while absolute size is increased, cross-sectional area of bone increases as the square of linear dimensions, but weight to be supported as their cube. After a certain limit the bone is unable to support the weight. For instance, human thigh-bones will break if called on to support about ten times the weight they now support. Thus a tenfold increase of man's linear dimensions would bring him to the point where he could no longer support his own weight, since cross-section of a thigh-bone would increase a hundredfold, while weight would increase a thousandfold, and so each square inch of femoral cross-section would be called upon to support ten times as much weight. (See D'Arcy Thompson, 1917, Chap. 2; Haldane, 1927b, p. 18.)

brate groups, reached the limits of specialization at latest by the Oligocene, and have shown negligible evolutionary changes in the succeeding 30,000,000 years (Wheeler, 1910). The titanotheres reached theirs long before most placental trends had been achieved, and accordingly were later extinguished by the competition of more efficient rivals. In general, the most successful mammalian groups reached their limits in the Pliocene.

One important fact must be stressed, since it is often overlooked by those who would uphold an orthogenetic as against a selectionist interpretation of such trends. It is that the environment to which a given line becomes adapted is organic as well as inorganic: it includes all other forms of life with which the type comes into ecological relation, as well as purely physical and climatic features. Sometimes the inorganic environment changes markedly, as when there is a climatic revolution, such as occurred at the end of the Cretaceous; but in general it is the organic environment which shows the more rapid and important alterations.

Thus the evolution of the ungulates is not adapted merely to greater efficiency in securing and digesting grass and leaves. It did not take place in a biological vacuum, but in a world inhabited, *inter alia*, by carnivores. Accordingly, a large part of ungulate adaptation is relative to the fact of carnivorous enemies. This applies to their speed, and, in the case of the ruminants, to the elaborate arrangements for chewing the cud, permitting the food to be bolted in haste and chewed at leisure in safety. The relation between predator and prey in evolution is somewhat like that between methods of attack and defence in the evolution of war. In recent naval history, for instance, an advance in the efficiency of big guns has immediately put an additional premium upon advance in armour-plating, and vice versa. Sometimes advance is so great that an entire method of attack or defence is rendered obsolete. The improvement of artillery led to the abandonment first of fortified castles and later of city fortifications as methods of defence: machine-guns and barbed wire forced the abandonment of the cavalry charge as a method of attack. Such radical changes have their biological parallels in the entire or almost entire extinction of a group.

The dependence of adaptive trends on the organic environment is shown in a diagrammatic manner in the relation between carnivores and herbivores; but more subtle dependence will exist wherever two types are brought into ecological competition or interrelation.

In addition, the organic environment of an individual includes the rest of the species. This is a truism so obvious as often to be forgotten; but since so much of selection depends on intraspecific competition, it is of great importance. When all ancestral horses could run only moderately fast, an additional premium would be placed on a little extra turn of speed; when the ancestral seal had first taken to the water, a better streamlining and a more efficient flipper would give their possessors a definite advantage over their fellows. When the biomechanical limit of specialization has been reached, such advances will no longer be possible, and selection can only act either by keeping the species up to the limit or by encouraging adaptive changes in other characters, such as intelligence or reproductive efficiency. (See pp. 478 seq.).

Thus partly in relation to other species, partly in competition with others of their own species, a constant selection-pressure will be exerted, causing adaptive trends, once begun, to be specialized towards a limit.

That adaptive radiation is essentially a product of selection, not the outcome of any intrinsic tendency, and is relative to environmental conditions, is further shown by the fact that when stocks are removed from competition or find themselves in special environments, they may show renewed adaptive radiation, although this has virtually ceased, at least does not take place, elsewhere. This is well exemplified by the gammarids in Lake Baikal (Korotneff, 1905-12), by the fish in certain African lakes (p. 324), and on a larger scale by such examples as the Australian radiation of the marsupials just mentioned. Similarly the enormous plasticity of e.g. pigeons under artificial selection is proof that their previous stability was the effect of selection-pressure, not of any reduction in intrinsic variability.

The same is demonstrated by the development of flightless or giant birds on oceanic islands, where selection will act in a new way. (See also p. 129.)

Theoretically, it may be possible to distinguish the problem of the *origin* of adaptive trends from that of their *maintenance*, once originated, at least in certain cases. For instance, the full evolution of all the adaptations associated with the habit of flatfish of lying on one side on the bottom, presents no particular difficulties in the way of a selectionist interpretation, while the first evolutionary step towards asymmetry is much harder to envisage. Even here, however, we find half-way stages. The primitive genus *Psettodes*, for instance, has the originally lower eye near the dorsal edge of the body, not on the secondarily upper surface as in all other pleuronectids. When we further consider that various fish have the habit of occasionally lying on one side on the bottom, the problem does not appear quite so serious as at first sight. Thus the suggestion put forward by Goldschmidt that this trend and others such as the asymmetry of gastropod molluscs were initiated by abrupt mutations, though afterwards maintained and perfected by selection, becomes improbable and redundant (pp. 456, 552).

3. THE APPARENT ORTHOGENESIS OF ADAPTIVE TRENDS

The only feature inviting orthogenetic explanation is the directive character of evolutionary trends, their apparent persistence towards a predetermined goal.* But on reflection this too is seen to be not only explicable but expected on a selectionist viewpoint. Over three-quarters of a century ago, Bates (1862) pointed out this fact. He wrote, with reference to mimicry, "The operation of selecting agents, gradually and steadily bringing about the deceptive resemblance of a species to some other definite object, produces the impression of there being some

---

* Berg in his book *Nomogenesis* (1926) gives numerous interesting examples of trends which he puts down to orthogenesis. Many of these, however, are covered by the consideration advanced in this section, while others would appear to fall under the head of consequential evolution (§ 6). The wealth of examples which he cites is worthy of detailed study from the selectionist viewpoint.

innate principle in species which causes an advance of organization in a special direction." And he later makes it clear that he would apply the same reasoning to all other adaptive trends (see also Poulton, 1931, who quotes Bates).

One difficulty that is often overlooked by believers in orthogenesis is the curious difference between related groups in regard to the number of separate divergent trends to which they give rise. Thus the horses are often considered as constituting but a single trend, though as we have seen there are numerous minor divergencies, and the extent of these has been stressed by Stirton's recent detailed studies (1940) as against Matthew's classical work (1926).

The evolution of this group can no longer be represented by "a pine-tree with one main stem and insignificant side branches" (H. E. Wood, 1941). But Wood goes on to point out, that even so, its development is extremely simple when compared with that of the closely-related group of the rhinoceroses. These show a considerable number of highly divergent trends, including that leading to the gigantic baluchitheres, and another to the semi-aquatic amynodonts. Sometimes one and the same sub-group shows a single-track trend in one geographical area, but complex polyphyletic divergence in another. There is a considerable amount of parallel evolution as well as divergence.

This is an extreme in the opposite direction from the horses. Most groups of comparable taxonomic rank show an intermediate degree of divergence.

It is impossible on orthogenetic principles to explain why one group should contain *in posse* the tendency to show marked divergent radiation and another comparable group should not, why one should form twice or four times as many orthogenetic trends as another. (See also *Crepis*, pp. 372 seq.).

To revert to the determination of single trends, it is clear that, once a trend has begun, much greater changes will be necessary to switch the stock over to some other mode of life than to improve the arrangements for the existing mode of life. T. H. Morgan (1925, p. 148) has put this point very clearly. "It has been pointed out that the power to reproduce itself puts the problem of the construction of a living organism on a different footing from the construction of a complex machine out of inorganic (non-living) material. This question is so important for the theory of evolution that its significance must be further indicated.

"Whenever a variation in a new direction becomes established, the chance of further advance in the same direction is increased. An increase in the number of individuals possessing a particular character has an influence on the future course of evolution—not because the new type is more likely to mutate again in the same direction, but because a mutation in the same direction has a better chance of producing a further advance since all individuals are now on a higher level than before." (Morgan might have added that for the same reason mutations in other directions will have a worse chance than before.) "When, for example, elephants had trunks less than a foot long, the chance of getting trunks more than one foot long would be in proportion to the length of the trunks already present and to the number of individuals in which such a character might appear. In other words, evolution once begun in a given direction is in a favourable position to go on in the same direction rather than in another, so long as the advance does not overstep the limit where further change is advantageous."

In the same way, too sudden an advance, even if mutations for it were all available at one time, would often be non-advantageous or even disadvantageous. We can see this from analogies with human constructions. In the evolution of the motor-car, the substitution of four for one or two cylinders was a great improvement: it had "survival-value". However, not until the majority of cars came to be four-cylindered was the additional advantage of still more cylinders of sufficient appeal to give the six- or eight-cylindered engine any considerable advantage in the market. Again, we can readily see that the sudden "development" of full modern armour-plate on the earliest ironclads would have been actually disadvantageous, since it would have reduced their speed relatively to less heavily protected ships, without conferring any corresponding benefit in the way of defence against the comparatively inefficient projectiles of the day. Only when the range and piercing power of the projectiles increased did increase of armour become advantageous.

Similarly a sudden large increase in size and power of a carnivore without corresponding advance in its prey might be disastrous to the species, since it might kill out or markedly reduce its own food-supply. Again, a marked improvement in one character might be non-advantageous in the absence of corresponding improvements in correlated characters.

This point, however, is only of theoretical interest for organic evolution, for the simple reason that the supply of mutations is so slow, and the mutations which can be used appear to be of such small extent, that really sudden and unadjusted advance is impossible. Most adaptive specialization therefore cannot help being gradual.

We may sum up the position as follows. Since selection can only build with the materials provided by mutation; since mutation is a slow process, and since the material it provides, to be useful for selection, must be in the nature of small bricks, it follows that the chances are overwhelmingly in favour of the small changes needed to confer advantage in preserving the existing trend, turning up (and therefore being acted upon) before the larger changes needed to confer advantage in another mode of life have had any likelihood of occurring. A specialized line thus finds itself at the bottom of a groove cut for it by selection; and the further a trend towards specialization has proceeded, the deeper will be the biological groove in which it has thus entrenched itself. Thus specialization, in so far as it is a product of natural selection, automatically protects itself against the likelihood of any change save further change in the same direction.

Plate (1913, p. 511), who reaches very similar conclusions, proposes the term *orthoselection* for selection promoting the continuance of an adaptive trend. It is surprising that this useful term has not come into more general use. That this apparent orthogenesis is determined functionally and not by some inner clockwork of the germ-plasm which predetermines a progressive change in structure, is excellently shown by the evolution of the elephants (see summary in Lull, 1917, p. 588). These began their career by an elongation of the muzzle, involving the enlargement of both jaws and both upper and lower incisor tusks. Before the beginning of the pliocene, this process had reached what appears to have been a mechanical limit. In the later evolution of the stock, the jaws were shortened, the trunk elongated, and the lower tusks abolished. The effective reach of the animal for its food was continuously increased: but the structural basis for this functional change was wholly altered, the elongation of the trunk being substituted for that of the jaw. It is impossible to stretch the principle of internal orthogenesis to cover a process of this type.

Another reversal of trend is that shown by the baboons (see e.g. Gregory, 1936), in which a secondary lengthening of the face into a muzzle has occurred subsequently to an original trend in the opposite direction, as exemplified by most Old World monkeys. This differs from the case of the elephants in that here the trend itself appears to have been reversed, while in the elephants the functional trend continues, and only the means for realizing it are altered.

While on the subject, we may deal with a cognate point, Dollo's so-called law of the irreversibility of evolution. This is an empirical fact of paleontology, but would appear to be merely the result of probability and what we may call biological convenience. That it involves no intrinsic necessity is shown by the experimental findings of geneticists on polydactyly in guinea-pigs. The tame guinea-pig, like other members of the genus *Cavia*, normally possesses but four digits (ii–v) on the front feet and three (ii–iv) on the hind. By selective breeding from the individuals possessing one or both hind little toes (digit v), which appear sporadically in certain domestic strains, a stock can be produced which always possesses this digit (see Pictet, 1933; Wright, 1934b). The basis for the character seems to be an alteration in the digital embryonic field, permitting it to be divided into more digital units than in the normal type (p. 550).

The little toes thus experimentally resurrected appear perfectly normal, so that man has been able to build up a stock which was in full possession of a hind little toe that the wild species and indeed the whole genus had definitely lost many millions of years ago. Thus nature no more abhors reverse evolution than she abhors a vacuum.*

Muller (1939), in a carefully reasoned review of the subject, comes to the same general conclusions. He points out that not only will the old characters resurrected by reversed evolution never rest on a genetically identical basis, but that with complex characters they will inevitably cease to be phenotypically identical or even closely similar. See also Needham's interesting discussion (1938).

The matter is complicated by the fact that the muscle and tendon supply is to a considerable extent independent of the bones and dermal structures (J. P. Scott, 1938), so that normal-looking digits may be abnormal functionally. In some cases, however, extra digits appear to be quite normal. This illustrates the difficulty of restoring (or independently evolving) a character depending on many distinct major factors.

Gregory (1936) also maintains the correctness of Dollo's Law. First he points out that Dollo himself asserted that the "Law" applied only when an organ is wholly lost. Thus cases of perfectly definite "reversal of evolution" which happen only to apply to changes in proportion are excluded by a quite arbitrary definition. Then Gregory maintains that structures which are regained are never entirely identical with the corresponding ones that were originally lost. Thus it has been shown that in the occasional three-toed horses that occur to-day, the extra digits "do not have the same coincidence with the carpal bones as do the side toes in the feet of the extinct *Hipparion*". Sometimes he goes further. Thus, though mastiffs and St. Bernards may show the big toe which is lacking in wild Canidae, "it would be

---

* Wright (op. cit.) has further produced another stock which, in addition to little toes, almost invariably possesses a thumb (fore digit i). This stock, however, can only be maintained in the heterozygous state, since the genes concerned are lethal when in double dose, although the thumbs produced appear quite normal.

difficult to prove that this so-called big toe is truly homologous with the true first digit of primitive mammals". Here the words *truly* and *homologous* appear to beg several questions, to which it is probably impossible to give an answer. If it is maintained that a regained organ is never absolutely identical with that which was lost, this is probably true in the great majority of instances. However, not only do some of the cases of extra toes in guinea-pigs seem to contradict this (though even here, certain characters such as coat-colour, etc., are almost certain to have altered since the organ was first lost, thus rendering it at its reappearance not *completely* identical), but wherever a "normal" character has been markedly altered (as in fowls' combs) or totally suppressed (as in the horns of cattle) by a dominant mutation, it is obviously possible, provided certain genetic precautions are observed, to re-obtain the identical normal character from the heterozygous form after an indefinite number of generations.

Regan (1924) has given an example, not based on experimental proof, of reversed evolution in fish. This concerns the re-acquisition by the Loricariidae of denticle-like structures on the scales. Another case is the return of later amphibians to the series of simple neuromast pits in place of the roofed-in groove constituting the lateral line of higher fish in early amphibia. The pit stage is ontogenetically and phylogenetically primitive. This case may be accounted for by a quite simple alteration in the time-relations of development.

Dollo's Law should thus in the first place be restated in more general form, and in the second place it should be regarded as a mere rule and not erected into a principle. It is true that the more complex an organ is, and the more completely it is lost, the less likely it is to be regained in identical form, but this depends on no absolute "principle of irreversibility"—only on the high degree of improbability of reversal in all of many factors concerned.

Many trends which at first sight appear useless may turn out on analysis to have functional significance. For instance, Malcolm Smith (1938) comments on the trend in agamid lizards towards reduction of the structures of the middle ear. The functional reason here may be the risk of damage to these delicate structures by living prey struggling in the mouth, as in the parallel trend seen in snakes, but Smith is inclined to a purely orthogenetic explanation.

The same principles seem to apply in general to small-scale adaptations as to long-range adaptive trends, except that since such adaptations frequently concern only one particular function and not the organism's main way of life, it should be easier for evolutionary direction to be changed, and for adaptation to set off on a new tack. In the matter of coloration in birds, for instance, there is a balance between the advantages to be derived from concealment and those to be derived from conspicuousness. The former will be higher for defenceless species and in open environments, the latter will be higher in males when there is polygamy (stimulative value of display characters) or when there is much rivalry between males as in territorial species (threat characters), and in both sexes in gregarious species (recognition markings). A slight change in habitat preference or reproductive behaviour will speedily tilt the balance in one direction or the other (see Huxley, 1923b, 1938a, 1938b; and p. 426).

4. NON-ADAPTIVE TRENDS AND ORTHOGENESIS

Besides the usual trends constituting the radiation of a group, most of which, as we have seen, appear clearly to be towards adaptive specialization, there are others for which no adaptive significance has as yet been found. The most striking are, naturally, those for which we have direct fossil evidence. Watson (1926) enumerates a number of trends observed in the extinct group of amphibia known as Labyrinthodonts. These include the flattening and broadening of the head and forepart of the body; the shortening of the skull, resulting in the hypoglossal nerve passing out posteriorly to the cranium instead of through the basioccipital; the gradual downward extension of the forepart of the cranial cavity; the progressive diminution in ossification of the cranium, and the final disappearance of certain bones; the development of an otic process in the pterygoid; etc.

These trends occur in a parallel way in a number of quite separate lines, and almost synchronously. They proceed on their course in spite of radical changes in the animals' biology, such as that from aquatic to terrestrial and back to secondarily aquatic life. And Watson states categorically that he can see no adaptive significance in any of them.

Certain trends have been assumed to be orthogenetically determined since their end-products appear to be more or less pathological. Nopcsa (1923) has termed such evolutionary simulations of diseased conditions *arrhostia*. In certain cases, as with the pachyostosis and osteosclerosis which occurs in various marine vertebrates, and which simulates certain accompaniments of leukaemia, this seems to be a temporary means of securing better respiratory adaptation to an aquatic life (Nopcsa, 1923) during the period when other more satisfactory but more elaborate adaptations are being evolved. We thus tend to find it in the early stages of secondary aquatic trends (the permian *Mesosaurus*, the triassic nothosaur *Pachypleura*, the lower cretaceous lacertilian *Eidolosaurus*, the lower cretaceous ophidian *Pachyophis*, the eocene cetacean *Zeuglodon*); only in the vegetable-feeding Sirenia is it a permanent feature, but even so it has been much reduced in the later history of the group. In one case only, the pliocene sirenian *Felsinotherium*, does it seem to have become so excessive as to contribute to extinction. Thus, since it does not represent an irreversible trend which becomes accentuated until it ends disastrously, there is no need to postulate an orthogenetic determination for it.

Aquatic vertebrates show another arrhostic condition of bone, namely a retardation of ossification, exclusively or mainly of cartilage bone. Nopcsa (1930) cites Stegocephalia, modern Amphibia, Chelonia, Ichthyosauria, and (to a slight extent) Plesiosauria as showing this tendency. He further points out that it is very similar to the retardation of ossification produced by hypothyroidism. He suggests that in some as yet unknown way, aquatic life damps down thyroid activity; if this view is correct, then the arrhostia is a consequential effect of aquatic life, and need not be regarded as the result of a special orthogenetic trend.

Nopcsa (1923) also points out that in certain cases of very large size in vertebrates, arrhostic conditions simulating symptoms of hyperpituitarism (acromegaly) may arise. It would, however, appear probable that this again is a purely consequential effect of the large size, which itself depends largely or mainly on increased pituitary functions. If, as appears likely, the large size itself (e.g. of certain dinosaurs), during the favourable climatic conditions when it was evolved, was itself of advantage, orthogenesis need not be postulated, and the condition is closely parallel with that produced in the St. Bernard breed of dogs by artificial selection (p. 71). This interpretation is strengthened by the facts concerning the role of the pituitary in the evolution of the giant birds of the family Aepyornithidae as determined on endocranial casts (Edinger, 1940). Here the size of the pituitary relative to that of the forebrain increases over fourfold as absolute size is increased from *Mullerornis* to the gigantic *Aepyornis maximus*. Finally H. E. Wood (1941) and Goldschmidt (1940) draw attention to the fact that numerous vertebrates—forms of rhinocerotids (amynodonts), cave-bears, a number of fishes, etc. —have developed a facies very similar to that of achondroplasia, notably the "bull-dog" type of face. Here the implications are not so clear as with acromegalic arrhostia, but at least there is no more necessity of adopting orthogenesis as an explanation than in any of the other cases cited. Arrhostia seems thus to be a consequential rather than an orthogenetic phenomenon (pp. 525 seq.). See also Stockard (1938) on "pituitary" characters.

A succinct account of other noteworthy examples, in some of which the non-adaptive nature of the change seems clearer, is given by Haldane (1932a, p. 23) and may be quoted here:

"Further observation of these marine races showing slow continuous evolution displayed an extraordinary group of phenomena which are not obviously explicable on any theory of evolution whatever. Characters appear to go on developing past their point of maximum utility. Thus the coiling of the *Gryphaea* shells [lamellibranch molluscs] went on until it must have been very difficult for them to open at all, and impossible to open widely. This state of affairs occurred several times, and always portended the extinction of the race. The same thing sometimes happened in land animals.

Thus in the Titanotheria [large oligocene hoofed mammals] gigantic size and horn development were the prelude to extinction in a number of separate lines of descent. One is left with the impression that the evolutionary process somehow acquired a momentum which took it past the point at which it would have ceased on a basis of utility.

"But sometimes another process occurred, which has been particularly studied in the Ammonites. These animals, which in a general way resembled cuttlefish, made spiral shells with many chambers, but only lived in the last of them, the others being presumably filled with water or gas. The inner chambers were made by the young animals, the latter by the adults. So we can contrast the shell-making activity of the same animal at different ages. We then find that the earlier chambers often resemble those produced by the adults of ancestral forms some millions of years earlier. The phenomenon can be especially well studied in the suture lines between different chambers. The correspondence is not exact, and often new features appear in the earlier stages which were not present in any ancestors. . . . This is quite analogous to the phenomenon of partial recapitulation seen in the early development of such forms as man. An early human embryo has rudimentary gill-slits and a tail. Later on it develops a thick coat of hair which is shed before birth. Of course the gill-slits and tail are unlike those of any adult animal, and it has special organs such as the umbilical cord which are not and never were found in adults. But many of its features recapitulate those of its adult ancestors.

"All this can be explained on Darwinian lines. The less a new adult character interferes with normal development the more likely it is to be a success. When, however, it has been fixed in the adult stage the complicated developmental process may well be slowly modified so that the advantages of the new character appear earlier and earlier in the life-cycle and its appearance is less and less abrupt. This process is, however, likely to be very slow.

"So far so good, but in the later stage of Ammonite history a much more surprising phenomenon occurred. A number of different lineages began to alter in the opposite direction. Features appeared which had not been seen for a hundred million years, but which strongly resembled those of the earliest known Ammonites. The suture-line became simplified, and the shell uncoiled. Sometimes the primitive features seem to have been present right through the animal's life-history. In other lines of descent (e.g. *Baculites*) the shell was at first coiled, but in the fully adult animal it was straightened out. This reversion to primitive type was always the prelude to extinction. It happened on a large scale in the late Trias, when most of the great Ammonite groups died out. Then there was a brilliant renaissance during the Liassic period, one of the older groups giving rise to many new types. But an epoch of archaism set in once more in the Cretaceous, and at the end of that period the last Ammonite died. The closing stages of Ammonite evolution were marked, not only by retrogression, but by the appearance of new shell types, with 'hairpin bends' as in *Hamites*, or an asymmetrical snail-like spire as in *Turritelites*. These bizarre forms, however, were only temporarily successful. After about 400 million years of life the Ammonites became extinct.

"The account here given is that due to Hyatt and Wurtemberger, and is, I think, accepted by most paleontologists. However, Spath's (1924) views on Ammonite lineages, which are easier to reconcile with Darwinism, command much support. I am not competent to judge between them, but wish to state the anti-Darwinian position as fairly as possible."

Among other examples often adduced by paleontologists as useless or eventually harmful trends are those towards spininess and over-ornamentation in trilobites, and towards excessive development of the arm-skeleton in brachiopods.

The second case which Haldane mentions, that of the titano-theres, can be more simply accounted for on Darwinian lines (p. 534). Indeed Haldane himself (op. cit., p. 141) later argues that the development of apparently unfavourable characters as a prelude to the extinction of a stock can in many cases (notably unwieldy size and exaggeratedly large horns), be put down to the biologically evil effects of intraspecific selection (p. 484).

On the other hand, no selectionist interpretation of the over-coiling of the *Gryphaea* lines, or of the secondary simplification of ammonites, or of other bizarre preludes to extinction in other groups, has as yet been given. A caveat should here be entered. No living ammonites are known. The complication of suture lines of the earlier ammonites and their simplification in later forms have at least a simple mechanistic basis in terms of rate-genes (p. 530). About their functional meaning we know next to nothing, so that it is dangerous to maintain that they were in no sense adaptive. This is the view to which Bather (1920) eventually came, after wide paleontological experience. It may even be that we are betraying our ignorance by not being able to perceive the direct functional utility of the latest strangely bent and partially involved types of shell. This, however, is unlikely, and with the *Gryphaea* still less likely. An additional complication is introduced by the fact that, as briefly noted by Haldane, *Gryphaea* is not a true genus, but merely a name for the final stage in the coiling of an ostreid shell, and that this stage has been reached by several lines, starting their evolution at different times (Arkell, 1933; p. 409). The fact that on several occasions certain oysters remained flat while others proceeded to show this tendency to over-coiling which was eventually to lead to their extinction, is difficult to account for on any hypothesis so far put forward, orthogenetic or otherwise.

It is, of course, possible that these trends, in themselves useless, are correlated with adaptive trends in other characters (pp. 63, 206). However, we must provisionally face an explanation in terms of orthogenesis—i.e. of evolution predetermined to proceed within certain narrow limits, irrespective of selective disadvantage except where this leads to total extinction. It should be noted that, even if the existence of orthogenesis in this cause be confirmed, it appears to be a rare and exceptional phenomenon, and that we have no inkling of any mechanism by which it may be brought about. It is a description, not an explanation. Indeed its existence runs counter to fundamental selectionist principles (p. 123).

Of course, if mutation-rate were high enough to overbalance counter-selection, it would provide an orthogenetic mechanism of a kind. However, as Fisher and others have shown, mutation-rates of this intensity do not exist, or at least must be very rare. Secondly, even if they did exist, they would not by themselves provide an explanation of the real problem at issue, which is the *long continuance* of apparently orthogenetic trends. For this, we should have to postulate not merely a high mutation-rate, but a restriction of the direction of mutation, so that new mutations with high frequency would always be arising to produce further effects of the same type. And of this there is no evidence whatever.*

---

* The work of Jollos (1930), claiming that induced mutations tend to occur in a series of successive steps with progressively greater effect, appeared to indicate a mechanism of this general type for mutations of low frequency. Later researches, however (e.g. Plough and Ives, 1934), have entirely failed to confirm the existence of such "directional" or "progressive" mutation.

Orthogenesis of this sort, playing the major part in guiding evolutionary change, with selection in a purely limiting and subsidiary role, may be called dominant or primary. While dominant orthogenesis, if it exists at all, is rare and exceptional, what we may call subsidiary or secondary orthogenesis is common enough. Under the head of subsidiary orthogenesis I include phenomena which in the first place are of an orthogenetic nature in that they limit the freedom of variation and therefore of evolutionary change, and in the second place are subsidiary in that they merely provide limits within which natural selection still plays the main guiding and shaping role.

The first phenomenon of subsidiary orthogenesis with which we must deal is parallel variation (pp. 99, 211, 395, 431). This is a comprehensive term which includes several distinct processes. In the first place there is homologous mutation—the alteration of homologous genes in the same kind of way. In the second place there is parallel character-change—a similar phenotypic effect, produced, however, by mutations in different genes. Parallel character-change may further be either (a) homologous or (b) purely superficial. When homologous, the same type of developmental process is usually affected in the same kind of way: when superficial, the phenotypic effect is similar, but is produced by different developmental processes. This important distinction between the different modes of parallel variation has not always been clearly envisaged. (We must also remember that truly homologous mutations may sometimes exert quite different phenotypic effects in different species.)

We will take examples of the different categories. In certain species of *Drosophila*, such as *D. melanogaster* and *D. simulans*, the possibility of obtaining offspring from interspecific crosses has enabled geneticists to prove that certain parallel variations, e.g. white eye and one yellow body variant, are due to truly homologous mutation—i.e. the same type of mutation has occurred in corresponding loci, or in other words in descendants of the same ancestral gene (see Morgan, Bridges, and Sturtevant, 1925). The proof consists in the offspring of two similar mutants showing the same mutant character, and not presenting a reversion to wild type, as would occur if the genes were not homologous. In other cases, though this complete proof cannot be given owing to sterility, the location of the genes in corresponding sections of apparently homologous chromosomes is strong presumption of true homologous mutation. The blood-group genes in man and apes are possibly another example. Interspecific grafting (Stubbe and Vogt, 1940a) may also demonstrate gene-homology.

In other cases the evidence is less cogent. Haldane (1927a), for instance, has collected the data on the colour mutations of domestic and wild rodents and has shown that much parallel variation has occurred in the various species and genera. To deduce, however, as he is inclined to do, that these are all due to true homologous mutation, though in several cases probable, is not logically justified; similar phenotypic effects are often produced by mutations in non-homologous genes. There are, for instance, several non-homologous mutations for pink eyes and two for yellow body-colour in *Drosophila* (Morgan, Bridges, and Sturtevant, 1925), and several for red eye-colour in *Gammarus chevreuxi* (Sexton and Clark, 1936b). In rabbits, three separate mutant genes may produce the "rex" coat-character (found also in other rodents): Castle and Nachtsheim (1933). Thus parallel variation may be due to non-homologous mutations producing parallel character-change.

Another similar line of approach is provided by the data on mutation-frequency in the laboratory, and on the proportion of wild-caught individuals carrying mutant genes in a heterozygous condition. From these it has been established that various mutational effects recur regularly in all organisms which have been thoroughly investigated (see p. 396). Here again the effects may sometimes be due to homologous mutation, sometimes merely to homologous character-effect. In either case, the presumption is strong that a number of corresponding mutational effects will recur independently in various related species of a group.

It is important to note that when non-homologous mutations affect the same developmental process in the same kind of way in different species, the resultant character-change may legitimately be called homologous, even though neither the final character, nor the steps of the developmental process by which it is generated, are precisely identical. In such cases the nature of the developmental process provides a certain limitation or canalization of the types of variation possible. Thus if melanin pigment is present, a reduction in the intensity of its production, however brought about, will result in dilution: a certain type of chemical alteration of the process will result in brown or yellow instead of black, and so on. When, as in many rodents, the agouti pattern is normally present, with a yellow section on a black hair, the chief modifications possible (apart from the dilution of black or its alteration to brown, and the total inhibition of all pigmentation) appear to be (i) either the extension of yellow to cover the whole hair or its reduction to leave the hair wholly black, or (ii) the presence or absence of a larger or smaller area of yellowish-white on the belly.

In a similar way, the process of wing-development in *Drosophila* is such that numerous non-homologous mutations can produce greater or lesser notching or truncation at the tip, and various others can reduce the width of wing (see list of genes in Morgan, Bridges, and Sturtevant, 1925). In general, the similarity of homologous character-changes is due to their influencing an identical developmental process in a similar way. Truncate wings provide an interesting special case. Here Altenburg and Muller (1920) showed that the chief gene for truncation in some fashion "sensitized" certain developmental processes in such a way that many quite independent mutations shortened wing-length much more in the presence of this gene than in its absence. Similar cases are now known for other processes in *Drosophila* and for other organisms, and will become frequent as work in physiological genetics progresses. In one sense, this is a case of parallel variation, in another, of consequential evolution (§§ 6, 7).*

Superficial parallel character-change is known specially for

---

* The fact that the processes of development restrict the possibilities of variation has a further consequential effect, in the frequent existence of what Goldschmidt (e.g. 1940, *passim*) has called *phenocopies*—modifications that are phenotypically indistinguishable from mutational effects. This phenomenon in its turn may provide the basis for processes of organic selection (pp. 304, 524).

mimetic insects. Here selection-pressure has been dominant, and has moulded dissimilar processes to give similar effects. A good example is *Papilio hector* and its mimic the *romulus* form of *P. polytes*, in which the red pigments are chemically distinct, the one turning yellow, the other purplish on application of acid (Ford, 1937). An even better case is that of a skipper butterfly, *Abantis levebu*, which mimics Pierines (whites): the white pigment of the skipper is a flavone, while that of the whites is a pterin (unpublished information from Mr. E. B. Ford).

A curious non-mimetic case is that of *Satyrus anthe*, in which two areas of apparently similar white are due to wholly different pigments, in one a pterin derived from metabolic breakdown, in the other a flavone derived by building up from a product of the food-plant.

Parallel variation may thus affect homologous genes and homologous processes: or non-homologous genes but homologous processes; or genes and processes both of which are non-homologous. The first two types, since they are often indistinguishable in practice, may conveniently be lumped together under the head of parallel mutation.

Finally, we must remember that owing to the alterability of gene-expression by the residual gene-complex (pp. 64, 87), even truly homologous mutations need not produce similar phenotypic effects.

These facts have interesting evolutionary bearings. In the first place, the existence of true homologous mutation shows us that the classical post-Darwinian concept of homology cannot be applied to species. That concept equated correspondence in plan of organization with common descent. This conclusion really involves two steps, one a generalization of observation, the other a historical deduction. The arm of a man, the wing of a bird, and the flipper of a whale can be shown to be built on a common plan: and it is deduced that the reason they are all built on a common plan is because their three possessors are all descended from a common ancestor (see pp. 391 seq.).

This explanation of the fact of homology by common ancestry undoubtedly holds good for complex structures for whose evolution a very large number of steps were required. No biologist would venture to suggest that the pentadactyle limbs of vertebrates or the mouth-parts of insects could have been separately evolved in more than one stock. But the fact of homologous mutation shows that it need not hold for characters involving only one or a few mutations. Both *Drosophila melanogaster* and *D. simulans* have red eyes, but both have produced white-eyed mutants. The white-eyed types are clearly homologous in that they are due to corresponding alterations in corresponding parts of the hereditary constitution: but they cannot be traced back to a common white-eyed ancestral species. The same is true of commonly recurring aberrations within a wild genus or species—e.g. white-flowered bluebells or gentians, which may even establish themselves as small local groups in nature. There is no ancestral white variety from which all the white-flowered specimens are descended.

More to our present purpose is the bearing of recurrent and parallel variations on the phenomena of convergence and parallel evolution. In this case both homologous mutation and homologous character-change will clearly be relevant.

We have mentioned (p. 488) the finding of paleontologists, that in fossil lineages with abundant documentation, numerous separate lines appear to pursue the same general trend, although the rate of change of separate characters may differ: e.g. in the horses, some lines, although often specifically or even generically distinct, will lag behind the mean for the period as regards complication and size of molars, while showing advance beyond the mean for reduction of digits; others will show the converse; and still others will be at the mean for both characters. The same is true of the sea-urchin *Micraster* (p. 32).

This can readily be explained if we assume that mutations with similar effects are likely to turn up in related lines. It must be observed, however, that selection-pressure is also necessary. Actually, it will be the dominant factor, since it alone prescribes the general direction of specialization.

The fact, noted above (p. 509), that the coiled *Gryphaea* type of shell was independently evolved in oysters at several different times and places may perhaps imply that it was of selective value under certain temporary and local conditions (e.g. of greater sedimentation). However, its apparent final harmfulness to the lineages in which it occurs appears to rule out any simple selectionist interpretation. As with so many paleontological riddles, we may never learn the answer.*

According to Osborn (1936) and le Gros Clark (1934), parallel evolution has played a considerable part in the geological history of the Proboscidea and the Primates respectively; and Brough (1936) gives interesting examples from bony fish. Parallel evolution in the titanotheres, and its probable explanation, is discussed on p. 534. Parallel evolution appears to have taken place in several separated lineages of Jurassic hexacorals, in each case tending to greater compactness of the corallites (W. D. Lang, 1938).

Various mimetic resemblances, especially in synaposematic "rings" of related species all sharing the Mullerian advantages of a common warning pattern, but also in some Batesian cases, will doubtless prove to depend largely on parallel mutations. On the other hand, many mimetic resemblances are demonstrably due to completely non-homologous character-changes (see Carpenter and Ford, 1933, p. 31), so that selection must be the essential agency in their production.

The same reasoning applies to the interesting case cited by le Gros Clark (1934, pp. 81–83) of the evolution of teeth in Primates. The two sub-families of fossil Lemuroidea, the Notharctinae and the Adapinae, both show the evolution of a quadritubercular from a trituberçular type of molar tooth. But whereas in the Adapinae this condition is brought about in the normal way by the development of a true hypocone as a wholly new cusp from the cingulum, in the Notharctinae a pseudo-hypocone is formed by the fission of the original protocone into two cusps.

---

* One of the features characterizing the evolution of the *Gryphaea* from the *Ostrea* type is a progressive increase in absolute size. Swinnerton (1940) studied the evolution of a lineage which rather more than doubled its linear dimensions during part of the Lower Liassic. He estimates that this change proceeded at the rate of an increase of 1 per cent in size in about 1,000 generations (cf. p. 61 n. on the rate of evolution in horses). Thus the effect *may* be consequential (p. 535).

The fact that the trend towards the quadritubercular condition cannot be due to parallel mutation constitutes additional evidence in favour of a selectionist interpretation.

In groups showing polymorphism, the same variant types may recur over and over again in different species. A classical case is the existence of apparently identical variant phases in banding and ground-colour in the snails *Cepaea hortensis* and *C. nemoralis* (p. 99). Recently Rubtzov (1935) has shown that complex colour-patterns recur as normal variants not only in related species but related genera of grasshoppers. Thus of six colour-phases, all recur in five species of *Chorthippus*, and four or five in six others, while two to five also recur in various species of seven other genera. Within genera, parallel evolution may often occur, sometimes to the confusion of the systematist who attempts a phylogenetic classification. Thus in the Australian bird genus *Acanthiza* (Mayr and Serventy, 1938) a brighter-coloured rump, a marked pattern on the head, streaking on the breast, and lengthening of the tail have all occurred more than once. In the butterfly genus *Colias*, Mr. E. B. Ford informs me, numerous species have yellow males and dimorphic females, yellow or white (cf. p. 98). In some cases this is due to a special genetic mechanism (p. 99). In others, selection acting on very similar germplasms with very similar capacities for mutation may produce such a result; this would in general apply to the numerous parallel regularities afforded by the "Geographical Rules" of systematists (see p. 211), though here non-homologous variation doubtless plays a larger role.

In general, it may be said that the fact of parallel mutation makes parallel evolution and certain types of convergence likely to occur, but only in such cases where parallel mutation is supplemented by parallel selection, or by special genetic mechanisms.

5. THE RESTRICTION OF VARIATION

Then we have restrictions on the amount of variation possible. There is, for example, a great contrast between the uniformity of snipe or most ducks as against the tendency of many species of passerine birds to break up into geographical subspecies, or the constancy of such plants as bracken (*Pteridium aquilinum*) or *Dryas octopetala* as against the great variability of field pansy (*Viola tricolor, sensu lato*), or chickweed (*Stellaria media, sensu lato*). It may be, of course, that the restriction of actual variability here depends on quite other causes than a restriction of the potentiality of variation. Much work must be done on the subject before we can do more than guess.

In any case we must beware of arguing that the inability of specialized forms to produce new types must be due to an inherent lack of genetic variability. This assertion is often made, but cannot be upheld. We have already seen (p. 500) that the failure lies in the difficulty for selection of utilizing any variations except those tending towards further specialization in the same direction. When the biomechanical limit has been reached, the type is stuck and can do nothing but either maintain itself or else become extinct. However, as we have seen (pp. 324 seq.), such limits are relative to the environmental situation: if this is radically altered, evolutionary radiation may again set in, showing that the previous standstill was not due to lack of genetic variability. The astonishing range of types produced by man in domesticated animals, even those like pigeons whose origin is free from the suspicion of hybridization, conclusively demonstrates the same fact. From another angle, the reserve of genetic variability, much of it waiting to be elicited by selection, is demonstrably enormous in most wild species (R. A. Fisher, 1930*a*, p. 96).

More to the point are the examples of restricted types of variation found in nature. Many groups appear to vary readily in certain directions, with difficulty in others.

The rarity of greens in adult butterflies (and, to a lesser extent, moths) is a case in point. In most other insect groups, green is a common colour; and in view of its selective value as protective (cryptic) coloration against a background of vegetation, this is what one would expect. Indeed numerous larval Lepidoptera show a green coloration which is obviously cryptic. The rarity of green in the adults is all the more remarkable.

Then among woodpeckers, reds, blacks, and whites are frequent, and yellows, greens, and browns may occur, but blues appear to be unknown. Gulls, on the other hand, show almost exclusively a combination of white with grey-blue or black: reds, yellows, and greens are never found in their plumage (though they occur frequently in their beaks or legs). Penguins, again, show no red in their plumage, though some have yellow. This is of interest, since Levick (1914) found that red possessed some special stimulating quality for the Adelie Penguin. This species is much addicted to the theft of the stones which constitute its nest-material. Levick painted stones of different colours, and found that the red ones travelled by theft across the colony much faster than those of any other colour. One may presume that red plumage would have an advantage in sexual selection; but the bird's plumage has remained black and white.

Here again we must beware of arguing that because certain characters are normally not found, therefore they cannot be produced. The pierines or white butterflies provide a good example to the contrary. As everyone knows, the prevailing colour of these is white, often with black or greenish markings, and sometimes with yellow or orange. In the Old World they are practically restricted to this range of colour, and to certain types of pattern. In South America, however, a number of pierines have become mimetic: and these, to copy their models, have developed a number of new colours and patterns not elsewhere found in the group. Even in these, however, there is some restriction, for all the pigments employed are pterins, belonging to the katabolic type of substances produced from the breakdown products of metabolism: no flavones, for instance, occur in pierines, save in one aberrant New World group (Ford, 1940b). Thus the group appears to be subject to a restriction as to the chemical nature of its pigments, though in respect of its patterns and to a certain extent of its actual coloration it must be regarded as conservative rather than as compulsorily limited.

Again, at first sight it might be supposed that the lower mammals (all groups except Primates) were genetically restricted as regards pigmentation, since they are confined to black, white, grey, brown, russet, and yellow, while in Primates scarlets, pinks, blues, and greens are also found. This, however, would appear to be a case of consequential evolution (see p. 525), the greater range of colours among Primates being a consequence of their acquisition (alone among mammalian groups, apparently) of colour-vision. A relevant fact is that, as I am informed by Dr. S. Zuckerman, the red of buttocks and occasionally of face in Primates is due, as in our own lips, to blood showing through their skin. This device for producing visible red would have been available to members of other mammalian groups, but would have been useless in the absence of colour-vision.

There are some cases, however, in which certain variations appear to be impossible or at best very difficult to produce. In spite of intensive and long-continued efforts, breeders have failed to give the world blue roses or black tulips. A bluish-purple in the rose and a deep bronze in the tulip are the limits reached: true blue and jet black have proved impossible.

We refer later to the small amount of new variation to be found in the introduced English sparrow (*Passer domesticus*) in the U.S.A. This was recently confirmed by Lack (1940c). No marked local races have been established, and the variance of individual populations has been scarcely or not at all increased. This rather surprising failure to vary may possibly be due to lack of time (p. 521).

Restriction of variability may also be due to quite other causes, namely to a lack of what is called modificational plasticity—the capacity to react by modification to differences in the environment (see p. 441). Various botanists (e.g. Turrill, 1936; and see Marsden-Jones and Turrill, 1938) have shown that different species of plants differ enormously in this respect, some, which we may call stenoplastic, remaining extremely constant under a wide range of environmental conditions, others, the euryplastic types, reacting by marked changes in size, habit, proportions, etc. p. 444). We have less information on the subject in animals.

This phenomenon is of great interest ecologically and in relation to minor systematics. We do not, however, know whether it is correlated with any difference in actual or potential genetic variability, and this alone will have long-range evolutionary effects.

This brings us to an allied problem, that of the great variability of certain species as opposed to the relative invariability of others. We have already touched on this in connection with the subject of polymorphism (p. 516).

Hornell (1917), after detailed study of the lamellibranch *Meretrix* in Indian seas, concludes that the three species involved differ markedly in their type of variability. *M. meretrix* and *M. attenuata* are very variable in colour, but "remarkably stable" in adult shape and size, whereas *M. casta* is highly variable both geographically and locally in these last respects.

Restriction of variation is sometimes only apparent. Thus the snails of the genus *Cepaea*, such as *C. hortensis* and *C. nemoralis* (see p. 202), appear at first sight to be far more variable in their ground-colour and banding pattern than the common garden snail *Helix aspersa*. However, as Mr. Diver has pointed out to me, the shell of the garden snail is heavily suffused with a general brown pigment, which masks any underlying variation. Actually, it would seem that variation in these concealed patterns is just as great as in the readily visible patterns of *Cepaea*.

Similarly, there are two North American species of the lamellibranch *Donax*, of which one (*D. gouldii*) is superficially very uniform, while the other (*D. variabilis*) owes its name to the striking variation which it exhibits (Anon., 1941). Examination of the illustration, however, seems to show that the apparent restriction of variability in *D. gouldii* is due to a general diminution in the intensity of pigmentation, which renders the various patterns much fainter.

Bateson (1913, pp. 24 seq.) gives a number of other examples. In some cases, however, if he had gone further into the subject, the facts would not seem so curious. For instance, he cites the case of two closely related British noctuid moths of the genus *Dianthoecia*, both common and wide-ranging: *D. capsincola* shows little variation, while *D. carpophaga* "exhibits a complex series of varieties". He further mentions that the common "Silver Y", *Plusia gamma*, shows little variation in the mark from which it takes its name, while the corresponding mark in *P. interrogationis* is so variable that no two specimens are alike. However, in the latter case, he omits to mention that in ground colour the two forms both show considerable variation, showing that *P. gamma* is not stable as a species.

With *Dianthoecia*, he has neglected the ecology of the two species. Although he states that they are similar in their habits, this is not true in one important respect, for Mr. E. B. Ford tells me that while the adults of *D. capsincola* rest in concealed situations at the base of herbage, those of *D. carpophaga*, predominantly a coastal species, tend to rest on exposed soil and rock. Their coloration is thus subject to selection for protective reasons, and the variation to which Bateson refers is mainly a regional one, forms from different localities being adapted to the prevalent colour of the local background. For instance on the south coast of Britain, whitish forms are found in the chalk areas, but beyond these, to the west, brownish types predominate.

These examples will serve to show the complexity of the problem, and the danger of hasty conclusions. None the less, some of Bateson's cases seem to satisfy all requirements. In Britain, for instance, the pheasant stock (if we disregard recombinational variation due to crossing) is less variable than the red grouse, in spite of the fact that the former has been introduced into alien surroundings. In the United States, the introduced house sparrow appears to be much less variable geographically than many indigenous species (p. 519; J. C. Phillips, 1915). However, the lapse of time may not have been sufficient to elicit geographical differentiation (see p. 194), for this appears to depend on selection as well as on inherent variability. In any case the species shows plenty of geographical variation in the Old World.

At the moment we can give no explanation, whether in terms of intrinsic nature or external selection-pressure, to account for the restriction of variability in some species as against others of the same genus, although we may say with some assurance that some species seem to show a greater readiness to vary genetically than do others, and further that a given type may produce certain kinds of mutational effects more frequently, others with great rarity or perhaps never. On the other hand, theoretical considerations show that evolutionary change will still occur, in spite of wide differences in general mutation-rate, provided that selection is operative. Thus it will be rare that lack of evolutionary change can be due to lack of raw materials in the shape of mutations.

So much for the possibility of a restriction of the raw material of variation, through the differential frequency of mutation in various directions. Another restriction, of much more frequent occurrence, is that of the utilizability of variation, through a differential effect upon the selective value of mutations in different directions. The former depends upon inherent properties of the germinal material; the latter upon the past history of the species, as embodied in its present organization, and upon its environment. We have given examples of the relativity of evolutionary change to environmental conditions (p. 430). As an example of past history limiting the advantageous directions of change, we have already considered the effect of past specialization in favouring further change in the same direction and inhibiting it in other directions. The principle is, however, of wider application. Once a given structural plan has been evolved, it will be much simpler (I use a shorthand mode of expression) to alter its parts quantitatively or to adapt it to new functions than to evolve new organs. For this reason, the great majority of evolutionary changes of structure consist in changes of proportion only, one part or organ being enlarged, another reduced. To take a striking example, the adult echinoderms have never succeeded in escaping fully from their radial symmetry. Asymmetrical and bilateral forms have been evolved, but never full bilaterality with development of a head. Numerous other examples of structures altering their function during evolution and of the past dictating the limits for the future (see p. 500), will readily occur to the mind. An interesting minor one is the fact that in groups with sporadic hearing, the evolution of this capacity in conjunction with that of functional sound-production may be followed by the evolution of a second distinct method of sound-production. This has occurred in several longicorn beetles; and in one (*Plagithysmus*) two subsidiary methods have been evolved (see the Cambridge Natural History for details). Numerous other examples of specialization in one type of sense-organ being followed in evolution by a series of allaesthetic acquisitions designed to stimulate that particular sense-organ, will occur to all biologists. Such restrictions, however, should strictly not be called orthogenetic. They are rather to be considered as cases of orthoselective evolution (p. 500), but consequential in the long·range or historical sense (p. 545).

The fact remains that evolutionary change is not completely at random. In the first place it is restricted environmentally. In saying this we are only reaffirming the fundamental Darwinian postulate of selection, for selection is always relative to the environment, both inorganic and biological. This relativity, however, is so basic that it is often neglected: its importance is thrust upon our notice only when a climatic revolution takes place, or, more frequently, when there is some alteration in the biological environment, as with the colonization of new areas where the balance of competitors or enemies is different.

It is, however, also restricted on account of peculiarities in the evolving organisms. Such internal restriction operates in two ways, orthogenetically and historically. Both types of restriction may play either a dominant or a subsidiary role in evolution. The historical restrictions depend on the previous evolutionary history of the stock and its effects on the machinery of selection. Dominant historical restrictions arise from what we may call the groove effect (p. 500), which Plate termed orthoselection: once adaptive specialization has begun in one direction it must become progressively harder, on the basis of the known facts of mutation, for selection to switch the trend onto another direction. The result is an apparent orthogenesis. Subsidiary (or consequential) historical restrictions simply make it easier for selection to act in certain ways than in others, while leaving the adaptive direction to be guided by selection.

A special case of subsidiary historical restriction is provided by the Baldwin and Lloyd-Morgan principle of Organic Selection, according to which an organism may in the first instance become adapted to an ecological niche merely by behaviour (whether genetic or purely habitual) and any consequent non-heritable modifications, after which mutations for the kind of structural change suitable to the particular mode of life will have a better chance of being selected. Where the modifications are extensive, the process of their replacements by mutations may closely simulate lamarckism (pp. 114, 296, 304). The principle is an important one which would appear to have been unduly neglected by recent evolutionists.

True orthogenetic restriction depends on a restriction of the type and quantity of genetic variation. When dominant it prescribes the direction of evolution: when subsidiary it merely limits its possibilities.

Dominant historical restriction is common, dominant orthogenetic restriction very rare, if indeed it exists at all. Subsidiary historical restriction is common. It may be important in barring certain major lines of advance, but allows considerable freedom in the direction of adaptive specialization. Subsidiary orthogenetic restriction is probably frequent, but we are not yet able to be sure in most cases whether a limitation of variation as actually found in a group is due to a limitation in the supply of mutations or to selection, or to other causes. It is, however, certain that some mutational effects recur regularly in some allied species, and probable that this phenomenon is widespread. This last fact may contribute to parallel evolution—a type of directional change in which orthogenetic and selectionist agencies are combined.

To sum up, the only important agency restricting the direction of evolutionary change is the historical one, leading to a purely apparent orthogenesis. The subsidiary restrictions are truly subsidiary, in that the supply of variation remains sufficient to allow a degree of freedom in the direction of change which is always considerable and in certain cases at least appears to be, for all practical purposes of adaptive specialization, unlimited.

6. CONSEQUENTIAL EVOLUTION: THE CONSEQUENCES OF
DIFFERENTIAL DEVELOPMENT

Under this head we may discuss types of trend which are initiated or maintained with special readiness as a consequence of the way in which genes operate to produce their effect during development.

Let us begin with an example neatly worked out by Haldane (1932a, p. 124; see also Castle, 1932), which demonstrates how the results of selection at one period of the life-cycle may have repercussions on other periods and affect the species and its evolution in unexpected ways. The phenomenon with which he deals is that of intra-uterine selection in mammals which are polytocous, i.e. bring forth a number of young at one birth. Here there must be an intense pre-natal selection, since a considerable percentage of every litter dies in utero. Rapidity of growth especially must be at a premium, since space and nutrition are limited, and any advantage gained by an embryo establishing itself early is likely to be of permanent advantage throughout the critical stages.

Haldane suggests with some plausibility that any rapidity of pre-natal growth thus acquired is likely to be transferred in whole or in part to post-natal life as well, and that intra-uterine selection may thus help to account for the progressive increase in size seen in so many mammalian lines during their evolution.*

At any rate, the converse seems to hold good, namely that on

---

* This cannot be the only factor responsible for such trends towards evolutionary increase in bulk. For one thing, size-increase (up to a certain limit) must often be directly advantageous in its own right; and for another, the phenomenon occurs also in other types, such as reptiles, in which no phase of intra-uterine existence is passed through. It might be interesting to compare the *rate* of evolutionary size-increase in monotocous and polytocous placental types; but we could never be sure at what period a type which at present is monotocous had ceased to have litters of several young. Haldane himself in a later work (1938, p. 125) points out that a similar trend towards increased size will operate in polygamous species in which the males fight for the females. In the first case, intersexual selection will operate to increase the size of the males; and then some of this increase in size will tend automatically to be transferred to the females (cf. Winterbottom, 1929 and 1932), so that the size of both sexes will tend to be pushed beyond the optimum, or what would be the optimum for other reasons.

account of intra-uterine selection it would be impossible for a polytocous mammal to slow down its rate of development. One of the most characteristic features of man, and one by which his capacity of learning is utilized to the fullest extent, is precisely such a slowing down of general rate of development. Without it he could not in all probability have become fully human or biologically dominant. Judged by the law (which applies to most other mammals so far investigated) which regulates the amount of food consumed before the adult phase is reached, man's immaturity has been lengthened some sevenfold. This could not have occurred in a polytocous form. It was only after man's ancestors ceased to have litters and began to bring forth a single young at a birth that the further evolution of man became possible.

Further, this general slowing down had numerous corollaries. The typical adult human condition of hair on the head but almost complete absence of hair on the body is passed through as a temporary condition at about the time of birth by the anthropoid ape. The hymen of the human female has been stated to represent the persistence of what in lower mammals is an embryonic stage in the development of the urino-genital system. Most striking of all, the general form of the human face and skull, with its absence of snout and of bony ridges on the cranium, is quite similar to that of the foetal or newborn ape, but quite dissimilar to that of the adult (see p. 555; and Bolk, 1926).*

The general slowing down of man's post-natal development is doubtless due in part to its possessing selective advantage. But, as Haldane points out, it may also be in part the indirect carry-over from a slowing of pre-natal development. In the circumstances of anthropoid apes and of primitive sub-man a foetus is on the whole better nourished and less exposed to danger than a newborn infant, so that pre-natal slowing, with consequent prolongation of the intra-uterine phase, is here advantageous in

---

* The slowing is already marked in anthropoid apes, but not so extreme as in man. Spence and Yerkes (1937) show that whereas the percentage rate of increase in bulk in domestic mammals and rodents varies from 400 to 1,200 per cent per annum during the juvenile period, in the chimpanzee it is 21–27 per cent, and in man about 10 per cent.

polytocous mammals. (The non-black eye- and hair-colours (except red hair) of certain human ethnic groups appear also to be due to a slowing of the processes concerned with melanin-deposition: McConaill and Ralphs, 1937.)

This prolongation of a more protected early phase may also apply to the larval period, for instance in insects with their coenogenetic larvae, which are often highly adapted to their secondary mode of life. One need only think of the mayfly with its imaginal phase reduced both in structure and in duration.

Sometimes this reduction is carried to its logical extreme, and the adult phase is wiped out of the life-history by neoteny. This has demonstrably occurred in various beetles, and in the axolotl. It has probably taken place in ourselves as well: there is every reason to suppose that our adult ancestors possessed heavy brow ridges and protruding jaws, and that our smooth foreheads and orthognathous faces represent primarily the prolongation into maturity of a foetal and neo-natal phase that we share with the apes.

Haldane in an interesting paper (1932*b*) discusses these and similar phenomena from the standpoint of the time of action of the genes controlling them. A more comprehensive view, however, such as that adopted by de Beer (1940*a*), would include as still more important the genes' *rate* of action.

As A. R. Moore (1910, 1912) first suggested, and as Goldschmidt (summarized 1927), Ford and Huxley (summarized 1929), and others have conclusively shown, a large number (possibly the majority) of genes exert their effects through the intermediation of a process operating at a definite rate. They may be the direct cause of the process, or they may influence the rate of a process originated in some other way: in either case mutations in the genes concerned will alter the rate of some process of development.

The speeds of processes which such rate-factors control are not absolute, but relative—relative to the speed of other processes of development and of development in general. Further, it is found that a decrease in the rate of a visible process is in general accompanied by a delay in the time of its initial onset, and vice versa. This may be merely a threshold effect, but clearly has important biological consequences, since it will affect the *duration* of any other characters which can only manifest themselves before the process visibly manifests itself.

Furthermore, such processes do not necessarily continue indefinitely. Often they reach an equilibrium; when this is so the final level of the equilibrium also appears to be correlated with the rate of the process. This is so, for instance, with eye-colour in *Gammarus* (Ford and Huxley, 1929) and probably in man. The physiological basis of this fact is obscure, but once more it may involve interesting biological consequences. In addition to such rate-genes, others are known which appear only to affect the time of onset of a process and not its rate.

Attempts have been made by representatives of the Morgan school (see e.g. Schultz, 1935) to minimize the importance of these discoveries, by asserting that they constitute only a re-description of old phenomena and add nothing truly new. On the contrary, I would maintain that the concept of rate-genes is as important for biology as is the concept of genic balance or the gene-complex. I need not go into its bearings upon physiological genetics—the problem of how the genes become translated into characters—save to say that it has in this field already proved itself an indispensable tool. Here we are concerned with its evolutionary implications (see also the excellent discussion in Goldschmidt, 1940, pp. 311 seq.).

In the first place, since rate-genes are common, it is a legitimate provisional assumption that the rates of developmental processes in general are gene-controlled. Further, the simplification introduced into an analysis of development by the concept of relative rates of processes—exemplified by work such as Goldschmidt's on intersexuality and other problems (summarized 1927), Huxley's (1932) on the proportion of parts in animals, Ford and Huxley's (1929) on rate-genes, and Sinnott's (1935; Sinnott and Dunn, 1932, p. 341) on the role of rate-genes in determining fruit-shape in plants—makes it desirable to try this key first of all when attacking any developmental problem.

Next, as Swinnerton (1932) has stressed, a progressive mutational change in the speed of processes controlled by rate-genes affords a complete formal explanation of many paleontological data, e.g. in various molluscan shells.

It further affords an explanation certainly of most and probably of all cases of so-called reversal of dominance. The classical example is that recorded by A. Lang (1908) in crosses between red- and yellow-shelled snails. The F2 when young showed a ratio of 3 yellow : 1 red, whereas in the older individuals the ratio was 3 red : 1 yellow. The explanation is that all those individuals with either one or two "red" genes eventually become red, but the rate at which this occurs is reduced when the gene is present in single dose. For other examples see p. 218; Goldschmidt (1927); Huxley and Ford (1929).

It also helps us to understand the presence, the persistence, and the variability of vestigial organs. I may here cite a previous discussion of the subject (Huxley, 1932, p. 235):

"As regards vestigial organs, the arm-chair critic often demands of the evolutionist how the last stages in their reduction could occur through selection, and why, if reduction has gone as far as it has, it could not go on to total disappearance. In the light of our knowledge of relative growth, we may retort that we would *expect* the organ to be formed of normal or only slightly reduced relative size at its first origin, but then to be rendered vestigial in the adult by being endowed with negative heterogony [allometry: see Huxley and Teissier, 1936].* If rate-genes are as common as they appear to be, then what we have called the line of biological least resistance would be to produce adult vestigiality of an organ by reducing its growth-coefficient. So long as it is reduced to the requisite degree of insignificance at birth (or at whatever period a larger bulk would be deleterious), there is no need for reduction of its growth-rate to be pressed further. But the negative heterogony with which it is endowed will continue to operate, and it will therefore continue to grow

---

* Needham and Lerner (1941) have now proposed the term *heterauxesis* to supersede allometry in cases of true relative growth, reserving the latter term for comparison of relative proportions in different types. It will probably be best to use *allomorphosis* for this latter use, keeping allometry as a general and inclusive term (Needham, Huxley and Lerner, 1941).

relatively smaller with increase of absolute size. This last fact may account for the apparently useless degree of reduction seen in some vestigial organs, e.g. that of the whale's hind-limb. The degree of reduction may be useless considered in relation to the adult, but the relative size in the adult may be merely a secondary result of the degree of negative heterogony needed to get the organ out of the way, so to speak, before birth. In addition threshold mechanisms will possibly be at work, so that the organ, after progressive reduction, eventually disappears entirely.

"In such cases quite small differences in growth-ratio, if the range of absolute size over which they operate is considerable, will make quite large differences in final relative size, a fact which indubitably will help to account for the high variability of vestigial organs. Even when the organ itself never grows, as in the imaginal structures of insects with a metamorphosis, a similar degree of variability may be brought about by relatively small variations in the rate-genes responsible."

Consideration of the threshold-effect of any genes acting as rate-controllers for vestigial organs will also show that such organs must be unusually variable (op. cit., pp. 236–7).

The concept of rate-genes indeed provides a great simplification of the facts of recapitulation and anti-recapitulation. Whenever the rate of a process is correlated with time of onset and with final equilibrium-level, a mutation causing an increase in rate will produce recapitulatory phenomena—it will drive the visible onset of the process further back in ontogeny, will add a new "hypermorphic" character at the end of the process, and will cause all the steps of the original process to be recapitulated, but in an abbreviated form, during the course of the new process. This will account, for instance, for many of the recapitulatory phenomena seen in the suture-lines of ammonites (p. 507).

Conversely, a mutation causing a decrease in rate will have anti-recapitulatory effects—it will prolong the previous phase longer in ontogeny, it will not only slow the process down but render it "hypomorphic" by stopping it at a lower level of completion, and it will remove certain previous adult characters and push them off the time-map of the life-history (see Huxley,

1932, pp. 239–40). Many of the phenomena of so-called "racial senescence" in ammonites, including the gradual uncoiling of the shell, may be due to phenomena of this type (p. 507). Swinnerton (1938) has given numerous examples of processes of both types revealed in actual fossil lineages.

Haldane (1933) has drawn attention to a still further consequence of these facts, coupled with Fisher's principle of the origin of dominance (p. 75). He begins with a reminder of Goldschmidt's generalization that dominant alleles tend to promote not only a greater intensity of action, but one with a greater range both in space, over the organism's body, and in time, during its development. (This "greater range in time" is a less accurate formulation of the principle of earlier onset of rate-genes promoting a greater speed of process, as found by Ford and Huxley, 1929.) This, he then points out, will mean that even when homozygote and heterozygote are alike in the final stages there will be an early period in which the process involved is more advanced in the homozygote. Thus, "in so far as developmental abnormality is disadvantageous, the Fisher effect will always be tending to increase the activity of the genes", and so extending their action further and further back into ontogeny. Where the form of early stages is closely adaptive, as it must be in larvae, this backward spread of gene-effects concerned with adult characters will be checked by natural selection.* But where there is a sheltered embryo, its form will have little survival value, and the process will tend to continue unchecked. This would promote phenomena of tachygenesis and recapitulation, for many genes would tend originally to come into action rather late, but gradually to extend their activity back into ontogeny, so that the phylo-genetically older characters of the adult would tend to manifest themselves earlier in development, and this would be more prominent in forms with embryos than in those with larvae. This tendency may explain why recapitulatory phenomena appear to be commoner than anti-recapitulatory.

* This conclusion is borne out by the fact mentioned by Ford (1937) that it is rare in Lepidoptera for mutations to affect the visible character of both the larva and the imago.

Castle (1932), from his data on rabbits, has drawn general evolutionary conclusions similar to Haldane's.

As de Beer (1930) has pointed out, when coenogenetic changes occur in the embryo or larva, the adult remaining unchanged, neither paleontology nor comparative anatomy would register any phylogenetic advance. But if now neoteny or foetalization occurs, the old adult characters may be swept off the map and be replaced by characters of a quite novel type.

This process, which he calls *clandestine evolution*, has been operative on a small scale in neotenous beetles and amphibia. Garstang (1922) has suggested that it has operated on a large scale in the ancestry of the vertebrates and of the gastropods. It is in any case a principle of far-reaching importance.

A clear-cut example comes from the species of the snail *Cepaea*. It seems quite plain that their non-banded varieties are produced not because they contain a gene causing the total absence of pigment, but because they contain one which slows down pigment-formation and delays its visible onset relatively to general growth, to such an extent that growth is completed before any pigment can be formed.

This is a comparatively unimportant effect; but when major processes are affected, such as metamorphosis, sexual maturity, or general rate of growth or development, the results may be far-reaching. Paedogenesis is caused by relative acceleration of the processes leading to sexual maturity. Neoteny in the axolotl and presumably in insects is due to the slowing down of the processes leading to metamorphosis. The condition seen in man should not strictly be called neoteny, but rather foetalization or perhaps juvenilization: this would seem to be produced by a general slowing of developmental rate, relative both to time and to sexual maturity.

The existence of rate-factors has a bearing upon the problem presented by apparently useless characters. For alterations in the rate of a process will often automatically produce a number of secondary and apparently irrelevant effects. These will persist if they are harmless, or if any harmful effect is more than counter-balanced by the favourable effect of the initial change; and once produced they may of course become utilized for other purposes. Numerous examples of such "correlated characters", as Darwin called them, are now known (pp. 188 seq.).

I will take a simple example from *Gammarus*. The depth of colour of the eye depends essentially upon the rate of deposition of melanin in an originally pure red eye. But the visible effect depends also on the size of the eye at a given time—when the eye is smaller, the melanin is more crowded and the eye looks darker (Ford and Huxley, 1929). In point of fact depth of eye-colour has been found to be modified, first by genes controlling the rate of melanin-formation, secondly by genes controlling relative eye-size, and thirdly by genes controlling the rate of development of the whole organism. Thus a mutation affecting the relative rate of eye-growth will alter the depth of eye-pigmentation.

It would seem inevitable that many of the apparently useless features used in diagnosing species are correlated characters of this type. This may well prove to be the case with many of the pigmentary and other visible characters of the subspecies of *Lymantria* (p. 216; Goldschmidt, 1934). In cotton species (*Gossypium*) flower-colour, apparently owing to some underlying metabolic difference, has corolla-size as a correlate (Silow, 1941).

Of course not all useless "correlated characters" need be dependent simply on alterations in the rate of a process. The white-eye series of mutants in *Drosophila* also cause alterations in the shape of the spermatheca and the colour of the testis-sheath. Ford's analysis (1930) of Dobzhansky's data has made it probable that while the eye-characters of the series have been selected against to make their expression recessive, no selection has been operative on the internal characters (p. 80), which would then be mere correlates. Even here, however, it is probable that the different eye-colours of the white series represent the cross-sections of a series of rate-curves.

Important examples of correlated characters are the higher mental faculties of man. It is obvious that natural selection cannot have been operative directly in bringing about the evolution of intense musical or mathematical ability, or indeed of many specifically human faculties. As H. S. Harrison (1936) puts it, writing as an anthropologist, "it seems clear, indeed, that whatever factors were concerned in the ancient evolution of the modern type of man, the upper limits of his powers and aptitudes of mind were not determined by the struggle for existence". Natural selection, however, could be and doubtless was operative in bringing about the evolution of speech and conceptual thought, with their corollaries of rational control in the practical sphere and freedom of association between the different compartments of mental powers. Once, however, this level of mental attainment was reached, the so-called higher faculties immediately became possible. They are implicit in the general type of brain organization required for speech and conceptual thought, and are therefore correlated characters in our sense. A somewhat similar case from lower organisms is that of bird song. Undoubtedly true song has important functions, notably as territorial threat and advertisement (Huxley, 1938c). But given the complex emotional make-up of song-birds, song is uttered in many circumstances where it has other functions or is even functionless, produced "for its own sake". The sedge-warbler (*Acrocephalus schoenobaenus*) will sing as an expression of anger. Many birds sing as an expression of general well-being; the autumn recrudescence of song in many species would seem to be due to this, and to have no function. The vocal mimicry of many birds would seem to be an entirely unselected resultant, wholly comparable to human higher faculties.

A peculiar correlated character is that of human scapular shape, a convex inner border to the shoulder-blade being correlated with general fitness and high expectation of life, and vice versa for a concave one (Graves, 1932). Here, however, the correlation is a comparatively low one.

The development of correlated characters during evolution may stimulate orthogenesis One of the most apparently convincing bits of evidence for the reality of orthogenesis was the discovery of Osborn (1929) and his school, that horns of the same type were evolved independently, in the same region of the skull, in four separate groups of titanotheres. Sturtevant

(1924), however, suggested that characters of this sort might be correlated characters, and the study of relative growth (Huxley, 1924; 1932, p. 218) has provided a simple explanatory basis for this view in this particular case. The horns of titanotheres are, like most horns, allometric, increasing in relative size with the absolute size of the animal, and not appearing at all below a certain absolute size. We have only to postulate the potentiality of frontal horns in the ancestral titanothere stock, for their independent actualization in the different groups to become inevitable so soon as a certain threshold of body-size is reached. Increase of body-size is probably advantageous up to a limit; if so the horns are the useless correlate of a useful character. It would be more accurate to say *initially useless*, since presumably once they appeared they were employed in fighting★ (and see footnote†).

The interesting analysis of Hersh (1934) has shown that evolutionary allometry can be quantitatively studied. Thus in titanotheres, the evolutionary development of horn-length relative to basilar skull-length obeys the law of simple allometry, but with an unusually high equilibrium-constant or partition-coefficient ($a =$ about 9·0), He has further pointed out that, provided no change in growth-mechanism occurs during geological time, the equilibrium-constant for the relative growth of an organ will be the same for the evolution of a stock as for the development of a single individual within the stock.

Extrapolation of his curve indicates that the primitive titanotheres of the Eocene should have horns about 0· 5 mm. long—in other words, of inappreciable size; and this is actually the case.

He also records the important fact that the equilibrium-constants for the relative growth of certain characters (e.g. zygomatic width and free nasal length relative to skull-length)

★ The fact that in rhinoceroses, horns appeared independently in three separate lines, but on *different* regions of the head, is not to be explained either orthogenetically or on the basis of simple allometry as in titanotheres. An allometric factor must presumably be involved, but also, it would appear, a selective factor.

† Hersh points out that while the horns originally appeared as correlated characters, presumably as a result of selection for increased general bulk, once they were established and were of use in fighting, selection for increased horn-size might occur, and would then bring about increased bulk as a "correlated character" in its turn.

may change at definite points in geological time, indicating changes (presumably mutational) in the underlying ontogenetic growth-mechanism at certain stages in the evolution of the group.

According to Robb (1935-6) face-length in horses shows the same growth-constant for its ontogenetic and phylogenetic allometry, so that the phylogenetic change in skull-proportions would be entirely consequential on general size-increase. However, Reeve and Murray (1942) have shown that this is incorrect, the growth-constant changing during ontogeny from 1·5 to 1.0, while the phylogenetic growth-constant for the more primitive genera is 1.8; thus in modern (hypsodont) horses, lengthening of the face has been anticipated in early embryonic life. Robb further maintains that whereas digits ii and iv show the same slightly negative phylogenetic allometry in 3-toed and 1-toed forms, there is an abrupt change in the constant (b) defining the initial size of the primordia. Hersh's work on titanotheres indicates similar abrupt changes in the relative growth-constant a, as does Reeve and Murray's on the horse's face; while Herzberg and Massler's (1940) on rodent incisors indicates a gradual increase in a during phylogeny. Thus studies on relative growth sometimes lay bare the genetic mechanisms underlying evolution. Similarly, related subspecies may differ either in their b or a values for certain allometric organs—e.g. the antennae of the amphipod *Corophium volutator* (Chevais, 1937).

Detailed studies as to the different rate of change with time of various characters involved in a trend, such as that of Swinnerton (1921) on carboniferous corals, are likely to throw considerable light on selection and on consequential evolution.

Allometric growth is also without doubt the explanation for Lameere's and Geoffrey Smith's rule, namely that a large number of organs, all of them apparently allometric in the individual, tend to be of larger relative size in those species or genera of a group which are of greater absolute size. This is most clearly shown in beetles, but appears also to exist in hornbills, anteaters, and other forms (see Champy, 1924; Huxley, 1932, p. 212).

This principle has obvious taxonomic bearings. In the first place, percentage measurements of the proportionate size of an organ will have no diagnostic value unless either the organ is isometric, or there is not only a fixed adult phase (as in insects or higher vertebrates), but one with a restricted adult size-range (which is not true in many insects, e.g. Lucanidae, and even some mammals, e.g. the red deer (*Cervus elaphus*), as discussed by Huxley (1932, pp. 42 and 205). For some of the taxonomic implications, see Klauber (1938) on relative head-length in rattlesnakes, and Swinnerton (1940) for shell-shape in *Ostrea-Gryphaea* lineages (pp. 508, 515 *n*.).

A recent important study of this question has been made by Reeve (1940) on the anteaters of the family Myrmecophagidae. These include three well-marked genera, *Cyclopes*, *Tamandua*, and *Myrmecophaga*, characterized by increasing size and increasing relative face-length, measurable by facial index (see Table).

	Adult Skull-length.	Facial Index.	Growth-coefficient (a) of Maxillary Region.
Cyclopes	4·5–5 cm.	0·5	1·26
Tamandua	13–14 cm.	0·8	1·36
Myrmecophaga ..	36–38 cm.	1·6	1·77

The facial index is the ratio of maxilla length to rest-of-skull length. *Cyclopes* has a distinctly short face, while in the other two genera the snout region is very obviously elongated, exceptionally so in *Myrmecophaga*, where the maxilla is over 11 times as long as the rest of the skull.

The degree of allometry in the snout was then found for each species by comparing skulls of different absolute sizes. It will be seen from the table that all three genera show positive allometry, though it is intensified with increase or absolute size.* This last feature is unusual, but is one which might be anticipated where we are dealing with stages in a trend towards a particular specialization.

Reeve shows that most, but not all, the differences in facial

---

* The difference between the growth-coefficient in *Cyclopes* and *Tamandua* is only doubtfully significant.

proportion and skull structure between the three genera, especially between the two small ones, are purely consequential on the differences in absolute size; and there is no ground whatever for the proposals that have been made by various systematists to erect a separate subfamily or even family for the reception of *Cyclops*, on the ground of its different facial proportions.

Intraspecifically, too, the allometry principle has interesting taxonomic implications. Thus the genus *Tamandua* has been divided by recent systematists into two species, including nine subspecies, many of which latter have been erected on the basis of differences in percentage snout-length. Reeve in a further analysis (1941) shows that this procedure is invalid, since many such percentage differences are purely consequential on not very large differences in absolute size. This entirely bears out the warning given by Huxley (1932, p. 204, etc.) as to the preference of taxonomists for employing percentage rather than absolute size-differences in diagnosis. In any case, to erect subspecies on a few skulls (sometimes only one) which happen to show slight differences in proportion from the type, as has been done by e.g. Lönnberg (1937), is bound to lead to confusion. Doubtless geographical subspeciation will have occurred in these wide-ranging animals; but to establish the subspecies properly, absolute measurements, allometric constants, and pelage characters must be taken into account as well as differences in proportion.

Allometry has applications even to craniometrical indices. In mammals increased dolicocephaly appears to accompany increased absolute skull-size (Kappers, 1928). In man, this may also hold, though the evidence is more definite for increase of relative skull-height with absolute size (see Huxley, 1932, p. 220).

A fact of considerable interest is that certain organs, notably the vertebrate brain, show different degrees of allometry intra- and inter-specifically (see full discussion in de Beer, 1940a). In the simple allometry formula, brain-weight $= b$ (body-weight)^a, the intraspecific value of the equilibrium-constant a lies between $0 \cdot 22$ and $0 \cdot 27$. This appears to be a consequence of the developmental facts that neuron-number is approximately constant within the species, and that increase of body-volume causes an increase of neuron-volume which is somewhat less than proportional to the 1/3 power of body-volume, or in other words to the linear dimensions of the body, apparently on account of the linear increase in axon-length necessitated by increased body-size.

A further fact is that the value of the equilibrium-constant for different-sized individuals is lower in domestic races than in wild species (though, of course, the size-range of the domestic forms will be much greater). Thus in wild Canidae the value is about 0·26, in the domestic dog 0·22. This may perhaps be correlated with the different type of selection operating in the two cases, that for domestic races here being essentially concerned with size, irrespective of detailed physiological adjustments of the brain to a particular size.

Interspecifically, the equilibrium-constant is more than twice as high, about 0·56. For this to be the case, it is necessary that more neurons as well as larger neurons should be present. The brain-volume is thus nearly proportional to the *surface* of the body. This must represent the optimal relation physiologically.

Finally, there is the curious fact that the constant of initial proportion *b* varies from one group of species to another by whole-number multiples of $\sqrt{2}$. Dubois has suggested that this is due to the cerebral neuroblasts undergoing a different number of cell-divisions before finally differentiating. Whether this be true or not, we may be sure that the fact is consequential upon some ontogenetic process.

Lumer (1940) has successfully applied allometric analysis to the classification of the domestic breeds of dog (*Canis familiaris*). This enabled him in the first place to rule out the great majority of earlier classifications as being based solely on adult proportions (percentage ratios of various measurements). By plotting various absolute adult measurements of different-sized breeds on a double logarithmic scale, he obtained evolutionary growth-constants, as Hersh did with the titanotheres (p. 535), and he was then able to group the various breeds into six "allometric tribes", each characterized by possessing a particular set of growth-coefficients.

Different tribes may show the same growth-coefficients for

certain organs. Thus, for example, the terrier tribe (Alsatian, setter, poodle, fox-terrier, etc.), the bulldog tribe, the Great Dane tribe (with St. Bernard and Newfoundland) and the greyhound tribe (Borzoi, greyhound, whippet, etc.), have the following growth-coefficients (a), representing the skull's growth-relations in length and in breadth respectively.

	Terriers.	Bulldogs.	Great Danes.	Greyhounds.
Snout length/lower jaw length	1·11	1·72	0·69	1·11
Palate width/palate length ..	0·69	0·24	1·12	0·60

The greyhounds share with the terriers the length-relations of the snout, and presumably diverged later in respect of their width-relations. The other two groups have become more extreme in both relations, but in opposite directions.

The measurements on wolves (*Canis lupus*) are interesting. For the snout-length/cranial-length relation, the wolf stands at the intersection of the two main curves on to which all the forms (except the toy terrier) fall. For other measurements it usually conforms to the terrier or the Great Dane type. Though some of the results must be regarded as tentative, it seems clear that the form of domestic breeds is dependent on two main factors—first, mutations affecting the growth-coefficients of particular regions, and secondly, changes in proportions consequential on changes in absolute size. These changes will, of course, be quite different in the various tribes because of their difference in growth-coefficients.

Size in snakes is correlated with the pattern of the scales. As this is used for taxonomic diagnosis, the consequential effects of size-changes may be of systematic importance. Thus Stull (1940) describes inter-group clines in the genus *Pituophis*, involving a progressive diminution in the number of scale-rows in passing outwards from the centre of distribution. In addition, other scale-characters are graded and the relative tail-length increases markedly. But all these characters appear to be directly consequential on decreased absolute length. In fishes (*Catastomus*) delay in development relative to growth leads to an increased number of scales (Hubbs, 1941).

It is in general fair to state that change in absolute size is almost certain to produce numerous correlated changes in proportions. It is also true that change in relative size of an organ is quite likely to be accompanied by correlated changes in various of its own characters: this fact is illustrated by the antlers of deer (Cervidae) and the mandibles of stagbeetles (Lucanidae), where it has important taxonomic consequences in denying taxonomic validity to groups distinguished on the basis of the form of allometric organs (see Huxley, 1932, p. 204 seq.). In addition, continued increase in absolute size will so increase the relative size of an organ with well-marked allometry that it will eventually approach the boundary of disadvantage. Selection may then operate to reduce its rate of growth and therefore its final size, or, if conditions alter rapidly, the organism may be caught napping in an evolutionary sense, and be extinguished. Such considerations would account for such apparent cases of orthogenesis as the antlers of the Irish elk and the fantastic horns of some beetles (see Champy, 1924), as well as the limited size of certain types, such as the fiddler-crabs (*Uca*), where males weighing 17 g. have large claws three-quarters as heavy as the rest of the body (Huxley, 1932, pp. 32, 216).

The principle also has practical implications, as to which I may again quote from a previous publication (Huxley, 1932, p. 88):

"Hammond (1928, see also 1921) has also shown that the growth-gradients in the limbs and elsewhere affect the muscles as well as the bones, so that the study is of practical as well as theoretical importance. An important point made by Hammond may be given in his own words.

" 'As the animal grows, it changes its conformation; at birth the calf or lamb is all head and legs, its body is short and shallow, and the buttocks and loin are comparatively undeveloped; but, as it grows, the latter—buttocks, loin, etc.—grow at a faster rate than the head and legs, and so the proportions of the animal change. . . . The extent to which these proportions change determines its conformation; those which develop most for their age have the best meat conformation, while those which develop least have the worst. . . . Breed improvement for meat, therefore, means pushing a stage further the natural change of proportion as the animal matures. . . . The adult wild mouflon ewe is in its proportions but little in advance of the improved Suffolk lamb at birth, although it is much larger.'

"Thus it would appear that one of the chief advances made by man in creating improved breeds of sheep and other meat animals has been simply to steepen growth-gradients which already operate during post-natal development in the wild ancestral forms. Hammond himself (1928) has expressed a similar idea: 'The improver of meat-producing animals has apparently not chosen mutations occurring in isolated points independently, but rather has based his selection on the generalized correlated changes of growth.' "

McMeekan (1940–1) gives a similar analysis for the pig.

Another case where alteration in the rate of processes may have results of taxonomic importance is found in flying-fish (Exocoetidae). In certain species barbels are only present in young specimens. But the size at which the barbel is lost varies very greatly, apparently owing to the time-relations of the process differing in different subspecies (Brunn, 1933, who quotes similar cases from other fish).

A possible further consequential evolutionary result of mechan-isms regulating the proportion of parts I owe to a suggestion by Mr. Moy-Thomas. In standard textbooks it is customary to classify the extinct group of Palaeoniscoid fishes into two separate groups, the Palaeoniscidae and the Platysomidae. The only essential distinction between the two, however, is one of body-form, the former being elongated, the latter short and deep in body. In the course of their history, the two groups show parallel evolutionary trends.

If the groups were truly distinct, of separate origin, this would be a remarkable case of parallel evolution. On the other hand, as D'Arcy Thompson (1917, Chap. 17) first showed, differences in body-form of even greater extent than those between these two groups can be brought about by quite simple geometrical transformations, and Huxley (1932) pointed out that the actual mechanisms of relative growth, in the shape of growth-gradients or growth-fields of relatively simple conformation, provide a biological basis for such transformations, since alteration in a growth-gradient would affect the proportionate size of all the parts in whose growth it was concerned (see also Goldschmidt, 1940, pp. 311 seq.).

An alternative hypothesis, therefore, is that the Palaeoniscidae and the Platysomidae in reality constitute but one natural group, and that in every epoch two main types, elongate and deep-bodied, were evolved in relation to different modes of life. Only further study can decide between these two alternatives.

Granted the basic growth-mechanism responsible for the spiral shells of gastropods (Huxley, 1932, Chap. 5), only a limited set of shell-forms is available. Rensch (1934, p. 89) has collected interesting examples of the extraordinary convergence produced by this determinism of growth-mechanism in land-snails.

The claim that the concept of rate-genes is as important as that of the gene-complex would thus seem to be justified. Without the concept of the gene-complex we could obtain little insight into the intricate phenomena of genic balance or the puzzles of the evolution of dominance and recessiveness. Similarly the study of developmental processes controlled by rate-genes has illuminated the reversal of dominance, and the evolutionary aspects of recapitulation, of neoteny, foetalization, clandestine evolution, and apparently useless characters, as well as helping to a simpler understanding of the innumerable cases of quantitative evolution.

7. OTHER CONSEQUENTIAL EVOLUTIONARY TRENDS

So far, we have been considering mainly the evolutionary effects of differences in rate of development, whether between different species, different variants of the same species, or different parts of the body. However, there are many other examples of consequential evolution. Let us begin with one from bony fish, which has been discussed by Moy-Thomas (1938). Here, the dermal bones of the skull appear to be determined primarily in relation to the system of sensory canals. Bones not formed in direct relation with the canal system are produced to fill gaps between the canals. The precise number of centres operative in such a gap varies (in relation to factors at present unknown, but partly in relation to the size of the gap), so that the parietal region, for instance, may be occupied by bones varying from one to four in number. The canal system is on the whole constant in plan throughout the class, but varies in the detail of position of its various parts.

This will cause variation in the limits of particular bones, in the total number of bones determined in relation to the canal system, and in the size of the gaps to be filled by other bones. The parietal gap, for instance, is in some fish so much reduced that there is no room for a separate centre in it, and the parietal region is filled by a canal-determined bone, the supra-temporal.

It is obvious that, in these circumstances, the classical concept of homology breaks down. We cannot expect to homologize individual bones throughout the class (see also Westoll, 1936). The evolution of the dermal bones of the fish's skull is entirely consequential on the changes in detailed pattern of the sensory canal system. The interminable disputes of morphologists brought up in the post-Darwinian school, determined to discover precise correspondence between individual bones and to draw phylo-genetic conclusions from their homologies, turn out to have no factual basis. The right answer was difficult to find for the simple reason that the wrong question was asked. We are reminded of the fact pointed out by Jacques Loeb (see Loeb, 1912) that in embryo fish (*Fundulus*) the wandering pigment-cells eventually arrange themselves along the blood-vessels, so that the visible colour-pattern follows the pattern of the circulatory system.

In the Malagasy insectivore *Hemicentetes semispinosus* an appar-ently adaptive reduction in tooth-size (p. 287) has certain consequential effects on skull-form (Butler, 1941). It would be interesting to see whether such effects are general.

An example of great evolutionary importance is that cited by Watson (1926) of the locomotion of vertebrates. Among fish, there are two main types of locomotion—that of most teleosts, in which movement is mainly restricted to the base of the tail, and that of various other forms, in which the whole body is markedly undulated. In this second group, the elasmobranchs hold their pectoral fins stiffly out, while the Dipnoi and *Polyp-*

terus and its relatives do not. Only from this last sub-type could the locomotion of the tailed Amphibia be derived. These were first aquatic, but even later their locomotion was "a swimming upon land" (but see the criticism of Moy-Thomas, 1934). This is an excellent example of what we may call historical evolutionary consequence, where the past history of an organism helps to determine its future mode of evolution. Some examples of this we have already mentioned (p. 522) under the head of historical restriction of variability. A striking case of this in the evolution of our own species is the effect of monotocy (p. 525). Our own evolution also provides an example of rather a different nature. The assumption of the erect posture at once converted many of our internal adjustments into maladjustments. Here was an immediate consequential step; the incipient counteraction of these maladjustments is a further one.

Sex has numerous consequential effects. In the first place, there is the tendency for characters acquired by one sex, e.g. by intrasexual selection, to be transferred in whole or in part to the other (see Meisenheimer, 1921, chap. 23; Winterbottom, 1929, 1932). This will in certain groups increase the amount of evolutionary diversification to be found between species. Conversely, the difference in internal environment provided by the two sexes may and frequently will give rise to sex-limited characters which are wholly non-adaptive at their origin, but may later be used as the basis for adaptive (e.g. epigamic) sex-limited characters (cf. discussion in C. and F. Gordon, 1940, who succeeded in building up stocks of *Drosophila* with a non-adaptive but definite sex-limited female character—brown palp).

Somewhat similarly, the sex-limited difference in hair-number varies considerably in different species of *Drosophila* (Mather, 1941). Thus in *D. melanogaster* and in *D. simulans* females have rather more hairs than males, but in *D. virilis* many fewer.

A very extraordinary case concerns the external genitalia of hyenas (see L. H. Matthews, 1939*b*). These are indistinguishable externally in males and non-parous females. Copulation, as a result, appears to be an elaborate and difficult feat. Matthews suggests that this apparently dystelic state of affairs is the consequence of some unusual upset of endocrine balance, the females having an excess of androgenic substances and presumably a deficiency of oestrogens. The condition is closely parallel to that seen in adrenal virilism in females of our own species.

Empirical observation reveals numerous other peculiarities of organic construction which may form the basis for consequential evolutionary trends.

In mammals, for example, the extremities ("points": ears, limbs, muzzle, and tail), either as a whole or in their terminal portions, are frequently of a different colour from the rest of the body. This undoubtedly depends on a physiological peculiarity of these regions, namely their lower temperature. Detailed studies have been made of the problem in the Himalayan breed of domestic rabbit, which is white with black points (see Iljin, 1931). The Himalayan pattern depends on an allele of the albino series which reduces the intensity of melanin-production. At this level of production, melanin can only be formed in regions below a certain critical temperature. In normal animals, these regions exist only in the points; but by experimental procedure (shaving and subsequent exposure to cold) black hair can be induced in any region of the body. Thyroidization also affects the reaction. The Siamese pattern in cats is similar (Iljin and Iljin, 1930).

In the most general terms, the points provide a differential environment for the manifestation of pigmentation-genes; and when these are working close to a threshold level of production, differential effects are readily produced in these areas. The quantitative restriction of this or that type of pigmentation depends on quantitative reduction in the activity of the genes responsible; but its localized distribution depends on a differential pattern in the construction of the organism, providing different opportunities for gene-expression in different areas.

The dorsal stripe present in so many breeds and species of mammals is doubtless a further example of the same principle. Numerous other examples may be found enumerated in works such as those of Haecker (1925, 1927).*

* It is necessary on theoretical grounds to draw a sharp distinction between such cases, dependent on the general construction of the organism, and others

The presence of such organizational patterns will result in a considerable amount of parallel evolution in regard to visible colour-pattern.

Mammalian extremities (points) also react to temperature in another way, namely by enlarging at higher temperatures (p. 213). This is again very likely due to the increase in their heat-loss and the lowering of their intrinsic temperature at lower external temperatures. In any case, this will account for a large number of parallel trends (character-gradients) affecting relative size of extremities, which are found in nature.

The most extensive type of organismal pattern is the organic gradient or as it is better styled gradient-field (Huxley, 1935). Although we are still in ignorance as to the physiological basis of such gradients, they undoubtedly exist, and by providing differential environments for gene-expression, open the door to consequential evolution. Such gradients may be total, extending through the whole organism, or partial, extending through a single organ or region.

The interesting effect of different regional gradients on pigmentation is well shown in the zebras, in which the striping is always at right angles to the main axis of the region, whether trunk or limb. Where hind-limb area meets trunk area, interaction of the stripe system occurs, giving curious patterns. These patterns differ from species to species (see Haecker, 1927), doubtless on account of slight differences in the form and relative intensity of the underlying gradients.

One of the most widespread results of the existence of such gradients is the common type of coloration in many vertebrates, which produces counter-shading with dark back and light belly, following the main dorso-ventral gradient of the embryo. According to the mode of gene-expression, the dark may grade into the light or be sharply delimited, and according to the

which depend on the existence of local fields—e.g. the sharply delimited plumage-fields of many birds (Haecker, op. cit.). These appear to have more analogy with the localized morphogenetic fields into which the developing embryo becomes divided, and which may persist into the adult, as revealed by regeneration experiments in urodeles (references in Huxley and de Beer 1934, and Huxley, 1935).

threshold of gene-activity, the light ventral area may be larger or smaller. Genetic analysis in rodents has revealed a series of alleles, whose differential effect within this gradient is quantitatively different. By altering the threshold of gene-activity, uniformity of coloration from mid-dorsal to mid-ventral line may be established, and by special mechanisms the normal pattern may be reversed, as in the offensive skunks and Cape polecats and the well-defended ratels (*Mephitis, Conepatus, Ictonyx*, and *Mellivora*), in order to enhance instead of to reduce conspicuousness, or replaced by quite different types of patterns; but the existence of the gradient has provided the basis for a great deal of parallel evolution in pigmentation characters.

The phenomenon known as determinate variability also depends undoubtedly on the existence of organismal or regional gradients. For instance, in the ladybird beetle *Adalia frigida* (Zarapkin, 1930) all stages occur from unspotted through spotted to nearly uniform black types. There is, however, a regularity in the order in which the seven pairs of spots appear and in that in which they are subsequently joined. The gradient-field appears to be a complex one, and there is accordingly a certain amount of variability, but the general regularity is marked.

Gause (1930) has made an interesting comparative study of the subject in three species of the coleopteran genus *Phytodecta*. All most commonly have five pairs of spots in a characteristic pattern on the elytra, but variants occur, especially in the minus direction. Variability in spot-number is least in *P. rufipes*, greatest in *P. viminalis*, with *P. linnaeanus* in an intermediate position. This difference, however, depends on some relation between an antero-posterior gradient and the threshold for pigment-deposition in the spot areas, since in all forms the anterior spots are rarely (or never) absent, but the posterior spots frequently, and increasingly so with increasing distance from the anterior end. The threshold for invariable pigment-deposition (spot present in 99 per cent of cases or over) is halfway down the elytra in *P. rufipes*, so that three pairs of spots are always present; in *P. linnaeanus* it is near the anterior end, leaving two stable pairs, and in *P. viminalis* still more anterior, leaving only one invariable pair of spots. This may be due either to alteration in the slope of the gradient or in the intensity of pigment-formation, or both. That the gradient is really a gradient-field and capable of alterations affecting spot-pattern is shown by a comparison of spot-frequency in *P. linnaeanus* and *P. viminalis*. Whereas in the latter the facts can only be interpreted as the basis of a uniform gradient running diagonally from the external anterior margin to the posterior point of junction of the elytra, the gradient of *P. linnaeanus* must be more complex, starting as in *P. viminalis*, but in the posterior half of the elytra running out towards the external margin again.

Thus the form of the gradient-field in the elytra has both general and special consequences, for the intra- as well as the inter-specific variation of the pigmentation of the genus.

A related phenomenon occurs in the pluteus larvae of sea-urchins. The skeleton of the plutei belonging to various echinoids of extremely different adult structure, and assigned to different suborders or even subclasses, is virtually identical. Von Ubisch (1933) suggests, on the basis of experimental analysis, that this is due to the existence of a general type of gradient-field determining skeleton-formation, shared by most typical plutei, and that simple quantitative alterations in this would bring about strong similarity in skeleton, irrespective of common descent or adult resemblance, thus simulating orthogenesis. In a later paper (1939) he shows that cytoplasmic viscosity is the chief agent affecting the form of the larval skeleton. By treatments altering viscosity, normally simple skeletons can be made more complex, and then show a close resemblance to the normally complex skeletons of other forms.

A slightly different phenomenon of the same sort occurs in another ladybird, *Epilachna chrysomelina* (Zarapkin and H. A. Timoféeff-Ressovsky, 1932). Here the shape of single spots was studied. It was found that with increase in absolute spot-size (antero-posterior length) most spots became increasingly elongated in form (higher ratio of length to breadth). The degree to which this occurs, however, is much greater in some spots than in others, and may differ markedly even in neighbouring spots.

The gradient-field affecting pigment-deposition must accordingly be distorted in different ways in different regions.

A genetic difference in spot-size will therefore bring about consequential differences in spot-form: such a difference was found to distinguish the races from Palestine and Corfu respectively. One spot (near the hind end of the elytra) was found to behave in a more complex manner, becoming first more and later less elongate with increase in absolute length.

Similar studies made by R. H. Johnson (1910) on the entire family Coccinellidae, have shown that some intrinsic plan of organization (gradient-field) has important consequential effects on the evolution of pattern in the whole group of ladybird beetles. A great volume of data on this and cognate subjects is discussed by Vogt and Vogt (1938).

Interesting work has also been done by Schwanwitsch (1924, 1926) on the patterns of butterflies' wings. He shows that in a large section of the Rhopalocera, all existing patterns can be derived from an original prototype through the modification of different markings by a limited number of methods. Both the existence of the original prototypic pattern and the limited modes of its alteration operate to restrict the evolution of pattern in the group in a consequential way.

Returning from colour-patterns to other characters, we find that the existence of the abnormal condition of the head known as otocephaly is in guinea-pigs due to a combination of genetic and environmental factors acting upon the primary gradient of the embryo (or that of the organizer). Similarly the suppression of digits in the course of evolution in the guinea-pig family, and their subsequent restoration by selective breeding (p. 501), appears not to have depended on genes acting on each digit separately or directly, but on genes affecting the general tendency of the limb primordium to break up into discontinuous parts (digits) at its distal end, by interfering with a controlling centre of the digit-forming field, situated on the post-axial side of the hand region of the limb-bud (discussion of both cases in S. Wright, 1934b, and of the latter in J. P. Scott, 1938). For instance, the same gene which in single dose tends to restore a normal thumb, and often a normal little toe also, in double dose is lethal, but permits development to a stage at which the embryo is seen to possess the rudiments of 8 to 12 toes per foot. Further, one modifier was found which promoted the development of thumbs but inhibited the development of little toes. This may most readily be interpreted as a gene steepening a gradient concerned with digit-separation, and running from the pre-axial to the post-axial side of the limb.

An interesting consequence of serial repetition of structures such as teeth is mentioned by Gregory (1936). The mammalian tooth-series of course early becomes differentiated into markedly distinct subseries. But the fundamental seriation, with its capacity for more extended repetition, remains, and when a character is added in one subseries, "as in the case of new cusps in the premolars or new cuspules in the molars, the whole tooth-row often tends to be glossed over, so to speak, with the same surface-features, so that all the cheek-teeth, as in the horses, come to look amazingly like each other". This phenomenon Gregory calls "secondary polyisomerism"; it frequently imparts a quite deceptive appearance of lack of differentiation, the new features which have spread over a large part of the series disguising the older characters differentiating the subseries.

A curious consequential effect is the weakening of feather-structure associated with the presence of red lipochrome pigment. This appears to be due to the inhibition of feather-differentiation by lipochrome (Desselberger, 1930). The chief result is the reduction or loss of barbules, while the barbs fail to show full differentiation into cortical and medullary layers.

In the barbets of the genus *Lybius*, black-, red- and white-headed forms are found. One of the last-mentioned, *L. torquatus zombae*, studied by Salomonsen (1938), appears to have been recently derived by mutation (of at least two genes) from a red form (see p. 195).

Red feathers, as we have seen, become worn much more rapidly and thoroughly than black; but the white feathers of *zombae* are so weak that they are almost pathological, the whole white portion rapidly disappearing with wear. Apparently, the presence of lipochrome confers a certain degree of mechanical solidity. Thus in *L. t. zombae*, the white feathers are doubly weak: they retain the weak structure characteristic of the red feathers from which they have arisen, and also, through the lack of all lipochrome, the remaining structure is further weakened. In certain other white-headed *Lybius*, however, the white feathers are normal. Presumably other mutations have occurred which restore the normal feather-structure. Salomonsen notes that some individuals of *L. t. zombae* have patches of normal white feathers on the head; possibly selection is already at work repairing some of the deleterious effects of the white mutations (cf. the similar "repair" of the St. Bernard dog; p. 71).

After this chapter was written, Goldschmidt (1940) published his *Material Basis of Evolution*, in which he pays considerable attention to the problem, devoting over 100 pages to "evolution and the potentialities of development". Already in 1920 he had recognized that "a change in the hereditary type can occur only within the possibilities and limitations set by the normal process of development", and had illustrated the point at some length. In this latter work he restates the matter more positively, e.g. p.322: "What is called in a general way the mechanics of development will decide the direction of possible evolutionary changes. In many cases there will be only one direction. This is orthogenesis without Lamarckism, without mysticism. . . ."

Among his examples we may cite a few. Where certain red pigments normally occur in Lepidoptera, yellow varieties (aberrations) occur, and white mutants may arise from the yellow forms (p. 12). This, however, is due to alteration in the rate and intensity of red pigment-formation (Ford, 1937).

He agrees that the demonstration of growth-gradients and growth-fields accounts for many examples of non-adaptive variation, and lightens the burden on natural selection by showing that numerous correlated changes in proportions will be expected to occur as the result of single mutations affecting the form of the growth-gradient.*

---

* It is worth recalling that developmental processes "lighten the burden on natural selection" in a number of other ways, though here by means of modifi-

Some of his most striking cases concern the morphogenetic effect of the ductless glands. For instance, once the thyroid has been evolved, certain changes in it will be expected to exert similar consequences in numerous types. It is no accident that the thyroid is associated with metamorphosis not only in Amphibia but in various fish such as eels, flounders, and mud-hoppers (*Periophthalmus*). In the last-named, the aquatic larva becomes an amphibious adult, but excess thyroid causes an intensification of all its adaptations to aerial existence, most notably in the pectoral fins, which come to simulate a tetrapod limb (p. 277; Harms, 1934).

Again, achondroplasia and other peculiarities in size or proportions, which are certainly or probably dependent on endocrine changes and which occur as aberrations in man and other forms and as breed-types in dogs, goldfish, etc., are closely similar to the normal condition in various wild species (short-legged carnivores, bulldog-faced fish, etc.). There is at least a *prima facie* case for regarding the primary change leading to the evolution of these species as being similar to that involved in the production of the peculiar breeds and aberrations. On the other hand, there is no reason to suppose that the change in the wild species must have been abrupt, as Goldschmidt assumes. It is more likely to have been a gradual process, accompanied by buffering with modifiers (cf. our discussion of Stockard's results with St. Bernard dogs, p. 71). It seems clear, however, that the endocrine system constitutes a "chemical skeleton" whose existence and nature prescribes certain limits to, and certain favoured modes of, evolutionary change in its possessors.

With the progress of what Haecker (1925) calls phenogenetics and of physiological genetics in general, numerous other examples will undoubtedly be unearthed in the most diverse groups of

cation, not by consequential effects of the type we have here been discussing. I refer to the extraordinary functional adaptation of fine structure and often size seen in bones, tendons, blood-vessels, etc. (see discussion in Huxley and de Beer, 1934, chap. 13, §§ 6, 7, pp. 431 seq.). These have frequently been held up as impossible of explanation on a selectionist view. So they would be if they were the result of genetic adaptation; but all the details appear to be due to modificational adaptation, produced anew by functional demands in each individual. The general framework is genetically adaptive, and so is the general capacity for reaction; the rest is modificational polish.

organisms. We are here concerned only to establish principles. It seems clear that the existence of organizational patterns in organisms, whether in the shape of general, regional, or local gradient-fields, or in some other form, will have consequential evolutionary effects. It will for one thing account for a great deal of otherwise mysterious parallel evolution, e.g. in pattern, in horn-development in titanotheres, in relative size of allometric organs, etc.

Aggregation, as in social hymenoptera, can also be regarded as a type of organization, and may have important consequential effects. To take but one example, the wood-eating habits of primitive termites, so important for their evolutionary success, could, it seems, only have arisen in a social form. For their digestion of cellulose depends on the presence of symbiotic protozoa; and these are lost at each moult, so that reinfection can only occur through association with other, non-moulting individuals (see discussion in Emerson, 1939).

One might perhaps also include a category of historical consequential effects, as when types evolved in relation to one habitat manage to invade another. Thus, as Professor Salisbury informs me in a letter, various species of trees in the neotropical rain-forests are deciduous; and all are closely related to deciduous temperate types. However, this is perhaps to extend the concept of consequential evolution too widely, until it becomes merged in the obvious fact that in evolution the present and future of an organic type is partly determined by its past.

Examples such as those of social insects (pp. 480, 482), of certation in pollen (p. 481), of selection in abundant as against rare species, and of intra-uterine selection in polytocous mammals, show how the type and course of evolutionary trends may be altered according to the type of competition and selection at work. A somewhat similar consequential trend in this field concerns the effect of inter-male competition in birds and other groups. The result has been that in general the males have become much more differentiated than the females, their secondary sexual characters being usually striking and specifically distinctive; and further that some of this masculine diversification has then been transferred to the females, although in them the characters are functionless (see Darwin, 1871; Meisenheimer, 1921, chap. 23; Winterbottom, 1929 and 1932 ; Huxley, 1938*a* and *b*; and p. 545).

The examples we have been considering in these sections show how the fact that most genes affect the rate, the time of onset, the duration, and the type of developmental processes, will provide the raw material for trends involving progressive alteration in one or other of these factors of development. Since the raw material is so abundant, consequential trends of this sort will be frequent. A description of some bearings of the subject is given by Huxley (1932, Chap. 7), and fuller evolutionary discussion is given, not only by Goldschmidt (see above), but by Haldane in his previously cited paper (1932*b*), by de Beer (1940*b*), and from the standpoint of physiological genetics by Waddington (1941*b*). The course of Darwinian evolution is thus seen as determined (in varying degrees in different forms) not only by the type of selection, not only by the frequency of mutation, not only by the past history of the species, but also by the nature of the developmental effects of genes and of the ontogenetic process in general.

POSTSCRIPT.—Weidenreich's important recent paper (1941) deals with consequential trends in mammalian skulls, dependent upon brain-growth. The brain's relative growth-rate is high in early embryonic life; in most mammals, it later slows down markedly, and the high allometry of the face then comes into play. In dwarf domestic breeds and small wild species, facial allometry is checked early. There normally results not only a relative orthognathism, but also absence of cranial superstructure (sagittal crest, supra-orbital ridges, etc.), persistent cranial sutures, rounded palate, smaller teeth, often with simplified pattern, relatively wide cranial cavity (brachycephaly), etc.; in young and dwarf dogs, the frontals are almost entirely cranial, while in adult large dogs their major part is facial. Man, though not a dwarf species, shows the "dwarf" type of skull. This is not due to the retention of visible foetal characters, as postulated by Bolk (p. 526), but to the persistence into later stages of the brain's early high relative growth-rate.

CHAPTER 10

EVOLUTIONARY PROGRESS

1. IS EVOLUTIONARY PROGRESS A SCIENTIFIC CONCEPT?

The question of evolutionary or biological progress remains. There still exists a very great deal of confusion among biologists on the subject. Indeed the confusion appears to be greater among professional biologists than among laymen. This is probably due to the common human failing of not seeing the wood for the trees; there are so many more trees for the professional!*

The chief objections that have been made to employing *progress* at all as a biological term, and to the use of its correlates *higher* and *lower* as applied to groups of organisms, are as follows. First, it is objected that a bacillus, a jellyfish, or a tapeworm is as well adapted to its environment as a bird, an ant, or a man, and that therefore it is incorrect to speak of the latter as higher than the former, and illogical to speak of the processes leading to their production as involving progress. An even simpler objection is to use mere survival as criterion of biological value, instead of adaptation. Man survives: but so does the tubercle bacillus. So why call man the higher organism of the two?

A somewhat similar argument points to the fact that evolution, both in the fossil record and indirectly shows us numerous examples of specialization leading to increased efficiency of adaptation to this or that mode of life; but that many of such

---

* For a fuller discussion of certain aspects of the problem see Huxley, 1923*a*, 1936, 1940; Wells, Huxley and Wells, 1930, Book 5, chap. 6, § 5.

specialized lines become extinct, while most of the remainder reach an equilibrium and show no further change.

This type of objection, then, points to certain fundamental attributes of living things or their evolution, uses them as definitions of progress, and then denies that progress exists because they are found in all kinds of organisms, and not only in those that the believers in the existence of progress would call progressive.

A slightly less uncompromising attitude is taken up by those who admit that there has been an increase of complexity or an increase in degree of organization, but deny that this has any value, biological or otherwise, and accordingly refuse to dignify this trend by a term such as progress, with all its implications.

Some sociologists, faced with the problem of reconciling the objective criteria of the physical sciences with the value criteria with which the sociological data confronts them, take refuge in the ostrich-like attitude of refusing to recognize any scale of values. Thus Doob in a recent book (1940) writes:

"In this way, the anthropologist has attempted to remove the idea of progress from his discipline. For him, there is just change, or perhaps a tendency towards increasing complexity. Neither change nor complexity is good or bad; there are differences in degree, not in quality or virtue. . . . The sweep of historical progress reveals no progressive trend. . . ."

By introducing certain objective criteria into our definition of progress, as we do in the succeeding section, this objection can be overcome, at least for pre-human evolution. In regard to human evolution, however, as we shall see in the concluding section of this chapter, the nettle must be grasped, and human values given a place among the criteria of human progress.

The second main type of objection consists in showing that many processes of evolution are not progressive in any possible sense of the word, and then drawing the conclusion that progress does not exist. For instance, many forms of life, of which the brachiopod *Lingula* is the best-known example, have demonstrably remained unchanged for enormous periods of several hundreds of millions of years; if a Law of Progress exists, the objectors argue, how is it that such organisms are exempt from its operations?

A variant of this objection is to draw attention to the numerous cases where evolution has led to degeneration involving a degradation of form and function, as in tapeworms, *Sacculina* and other parasites, in sea-squirts and other sedentary forms: how, it is asked, can the evolutionary process be regarded as progressive if it produces degeneration?

This category of objections can be readily disposed of. Objectors of this type have been guilty of setting up an Aunt Sally of their own creation for the pleasure of knocking her down. They have assumed that progress must be universal and compulsory: when they find, quite correctly, that universal and compulsory progress does not exist, they state that they have proved that progress does not exist. This, however, is an elementary fallacy. The task before the biologist is not to define progress *a priori*, but to proceed inductively to see whether he can or cannot find evidence of a process which can legitimately be called progressive. It may just as well prove to be partial as universal. Indeed, human experience would encourage search along those lines; the fact that man's progress in mechanical arts, for instance, in one part of the world is accompanied by complete stagnation or even retrogression in other parts, is a familiar fact. Thus evolution may perfectly well include progress without being progressive as a whole.

The first category of objections, when considered closely, is seen to rest upon a similar fallacy. Here again an Aunt Sally has been set up. Progress is first defined in terms of certain properties: and then the distribution of those properties among organisms is shown not to be progressive.

These procedures would be laughable, if they were not lamentable in arguing a lack of training in logical thought and scientific procedure among biologists. Once more, the elementary fact must be stressed that the only correct method of approach to the problem is an inductive one. Even the hardened opponents of the idea of biological progress find it difficult to avoid speaking of higher and lower organisms, though they may salve their consciences by putting the words between inverted commas. The unprejudiced observer will accordingly begin by examining various types of "so-called higher" organisms and trying to discover what characters they possess in common by which they differ from "lower" organisms. He will then proceed to examine the course of evolution as recorded in fossils and deduced from indirect evidence, to see what the main types of evolutionary change have been; whether some of them have consistently led to the development of characters diagnostic of "higher" forms; which types of change have been most successful in producing new groups, dominant forms, and so forth. If evolutionary progress exists, he will by this means discover its factual basis, and this will enable him to give an objective definition.

2. THE DEFINITION OF EVOLUTIONARY PROGRESS

Proceeding on these lines, we can immediately rule out certain characters of organisms and their evolution from any definition of biological progress. Adaptation and survival, for instance, are universal, and are found just as much in "lower" as in "higher" forms: indeed, many higher types have become extinct while lower ones have survived. Complexity of organization or of life-cycle cannot be ruled out so simply. High types *are* on the whole more complex than low. But many obviously low organisms exhibit remarkable complexities, and, what is more cogent, many very complex types have become extinct or have speedily come to an evolutionary dead end.

Perhaps the most salient fact in the evolutionary history of life is the succession of what the paleontologist calls dominant types.* These are characterized not only by a high degree of complexity for the epoch in which they lived, but by a capacity for branching out into a multiplicity of forms. This radiation seems always to be accompanied by the partial or even total extinction of competing main types, and doubtless the one fact is in large part directly correlated with the other.

In the early Paleozoic the primitive relatives of the Crustacea

* For fuller summary, see Wells, Huxley, and Wells (1930), Book 5.

known as the trilobites were the dominant group. These were succeeded by the marine arachnoids called sea-scorpions or eurypterids, and they in turn by the armoured but jawless vertebrates, the ostracoderms, more closely related to lampreys than to true fish. The fish, however, were not far behind, and soon became the dominant group. Meanwhile, groups both from among the arthropods and the vertebrates became adapted to land life, and towards the close of the Paleozoic, insects and amphibians could both claim the title of dominant groups. The amphibia shortly gave rise to the reptiles, much more fully adapted to land life, and the primitive early insects produced higher types, such as beetles, hymenoptera and lepidoptera. Higher insects and reptiles were the dominant land groups in the Mesozoic, while among aquatic forms the fish remained pre-eminent, and evolved into more efficient types: from the end of the Mesozoic onwards, however, they show little further change.

Birds and mammals began their career in the Mesozoic, but only became dominant in the Cenozoic. The mammals continued their evolution through the whole of this epoch, while the insects reached a standstill soon after its beginning. Finally man's ancestral stock diverged, probably towards the middle of the Cenozoic, but did not become dominant until the latter part of the Ice Age.

In these last two cases, the rise of the new type and the downfall of the old was without question accompanied and facilitated by world-wide climatic change, and this was probably true for other biological revolutions, such as the rise of the reptiles to dominance.

When the facts concerning dominant groups are surveyed in more detail, they yield various interesting conclusions. In the first place, biologists are in substantial agreement as to what were and what were not dominant groups. Secondly, some groups once dominant have become wholly extinguished, like the trilobites, eurypterids and ostracoderms, while others survive only in a much reduced form, many of their sub-groups having been extinguished, as with the reptiles or the monotremes, or their numbers enormously diminished, as with the larger non-human placentals. Those which do not show reduction of one or the other sort have remained to all intents and purposes unchanged for a longer or shorter period of geological time, as with the insects or the birds. Finally, later dominant groups normally arise from an unspecialized line of an earlier dominant group, as the birds and reptiles from among the early reptiles, man from the primates among the mammals (p. 525, footnote). They represent, in fact, one among many lines of adaptive radiation; but they differ from the others in containing the potentiality of evolving so as to become dominant on a new level, with the aid of new properties. Usually the new dominance is marked by a fresh outburst of radiation: the only exception to this rule is Man, a dominant type which shows negligible radiation of the usual structurally-adapted sort, but makes up for its absence by the complexity of his social life and his division of labour.

If we then try to analyse the matter still further by examining the characters which distinguish dominant from non-dominant and earlier from later dominant groups, we shall find first of all, efficiency in such matters as speed and the application of force to overcome physical limitations. The eurypterids must have been better swimmers than the trilobites, the fish, with their muscular tails, much better than either; and the later fish are clearly more efficient aquatic mechanisms than the earlier. Similarly the earlier reptiles were heavy and clumsy, and quite incapable of swift running. Sense-organs also are improved, and brains enlarged. In the latest stages the power of manipulation is evolved. Through a combination of these various factors man is able to deal with his environment in a greater variety of ways, and to apply greater forces to its control, than any other organism.

Another set of characteristics concerns the internal environment. Lower marine organisms have blood or body-fluids identical in saline concentrations with that of the seawater in which they live; and if the composition of their fluid environment is changed, that of their blood changes correspondingly. The higher fish, on the other hand, have the capacity of keeping their internal environment chemically almost constant. Birds and mammals have gone a step further: they can keep the temperature of their internal environment constant too, and so are independent of a wide range of external temperature change.

The early land animals were faced with the problem of becoming independent of changes in the moisture-content of the air. This was accomplished only very partially by amphibia, but fully by adult reptiles and insects through the development of a hard impermeable covering. The freeing of the young vertebrate from dependence on water was more difficult. The great majority of amphibians are still aquatic for the earlier part of their existence: the elaborate arrangements for rendering the reptilian egg cleidoic (J. Needham, 1931, pp. 1132 seq.) were needed to permit of the whole life-cycle becoming truly terrestrial.

There is no need to multiply examples. The distinguishing characteristics of dominant groups all fall into one or other of two types—those making for greater control over the environment and those making for greater independence of changes in the environment. Thus advance in these respects may provisionally be taken as the criterion of biological progress.

3. THE NATURE AND MECHANISM OF EVOLUTIONARY PROGRESS

It is important to realize that progress, as thus defined, is not the same as specialization. Specialization, as we have previously noted, is an improvement in efficiency of adaptation for a particular mode of life: progress is an improvement in efficiency of living in general. The latter is an all-round, the former a one-sided advance. We must also remember that in evolutionary history we can and must judge by final results. And there is no certain case on record of a line showing a high degree of specialization giving rise to a new type. All new types which themselves are capable of adaptive radiation seem to have been produced by relatively unspecialized ancestral lines.*

* If Garstang's suggestion be true (see p. 532) that "clandestine evolution" has enabled new large-scale radiations to start by utilizing a *larval* organization and driving the adult organization off the stage, we have here an apparent

Looked at from a slightly different angle, we may say that progress must in part at least be defined on the basis of final results. These results have consisted in the historical fact of a succession of dominant groups. And the chief characteristic which analysis reveals as having contributed to the rise of any one of these groups is an improvement that is not one-sided but all-round and basic. Temperature-regulation, for instance, is a property which affects almost every function as well as enabling its possessors to extend their activities in time and their range in space. Placental reproduction is not only a greater protection for the young—a placental mother, however hard-pressed, cannot abandon her unborn embryo—but this additional protection, together with the later period of maternal care, makes possible the extension of the plastic period of learning which then served as the basis for the further continuance of progress.

It might, however, be held that biological inventions such as the lung and cleidoic shelled egg, which opened the world of land to the vertebrates, are after all nothing but specializations. Are they not of the same nature as the wing which unlocked the kingdom of the air to the birds, or even to the degenerations and peculiar physiological changes which made it possible for parasites to enter upon that hitherto inaccessible habitat provided by the intestines of other animals? This is in one sense true; but in another it is untrue. The bird and the tapeworm, although they did conquer a new section of the environment, in so doing were as a matter of actual fact cut off from further progress. Theirs was only a specialization, though a large and notable one. The conquest of the land, however, not only did not involve any such limitations, but made demands upon the organism which could be and in some groups were met by further changes of a definitely progressive nature.* Temperature-regulation, for

exception. It is only fair to say, however, that this view is still highly speculative, and that in any case we would presume that a relatively unspecialized larval type would have served as the new starting-point.

 * Morley Roberts (1920, 1930, etc.) gives numerous interesting examples in which new and in a sense abnormal demands upon organisms result eventually in adjustments which are more or less adaptive in relation to the new situation. Unfortunately he postulates a lamarckian transmission of modifications which vitiates or obscures much of his evolutionary discussion.

instance, could never have arisen through natural selection except in an environment with rapidly-changing temperatures: in the less changeable waters of the sea the premium upon it would not be high enough.* The same is true for eurythermy (p. 444).

Of course a progressive advance may eventually come to a dead end, as has happened with the insects, when all the biological possibilities inherent in the type of organization have been exploited. From one point of view it might be permissible to call such a trend a long-range specialization; but it would appear more reasonable to style it a form of progress, albeit one which is destined eventually to be arrested. It is limited as opposed to unlimited progress.

A word is needed here on the restricted nature of biological progress. We have seen that evolution may involve downward or lateral trends, in the shape of degeneration or certain forms of specialization, and may also leave certain types stable. Further, lower types may persist alongside higher, even when the lower are representatives of a once-dominant group that includes the higher types. From this, it will first be seen, as we already mentioned, that progress is not compulsory and universal; and secondly that it will not be so marked in regard to the average of biological efficiency as to its upper limit. Progress, in other words, can most readily be studied by examining the *upper levels* of biological efficiency (as determined by our criteria of control and independence) attained by life at successive periods of its evolution.

For this, during the earlier part of life's history, we must rely upon the indirect evidence of phylogeny, drawn from comparative morphology, physiology, and embryology, while for the last thousand million years this is further illuminated by the light of paleontology, with its direct evidence of fossils.

We have thus arrived at a definition of evolutionary progress as consisting in a raising of the upper level of biological efficiency, this being defined as increased control over and independence of

---

* Once evolved on land, however, it proved its value even in the sea, as evidenced by the success of the Cetacea and other secondary aquatics among mammals (see p. 452).

the environment.* As an alternative we might define it as a raising of the upper level of all-round functional efficiency and of harmony of internal adjustment.†

This brings us to a further objection which is often raised to the idea of progress, namely, that it is a mere anthropomorphism. This view asserts that we judge animals as higher or lower by their greater or lesser resemblance to ourselves and that we give the name of progress to the evolutionary trend which happens to have culminated in ourselves. If we were ants, the objectors continue, we should regard insects as the highest group and resemblance to ants as the essential basis of a "high" organism: while if we were eagles our criterion of progress would be an avian one.

Even Haldane (1932a, p. 153) has adopted this view. He writes, "I have been using such words as 'progress', 'advance, and 'degeneration', as I think one must in such a discussion, but I am well aware that such terminology represents rather a tendency of man to pat himself on the back than any clear scientific thinking. . . . Man of to-day is probably an extremely primitive and imperfect type of rational being. He is a worse animal than the monkey. . . . We must remember that when we speak of progress in Evolution we are already leaving the relatively firm ground of scientific objectivity for the shifting morass of human values."

This I would deny. Haldane has neglected to observe that man possesses greater power of control over nature, and lives in greater independence of his environment than any monkey. The use of an inductive method of approach removes all force from such objections. The definitions of progress that we were able to name as a result of a survey of evolutionary facts, though admittedly very general, are not subjective but objective in their character. That the idea of progress is not an anthropomorphism can immediately be seen if we consider what views would be taken by a philosophic tapeworm or jellyfish. Granted that such organisms could reason, they would have to admit that they

---

* Herbert Spencer recognized the importance of increased independence as a criterion of evolutionary advance: see references in Needham (1937).

† See also R. W. Gerard (1940), "Organism, Society, and Science", *Sci. Mo.*, **50**: 340.

were neither dominant types, nor endowed with any potentiality
of further advance, but that one was a degenerate blind alley,
the other a specialization of a primitive type long left behind
by more successful forms of life. And the same would be equally
true, though not so strikingly obvious, of ant or eagle. Man *is*
the latest dominant type to be evolved, and this being so, we are
justified in calling the trends which have led to his development
progressive. We must, however, of course beware of subjectivism
and of reading human values into earlier stages of evolutionary
progress. Human values are doubtless essential criteria for the
steps of any future progress: but only biological values can have
been operative before man appeared.

The value of such a broad biological definition of progress
may be illustrated by reference to a recent definition of human
progress by Professor Gordon Childe (1936). Professor Childe,
too, is seeking for an objective criterion for progress; but the
criterion he adopts is increase of numbers. Quite apart from the
logical difficulty that increase in population must, on a finite
earth, eventually approach a limit, it is clear that this criterion
is at once invalidated by the facts of general biology.

There are many more of various common plankton organisms
than of men or of any bird or mammal. There are in all probability
many more houseflies than human beings, more bacteria, even
of a single species, than of any metazoan. If we apply our criterion
of increased control and independence, we see that it would be
theoretically quite possible (though difficult with our present
type of economy) to obtain progressive changes in human
civilization with an accompanying decline in population.

Here let me interject a further word concerning objective and
subjective criteria for progress. As regards human progress, it
is clear that subjective criteria cannot and should not be neglected;
human values and feelings must be taken into account in deciding
on the future aims for advance. But in comparing human with
pre-human progress, we must clearly stick to objective standards.
I would thus like to make a distinction between biological or
evolutionary progress and human progress. The former is a
biological term with an objective basis: it includes one aspect of

human progress. Human progress, on the other hand, has connotations of value as well as of efficiency, subjective as well as objective criteria.★

Returning to biology, we may sum up as follows. Progress is all-round biological improvement. Specialization is one-sided biological improvement: it always involves the sacrificing of certain organs or functions for the greater efficiency of others. It is the failure to distinguish between these two types of evolutionary process that vitiates the generalizations of many biologists (e.g. Hawkins, 1936).

Degeneration is a form of specialization in which the majority of the somatic organs are sacrificed for greater efficiency in adaptation to a sedentary or a parasitic life. Locomotor organs disappear, sensory and nervous systems are much reduced, and in parasites the digestive system may be abolished. Reproductive mechanisms, however, may be inordinately specialized, as in certain parasites.

Besides these types of evolutionary process, we may have stability, as in the lamp-shell *Lingula*, or in ants during most of the Cenozoic epoch. Stable types are presumably either extremely well-adapted to a permanent biological niche or have reached the limit of specialization or of progress possible to them.

Finally, we may have the type of evolutionary trend best known among the Ammonites, of increasing complication followed by simplification. This we have already discussed in our section on orthogenesis.

A possible method of evolutionary escape from specialization is afforded by changes in rate of sexual maturity relative to general development, leading to neoteny or foetalization, as

★ On the other hand, to confine the term *progress* entirely to human affairs, and to contrast it with *evolution* in pre-human history, as does Marett (1933, 1939), is to restrict the meaning of progress unduly, while distorting that of evolution. On three successive pages Marett describes or defines progress in three different ways: (1) the moral of human history and pre-history would seem to be that "progress in the direction of the spiritual is implicit in normal human endeavour". (2) Progress in spirituality in the future "may be conceived in terms of the greatest self-realization of the greatest number". (3) "Real progress is progress in charity." It should be clear how important it is to give greater universality and concreteness to the idea of progress by considering human progress as a special case of biological progress.

discussed in a previous chapter (pp. 526 ff., 555). This may abolish a specialized adult phase and give the opportunity for the progressive evolution of a new generalized type.

As revealed in the succession of steps that have led to new dominant types, progress has taken diverse forms. At one stage, the combination of cells to form a multicellular individual, at another the evolution of a head; later the development of lungs, still later of warm blood, and finally the enhancement of intelligence by speech. But all, though in curiously different ways, have enhanced the organism's capacities for control and for independence; and each has justified itself not only in immediate results but in the later steps which it made possible.

We have now dealt with the fact of evolutionary progress, and with the philosophical and biological difficulties inherent in the concept. What of its mechanism? It should be clear that if natural selection can account for adaptation and for long-range trends of specialization, it can account for progress too. Progressive changes have obviously given their owners advantages which have enabled them to become dominant. Sometimes it may have needed a climatic revolution to give the progressive change full play, as seems to have been the case at the end of the Cretaceous with the mammal-reptile differential of advantage; but when it came, the advantage had very large results—wholesale extinctions on the one hand, wholesale radiation of new types on the other. It seems to be a general characteristic of evolution that in each epoch a minority of stocks give rise to the majority in the next phase, while conversely the majority of the rest become extinguished or are reduced in numbers.

There is no more need to postulate an *élan vital* or a guiding purpose to account for evolutionary progress than to account for adaptation, for degeneration or any other form of specialization.*

One point is of importance. Although we can quite correctly speak of evolutionary progress as a biological fact, this progress

---

* A small minority of biologists, such as Broom (1933), still feel impelled to invoke "spiritual agencies" to account for progressive evolution, but their number is decreasing as the implications of modern selection theories are grasped.

is of a particular and limited nature. It is, as we have seen, an empirical fact that evolutionary progress can only be measured by the upper level reached: for the lower levels are also retained. This has on numerous occasions been used as an argument against the existence of anything which can properly be called progress; but its employment in this connection is fallacious. It is on a par with saying that the invention of the automobile does not represent an advance, because horse-drawn vehicles remain more convenient for certain purposes, or pack animals for certain localities. A progressive step in evolution will normally and probably invariably bring about the extermination of some types at a lower level; but the variety of environments and of the available modes of filling them is such that it is extremely unlikely to exterminate them all. The fact that protozoa should be able to exist side by side with metazoa, or a considerable army of the "defeated" group of reptiles together with their mammalian "conquerors", is not in any way surprising on selectionist principles: it is to be expected.

4. THE PAST COURSE OF EVOLUTIONARY PROGRESS

One somewhat curious fact emerges from a survey of biological progress as culminating for the evolutionary moment in the dominance of *Homo sapiens*. It could apparently have pursued no other general course than that which it has historically followed: or, if it be impossible to uphold such a sweeping and universal negative, we may at least say that among the actual inhabitants of the earth, past and present, no other lines could have been taken which would have produced speech and conceptual thought, the features that form the basis for man's biological dominance.*

Multicellular organization was necessary to achieve the basis for adequate size: without triploblastic development and a blood-system, elaborate organization and further size would have been impossible. Among the coelomates, only the vertebrates were eligible as agents for unlimited progress, for only they were able

* So far as I am aware, this was first emphasized by Huxley, 1930.

to achieve the combination of active efficiency, size, and terrestrial existence on which the later stages of progress were of necessity based. Only in the water have the molluscs achieved any great advance. The arthropods are not only hampered by their necessity for moulting; but their land representatives, as was first pointed out by Krogh, are restricted by their tracheal respiration to very small size. They are therefore also restricted to cold-bloodedness and to a reliance on instinctive behaviour (see discussion in Wells, Huxley and Wells, 1930, Book 5, chap. 5, § 7). Lungs were one needful precursor of intelligence. Warm blood was another, since only with a constant internal environment could the brain achieve stability and regularity for its finer functions. This limits us to birds and mammals as bearers of the torch of progress. But birds were ruled out by their depriving themselves of potential hands in favour of actual wings, and perhaps also by the restriction of their size made necessary in the interests of flight.

Remain the mammals. During the Tertiary epoch, most mammalian lines cut themselves off from the possibility of ultimate progress by concentrating on immediate specialization. A horse or a lion is armoured against progress by the very efficiency of its limbs and teeth and sense of smell: it is a limited piece of organic machinery. As Elliot Smith has so fully set forth, the penultimate steps in the development of our human intelligence could never have been taken except in arboreal ancestors, in whom the forelimb could be converted into a hand, and sight inevitably became the dominant sense in place of smell. But, for the ultimate step, it was necessary for the anthropoid to descend from the trees before he could become man. This meant the final liberation of the hand, and also placed the evolving creature in a more varied environment, in which a higher premium was placed upon intelligence. Further, the foetalization necessary for a prolonged period of learning could only have occurred in a monotocous species (pp. 525, 555; Haldane, 1932a, p. 124; Spence and Yerkes, 1937). Weidenreich (1941) maintains that the attainment of the erect posture was a necessary prerequisite for the final stages in human cerebral evolution.

The last step yet taken in evolutionary progress, and the only one to hold out the promise of unlimited (or indeed of any further) progress in the evolutionary future, is the degree of intelligence which involves true speech and conceptual thought: and it is found exclusively in man. This, however, could only arise in a monotocous mammal of terrestrial habit, but arboreal for most of its mammalian ancestry. All other known groups of animals, except the ancestral line of this kind of mammal, are ruled out. Conceptual thought is not merely found exclusively in man: it could not have been evolved on earth except in man.

Evolution is thus seen as a series of blind alleys. Some are extremely short—those leading to new genera and species that either remain stable or become extinct. Others are longer—the lines of adaptive radiation within a group such as a class or sub-class, which run for tens of millions of years before coming up against their terminal blank wall. Others are still longer—the lines that have in the past led to the development of the major phyla and their highest representatives; their course is to be reckoned not in tens but in hundreds of millions of years. But all in the long run have terminated blindly. That of the echino-derms, for instance, reached its climax before the end of the Mesozoic. For the arthropods, represented by their highest group, the insects, the full stop seems to have come in the early Cenozoic: even the ants and bees have made no advance since the Oligocene. For the birds, the Miocene marked the end; for the mammals, the Pliocene.

Only along one single line is progress and its future possibility being continued—the line of man. If man were wiped out, it is in the highest degree improbable that the step to conceptual thought would again be taken, even by his nearest kin. In the ten or twenty million years since his ancestral stock branched off from the rest of the anthropoids, these relatives of his have been forced into their own lines of specialization, and have quite left behind them that more generalized stage from which a conscious thinking creature could develop. Although the reversibility of evolution is not an impossibility *per se*, it is probably an actual impossibility in a world of competing types. Man might con-ceivably cause the capacity for speech and thought to develop by long and intensive selection in the progeny of chimpanzees or gorillas; but Nature, it seems certain, could never do so.

One of the concomitants of organic progress has been the progressive cutting down of the possible modes of further progress, until now, after a thousand or fifteen hundred million years of evolution, progress hangs on but a single thread. That thread is the human germ-plasm. As Villiers de l'Isle-Adam wrote in *L'Ève Future*, "L'Homme . . . seul, dans l'univers, n'est pas fini."

5. PROGRESS IN THE EVOLUTIONARY FUTURE

What of the future? In the past, every major step in evolutionary progress has been followed by an outburst of change. For one thing the familiar possibilities of adaptive radiation may be exploited anew by a number of fresh types which dominate or extinguish the older dispensation by the aid of the new piece of organic machinery which they possess. Or, when the progressive step has opened up new environmental realms, as was the case with lungs and the shelled egg, these are conquered and peopled; or the fundamental progressive mechanism may itself be improved, as was the case with temperature-regulation or the pre-natal care of the young in mammals.

Conscious and conceptual thought is the latest step in life's progress. It is, in the perspective of evolution, a very recent one, having been taken perhaps only one or two and certainly less than ten million years ago. Although already it has been the cause of many and radical changes, its main effects are indubitably still to come. What will they be? Prophetic phantasy is a dangerous pastime for a scientist, and I do not propose to indulge it here. But at least we can exclude certain possibilities. Man, we can be certain, is not within any near future destined to break up into separate radiating lines. For the first time in evolution, a new major step in biological progress will produce but a single species. The genetic variety achieved elsewhere by radiating divergence will with us depend primarily upon crossing and recombination (see Huxley, 1940).

We can also set limits to the extension of his range. For the planet which he inhabits is limited, and adventures to other planets or other stars are possibilities for the remote future only.

During historic times, all or almost all of the increase in man's control over nature have been non-genetic, owing to his exploitation of his biologically unique capacity for tradition, whereby he is provided with a modificational substitute for genetic change. The realization of the possibilities thus available will continue to play a major part in human evolution for a very long period, and may contribute largely to human progress.

More basic, however, though much slower in operation, are changes in the genetic constitution of the species, and it is evident that the main part of any large genetic change in the biologically near future must then be sought in the improvement of the fundamental basis of human dominance—the feeling, thinking brain, and the most important aspect of such advance will be increased intelligence, which, as A. Huxley (1937, p. 265) has stressed, implies greater disinterestedness and fuller control of emotional impulse.*

First, let us remind ourselves that, as we have already set forth (p. 482), we with our human type of society must give up any hope of developing such altruistic instincts as those of the social insects. It would be more correct to say that this is impossible so long as our species continue in its present reproductive habits. If we were to adopt the system advocated by Muller (1936) and Brewer (1937), of separating the two functions of sex—love and reproduction—and using the gametes of a few highly endowed males to sire all the next generation, or if we could discover how to implement the suggestion of Haldane in his *Daedalus* and reproduce our species solely from selected germinal tissue-cultures, then all kinds of new possibilities would emerge. True castes might be developed, and some at least of them might be endowed with altruistic and communal impulses. In any case, as A. Huxley (1937) points out in an interesting

* Of course great increases in man's control over and independence of his environment may be produced by the better utilization of his existing capacities (see e.g. G. H. Thomson, 1936); but these represent modifications, not genetic changes.

discussion, progress (or, I would prefer to say, future human progress) is dependent on an increase of intraspecific co-operation until it preponderates over intraspecific competition.

Meanwhile there are many obvious ways in which the brain's level of performance could be genetically raised—in acuteness of perception, memory, synthetic grasp and intuition, analytic capacity, mental energy, creative power, balance, and judgment. If for all these attributes of mind the average of our population could be raised to the level now attained by the best endowed ten-thousandth or even thousandth, that alone would be of far-reaching evolutionary significance. Nor is there any reason to suppose that such quantitative increase could not be pushed beyond its present upper limits.

Further, there are other faculties, the bare existence of which is as yet scarcely established: and these too might be developed until they were as commonly distributed as, say, musical or mathematical gifts are to-day. I refer to telepathy and other extra-sensory activities of mind, which the painstaking work of Rhine (1935), Tyrrell (1935), and others is now forcing upon the scientific world as a subject demanding close analysis.

If this were so, it would be in a sense only a continuation of a process that has already been at work—the utilization by man for his own ends of hitherto useless by-products of his mental constitution. The earlier members of the Hominidae can have had little use for the higher ranges of aesthetic creation or appreciation, for mathematics or pure intellectual construction. Yet to-day these play a large part in human existence, and have come to possess important practical consequences as well as value in and for themselves. The development of telepathic knowledge or feeling, if it really exists, would have equally important consequences, practical as well as intrinsic.

In any case, one important point should be borne in mind. After most of the major progressive steps taken by life in the past, the progressive stock has found itself handicapped by characteristics developed in earlier phases, and has been forced to modify or abandon these to realize the full possibilities of the new phase (see M. Roberts, 1920, 1930, for various examples of forced adjustment to new conditions, but with the caveat that some are highly speculative, and that all are presented in a lamarckian frame of reference which often obscures their true significance). This evolutionary fact is perhaps most obvious in relation to the vertebrates' emergence from water on to land. But it applies in other cases too. The homothermy of mammals demanded the scrapping of scales and the substitution of hair; man's erect posture brought with it a number of anatomical inconveniences. But man's step to conscious thought is perhaps more radical in this respect than any other.

By means of this new gift, man has discovered how to grow food instead of hunting it, and to substitute extraneous sources of power for that derived from his own muscles. And for the satisfaction of a few instincts, he has been able to substitute new and more complex satisfactions, in the realm of morality, pure intellect, aesthetics, and creative activity.

The problem immediately poses itself whether man's muscular power and urges to hunting prowess may not often be a handicap to his new modes of control over his environment, and whether some of his inherited impulses and his simpler irrational satisfactions may not stand in the way of higher values and fuller enjoyment. The poet spoke of letting ape and tiger die. To this pair, the cynic later added the donkey, as more pervasive and in the long run more dangerous. The evolutionary biologist is tempted to ask whether the aim should not be to let the mammal die within us, so as the more effectually to permit the man to live.

Here the problem of values must be faced. Man differs from any previous dominant type in that he can consciously formulate values. And the realization of these in relation to the priority determined by whatever scale of values is adopted, must accordingly be added to the criteria of biological progress, once advance has reached the human level. Furthermore, the introduction of such criteria based upon values, in addition to the simpler and more objective criteria of increasing control and independence which sufficed for pre-human evolution, alters the direction of progress. It might perhaps be preferable to say that it alters the level on which progress occurs. True human progress consists in increases of aesthetic, intellectual, and spiritual experience and satisfaction.

Of course, increase of control and of independence is necessary for the increase of these spiritual satisfactions; but the more or less measurable and objective control over and independence of external environment are now merely subsidiary mechanisms serving as the material basis for the human type of progress; and the really significant control and independence apply to man's mental states—his control of ideas to give intellectual satisfaction, of form and colour or of sound to give aesthetic satisfaction, his independence of inessential stimuli and ideas to give the satisfaction of mystic detachment and inner ecstasy.

The ordinary man, or at least the ordinary poet, philosopher, and theologian, is always asking himself what is the purpose of human life, and is anxious to discover some extraneous purpose to which he and humanity may conform. Some find such a purpose exhibited directly in revealed religion; others think that they can uncover it from the facts of nature. One of the commonest methods of this form of natural religion is to point to evolution as manifesting such a purpose. The history of life, it is asserted, manifests guidance on the part of some external power; and the usual deduction is that we can safely trust that same power for further guidance in the future.

I believe this reasoning to be wholly false. The purpose manifested in evolution, whether in adaptation, specialization, or biological progress, is only an apparent purpose (p. 412). It is as much a product of blind forces as is the falling of a stone to earth or the ebb and flow of the tides. It is we who have read purpose into evolution, as earlier men projected will and emotion into inorganic phenomena like storm or earthquake. If we wish to work towards a purpose for the future of man, we must formulate that purpose ourselves. Purposes in life are made, not found.

But if we cannot discover a purpose in evolution, we can discern a direction—the line of evolutionary progress. And this past direction can serve as a guide in formulating our purpose for the future. Increase of control, increase of independence, increase of internal co-ordination; increase of knowledge, of means for co-ordinating knowledge, of elaborateness and intensity of feeling—those are trends of the most general order. If we do not continue them in the future, we cannot hope that we are in the main line of evolutionary progress any more than could a sea-urchin or a tapeworm.

As further advice to be gleaned from evolution there is the fact we have just discussed, that each major step in progress necessitates scrapping some of the achievements of previous advances. But this warning remains as general as the positive guidance. The precise formulation of human purpose cannot be decided on the basis of the past. Each step in evolutionary progress has brought new problems, which have had to be solved on their own merits; and with the new predominance of mind that has come with man, life finds its new problems even more unfamiliar than usual. This last step marks a critical point in evolution, and has brought life into situations that differ in quality from those to which it was earlier accustomed.

The future of progressive evolution is the future of man. The future of man, if it is to be progress and not merely a standstill or a degeneration, must be guided by a deliberate purpose. And this human purpose can only be formulated in terms of the new attributes achieved by life in becoming human. Man, as we have stressed, is in many respects unique among animals:* his purpose must take account of his unique features as well as of those he shares with other life.

Human purpose and the progress based upon it must accordingly be formulated in terms of human values; but it must also take account of human needs and limitations, whether these be of a biological order, such as our dietary requirements or our mode of reproduction, or of a human order, such as our intellectual limitations or our inevitable subjection to emotional conflict.

Obviously the formulation of an agreed purpose for man as a whole will not be easy. There have been many attempts already. To-day we are experiencing the struggle between two opposed

* For a full analysis of the biological peculiarities of our species see Huxley, 1940.

ideals—that of the subordination of the individual to the community, and that of his intrinsic superiority. Another struggle still in progress is between the idea of a purpose directed to a future life in a supernatural world, and one directed to progress in this existing world. Until such major conflicts are resolved, humanity can have no single major purpose, and progress can be but fitful and slow. Before progress can begin to be rapid, man must cease being afraid of his uniqueness, and must not continue to put off the responsibilities that are really his on to the shoulders of mythical gods or metaphysical absolutes (see Everett, 1932).*

But let us not forget that it is possible for progress to be achieved. After the disillusionment of the early twentieth century it has become as fashionable to deny the existence of progress and to brand the idea of it as a human illusion, as it was fashionable in the optimism of the nineteenth century to proclaim not only its existence but its inevitability. The truth is between the two extremes. Progress is a major fact of past evolution; but it is limited to a few selected stocks. It may continue in the future, but it is not inevitable; man, by now become the trustee of evolution, must work and plan if he is to achieve further progress for himself and so for life.

This limited and contingent progress is very different from the *deus ex machina* of nineteenth-century thought, and our optimism may well be tempered by reflection on the difficulties to be overcome. None the less, the demonstration of the existence of a general trend which can legitimately be called progress, and the definition of its limitations, will remain as a fundamental contribution of evolutionary biology to human thought.

* See also Huxley, 1943, *Evolutionary Ethics* (Romanes Lecture) University Press, Oxford.

ADDENDUM 1955

For recent developments readers are referred to the following works:
PALEONTOLOGY, COURSE OF EVOLUTION: G. G. SIMPSON " The Major Features of Evolution." New York, 1953.
SPECIATION AND GENETICS: T. DOBZHANSKY " Genetics and the Origin of Species." (3rd. edition) New York, 1951. E. MAYR " Systematics and the Origin of Species." New York, 1942.
GEOGRAPHICAL RULES: and GENERAL SYNTHESIS: B. RENSCH " Neuere Probleme der Abstammungslehre." (2nd. edition) Stuttgart, 1954.
EVOLUTIONARY ETHICS: and PROGRESS: T. H. AND J. S. HUXLEY. " Evolution and Ethics." London, 1947.

INTRODUCTION TO THE SECOND EDITION

In the twenty years since this book was first published, there has been an enormous volume of new work and new ideas on the subject of evolution. To do justice to this vast material within the limits of a short introduction is impossible. All I can do is to mention some of the more interesting discoveries, new ideas and new lines of study in this field, together with some of the more important books on the subject that have been published since 1942. I have restricted myself almost entirely to books and papers published in English: these contain references to the important work published in other languages during the period.

The main fact to note is that the neo-Darwinian, synthetic, or integrative theory of evolution that I maintained in 1942 has gained many new adherents and may now be regarded as the established view. It has been supported by Rensch in his *Evolution above the Species Level* (1959a); by G. G. Simpson in *Tempo and Mode in Evolution* (1944) and *Major Factors in Evolution* (1953), by Ernst Mayr in *Systematics and the Origin of Species* (1942), by Dobhansky in *Genetics and the Origin of Species* (1951) and in *Mankind Evolving* (1962), by Stebbins in *Variation and Evolution in Plants* (1954), by Carter in *A Hundred Years of Evolution* (1957): also by the mass of the contributors to *The Evolution of Life*, Vol. I of the University of Chicago centennial on *Evolution after Darwin* (1960), to the Society of Experimental Biology's Symposium on *Evolution* (1953), to *Hundert Jahre Evolutionsforschung*, edited by Heberer and Schwanitz (1960), to *Darwin's Biological Work*, edited by P. R. Bell (1959), and to *A Century of Darwin*, edited by S. A. Barnett (1958). See also Waddington's *The Nature of Life* (1961) and Moody's *Introduction to Evolution* (1953).

It underlies most recent works on genetics, like L. C. Dunn's symposium on *Genetics in the 20th Century* (1951) Srb and Owen's text-book of *General Genetics* (1952) or King's up-to-date *Genetics* (1962), and modern treatments of major animal groups such as J. Z. Young's remarkable *The Life of Vertebrates* (1950). Finally, it has been adopted or assumed by the great majority of the contributors to *Evolution*, the first scientific journal devoted to the subject, whose successful launching in 1947 marked a major step in the progress of evolutionary biology.

Darwin's original contention, that biological evolution is a natural process, effected primarily by natural selection, has thus become increasingly confirmed, and all other theories of evolution requiring a supernatural or vitalistic force or mechanism, such as Bergson's creative evolution, and all "autogenetic" theories (Dobzhansky) such as Berg's nomogenesis, Osborn's aristogenesis, and orthogenesis in the strict sense, together with all Lamarckian theories involving the inheritance of acquired characters, have become increasingly untenable.

Only in the U.S.S.R. has Lamarckism found favour. Here, under the influence of Lysenko, the peculiar brand of Lamarckism styled Michurinism was given official sanction, and extravagant and ill-founded claims were made on its behalf, while neo-Mendelian genetics, which everywhere else was advancing in a spectacular way, was officially condemned as bourgeois or capitalist "Morganist-Mendelist," and Soviet geneticists were exiled or lost their jobs. See J. S. Huxley, *Soviet Genetics and World Science*, 1949; and C. Zirkle, *Evolution, Marxian Biology and the Social Scene*, 1959.

The Soviet opposition to genetical science was particularly strong in the field of human genetics, since the orthodox Marxists believed or wanted to believe that a few generations of socialism would improve the genetic quality of the population. Eventually Lysenko lost his dominant position. But though orthodox genetics is now once more permitted, some official encouragement is given to an uneasy mixture of Mendelism and Michurinism.

Meanwhile in Britain, Waddington (1957, 1960) has made a notable contribution to evolutionary theory by his discovery that Lamarckian inheritance may be simulated by a purely neo-Darwinian mechanism. This he called *genetic assimilation*. It operates through the natural selection of genes which dispose the developing organism to become modified in reaction to some environmental stimulus. Waddington showed experimentally that after a number of generations of selection for individuals which showed the most pronounced reaction, a strain could be

obtained which developed the modified character in the absence
of the environmental stimulus. This applies to adaptive as well as
to non-adaptive modifications, and, as Haldane (1959, p. 146)
points out, could clearly be effective in regard to the origin of
various types of instinctive behaviour, by the genetic assimilation
of behavioural modifications. (See also Stern, 1959).

The upholders of orthogenetic evolution had claimed that good
fossil series showed unvarying evolutionary trends in one definite
direction, and that this could not be explained except by postulating some inherent directive force. Their standard example was
the evolution of the horse. However, G. G. Simpson in his book
Horses (1951) conclusively demonstrated that the facts are otherwise: not only are trends sometimes reversed in single branches
of the group, but the main trend shows definite changes of direction during its course. This is consonant with the view that
natural selection is "opportunistic" in its operations, a view
especially championed by G. G. Simpson and accepted by most
other modern authorities, such as Dobzhansky and Mayr.

Sheppard in his book *Natural Selection and Heredity* (1958) has
analysed the operation of natural selection in detail, especially
in relation to population genetics, speciation, and adaptations such
as mimicry.

The most comprehensive and up-to-date exposition of the synthetic theory of evolution has just been given by Ernst Mayr in
his magistral book *Animal Species and Evolution* (1963). As he points
out, a radical change in recent evolutionary theory has been "the
replacement of typologic thinking by population thinking."
However, the modern synthetic theory still retains the combination of induction and deduction that underlay Darwin's original
theory of evolution by natural selection.

His main point is that the species is a highly organised unit of
evolution, based on an integrated pattern of co-operative genes
co-adapted to produce an optimal phenotype, highly homeo-
static and resistant to major change. This results in what has been
termed *genetic relativity*. No gene has a fixed selective value: one
and the same gene may be highly advantageous on one genetic
background, highly disadvantageous on another. A long term

consequence is that the range of mutations and recombinations available to any particular organism or taxon is a restricted one and its evolutionary possibilities are correspondingly limited. This presumably accounts for some so-called orthogenetic trends, and for various phenotypic tendencies of different families and orders of animals and plants.

As a further result, speciation, in the sense of the splitting of one species into two, appears to occur most frequent by divergence of isolated populations near the margins of a species' range. These, under the pressure of new selective forces and in the absence of gene-flow from the central gene-pool of the species, are able to escape from the old integration and undergo genetic reconstruction with formation of a new integrated genotypic pattern.

Mayr (opp. cit) has synthesized a great mass of work concerning speciation and the nature of species and subspecies. In general, he maintains that some degree of spatial isolation is a necessary prerequisite for species-formation. This definitely seems to hold for groups like birds (with which Mayr is especially familiar) and for other higher vertebrates such as mammals, and certainly applies in the great majority of other cases; but workers on other groups like fish and insects have adduced various examples in which ecological or habitudinal divergence appears at first sight to have led to speciation without the prior intervention of geographical or spatial isolation. And E. B. Ford and his associates have shown that definite intra-specific differentiation of adjacent non-isolated populations (of butterflies) may occur in the apparent absence of any geographical or ecological barrier (Creed, Dowdeswell, Ford and McWhirter, 1959). In plants, of course, speciation can take place suddenly, by allopolyploidy (see e.g. Stebbins, 1950; Haldane, 1959).

Numerous examples are now known where it is really a matter of taste whether to call two distinct groups subspecies or full species. The most interesting are those where the end links of a chain or ring of geographical subspecies come to overlap, and yet do not interbreed, either at all or fully, and must therefore be regarded as having become good species. (See Mayr, 1963).

Monophyletic assemblages of essentially allopatric populations that are morphologically too different to be included in a single species are frequent in most animal groups. Mayr calls such assemblages *superspecies*, and their distinctive allopatric components *semispecies*.

Most so-called biological races turn out on analysis to be sibling species, phenotypically very similar, but with distinctive and incompatible genotypes.

The majority of animal species appear to be *polytypic*, composed of a number of allopatric subspecies. In some groups the total number of existing species is now known with considerable accuracy, and also the number of subspecies per species. Thus there are approximately 8,600 species and 28,500 subspecies of birds. The number of subspecies per species is approximately the same in tiger-beetles, but considerably higher in small rodents and notably in tropical land-snails.

Recently, increasing importance has been attached to habitat selection as an intrinsic factor leading to localisation and isolation of animal groups. Changes in habitat preference, whether modificational or genetic, facilitate rapid speciation. In higher vertebrates, notably birds, habitat selection is based on psychological capacities. For recent work on the subject, see Mayr, 1963, Chap. 18.

Both in animals and plants, increasing attention has been given to regularities of intraspecific variation. Rensch (op. cit. chap. 3, p. 43f.) has tabulated a large number of "geographical rules" of variation. Most of these are clinal, and merely extend the results already summarized by me in the present work: however, the demonstration of the general occurrence of such adaptive responses to graded environmental differences is of considerable importance.

Rensch has paid special attention to the allometric consequences of change in absolute size, not only intra-specifically but also trans-specifically (op. cit. p. 133f., p. 292). The most interesting result is the effect of increased brain-size in promoting greater intelligence. This appears to be effected partly by the absolute increase in number of neurons, partly by the positive allometry of higher cerebral areas.

Clines in some characters appear to be present in the majority of animal species studied, and are indices of adaptive geographical variation. In plants, ecotypic variation may or may not be clinal: see Stebbins, *Variations and Evolution in Plants*, 1950. Regular but non-clinal variation is also seen in some animals, notably in cryptic coloration in relation to background.

The establishment of adaptive cryptic coloration under the influence of natural selection in local populations of moths in industrial areas has been brilliantly and exhaustively studied by Kettlewell, and is well summarised in Sheppard (1958, p. 68 f.); it affords the best-documented example of Darwinian evolution brought about by natural selection.

However, there have been numerous other studies, both theoretical and experimental, of natural selection operating in natural and experimental populations, often at intensities much greater than was earlier supposed possible. Valuable summaries of these have been given by Sheppard (1958), by Maynard Smith in *The Theory of Evolution* (1958), by Dobzhansky (1955, 1962), and by Ford (1963).

As a result of the marked increase of interest in population genetics as against formal genetics, selection theory has undergone various changes. One striking and in my opinion undesirable innovation concerns the concept of *fitness*. It is now fashionable to define fitness solely in terms of differential reproductive advantage, without any reference to phenotypic fitness ensuring individual survival. Some authors, like Dobzhansky (op. cit.), go so far as to call differential reproductive advantage "Darwinian fitness," although Darwin never used fitness in this sense, and although it was Herbert Spencer who first introduced the term into evolutionary theory by his unfortunate phrase *The Survival of the Fittest*, which Darwin did not employ in the earlier editions of the *Origin of Species*. On p. 129, Dobzhansky writes that "Darwinian fitness is measurable only in terms of reproductive proficiency," and later (p. 221) that "the only trend [or] direction . . . discernible in life and its evolution is the production of more life." Accordingly (p. 11) "natural selection *means* differential*

---

* It would be more logical to say *operates by means of*.

reproduction of carriers of different genetic endowments . . . "

When we examine the problem more critically, we find that we must differentiate between two quite distinct modes of natural selection, leading to different types of evolutionary trend, which we may call *survival selection* and *reproductive selection*. Haldane (1959) also distinguishes these two modes of natural selection, but calls them phenotypic and genotypic respectively. I prefer my terminology for natural selection, but suggest using *phenotypic* and *genotypic* for the corresponding types of social selection (see below).

In the actual processes of biological evolution, survival selection is much the more important: selection exerts its effects mainly on individual phenotypes, and operates primarily by means of their differential survival to maturity. This will produce evolutionary effects because, as Darwin saw, (a) the majority of individuals which survive to maturity will mate and leave offspring; (b) much of the phenotypic variance promoting survival has a genetic basis.

Natural selection clearly may also operate by means of the differential reproduction of mature individuals, but in point of fact this *reproductive selection* has only minor evolutionary effects. Its most general effect is to promote an optimum clutch-size, litter-size, or in general terms progeny-number. Its effect in organisms with separate sexes is to promote mechanisms for securing successful matings, from flower-colour in entomophilous plants to mating behaviour in birds (see Maynard Smith, chaps. 8 and 11). Only when there is strong intra-sexual competition with a high premium on mating success, does reproductive selection promote special trends like those to striking display characters in polygamous-promiscuous birds like Birds of Paradise and Argus Pheasants; or those to large size, special weapons, and general combative character in mammals with a harem-system, like deer and Elephant Seals. Darwin recognized the basic difference between these two forms of selection when he coined the term *sexual selection* for reproductive selection operating by inter-male competition. (For important discussions of sexual selection, see chap. 6 of R. A. Fisher's *Genetical Theory of Natural Selection;* and Maynard Smith, op. cit., and in Barnett's *A Century of Darwin*, 1960).

Survival selection, on the other hand, as Darwin saw in 1859, inevitably promotes all kinds of trend leading to biological improvement, whether improvement in close adaptation to environment, in specialisation, in functional efficiency of particular organ-systems, in self-regulation, or in general organisation.

As R. A. Fisher pointed out in chapters 8 to 11 of his great book *The Genetical Theory of Natural Selection*, man is reproductively unique among organisms in showing an enormous range of individual variation in fertility, instead of a single optimum value with low variance. Man is also unique in having markedly reduced the impact of natural selection on the survival of individuals by artificial means, such as medical care and sanitation. The relative importance of differential survival and differential reproduction has thus been completely reversed in most present-day communities.

The human situation is so different from the biological that it may prove best to abandon the attempt to apply concepts like natural selection to modern human affairs. All the evolutionary differentials now operating, whether in survival or in reproduction, have their roots in the special psychosocial character of human evolution. It would seem best to accept the fact that a novel form of selection, *psychosocial selection*, or more simply *social selection*, is now operating; to attempt to define and analyse it more closely; and to see how it could be applied to produce eugenic results. Both phenotypic (survival) social selection and genotypic (reproductive) social selection are now probably dysgenic in their effects.

Thus R. A. Fisher (op. cit. p. 245) says that evolution in certain early types of society proceeds by "the social promotion of fertility," whereas in most modern societies there is a "social selection of infertility." I have coined the word *euselection* to denote deliberate selection for what are deemed desirable genetic qualities (Huxley, 1962). Herbert Brewer uses *eutelegenesis* to denote eugenic improvement by means of artificial insemination from selected donors; and H. J. Muller (1959 and 1962) and he have pointed out how it could be rendered much more effective by the use of the recent technique of preserving mammalian sperm (and eventually ova and immature germ-cells) in a deep-frozen state.

Eugenics and the general relation of human genetics to human evolution has been much discussed recently, notably by Dobzhansky (op. cit.), by Crow, Muller and others in the first part of the symposium on *Evolution and Man's Progress* (Hoagland and Burhoe, 1962), by Medawar in his Reith Lectures (1960), and by myself in my Galton Lecture (1962). It is becoming clear that social euselection (eugenic selection for the deliberate genetic improvement of man) will differ radically from artificial selection for the deliberate genetic improvement of domesticated plants and animals; and also from natural selection, which operates automatically to produce biological improvement in natural species of groups. It is also clear that , in so far as immediate threats to human progress are overcome, such as over-population, atomic war, and over-exploitation of natural resources, eugenic improvement will become an increasingly important goal of evolving man.

Much theoretical and experimental work has been done on selection in general. In addition to survival (phenotypic) and reproductive (genotypic), sexual, and social (psychosocial) selection (see above), the following main types of natural selection are now usually distinguished (see Dobzhansky, 1962; Haldane, 1959; Sheppard, 1958; Thoday, 1958; etc. Haldane in particular has helped to quantify the subject):

(1) *Normalizing*, centripetal, or stabilizing selection: tending to reduce variance, to promote the continuance of the "normal" type, and to prevent change in a well-adapted organisation.

(2) *Directional*, directed, or dynamic selection: tending to produce change in an adaptive direction.

(3) *Diversifying*, disruptive, or centrifugal selection: tending to separate a single population into two genetically distinct populations.

(4) *Balancing* selection: tending to produce balanced polymorphisms and heteroses in populations.

(5) Selection for variability: leading to high variance in

cryptic adaptation in certain conditions (see Sheppard, 1958). To which we may perhaps add

(6) *Post hoc* selection, as when a viable new species originates suddenly by allopolyploidy.

In recent years, much attention has been paid to the effects of population-density on survival, and a careful analysis has been made of the various density-dependent and density-independent factors involved and of their selective effects. See e.g. Allee et al, 1949; Sheppard, 1958, chap. 11; Wynne-Edwards, 1962; Mayr, 1963.

In numerically very small populations, as Sewall Wright first pointed out, change in gene-frequency may occur by chance, through random survival without the intervention of selection. When this occurs through the loss of alleles which inevitably takes place in such populations, it is termed *genetic drift*, and may actually override selection-pressure and even lead to reduction or extinction of the population. Further, as discussed in chaps. 2 and 5 of the present work it may also occur when an isolated habitat, such as an island or a lake, is colonized by a handful of invaders. These will almost certainly not have a full complement of the alleles in the gene-complex of the species, so that the local population will be genetically distinct from the outset, and will frequently show further divergence owing to genetic drift and to local selection (see below). This has been called the *founder principle* by Mayr, who gives numerous examples of its effects. The most striking result occurs when an isolated habitat has been twice invaded by members of the same parent species: such double invasion not uncommonly leads to the formation of two original subspecies, derived from two distinct samples of one ancestral gene-complex, which may differentiate into separate species. However, Dr. E. B. Ford informs me that my statement on p. 233 of the present work that the high geographical diversity of Partula spp. in the Society Islands is not due to such colonization of isolated areas by non-representative samples of the population: Partula populations may change markedly over quite short distances, apparently in selective adjustment to the micro-habitat. In his *Ecological Genetics* (1963) he gives numerous further examples of the inadequacy of drift and the efficacy of natural selection in accounting for local differentiation, including that of snails like *Cepaea* (Cain and Curry, 1963).

A further step from double invasion is what Mayr (1963) calls "archipelago speciation", or the evolution from a few original "founders" of an adaptive radiation comprising a number of species, on archipelagoes like Hawaii or the Galapagos. Similar phenomena occur in regions with groups of lakes or of isolated mountain peaks.

Drift in the extended sense can have definite evolutionary consequences when a novel mutant, segregant, or chromosomal inversion occurs in a small isolated population with a restricted complement of genes. Its original establishment in the population will be a matter of drift. But if it is advantageous in relation to the population's local environment and new gene-complex, its full spread will be promoted by selection, unhindered by gene-diffusion from the original gene-complex of the species. For recent discussions of genetic drift and the founder principle, see Sheppard, 1958, chap. 7; Maynard Smith, 1958, chap. 13; Mayr, 1942 and 1963; Rensch, 1959, chap. 3; Ford, 1963; and, for man, Dobzhansky, 1962, chap. 10.

Perhaps the most important fact to emerge from research in population genetics is that in most animal species, the majority of wild populations have a surprisingly high genetic variance, but that much of it is potential, and is not manifested phenotypically unless released under the influence of selection. This capacity of the integrated genotype for storing variance is highly adaptive in relation to the evolutionary survival of species. On the other hand, the species has to pay a considerable price for this capacity, in the shape of the genetic load of disadvantageous variations which may be released by recombination.

Most such populations are not even approximately homozygous, but are heterozygous for a large proportion, perhaps a majority, of their genes. There is considerable dispute as to how much of this heterozygosity is maintained through selectively balanced morphisms, through straight heterozygote advantage in single genes, through traditional heterosis due to the co-operation of complementary genes, through the establishment of complementary linked polygenic systems as described by Mather, or through that of complementary chromosomal types (chromosome morphisms) as found by Dobzhansky in wild Drosophila. In any case, the widespread existence of heterozygosity will lock up a great deal of the variance of a natural population in potential form. Linked polygenic systems are normally balanced so as to secure an optimum mean effect on a given character (or on a pair or set of balanced morphic characters; see below). Long-continued selection can change the manifestation of the character, by a slow but stepwise release of their latent (stored) variance, as shown for instance, by the work of Mather (1953 and 1956) and Thoday (1953 and 1958).

In this and other ways high heterozygosity confers a marked degree of stability on a population, but it also ensures a large store of potential variance, which can be released by selection if circumstances demand it. Darwin's postulate that long-term and major evolution by natural selection is normally slow and manifested by gradual trends of change, largely in quantitative characters, has thus been confirmed, though modern population-genetics has shown that short-term minor changes may occur with surprising rapidity, under the influence of unexpectedly high selective pressures.

Mere heterozygosity grades into definite balanced genetic polymorphism, or *morphism* as it is more conveniently called. Much work has recently been done on this subject. Already in 1930 R. A. Fisher demonstrated on theoretical grounds that two genetic variants whose frequencies cannot be due solely to mutation, could not coexist in the same population unless there is a balance of advantage and disadvantage between them.

The balance may be determined purely by the variations in intensity of selection with morph-frequency: e.g. in morphic mimetic butterflies, the advantage enjoyed by a particular mimetic morph will decrease if its numbers increase above a certain point (see Sheppard, op. cit.). In most cases, however, the permanent maintenance of the balance is achieved genetically, by means of heterozygote advantage, or by double-dose (homozygous) phenotypic disadvantage of one of the alleles or allelic systems concerned. The latter mechanism is often achieved by close linkage of a recessive lethal or sublethal allele with one of the alleles determining the phenotypic effects of the morphism (see Ford, 1963).

In a general survey of the subject (Huxley, 1955) I showed how surprisingly widespread morphism is in nature, both in animals and plants (though visible morphism is much more prevalent in some groups of animals than in others). Ford (1963) gives a valuable treatment of the subject from the angle of ecological genetics. To take a few examples, Sheppard, Cain and their co-workers have analysed the morphism of the land snail *Cepaea nemoralis* in detail, and have shown that in some areas the balance is maintained by visual predation, in others by genetic viability factors (see Sheppard, 1958; Cain and Currey, 1963). The immense diversity of colour and pattern in various beach-dwelling forms like *Donax* and other small bivalve molluscs is apparently advantageous *per se*, in making recognition by sandpipers and other predators more difficult. Such massive polymorphism, where the degree of variation itself is adaptive, by minimising losses through predation, seems also to occur in brittle-stars, sea-anemones, tubicolous polychaetes and various grasshoppers (Moment, 1961).

The polymorphic mimicry of the eggs of the European Cuckoo appears to depend on a combination of genetic morphism with the existence of partially localized strains or *gentes* which prefer different fosterer (host) species. The precise methods involved in the genetic determination of the often amazingly accurate mimetic egg-morphs and in the distinctiveness and the geographical restriction of the gentes still remain to be elucidated (see Southern, 1954; summary in Rothschild and Clay, 1952, chap. 16).

In the butterfly *Colias eurythema*, Hovanitz (1953; see also Remington, 1954, Adv. Genetics, **6,** 403) was able to show that the white morph was selectively favoured at lower temperatures, and therefore at higher altitudes and latitudes.

In this and many other species, there is thus a *dimorph ratio cline* — a geographical cline manifested in the changing proportions of the two morphs. Numerous cases of morph-ratio clines have now been studied, and in one of them (bridled pattern in guillemots, *Uria aalge*) field studies of the cline have been repeated at two ten-year intervals. These confirm that the cline is definitely correlated with climate, cold and humidity favouring the bridled morph; but have revealed slight but significant changes in the bridling percentage, a decrease over the first ten-year period being followed by an increase in the second (Southern, 1951 and 1962).

Balanced morphisms involving whole chromosomes instead of single genes or small groups of genes can also play an important role, e.g. in Drosophila, where they have been brilliantly studied by Dobzhansky (1951, 1955); see also White (1961, chap. 10). Here, too, morph-ratio differences may exist in relation to environmental factors: the frequency of the different morphs (chromosome types) shows seasonal and geographical variation, the latter often manifested in climatic ratio-clines.

Recently the classical and most complex case of polymorphic mimicry, the swallowtail butterfly *Papilio dardanus*, has been thoroughly investigated (see Clarke and Sheppard, 1959). It is now clear that it is a true genetic morphism, with the different phenotypic morphs selectively balanced against each other by ecological as well as genetic factors. The basic differences between the main morphic types are determined by major switch-genes or supergenes, while the detailed resemblance of mimetic type to model is brought about by dependent polygenic systems. Where the range of a mimic extends beyond that of its model, the accuracy of the mimetic resemblance breaks down, showing that selection is needed to maintain it (Ford, 1936). See also Ford, 1963; and P. M. Sheppard in *Cold Spring Harbor Symposium*, 1959. Here, as in many other cases of adaptation, the indispensability of natural selection in producing teleonomic results (see later) has been established.

The stability of such selectively balanced morphic systems is shown by the morphism for sensitivity to PTC (phenylthiocarbamide). To most human beings PTC tastes disagreeably bitter; but a minority of about 25%, though varying slightly in different ethnic groups, have a higher genetic threshold for it, and cannot taste it at all except in high concentrations. It was later found that the same is true for chimpanzees, showing that this particular balanced morphism must have persisted in the gene-complex of higher primates for 10 millions years or so (see p. 53 of the present volume). It has recently been shown that PTC sensitivity is correlated with thyroid function; this is presumably implicated in the balance of advantage concerned. For sensory and other morphisms in man, see Kalmus, 1957.

Perhaps the most important and certainly the best-investigated of such stable morphisms is the ABO blood-group system.* which occurs in fundamentally the same form in man and the anthropoid apes and again must have existed for millions of year (see e.g. Mourant, 1954; Mourant et al. 1958; Boyd, 1950; Race and Sanger, 1962).

For a long time it was maintained, even by professional geneticists, that blood-group genes were selectively neutral, in spite of R. A. Fisher's theoretical proof to the contrary, and Ford's prophecy of the association of blood-groups with specific disease in 1949, six years before its discovery. However, recent studies have shown that this is not so. Blood-group genes are concerned with proneness to pernicious anaemia, to early broncho-pneumonia and to certain types of ulcer and cancer; probably with general viability; and possibly with fertility. These discoveries are opening up a new branch of medicine (see Clarke, 1961). There can be no doubt that the numerous other morphic blood-group systems in higher vertebrates (e.g. in cattle and pigeons) are also maintained by some form of selective balance and are equally important physiologically and biologically.

The case of sickle-cell anemia is particularly illuminating. It shows how a mutant allele concerned in the production of an abnormal type of haemoglobin, which is lethal or sublethal when

* The genetic terminology usually employed for the blood-groups is most unfortunate and should be replaced by that of Ford (1955). In this G^A, G^B, and g denote the main multiple alleles concerned. Persons of O blood-type will thus be gg in genetic constitution, those of B blood-type will be G^BG^B or G^Bg, those of A blood-type will be $G^A G^A$ or $G^A g$, and those of AB blood-type will all be $G^A G^B$. If desired, the terminology can be extended from the genes to cover the antigens and antibodies for which they are responsible. In point of fact the situation is more complex, since there are 3 alleles of different strength (dominance) responsible for A characters — G^{A1}, G^{A2}, and G^{A3}, which interact with G^B in various ways; but it remains true that blood-group genetics cannot be properly understood without a proper 'allelic nomenclature.

Similarly but more simply, in the MN blood-group two alleles are involved, L^M and L^N. Persons of blood-type M will be $L^M L^M$ in constitution; of blood-type MN, $L^M L^N$; of blood-type N, $L^N L^N$.

in double dose (homozygous) may when in single dose (heterozygous) confer such advantage in certain conditions (in this case in regions of high incidence of malaria) that it enters into morphic balance with its normal homologue. The sex-linked gene for favism seems to have a similar effect (see Fraser Roberts, 1959 Kalmus, 1957; Mourant, 1962).

Several dozen other genetical variants of haemoglobins, haptoglobins, and transferrins are now known, many of them so abundant in particular areas that they must be maintained in morphic balance by selection (see Mourant, 1962).

However, Fisher's basic thesis that genetic polymorphism must always involve a balance of selective advantage and disadvantage, has been put in question by recent discoveries in haematology, enzymology and immunology. It now appears that many — perhaps all — polypeptides and polysaccharides in higher vertebrates, as well as, of course, polynucleotides, exist in a large number of chemical forms some differing markedly, others only slightly, in their effects. In the case of gammaglobulin, Oudin (1958) calls these variants *allotypes:* the term can usefully be extended to all such cases of biochemical polymorphism: e.g. all enzymes so far investigated appear to exist in a number of allotypic forms. Smithers et. al (1962) suggest a cytogenetic mechanism which would account for the origin of numerous allotypes.

In discussing the matter, the following points are relevant. (1) It now turns out (see Pontecorvo, 1959) that genes in the customary sense are functional units of physiological action, technically known as *cistrons*. They are structurally compound, consisting of a series of ultimate units of crossing-over (sometimes called *recons*) and of mutation (mutational sites, sometimes called *mutons*). These in turn are each composed of a small number of nucleotide pairs. The particular sequence of nucleotides is what gives the whole gene its specific character. The maximum estimated number of mutational sites per gene range from something under 100 in Drosophila to over 300 in phage T4 and over 350 in Aspergillus. The total number of mutational sites even in such a comparatively simple organism as Aspergillus is over six million.

Modern work on DNA (see e.g. Davidson, 1960; Chargaff and Davidson, 1955-60; New Biology, 1960), has made it reasonably certain that the constitution of particular proteins is specifically related to the structure of particular genes — in other words to particular sequences of nucleotides in the genetic code provided by the genic DNA. This appears to be effected by a double template action, first of DNA on RNA and then of RNA on protein-formation.

It is also resonably certain that the complexity of DNA is so great that it is liable to slight changes in local chemical structure. These may be produced by radiation or chemical action, or by spontaneous rearrangement. When these changes are of considerable effect, they result in the obvious mutations of the mendelian geneticist. But it may be presumed that the majority are of very slight extent. The existence of some of these, the so-called modifiers, can be deduced from genetic experiment (see e.g. Mather, 1953, 1961), though they cannot be individually identified. Others can be detected and identified, but only by special genetic techniques, notably those of microbial genetics, where the research worker has vast numbers of individuals available and can utilize delicate chemical techniques for detecting slight genetic differences (see e.g. Pontecorvo, 1958; Jacob and Wollman, 1961).

The tentative suggestion may now be made that mutants of considerable extent and definite effect will either be reduced by selection to a very low frequency, or in certain circumstances will be utilized in establishing balanced morphisms of the type envisaged by Fisher or Ford. Mutations of very small extent, on the other hand, will not be subject to negative selection so long as their effects remain within what may be called the permitted spectrum of variation for the species; while some (e.g. presumably many minor modifiers) may indeed be advantageous in increasing the flexibility of the gene-complex and its capacity to cope with a fluctuating environment. They will then not be selected against and will not only persist but will accumulate, through repeated mutation at the same site, to a frequency much higher than mutation frequency.

Such persistent allotypy is clearly quite distinct from balanced morphism, though of course allotypes may be selectively utilized in morphisms like the blood-groups, while in the same blood-groups other multiple alleles (e.g. those within the A blood-type in the ABO system) may possibly be allotypes without significant selective value.

In any case, it seems clear that the genetics of poly-morphism, including allotypy as well as morphism in the strict sense, is destined to be of great importance not only for medicine but for immunology and biochemistry and for the rapidly growing science of individual difference (see e.g. Williams 1960). Polymorphism gives a new dimension to the gene-complex.

A remarkable special case of intra-individual allotypy is pro-vided by the diversity of transplantation antigens in the tissues. The presence of these normally prohibits the transplantation of tissues between conspecific individuals. A multiplicity of antigens implies a multiplicity of response, and there has been much dis-cussion of whether one future antibody-forming or "immunologi-cally competent" cell can respond to any antigen, or whether, as in the clonal theory (see Burnet 1959; also Lederberg, 1959) there is some restriction of competence. Burnet's theory envisages a genetical polymorphism of the lymphocytes produced by a single zygote, arising by somatic mutation; but this rather improbable hypothesis is still very much in doubt. True genetic allotypy may also be involved. Thus in mice there are over 20 antigenic loci, some of complex nature with up to 20 pseudo-alleles, presumably as a result of slight allotypic mutation.

In any case, immunological research has cleared up the old evolutionary puzzle of the thymus, whose function is now firmly established as provider of adequate supplies of two types of immunologically effective cells early in life. In birds, the thymus produces one such cell-type, while the hitherto mysterious bursa fabricii is now known to produce the other (see Burnet 1962). Meanwhile, the evolution of the immunological mechanisms of vertebrates, including their auto-immunity, remains obscure, though work such as that of Medawar (1958; see also Burnet,

1959) on homografts and immunological tolerance has shed much light on their operations.

The perennial discussions about adaptation, directional trends and their limitations, and apparent purpose in evolution and its products have entered on a new phase, which may be conveniently dated to the world-wide re-evaluation of Darwinism that took place in 1958 and 1959 around the centenary of its birth.

For one thing, there was a belated recognition that Darwin's own conception of (biological) improvement is fundamental. In the *Origin* he had written that natural selection "has as its ultimate result . . . that each creature tends to become more and more improved in relation to their [sic] conditions. This improvement inevitably leads to the gradual advancement of the organisation of the greater number of living beings." It remains for modern biologists to define and analyse the concept of improvement in detail.

Pittendrigh (1958) has performed a useful service by coining the term *teleonomy* to denote this inevitable effect of natural selection, which simulates purpose by imposing an essentially directional character on biological evolution. The evolutionary process is thus not *teleological*, directed by some consciously purposeful urge, but *teleonomic*, automatically moving in the direction of adaptation and improvement.

Considerable work has been done on trends in evolution, as revealed by fossil evidence. Much of this is presented by G. G. Simpson in his book *The Major Features of Evolution* (1953) and has been summarized by Haldane (1959, p. 134). Simpson has also assembled an important body of facts about rates of evolution, showing (a) that measurable evolution proceeds at different rates at different times during the period when a group is undergoing adaptive radiation; (b) that different major groups such as phyla and classes show different mean rates of evolutionary change, the earlier-evolved and lower or more primitive types in general showing slower rates. To take a couple of examples, the rate of increase in length of equid teeth was around $3\frac{1}{2}$ per cent per million years; the average duration of a genus in the Carnivora and most other groups of placental mammals is around 8 million years, while that in some lower molluscs may be tenfold this.

Haldane (1959) has an interesting discussion of the problem, pointing out that "Darwin was unique in his time in giving the rate of evolution approximately correctly." He has proposed the term *darwin* for a rate of change in dimensions by e (2.718) per million years, which is equivalent to 1.001 per millennium. The rate for horse teeth was between 20 and 40 millidarwins, and only very rarely has natural evolution reached a rate of 1 darwin, whereas artificial selection produces rates very much higher, up to 10 kilodarwins.

To facilitate thinking in terms of evolutionary time, I have suggested the term *cron* for a period of 1 million years (Huxley, 1957). In this terminology, the whole evolution of life has taken under 3 kilochrons, and that of man about 1 cron, while human history since the end of the last glaciation is measured in millicrons.

The time needed for the formation of a new species varies greatly (Mayr, 1963, chap. 18). In the absence of radical and relatively rapid reorganisation of the gene-complex by "genetic revolution", as is the case when two populations are isolated only by distance, speciation will be slow and may take up to several million years. But when an isolated marginal population passes through an evolutionary bottleneck, the process will be accelerated, and in exceptional cases may take only a few thousand years or even less.

Much thought has been given to the study of evolution as a process, and of the major trends and sub-processes involved in its operation. Rensch (1954) distinguished two major sub-processes—cladogenesis* and anagenesis. Cladogenesis or branching evolution leads to progressively greater divergence and diversification of organisms. Anagenesis or upward evolution leads to major advance in organization and biological efficiency. Later, I (see Huxley, 1961), suggested expanding *anagenesis* to cover all types of improvement, including improved detailed adaptation, improved specialisation for a particular way of life, more efficient organisation of some major functional organ-system, like diges-

---

* For some extraordinary reason this is spelt *Kladogenesis* in the English translation of Rensch's book.

tive, nervous or locomotory system, and improvement of the pattern of general organisation, e.g. as between diploblastic and tribloplastic animals or between reptiles and placental mammals.

Considerable attention has been given to the evolutionary aspects of functional morphology. Thus Manton (1961) has shown how different successful arthropod groups (e.g. centipedes and millipedes) are characterized by different patterns of locomotor functions and structure, each facilitating a particular habit of life.

I also attempted to re-analyse the most significant of all anagenetic processes, the trend to biological progress, to which I had devoted the final chapter of the present book, and came to the conclusion that evolutionary progress could best be defined as "advance in organisation which leaves the door open for further advance" (Huxley, 1947).

In addition, I proposed (see Huxley, 1957 and 1958) distinguishing a third major subprocess, which I termed *stasigenesis*—the tendency to limitation of anagenetic trends and their eventual stabilisation. The resultant stabilized types then persist for long periods, sometimes indefinitely.

Over three-quarters of a century ago, T. H. Huxley had drawn attention to the existence of "persistent types" as evidence that evolution was not always progressive or directional: we now see that they testify to the frequency of stasigenesis. Persistent types include the so-called "living fossils." Two notable examples have recently come to light—the coelacanth fish *Latimeria*, belonging to a group which was supposed to have become extinct at the end of the cretaceous, about 70 million years ago; and the spectacular deep-sea form *Neopilina*, an exceedingly primitive mollusc not far removed from the common ancestor of molluscs and annelids, whose nearest fossil relatives date back to at least 400 million years ago (Lemche, 1957). Both these discoveries illustrate the well-known fact, also seen in the monotremes and the lungfish, that living fossils, though belonging to a persistent type of general organisation, are often highly specialized in regard to habitat or particular way of life.

Further consideration has made it clear that even the most successful and abundant types may show apparently indefinite persistence. Basic avian organisation has persisted unchanged for about 20 million years, and basic ant organisation for over 50 million. In both groups, later evolution has been confined to specialized divergences, occasionally up to the rank of Family, but mostly generic and sometimes even only specific.

The prevalence of persistent types means that, in paleontology, chronological sequence need not imply phylogenetic sequence. The three-toed type of foot pattern represented a definite grade (see below) in the evolution of horses. But it persisted as such, for a considerable time after the evolution of one-toed forms (Simpson, 1951). Similarly, the Australopith type seems certainly to have persisted for a considerable time after the evolution of definitely human types.

Consideration of persistent and progressive types and lineages and of the widespread existence of parallel or convergent evolution, has led to changes in taxonomy. It is theoretically necessary to distinguish between two types of assemblage—*grades* and *clades*. A clade is a phylogenetic unit with a single evolutionary origin; whereas a grade is an assemblage of forms at a common level of evolutionary stabilisation and persistence. In many cases, named taxa must be simultaneously clades and grades. However, in some cases, e.g. the Subholostei and probably the Teleostei in bony fish, it is only a grade, which has been independently reached by the parallel evolution of two or more separate clades (see Huxley, 1958 and the interesting symposium on *The Species Concept in Taxonomy*, edited by Sylvester-Bradley, 1956). This subject has been well summarised by G. G. Simpson in his *Principles of Animal Taxonomy* (1961), chap 4; he also deals illuminatingly with many other implications of evolutionary fact and theory for taxonomy and classification, including the objective reality of higher taxa.

Meanwhile, it became clear that improvement of general organisation is brought about by a succession of successful types. Each new type achieves its evolutionary success by virtue of superior organisation, and as a result evolves into a new taxonomic group which radiates (undergoes cladogenesis) at the expense of the earlier groups in competition with it, including the group of similar taxonomic rank from which it has originated, though this may and does usually persist in reduced numbers. This process appears to apply to the anagenesis of all taxa from genus upwards, and indeed inevitably results in a taxonomic hierarchy.

Looked at from the angle of biological improvement, major anagenetic transformations, such as those leading to the formation of a new successful type like a new Class or Subclass, appear to involve a series of improvements in one important character after another: e.g. in the evolution of Birds from Reptiles (de Beer, 1954) and of man from lower Primates (le Gros Clark, 1955, 1961). This process of stepwise coadaptation has been called *mosaic evolution* by de Beer.

Each step of improvement presumably permits a minor radiation of the new improved type, the next step then being taken only by one or a very few of its radiating lineages, while others persist stasigenetically. This seems definitely to have happened in the evolution of horses and man (see above). In other cases, such as birds, fossil remains are so scarce that all we have left are isolated representatives of the main stages or grades, though presumably the type of each stage would have undergone some radiation and some of its representatives would have persisted into the next stage.

The process of step-by-step anagenesis is especially clear and especially important in relation to large-scale evolutionary advance or progress. This appears to be brought about by a succession of so-called dominant types of organization, each new successful type becoming dominant in its particular major habitat, and embodying the highest level of biological organisation found in that habitat.* Familiar examples include the succession of cephalopod types culminating in the dominance of the squids and octopuses, of bony fish culminating in that of the Teleostei, and the most interesting for ourselves, the succession from amphibian through reptile to mammal and man.

A fourth sub-process is that of diffusion, leading to convergence

---

* This evolutionary dominance, as also the ethological dominance seen in animal behaviour, has, of course, nothing to do with mendelian dominance as found in genetics. In particular, it must be pointed out that the development of evolutionary dominance does not depend on dominant mutations or alleles.

instead of divergence. In biological evolution it operates only on a very minor scale by diffusion of genes between separate species or more rarely genera, and much more commonly in plants (though gene-diffusion between animal subspecies is common). The usual method by which interspecific gene-diffusion occurs in animals is by *introgression*, in which one species becomes modified by the incorporation of a proportion of the genes of another. In plants, introgression is also common, but full hybridisation also frequently occurs with the formation of hybrid swarms: this is much rarer in animals.

In psychosocial evolution gene-diffusion owing to migration is common, and has prevented human subspecies (primary races) from evolving to full species (see Coon, 1962; Mayr, 1963). In addition, the cultural diffusion of ideas, art-forms, machines and other products, has played an increasingly important role, and is now preparing the way for the birth of a single world cultural and sociogenetic system.

Meanwhile, following C. D. Darlington's earlier work, considerable attention has been devoted to the evolution of the genetic system itself (see e.g. Darlington, 1958; White, 1954, 1961; Dobzhansky, 1955). The major stages in the evolution of the genetic system would appear to be as follows.

(1) The viroid or "naked gene" stage. The pre-cellular organism consists of a single "gene" or gene-string of nucleic acid, together with a limited equipment of proteins.

(2) The bacterial stage. The genetic system consists of a single chromosome without nuclear membrane, but enclosed in a cytoplasmic cell-body provided with a cell-membrane. The genes can thus interact with various cytoplasmic constituents (see Pontecorvo, 1963).

(3) The haploid nuclear stage. These are several chromosomes, enclosed in a nuclear membrane. The chromosomal genes can thus interact with each other within the nucleus, as well as with cytoplasmic constituents across the nuclear membrane (Pontecorvo, 1963). Diploidy only exists momentarily after sexual fusion.

(4) The diploid stage. The genetic system is diploid for a long period, in higher animals and land plants for almost the entire life-cycle. This makes possible much greater genetic variance, by permitting higher degrees of ploidy and by providing for the storage of recessive mutants in the shelter of their recessive homologues, the formation of linked polygene systems ensuring stability but allowing the slow release of variability under selection (Mather, 1953, 1961; Mayr, 1963); permitting the production of small chromosome rearrangements determining novel protein and other allotypes (p. xxviii; Smithers et. al., 1962) and of large chromosome rearrangements leading to intra- and interspecific differentiation; and the building up of balanced gene, supergene and chromosome morphisms (p. xxvf). See e.g. White, 1961, chap. 19; King, 1962; Dobzhansky, 1951, 1955.

There has also been a great development of animal ecology, including the study of the teleonomic character of integrated ecological communities, and the ways in which they develop and evolve in time (see e.g. Elton, *Animal Ecology*, 1947; Allee et al., *Principles of Animal Ecology*, 1948, Section V; Darling, *Wild Life in an African Territory*, 1960; Andrewartha, 1961).

Communities which have evolved in continuous coadaptation over long geological periods become tightly integrated and highly resistant to invasion by fresh species, whereas younger communities, especially in areas which have been exposed to major environmental change in the recent geological past, show looser organisation and are more readily colonized by new or alien species.

Ecological concepts have been clarified, notably that of *niche* as something quite different from *habitat*. The niche of a species, as Mayr puts it, is the outward projection of its needs. A habitat will contain a large number of ecological niches. These may be of very different extent; for instance, a single host-plant may provide several micro-niches for a corresponding number of phytophagous insect species, a single culture-bottle may contain micro-niches for more than one species of Drosophila. On the other hand two related species cannot coexist in a single identical ecological niche: one will exclude the other (exclusion principle: Gause's Law). This has been experimentally demonstrated with Paramecium, flour-beetles (Tribolium) and Drosophila. (See Mayr, 1963).

A new niche may develop into a whole new *adaptive zone*, as with the earliest invasion of the land by vertebrates, the colonisation of a biologically "empty" area by the ancestral Geospizid finch on the Galapagos archipelago, or the opening up of the rodent adaptive zone by the evolution of a dentition adapted for gnawing (see Mayr, 1963; Simpson, 1953). The successful invasion of a new adaptive zone permits the evolution of a new higher category or taxon, such as an Order or Suborder. This of course is accompanied by rapid cladogenesis, leading to an adaptive radiation, during which the new taxon occupies an increasing number of smaller adaptive zones and ecological niches. Such radiations usually go through an "explosive" phase when normalizing selection is low and evolution rapid. During this phase a number of new types may appear and evolve for a short time before becoming extinct, while other types increase their successful exploitation of the taxon's adaptive zone.

Considerable advances have been made in understanding the first evolution of life from non-living compounds on this planet (see e.g. J. W. S. Pringle in *Evolution*, Symp. Soc. Exp. Biol. VII, Cambridge, 1953; A. Oparin, *The Origin of Life*, 1957; Calvin, 1957b; Horizons in Biochemistry, 1962). The most interesting point for general evolution theory is that we must postulate a form of natural selection acting during the transition period from non-life to life, operating not via the differential reproduction of particular organic compounds but via the differential time of their persistence.

Much interesting and indeed exciting work has been done in ethology, notably on the origin of behaviour-patterns in animals, and their further evolutionary implications and consequences. I would specially mention the studies on communication in higher animals, notably on imprinting and critical periods for learning (including the surprising discovery that some song-birds have to learn their full song, while others do not), on appeasement and displacement activities, on ritualisation, on the language of bees, on the formation of social bonds in vertebrates and insects, on orientation (including the extraordinary fact that night-migrant birds steer by the stars), on "internal clocks" and other endogenous activities independent of peripheral stimulation, on the origins of tradition and on the role of exceptional individuals in modifying it. As regards the evolution of learning, it is now clear that complex instincts usually include an important learned component; and conversely that in learned behaviour there is usually an important genetic element, both in regard to the type and range of what can be learned and to the speed and timing of learning. See e.g. Tinbergen, 1951; Thorpe, 1956, 1961; von Frisch, 1955; Lorenz, 1952; Marler, 1959; Frisch, 1959, and Dobzhansky, 1962, p. 212, on tradition in monkeys; Roe and Simpson (ed.) 1958; Matthews, 1955; chap. 9 on *The Expression of the Emotions*, in Barnett, 1958; Section 10, *Evolution of phenomena of consciousness*, in Rensch, 1959; and, on the relations between animal ethology and human behaviour, Thorpe and Zangwill, 1961.

Recent work has made it clear that two processes are contained in memory, the first dynamic, involving the circuiting of impulses, the second structural, involving material changes in the neurones, synapses, and terminal knobs concerned in the circuiting (see Thorpe, 1961; Gerard, 1961). It has been suggested that RNA is structurally modified in the process of learning, and so facilitates the permanence of the transmission of the learned pattern of impulses (Hyden, 1961). In planarians, it has been maintained that the altered RNA is stored in various parts of the body, and can make possible the transmission of learning to a new brain (cephalic ganglion) produced by regeneration from a posterior half-animal (Coming and John, 1961, McConnell, 1962).

In Chap. 9 of the present work, I described numerous consequential trends resulting from past evolution. These all concerned structural or physiological characters. An interesting point emerging from recent work is that evolution has endowed higher animals with many consequential potentialities of behaviour which are not normally utilized. These include the counting ability of Jackdaws, the string-pulling activities of various small birds, the discovery by individual Blue Tits of how to remove the lids of milk bottles, the painting abilities of anthropoid apes, the capacity of cetaceans for communication and emotional attachment, and of large carnivores like lions for personal friendship with human beings. (See Thorpe, 1956; Lilly, 1961; Huxley, 1962b; Adamson, 1961; Morris, 1962). Psychedelic drugs appear to be revealing a vast range of almost untapped psychological possibilities of the human mind (Ropp, 1957; and references in Huxley, 1962b).

Recent research has cleared up a particular evolutionary problem which especially puzzled Darwin—the origin of powerful electric organs in a few separate groups of fish.

It has now been shown (a) that the swimming musculature of fish can generate electric potentials which can be experimentally detected in an aquarium; (b) that a considerable number of fish have independently evolved low-power electric effector organs from their musculature, and highly sensitive electric receptors from receptor elements of their lateral line system; and (c) that by these means they are able to detect obstacles and to find their prey in muddy waters (see Lissman, 1961).

Wynne-Edwards in his big book, *Animal dispersion in relation to social behaviour* (1962) has collected a large number of facts on which he bases some important and stimulating, not to say revolutionary, theories as to what he calls the *epideictic* relation, between signals and display and other aspects of social behaviour on the one hand, and the adaptive regulation of animal numbers in various species on the other hand.

Salisbury (1961) gives a summary of the evolution of weeds and the pre-adaptations or prerequisites which make for the success of alien introduced plant species, while Elton (1958) has provided a valuable account of the results of introducing alien animal and plant species into various countries.

The establishment by natural selection of strains of insects and other arthropods resistant to insecticides, mentioned on p. 471 of the present work, has now been brought about in numerous other organisms and is impeding the progress of pest-control, while the extended use of chemical sprays and other mass pesticides is seriously upsetting the ecological balance and in some cases damaging human health (see R. Carson, 1962; Babers and Pratt, 1961; Brown, 1958). The similar establishment of bacterial strains resistant to antibiotics, which was not mentioned in the original text, is now all too clearly demonstrating the efficacy of natural selection by the serious effects it is having in hospitals, and indeed on the treatment of infectious diseases in general.

Biochemical evolution concerns the evolution of chemical compounds or mechanisms which play key roles in the processes of life, such as chlorophyll, haemoglobin, actomyosin, ATP (adenosine triphosphate), thyroxin in chordates, uric acid excretion in cleidoic-egg vertebrates. It has received considerable attention in recent years. Here I can only refer to such books as Baldwin, 1949; Florkin and Morgulis, 1949; Williams, 1956 and 1960; and Haldane, 1952: to Baldwin's chapter in *Evolution*, Symp. Soc. Exp. Biol. VII, 1953, to Bernal's, Platt's and Calvin's articles in *Horizons in Biochemistry* (1962), and Calvin's article (1962) on the evolution of photosynthesis.

I must, however, draw attention to the outstanding event in this field, namely the dethronement of the proteins from their biological pre-eminence. It used to be held that life was based on proteins. Today, we know that DNA is the basis of life and its evolution, and that proteins, though essential for its operations, owe their production to the activities of DNA (see p. xxix).

Since 1942, the study of epigenetics (individual development) has contributed materially to a better understanding of evolutionary process. I have aready referred to Waddington's discovery of genetic assimilation: numerous other examples, notably concerning the evolution of epigenetic canalization, whereby the processes of normal development are channelled along adaptive pathways or *creodes*, will be found in his *The Strategy of the Genes* (1957), *New Patterns in Genetics and Development* (1962), and *The Nature of Life* (1961); the latter discusses the general cybernetics of development and evolution in an illuminating way, as well as the interaction of the two processes. Meanwhile, Bonner has approached the same subject from a somewhat different angle in his stimulating book *The Evolution of Development* (1958). See also

Lehmann, 1945, for the classical approach to the subject.

I have referred to the evolutionary importance of phenocopies (p. xivf.) and of the epigenetics of behaviour, notably of learning capacity (p. xxxix). In the present book (p. 525 ff.) I devoted a section to the evolutionary implications of that striking but still unexplained epigenetic mechanism controlling the relative size of parts in the organism, the growth-gradient or gradient-field: for later discussions of this see Reeve and Huxley, 1945; Rensch, 1959a, pp. 135, 292.

Though De Beer (1958) has abundantly demonstrated that the relation between ontogeny and phylogeny is not the recapitulation postulated by Haeckel in his biogenetic law, men like Wadding-ton and the other authors I have cited have made it clear that epigenetic mechanisms are as highly adapted or teleonomic as adult characters, and constitute an essential and often very import-ant part of the evolutionary process in all organisms higher than bacteria.

Epigenetics implements genetics and produces the phenotypes on which selection acts. It does so by generating increasingly complex and adaptive patterns of structure and function: in other words, higher degrees of organisation. Organisation, indeed, is a primary category of biology still demanding proper definition; and its anti-entropic increase, in ontogeny and during evolution, constitutes a major problem for the biological sciences, whose satisfactory resolution will demand a great deal of hard thinking. (See e.g. Waddington, 1957, p. 3 and passim; Huxley, 1962c; J. Z. Young, 1950, chap. 32; Sholl, 1956; Blum, 1955, ch. 12; Berrill, 1961; etc.).

Although most processes of differentiation can best be explained without recourse to somatic mutation or other genetic alteration (Waddington, 1962), it seems that what we may call *somatic genetics* — changes in genetic constitution in somatic tissues — may occasionally play a role in epigenetic ontogeny. Thus, in some organisms various tissues may come to show various degrees of polyploidy, either as a result of abnormal mitotic division or through endopolypoidy, when the chromosomes-strands undergo intracellular multiplication without nuclear division. Endopolypoidy is probably widespread in vertebrates, and occurs in all insects, though never in nerve-cells. The best known and most striking case is that of the polytene (many-strand) giant chromosomes in the salivary gland tissues of Drosophila and other Diptera, which may consist of as many as 1,024 unit chromosomes, the result of 10 replications. (See e.g. White, 1954, 1961; King, 1962). It is not known what phenotypic results are produced.

Plants and a few animals may show somatic areas with characteristics due to somatic mutation followed by cell-multiplication (see any modern text-book of genetics). Clones of mammalian tissues in tissue-culture may eventually mutate and become malignant; and malignant tissues often show chromosomal irregularities of various types (references in Huxley, 1958b).

The detailed study of zoogeography made by P. J. Darlington (1957) brings out a number of interesting evolutionary points. However, his conclusions are based on the postulate of continental stability. Now that the remarkable researches on paleomagnetism, summarized by Blackett (1960, 1961), have shown that this is no longer tenable, and consequently that Wegener's idea of continental drift was basically sound, the whole subject of evolution in relation to geographical distribution is in need of re-evaluation. In particular, we need to know the date, direction and distance of drift for different continental blocks. The changes in climate which they underwent in the process must have promoted many evolutionary changes in their animal and plant inhabitants.

It was not my intention to describe or discuss the historical origins or special characteristics of man in detail in this book. However, I must just mention the remarkable discoveries of Dart, Broom, and especially Leakey, which point strongly to Africa as the continent of man's origin, and to an australopithecoid as his immediate ancestor. For details, readers should consult works like Le Gros Clark's *The Fossil Evidence of Human Evolution* (1955), and *The Antecedents of Man* (1959) and his chapter in Barnett's *A Century of Darwin* (1959), Rensch (1959), Dobzhansky (1962), and Mayr (1963). For a biological characterization of man and the process of human subspeciation and subsequent convergence, see e.g. A. Barnett's *The Human Species* (1950), Boyd's *Genetics and the Races of Man* (1950), Carleton Coon's *The Origin of Races* (1962), Rensch's *Homo Sapiens* (1959b), and the final chapter of Mayr's *Animal Species and Evolution* (1963).

Mayr mentions that recent work on primate haemoglobins and serum proteins indicates that the hominid (proto-human) line branched off from the African branch of the Pongid line (chimpanzees and gorillas) at a comparatively late date, long after this had diverged from the Asian branch (orang-utans). He further points out that the evolution of hominids provides "an almost classical demonstration of mosaic evolution," with each organ and system of organs showing a different rate and pattern of evolutionary change. The "most astounding" feature of the process was the rapid increase in brain-size during the Pleistocenc, from 450–650 cm^3 in the Australopiths to 1200–1600 cm^3 in Neanderthal and Recent man. This, as Muller has pointed out, must have been facilitated by strong selection-pressure during the period when the evolving hominids were organized in small groups, whose survival depended on a combination of intelligence, communicative ability, parental care, and altruistic cooperation. As social units increase in size, as improvement in cultural tradition becomes relatively more important and dysgenic tendencies begin to operate, and as layer brain-size makes birth increasingly difficult, the selection-pressure is relaxed, or even partly reversed, and brain-size and genetic intelligence no longer increase.

Mayr also makes the point that the critical human characteristics, on which man's unique capacity for cumulative culture depend, are "intelligence, inventiveness, imagination, compassion and other traits that are difficult to measure and to compare." He emphasizes that early hominid species, like H. sapiens today, must have been highly polytypic, and that the "racial" differences between the various geographical subgroups (incipient subspecies) are primarily adaptive: classical racism on the other hand, based on false typological thinking, is erroneous. Though individual variation is exceptionally high in populations of modern man, it appears to be even higher in some of the anthropoids.

In my original text, I made no attempt to analyse the workings of the evolutionary process in the human or psychosocial phase.

All I did was to point out that man was the latest dominant type to be evolved, that he owed this position to a combination of unique properties, notably bipedalism, the capacity for conceptual thought and true (symbolic) speech, for domesticating other animals (Zeuner, 1963), and for making adaptive exosomatic "organs" like tools, weapons, and machines; that for any further progress, conscious purpose based on human values is needed, as well as automatic (natural) selection; and that "the new predominance of mind that has come with man" marked a critical point in evolution.

Since then there has been considerable further exploration of the subject. Its implications are, of course, far-reaching. If a process passes a critical point, it enters on a new phase, in which new properties emerge and new modes of operation become effective. Thus, to take an obvious example, the chemical substance H_2O has quite different properties in its solid, liquid and gaseous phases. In the same sort of way the process of evolution changes its character as it passes from the inorganic to the organic and from the organic to the psychosocial phase. In each phase it has a different mechanism of change, operates at a different tempo, and produces quite new kinds of results; but it is still evolution throughout.

One of the most important events of the last 20 years has been the recognition that evolution is still at work in the psychosocial phase, but operates in new ways; it is not a mere extrapolation of biological evolution. During the early part of this century, sociologists and social anthropologists strongly resisted the idea that evolutionary ideas could be applied to the study of social and historical processes. This was a reaction against the undue zeal and over-simplification of their late nineteenth century predecessors, whose concept of evolution was confined to an inevitable and unilinear progress from "lower" to "higher" levels or patterns of social organisation.

Now that biologists have shown that biological advance is neither inevitable nor unilinear, and that thinkers have been able to provide general definitions of evolution more satisfactory than those of earlier evolutionary philosophers like Herbert Spencer or Bergson, this inhibition has been overcome, and social scientists, often in conjunction with biologists, physicists and philosophers, are beginning to undertake a serious analysis of the exceedingly complex and difficult subject of evolution in its human or psychosocial phase. A notable advance was made in the symposium at the Darwin Centennial at Chicago in 1959, whose results were published in *The Evolution of Man*, Vol. 2 of *Evolution after Darwin*, Chicago, 1960. Reference should also be made to Rensch's *Homo Sapiens: vom Tier zum Halbgott* (Göttingen, 1959), to Dobzhansky (1962), to Waddington's *The Ethical Animal* (London, 1960), to Sahlin's and Service's *Evolution and Culture* (Ann Arbor, 1950), to part 5 of *Behaviour and Evolution*, edited by A. Roe and G. G. Simpson (New Haven, 1958), to Dobzhansky (1962), to Hoagland and Burhoe (1961), and to various essays in *The Humanist Frame*, edited by myself (London and New York, 1961).

Certain general conclusions are beginning to emerge. First, evolution in the psychosocial phase is primarily cultural, manifested in cultural change, and only secondarily genetic. Secondly, the same three sub-processes seen in biological evolution—cladogenesis, anagenesis, and stasigenesis—continue to operate in the psychosocial phase, but now with reference to cultures, leading respectively to cultural diversity, cultural improvement and advance, and cultural stabilisation and persistence. However, a fourth sub-process is now increasingly active—diffusion, leading to unification and convergence instead of divergence. As I have already mentioned, diffusion of genes occurs to a small extent in biological evolution, mainly in plants and only between closely related forms such as species and genera. But in psychosocial evolution, cultural diffusion of artefacts, techniques, symbols and ideas, as well as physical diffusion by migration, enslavement, and intermarriage, is universal and operates at all levels of cultural divergence.

Organisms possess an evolutionary mechanism for ensuring a combination of continuity and change (heredity and variation), in the shape of their chromosome-borne gene-complex. Through the operation of natural selection the gene-complex itself evolves, as a result of the organism's vicissitudes in time, so that each evolving population of organisms possesses a more or less adaptively integrated (co-adapted) gene-pool on which it draws for its future maintenance and evolution; (see Dobzhansky, 1962, Mather, 1961, etc.). Man possesses a second (evolutionary) system for ensuring a combination of continuity and change by means of his mechanism for the cumulative storage and application of experience, in the shape of the complex of ideas, beliefs, and attendant behaviour included under the general head of tradition, which we may call his idea-system for short. Through the operation of psychosocial selection, the idea-system itself evolves as a result of man's changing experiences during pre-history and history, so that each evolving human population possesses a more or less integrated or co-adapted pool of ideas on which it can draw for its maintenance and evolutionary requirements.

Owing to man's possessing this cumulative mechanism of utilizing and storing experience, all the processes of psychosocial evolution not only operate at a faster tempo than those of biological evolution, but exhibit acceleration, very markedly so in recent centuries.

As in the biological phase, major advance occurs through a succession of dominant types or patterns of organisation; however, these are organisations not of bodily organs and physiological functions but of thoughts and beliefs and associated social and cultural patterns—in brief, dominant idea-systems. Thus the scientific revolution marked the emergence of the scientific idea-system as the dominant pattern of human thought, while today there are signs that this may soon be succeeded by a humanist system.

Psychosocial selection, involving some sort of selection between competing ideas and values, must operate in the human phase, and is clearly very different from natural selection. However, not much progress has been made in its analysis, or in the detailed investigation of its results in the actual processes of cultural evolution, though pioneering studies like those of Sahlins and Service (op. cit.) and of Steward and Shimkin (in Hoagland and Burhoe, 1961), have opened up a fruitful methodological approach, and are beginning to produce interesting results.

Major trends for future psychosocial progress have been indicated by various writers, including Rensch (1959), myself (1961, 1962), and by Teilhard de Chardin in *The Phenomenon of Man* (1959), but a much more detailed and rigorous analysis is necessary before they become acceptable. On the other hand, increasingly valuable studies are being made on the past evolution of particular psychosocial functions, organs and techniques, such as the history of science, comparative religion, art, history, law and linguistics.* Unfortunately, some of the most exhaustive of such studies, e.g. of Toynbee on history, are vitiated through not having adopted an evolutionary approach. Meanwhile, serious obstacles to psychosocial progress have recently arisen, notably undue concentration on military technology and expenditure, over-exploitation of renewable resources, the atomic threat both to civilisation and to the human gene-complex, and above all, the excessive increase of human population.

I have left to the end the most important scientific event of our times—the discovery by Watson and Crick that the desoxyribonucleic acids—DNA for short—are the true physical basis of life, and provide the mechanism of heredity and evolution.† Their chemical structure, combining two elongated linear sequences in a linked double spiral or bihelix, makes them self-reproducing, and ensures that they can act as a code, providing an immense amount of genetical "information," together with occasional variations of information (mutations) which also reproduce themselves. Linear constructions of DNA are, of course, the primary structures in the genetic organelles we call chromosomes. In some primitive organisms there is only a single chromosome, including the species' entire apparatus of DNA (see Chargaff and Davidson, 1955-1960).

Specific DNA also plays the key role in determining the specific proteins, including enzymes, in living cells, through the intermediary of specific forms of RNA (ribose nucleic acid). The particular DNA code of each species thus provides epigenetic

---

* See, for example, the brilliant studies of Pisani (1962) on the processes operative in the evolution of Indo-European languages.

† For a brief account, see Davidson, 1960 and for a general discussion, see New Biology, No. 31, *Biological Replication*, 1960.

"instruction" as well as phylogenetic "information." Mayr (1963) makes the same distinction in slightly different terms. In his formulation, the phenomena of ontogeny and physiology are manifestations of the decoding of the information provided by the genotypic DNA, while those of evolutionary change are the result of the provision of ever-new codes of genetic information.

It may well prove that DNA structure has the further intrinsic property of ensuring recombination of mutants by interchange between separate homologous sections of DNA (chromosomes). Even if this essentially sexual process were not intrinsic *ab origine*, it confers such a high degree of evolutionary advantage that it must have been incorporated into the stream of life very early in its evolution. As a result (contrary to the views stated on p. 131 of the original text of this book), some form of sexual or para-sexual interchange process between chromosome-like bodies is found even among the most primitive types of organisms, including even blue-green algae (Kumar, 1962) and viruses (see below).

Thanks to a combination of electron microscopy, chemical study and genetic analysis, there has been a notable advance in our knowledge of the structure and behaviour of viruses. Viruses consist either of DNA or RNA, and act so as to deviate their host's metabolic processes to their own advantage, in a number of cases causing cancer in doing so.

Different viruses may interact, both genetically and non-genetically (Fenner, 1962). Some viruses may even temporarily become part of the genetic outfit of their host, re-emerging as parasites in response to certain stimuli. This is notably so with the so-called temperate phage parasites of bacteria, where the phage (prophage) particle is attached to, or perhaps partly replaces, a single bacterial gene, which then may be transferred to another host by so-called *transduction*. Some bacteria may undergo *transformation*, by DNA from other bacterial strains: particles of puri-fied DNA may, it appears, even replace existing alleles in the bacterium's gene-complex.

In other cases the virus or other parasite acts as a permanent or temporary plasmagene: e.g. the CO_2-sensitivity virus in Droso-phila (see l'Heritier, 1962) or the Kappa particle in Paramecium (see Beale, 1954). However, though such facts are of great genetic interest, and shed light on early types of organisation in living systems, their main evolutionary implication seems to be that they make certain new forms of symbiosis possible. (For microbial genetics, parasexual processes, viruses, transduction and trans-formation, see Jacob and Wollman, 1961; Catcheside, 1951; Braun, 1953; Pontecorvo, 1959 and 1963; Hayes and Clowes, 1960; Burnet, 1960; Burnet and Stanley, 1960; Fenner, 1962; K. Smith, 1962; Huxley, 1958b; Lederberg, 1957).

I did not mention cancer in the original text. Today we know a good deal about its manifestation in different types of plants and animals. The implications of the facts, notably the marked differences in manifestation between related groups, are often puzzling, and demand detailed exploration. One problem which should be carefully investigated is the following. It is known that the time to first cancer after application of carcinogens is broadly correlated with the size of the experimental animal. The question is whether rate of development of carcinogenetically induced tumours to first manifestation is correlated with the animal's rate of development and growth, or with its longevity. Experiments with small birds and mammals should give the answer: their rates of development are similar, but the birds' longevity is much greater.

One thing appears certain — that cancer is a blanket term cover-ing a wide range of abnormal growths, and that cancerous condi-tions may arise as a result of genetic imbalance, of virus infection, of carcinogenic treatment, chemical and physical, and apparently of some sort of somatic mutation, even in tissue-culture. It appears possible that in vertebrates abnormal growth is normally inhibited by some substance produced by the various tissues of the body. In some arthropods, the inhibitory control seems to be exerted via the nervous system. (For a brief summary from the biological angle, see Huxley, 1958b; also Burnet, 1959).

The various properties of DNA which I have mentioned make evolution inevitable. The existence of an elaborate self-reproduc-ing code of genetical information ensures continuity and speci-ficity; the intrinsic capacity for mutation provides variability; the capacity for self-reproduction ensures potentially geometric increase and therefore a struggle for existence; the existence of genetic variability ensures differential survival of variants and therefore natural selection; and this results in evolutionary transformation.

Our detailed knowledge of the constitution and operation of DNA and RNA will help in the unravelling of many particular genetic-evolutionary problems. Among these may be mentioned the relation of genes to developmental processes, the interaction of different genes, and the relations of genes to immunology via antigens and antibodies. Light is already being shed on the fine structure of genes, which are proving to be far more complex than was originally supposed (see Pontecorvo 1959).

It would also seem certain that more detailed knowledge about DNA will give us fuller understanding of mutation and the ways in which it depends on chemical structure, with the eventual possibility of influencing the type and direction of mutation by artificial means. In general, however, the discovery of DNA and its properties has not led to important new developments or significant modifications in evolutionary theory or in our understanding of the course of biological evolution. What it has done is to reveal the physical basis underlying the evolutionary mechanisms which Darwin's genius deduced must be operative in nature, and to open up new possibilities of detailed genetic analysis and of experimental control of the genetic-evolutionary process. The edifice of evolutionary theory is still essentially Darwinian after the incorporation of all our new knowledge of mendelian (particulate) genetics; it will remain so long after the incorporation of our knowledge of its detailed chemical basis.

BIBLIOGRAPHY

ADAMS, C. C. (1915). "The Variations and Ecological Distribution of the Snails of the Genus *Io*." Mem. Nat. Acad. Sci. **12**: (2).

ALDRICH, J. W., and NUTT, D. C. (1939). "Birds of Eastern Newfoundland." Sci. Pub. Cleveland Mus. Nat. Hist. **4**: 13.

ALEXANDER, W. B. (1941). "The Index of Heron Population, 1940." Brit. Birds **34**: 189.

ALLAN, H. H. (1940). "Natural Hybridization in Relation to Taxonomy," in "The New Systematics," ed. J. S. Huxley. Oxford.

ALLEE, W. C. (1938). "The Social Life of Animals." New York.

ALLEE, W. C. (1940). "Concerning the Origin of Sociality in Animals." Scientia **34**: 154.

ALLEN, J. A. (1876). "Geographical Variation Among North American Mammals, etc." Bull. U.S. Geol. Surv. **2**: 309.

ALPATOV, W. W. (1929). "Biometrical Studies on Variation and Races of the Honey Bee (*Apis mellifica*)." Quart. Rev. Biol. **41**: 1.

ALTENBURG, E., and MULLER, H. J. (1920). "The Genetic Basis of Truncate Wing, etc." Genetics **5**: 1.

ANDERSON, E. (1928). "The Problem of Species in the Northern Blue Flags, *Iris versicolor* L. and *Iris virginica* L." Ann. Mo. Bot. Gard. **15**: 241.

ANDERSON, E. (1937). "Cytology in its Relation to Taxonomy." Bot. Rev. **3**: 335.

ANON. (1941). "Related Mollusk Species Show Opposite Tendencies." Sci. News Letter **39**: 72.

ARKELL, W. J. (1933). "The Oysters of the Fuller's Earth, etc." Proc. Cotteswold Nat. Field Cl. **25**: 1.

ARKELL, W. J., and MOY-THOMAS, J. A. (1940). "Palaeontology and the Taxonomic Problem" in "The New Systematics," ed. J. S. Huxley. Oxford.

BABCOCK, E. B. (1939). "Recent Progress in Plant Breeding." Sci. Mon. N.Y. **1939**: 393.

BABCOCK, E. B., and STEBBINS, G. L. (1938). "The American Species of *Crepis*, etc." Publ. Carneg. Instn. no. **504**.

BADENHUIZEN, N. P. (1941). "Colchicine-induced Tetraploids obtained from Plants of Economic Value." Nature **147**: 577.

BAILY, J. L. (1939). "Physiological Group Differentiation in *Lymnaea columella*." Baltimore.

BAILY, J. L. (1941). Amer. Nat. **75**: 213.

BAKER, E. C. STUART (1930). "The Game Birds of India, Burma and Ceylon." (Vol. **3**.) London.

BAKER, E. C. STUART (1931). "The Game Birds of the Indian Empire." Vol. **5**, pt. 15. J. Bombay Nat. Hist. Soc. **35**: 241.

BALDWIN, J. M. (1896). "A new Factor in Evolution." Amer. Nat. **30**: 441, 536.

BALDWIN, J. M. (1902). "Development and Evolution." New York and London.

BALL, G. H. (1922). "Variation in Fresh-Water Mussels." Ecology **3**: 93.

BANKS, E. (1929). "Interbreeding among some Bornean Leaf-Monkeys of the Genus *Pithecus*." Proc. Zool. Soc. Lond. **1929**: 693.

BANTA, A. M., and WOOD, T. R. (1928). "A Thermal Race of Cladocera Originating by Mutation." Verh. V. Int. Kongr. Vererb. (Berlin, 1927) 1: 397.

BARBER, H. N. (1941). "Evolution in the genus Paeonia." Nature 148: 227.

BARBOUR, T., and SHREVE, B. (1937). "Novitates Cubanae." Bull. Mus. Comp. Zool. 80: 377.

BARRETT-HAMILTON, G. E. H., and HINTON, M. A. C. (1910—). "A History of British Mammals." London.

BARROWS, E. F. (1934). "Modification of the Dominance of Agouti to Non-Agouti in the Mouse." J. Genet. 29: 9.

BARTON-WRIGHT, E. C. (1932). "Recent Advances in Botany." London.

BATES, G. L. (1931). "On Geographical Variations within the Limits of West Africa: some Generalizations." Ibis (13) 1: 255.

BATES, H. W. (1862). "Contributions to an Insect Fauna of the Amazon Valley. Lepidoptera: Heliconidae." Trans. Linn. Soc. Lond. 23: 495.

BATES, R. W., RIDDLE, OSCAR, and LAHR, ERNEST L. (1939). "The Racial Factor in the Pigeon Crop-Sac Method, etc." Amer. J. Physiol. 125: 722.

BATESON, W. (1894). "Materials for the Study of Variation, etc." London.

BATESON, W. (1913). "Problems of Genetics." Oxford.

BATESON, W., and BATESON, G. (1925). "On Certain Aberrations of the Red-Legged Partridges, etc." J. Genet. 16: 101.

BATHER, F. A. (1920). "Fossils and Life." Rep. Brit. Ass. 1920: 61.

BAUR, E. (1923). "Einführung in die experimentelle Vererbungslehre," Berlin.

BAUR, E. (1932). "Artumgrenzung und Artbildung in der Gattung Antirrhinum, etc." Z. ind. Abst. Vererb.l. 63: 256.

BEADLE, L. C., and CRAGG, J. B. (1940). "Osmotic Regulation in Freshwater Animals." Nature 146: 588.

BEAUCHAMP, R., and ULLYOTT, P. (1932). "Competitive Relationships between Certain Species of Freshwater Triclads." J. Ecol. 20: 200.

BEEBE, C. W. (1907). "Geographic Variation in Birds with Especial Reference to the Effects of Humidity." Zoologica (N.Y.) 1: 1.

BEEBE, W. (1921). "A Monograph of the Pheasants," Vol. 2. London.

BEEBE, W. (1924). "Galapagos: World's End." New York.

BENEDICT, R. C. (1932). "Variation in Nephrolepis." Proc. VI. Int. Congr. Genet. (Ithaca) 2: 283.

BENEDICT, F. G., LANDAUER, W., and FOX, E. L. (1932). "The Physiology of Normal and Frizzle Fowl, etc." Storrs Agric. Exper. Sta. Bull. 177: 1.

BENSON, C. W. (1941). "Further Notes on Nyasaland Birds, etc., Pt. IV." Ibis (14), 5: 1.

BENT, A. C. (1939). "Life-Histories of North American Woodpeckers." Bull. U.S. Nat. Mus. no. 174.

BEQUAERT, J. (1918). "A Revision of the Vespidae of the Belgian Congo, etc." Bull. Amer. Mus. Nat. Hist. 39: 1.

BERG, L.S. (1926). "Nomogenesis: or Evolution Determined by Law." tr. J. N. Rostovtsow. London.

BERG, L. S. (1935). "Über die vermeintlichen marinen Elemente in der Fauna und Flora des Baikalsees." Zoogeographica 2: 455.

BERG, R. L. (1941). "A Genetical Analysis of Wild Populations, etc." Drosoph. Inf. Serv. no. 15: 20.

BIDDLE, R. L. (1932). "The Bristles of Hybrids between Drosophila melanogaster and Drosophila simulans." Genetics 17: 153.

BIRD, C. C., and BIRD, E. G., (1941). "The Birds of North-East Greenland." Ibis (14) 5: 118.

BLAIR, A. P. (1941a). "Isolating Mechanisms in Tree-frogs." Proc. Nat. Acad. Sci. 27: 14.

BLAIR, A. P. (1941b). "Variation, Isolation Mechanisms, and Hybridization in Certain Toads." Genetics 26: 398.

BLAIR, R. H., and TUCKER, B. W. (1941). "Nest-Sanitation." Brit. Birds 34: 206, 226, 250.

BLAKESLEE, A. F. (1928). "Genetics of Datura." Verh. V. Int. Kongr. Vererb. (Berlin, 1927) 1: 117.

BLAKESLEE, A. F., BERGNER, A. D., and AVERY, A. G. (1936). "A New Method of Synthesizing Pure-Breeding Types, etc." Amer. Nat. 70: 255.

BLAKESLEE, A. F., BERGNER, A. D., and AVERY, A. G. (1937). "Geographical Distribution of Chromosomal Prime Types in Datura stramonium." Cytologia, Fujii Jubilee Vol.: 1070.

BLAKESLEE, A. F., and FOX, A. L. (1932). "Our Different Taste Worlds." J. Hered. 23: 97.

BÖKER, H. (1924). "Begründung einer biologischen Morphologie." Z. Morph. Anthr. 24: 1.

BOLK, L. (1926). "Das Problem der Menschenwerdung." Jena.

BONNEVIE, K. (1934). "Embryological Analysis of Gene Manifestation in Little and Bagg's Abnormal Mouse Tribe." J. Exper. Zool. 67: 443.

BONNIER, G. (1895). "Recherches Experimentales sur l'Adaptation des Plantes au Climat Alpin." Ann. Sci. Nat. 7: 20, 225.

BORGSTRÖM, G. (1939). "Formation of Cleistogamic and Chasmogamic Flowers in Wild Violets, etc." Nature 144: 514.

BOWATER, W. (1914). "Heredity of Melanism in Lepidoptera." J. Genet. 3: 299.

BREWER, H. (1937). "Eugenics and Politics." The Eugenics Society, London.

BRIERLEY, J. (1938). "An Exploratory Investigation of the Selective Value of Certain Genes and their Combinations in Drosophila." Biol. Bull. 75: 475.

BROOM, R. (1933). "Evolution—Is There Intelligence Behind It?" S. Afr. J. Sci. 30: 1.

BROUGH, J. (1936). "On the Evolution of Bony Fishes, etc." Biol. Rev. 11: 385.

BRUNN, A. F. (1933). "On the Value of the Number of the Vertebrae, etc." Vidensk. Medd. Dansk. naturh. Forening 94: 375.

BUCHNER, P. (1928). "Holznahrung und Symbiose." Berlin.

BUMPUS, H. C. (1897). "The Variations and Mutations of the Introduced Sparrow." Biol. Lect. Woods Hole 1897: 1.

BUMPUS, H. C. (1899). "The Elimination of the Unfit as Illustrated by the Introduced Sparrow, etc." Bird Lect. Woods Hole 1898: 209.

BURKITT, J. P. (1924–1925). "A Study of the Robin by Means of Marked Birds (Parts 2 and 4)." Brit. Birds 18: 97 and 19: 120.

BUTLER, P. M. (1941). "A Comparison of the Skulls and Teeth of the Two Species of Hemicentetes." J. Mammal. 22: 65.

BUXTON, P. A. (1923). "Animal Life in Deserts." London.

BUXTON, P. A. (1935). "Insects of Samoa, etc., Summary," Pt. 9 (Fasc. 2): 33. Brit. Mus. (Nat. Hist.). London.

BUZZATI-TRAVERSO, A., JUCCI, C. and TIMOFÉEFF-RESSOVSKY, N. W. (1938). "Genetica di popolazione." Ricerca Scientifica, year 9, vol. 1 (nos. 11–12) 1.

CALMAN, W. T. (1940). "A Museum Zoologist's View of Taxonomy," in "The New Systematics," ed. J. S. Huxley. Oxford.

CAMERON, E. (1938). "A Study of the Natural Control of the Pea Moth, Cydia nigricana, Steph." Bull. Entom. Res. 29: 277.

CAROTHERS, E. E. (1941). "Interspecific Grasshopper Hybrids, etc." Proc. VII. Int. Genet. Congr. (Edinburgh, 1939): 84.

CARPENTER, G. D. H. (1925). "Speke's Tragelaph on the Sese Isles of Lake Victoria." Proc. Zool. Soc. Lond. **1925**: 1423.

CARPENTER, G. D. H. (1932). "The Forms of *Acraea johnstoni*, Godm., etc." Trans. Ent. Soc. Lond. **80**: 251.

CARPENTER, G. D. H. (1939). "Birds as Enemies of Butterflies, with Special Reference to Mimicry." Proc. VII. Int. Kongr. Entom. (1938): 1061.

CARPENTER, G. D. H., and FORD, E. B. (1933). "Mimicry." London.

CASTLE, W. E. (1932). "Body Size and Body Proportions in Relation to Growth Rates and Natural Selection." Science **76**: 365.

CASTLE, W. E. (1934). "Genetics and Eugenics" (4th ed.). Harvard.

CASTLE, W. E., and NACHTSHEIM, H. (1933). "Linkage Interrelations for the Three Genes for Rex (short) Coat in the Rabbit." Proc. Nat. Acad. Sci. **19**: 1006.

CASTLE, W. E., and PINCUS, G. (1928). "Hooded Rats and Selection, etc." J. Exper. Zool. **50**: 409.

CESNOLA, A. P. DI (1907). "A First Study of Natural Selection in *Helix arbustorum*." Biometrika **5**: 387.

CHAMPY, C. (1924). "Sexualité et Hormones." Paris.

CHAPMAN, A., and BUCK, W. J. (1893). "Wild Spain." London.

CHAPMAN, F. M. (1923). "Mutation among Birds in the Genus *Buarremon*." Bull. Amer. Mus. Nat. Hist. **48**: 243.

CHAPMAN, F. M. (1924). "Criteria for the Determination of Subspecies in Systematic Ornithology." Auk **41**: 17.

CHAPMAN, F. M. (1926). "The Distribution of Bird-Life in Ecuador." Bull. Amer. Mus. Nat. Hist. **55**: 1.

CHAPMAN, F. M. (1927). "The Variations and Distribution of *Saltator aurantiirostris*." Amer. Mus. Novit. no. **261**.

CHAPMAN, F. M. (1928). "Mutation in *Capito auratus*." Amer. Mus. Novit. no. **335**.

CHAPMAN, F. M. (1935). "Further Remarks on the Relationship of the Grackles of the Subgenus *Quiscalus*." Auk **52**: 21.

CHAPMAN, F. M. (1936). "Further Remarks on *Quiscalus* with a Report on Additional Specimens from Louisiana." Auk **53**: 405.

CHAPMAN, F. M. (1939). "Nomenclature in the Genus *Quiscalus*." Auk **56**: 364.

CHAPMAN, F. M. (1940a). "Further Studies of the Genus *Quiscalus*." Auk **57**: 225.

CHAPMAN, F. M. (1940b). "The Post-Glacial History of *Zonotrichia capensis*." Bull. Amer. Mus. Nat. Hist. **77**: 381.

CHAPMAN, F. M., and GRISCOM, L. (1924). "The House Wrens of the Genus *Troglodytes*." Bull. Amer. Mus. Nat. Hist. **50**: 279.

CHEESMAN, R. E., and HINTON, M. A. C. (1924). "On the Mammals Collected in the Desert of Central Arabia by Major R. E. Cheesman." Ann. Mag. Nat. Hist. (9) **14**: 548.

CHEVAIS, S. (1937). "Croissance et Races Locales de *Corophium volutator*." Trav. Stat. Biol. Roscoff. no. **15**.

CHILDE, V. G. (1936). "Man Makes Himself." London.

CHRISTOFF, M. (1941). "Polyploidy and Apomictic Development in the Genus *Potentilla*." Proc. VII. Int. Genet. Congr. (Edinburgh, 1939): 88.

CHRISTY, C. (1929). "The African Buffaloes." Proc. Zool. Soc. Lond. **1929**: 445.

CHRISTY, MILLER (1897). "*Primula elatior* in Britain, etc." J. Linn. Soc. (Bot.) **33**: 172.

CLANCEY, P. A. (1938). "Some Remarks on Western Scottish Birds." Ibis (14) 2: 746.

CLARK, W. E. LE GROS (1934). "Early Forerunners of Man, etc." London.

CLAUSEN, J. (1927). "Chromosome-Numbers and the Relationship of Species in the Genus *Viola*." Ann. Bot. 41: 677.

CLAUSEN, J., KECK, D. D., and HIESEY, W. M. (1937). "Experimental Taxonomy." Yearb. Carneg. Instn. 36: 13.

CLAUSEN, J., KECK, D. D., and HIESEY, W. M. (1938). "Experimental Taxonomy." Yearb. Carneg. Instn. 37: 218.

CLAUSEN, J., KECK, D. D., and HIESEY, W. M. (1940). "Experimental Studies on the Nature of Species. I. Effect of Varied Environments on Western North American Plants." Publ. Carneg. Instn. no. 520.

CLELAND, R. E. (1928). "The Genetics of *Oenothera* in Relation to Chromosome Behaviour, with Special Reference to Certain Hybrids." Verh. V. Int. Kongr. Vererb. (Berlin, 1927) 1: 554.

CLEMENTS, F. E. (1929). "Experimental Methods in Adaptation and Morphogeny." J. Ecol. 17: 356.

CLEMENTS, F. E. (1932). "Investigations in Ecology." Yearb. Carneg. Instn. 31: 211.

COLEMAN, E. (1927). "Pollination of the Orchid *Cryptostylis leptochila*." Vict. Nat. Melbourne 44: 20.

COLLINS, J. L. (1927). "A Low Temperature Type of Albinism in Barley." J. Hered. 18: 331.

COLLINS, J. L., HOLLINGSHEAD, L., and AVERY, P. (1929). "Interspecific Hybrids in *Crepis*, III." Genetics 14: 305.

COLMAN, J. (1932). "A Statistical Test of the Species Concept in *Littorina*." Biol. Bull. 62: 223.

CORNES, J. J. S. (1937). "Attitude and Concealing Coloration." Nature 140: 684.

COTT, H. B. (1940). "Adaptive Coloration in Animals." London.

COWAN, J. M. (1940). "Rhododendrons of the *Rh. sanguineum* Alliance." Notes Roy. Bot. Gdn. Edinb. 20: 55.

CRAMPTON, H. E. (1916). "Studies on the Variation, Distribution and Evolution of the Genus *Partula*, etc." Publ. Carneg. Instn. no. 228.

CRAMPTON, H. E. (1925). "Contemporaneous Organic Differentiation in the Species of *Partula* living in Moorea, Society Islands." Amer. Nat. 59: 5.

CRAMPTON, H. E. (1932). "Studies on the Variation, Distribution and Evolution of the Genus *Partula*, etc." Publ. Carneg. Instn. no. 410.

CRANE, M. B., and THOMAS, P. T. (1939). "Segregation in Asexual (Apomictic) Offspring in *Rubus*." Nature 143: 684.

CREW, F. A. E. (1936). "A Repetition of McDougall's Lamarckian Experiment." J. Genet. 33: 61.

CREW, F. A. E., and LAMY, R. (1932). "A Sex-linked Recessive 'Lethal' in *Drosophila obscura*." J. Genet. 25: 257.

CREW, F. A. E., and MIRSKAIA, L. (1931). "The Character 'Hairless' in the Mouse." J. Genet. 25: 17.

CROSBY, J. L. (1940). "High Proportions of Homostyle Plants in Populations of *Primula vulgaris*." Nature 145: 672.

CROSS, E. C. (1941). "Colour Phases of the Red Fox (*Vulpes fulva*) in Ontario." J. Mammal. 22: 25.

DALE, F. H. (1939). "Variability and Environmental Responses of the Kangaroo Rat, *Dipodomys heermanni saxatilis*. Amer. Midl. Nat. 22: 703.

DALE, F. H. (1940). "Geographic Variation in the Meadow Mouse, etc." J. Mammal. 21: 332.

DAVIS, V. (1937). "Etude critique des différentes formes de *Picus canus* Gmelin." Oiseau, Paris, n. ser. 7: 247.

DANSER, B. H. (1929). "Ueber die Begriffe Komparium, Kommisküum und Konvivium, etc." Genetica 11: 399.

DARLING, F. F. (1939). "Bird Flocks and the Breeding Cycle, etc." Cambridge.

DARLINGTON, C. D. (1933). "Chromosome Study and the Genetic Analysis of Species." Ann. Bot. 47: 811.

DARLINGTON, C. D. (1937). "Recent Advances in Cytology" (2nd ed.). London.

DARLINGTON, C. D. (1939). "The Evolution of Genetic Systems." Cambridge.

DARLINGTON, C. D. (1940). "Taxonomic Species and Genetic Systems," in "The New Systematics," ed. J. S. Huxley. Oxford.

DARLINGTON, C. D., and UPCOTT, M. B. (1941a). "The Activity of Inert Chromosomes in *Zea mays*." J. Genet. 41: 275.

DARLINGTON, C. D., and UPCOTT, M. B. (1941b). "Spontaneous Chromosome Change." J. Genet. 41: 297.

DARWIN, C. (1868). "The Variation of Animals and Plants under Domestication." London.

DARWIN, C. (1871). "The Descent of Man and Selection in Relation to Sex." London.

DARWIN, C. (1875). "The Origin of Species by Means of Natural Selection, etc." (6th ed.). London.

DARWIN, C. (1877). "The Various Contrivances by which Orchids are Fertilized by Insects" (2nd ed.). London.

DAVENPORT, C. B. (ed.) (1928). "Mutations of Physiological Import, etc." Yearb. Carneg. Instn. 27: 45.

DAVENPORT, C. B. (ed.) (1933). "Accumulation of Recessive Mutations during Long-continued Parthenogenesis." Yearb. Carneg. Instn. 32: 49.

DE BEER, G. R. (1930). "Embryology and Evolution." Oxford.

DE BEER, G. R. (1940a). "Embryology and Taxonomy," in "The New Systematics." ed. J. S. Huxley. Oxford.

DE BEER, G. R. (1940b). "Embryos and Ancestors." Oxford.

DEMENTIEV, G. P. (1938). "Sur la distribution géographique de certains oiseaux paléarctiques, etc." Proc. VIII. Int. Orn. Congr. (1934): 243.

DESSELBERGER, H. (1930). "Ueber das Lipochrom der Vogelfeder." J. Orn. 78: 328.

DEWAR, D., and FINN, F. (1909). "The Making of Species." London and New York.

DICE, L. R. (1931). "The Occurrence of Two Subspecies of the Same Species in the Same Area." J. Mammal. 12: 210.

DICE, L. R. (1933a). "The Inheritance of Dichromatism in the Deer-Mouse, *Peromyscus maniculatus blandus*." Amer. Nat. 67: 571.

DICE, L. R. (1933b). "Fertility Relationships between some of the Species and Subspecies of Mice in the Genus *Peromyscus*." J. Mammal. 14: 298.

DICE, L. R. (1937). "Variation in the Wood-Mouse, etc." Occ. Pap. Mus. Zool. Univ. Michigan no. 352: 1.

DICE, L. R. (1939). "Variation in the Deer-Mouse (*Peromyscus maniculatus*) in the Columbia Basin of South-Eastern Washington and Adjacent Idaho and Oregon." Contrib. Lab. Vert. Genet. Univ. Mich. no. 12: 1.

DICE, L. R. (1940a). "Relationships between the Wood-Mouse and the Cotton-Mouse in Eastern Virginia." J. Mammal. 21: 14 .

DICE, L. R. (1940b). "Ecologic and Genetic Variability within Species of Peromyscus." Amer. Nat. 74: 212.

DICE, L. R. (1940c). "Speciation in Peromyscus." Amer. Nat. 74: 289.

DICE, L. R., and BLOSSOM, P. M. (1937). "Studies of Mammalian Ecology, etc." Publ. Carneg. Instn. no. 485.

DICKSON, R. C. (1941). "Inheritance of Resistance to Hydrocyanic Acid Fumigation in the California Red Scale." Hilgardia, 13: 515.

DISCOVERY COMMITTEE (1937). "Report on the Progress of the Discovery Committee's Investigations." London.

DIVER, C. (1929). "Fossil Records of Mendelian Mutants." Nature 124: 183.

DIVER, C. (1932). "Mollusc Genetics." Proc. VI. Int. Congr. Genet. (Ithaca) 2: 236.

DIVER, C. (1938). "The Plant-carpet in Relation to Animal Distribution." Proc. Linn. Soc. Lond. 150: 124.

DIVER, C. (1939). "Aspects of the Study of Variation in Snails." J. Conchol. 21: 91.

DIVER, C. (1940). "The Problem of Closely-Related Species Living in the Same Area," in "The New Systematics," ed. J. S. Huxley. Oxford.

DOBZHANSKY, T. (1927). "Studies on the Manifold Effect of Certain Genes in Drosophila melanogaster." Z. ind. Abst. Vererb.l. 43: 330.

DOBZHANSKY, T. (1933). "Geographical Variation in Lady-Beetles." Amer. Nat. 67: 97.

DOBZHANSKY, T. (1936). "Position Effects of Genes." Biol. Rev. 11: 364.

DOBZHANSKY, T. (1937). "Genetics and the Origin of Species." New York.

DOBZHANSKY, T. (1939a). "Genetics of Natural Populations. IV. Mexican and Guatemalan Populations of Drosophila pseudoobscura." Genetics 24: 391.

DOBZHANSKY, T. (1939b). "Experimental Studies on Genetics of Free-Living Populations of Drosophila." Biol. Rev. 14: 339.

DOBZHANSKY, T. (1940). "Speciation as a Stage in Evolutionary Divergence." Amer. Nat. 74: 312.

DOBZHANSKY, T. (1941). "On the Genetic Structure of Natural Populations of Drosophila." Proc. VIII. Int. Genet. Congr. (Edinburgh, 1939): 104.

DOBZHANSKY, T., and TAN, C. C. (1936). "Studies in Hybrid Sterility. III. Z. ind. Abst. Vererb.l. 72: 88.

DONISTHORPE, H. (1940). "Mimicry in Ants." Ent. mon. Mag. 76: 254.

DONOVAN, C. (1936). "Catalogue of the Macrolepidoptera of Ireland." Cheltenham and London.

DOOB, L. W. (1940). "The Plans of Men." New Haven.

DOWDESWELL, W. H., FISHER, R. A., and FORD, E. B. (1940). "The Quantitative Study of Populations in the Lepidoptera. I. Polyommatus icarus Rott." Ann. Eugen. 10: 123.

DUBININ, N. P., and others (1934). "Experimental Study of the Ecogenotypes of Drosophila melanogaster." Biol. J. (Moscow) 3: 166.

DUBININ, N. P., and others (1936). "Genetic Constitution and Gene-dynamics of Wild Populations of Drosophila melanogaster." Biol. J. (Moscow) 5: 939.

DUKE, H. C. (1921). "On the Zoological Status of the Polymorphic Mammalian Trypanosomes, etc." Parasitol. 13: 352.

DUNN, L. C., and LANDAUER, W. (1934). "The Genetics of the Rumpless Fowl, etc." J. Genet. 29: 217.

DUNN, L. C., and LANDAUER, W. (1936). "Further Data on Genetic Modification of Rumplessness in the Fowl." J. Genet. **33**: 401.

DÜRKEN, B. (1923). "Über die Wirkung farbigen Lichtes auf die Puppen des Kohlweisslings (*Pieris brassicae*), etc." Arch. mikr. Anat. **99**: 222.

EDINGER, T. (1940). [Exhibition of brain endocasts of Malagasy ratite birds.] Proc. Zool. Soc. Lond. (A) **110**: viii.

EIGENMANN, C. H. (1909). "Adaptation," in "Fifty Years of Darwinism." New York.

EKER, R. (1935). "The Short-wing Gene in *D. melanogaster* and the Effect of Temperature on its Manifestation." J. Genet. **30**: 357.

ELLERS, K. (1936). "Die Rassen von *Papilio machaon* L." Abh. Bayer Akad. Wiss. (N.F.) **36**: 1.

ELOFF, G. (1936). "Behaviour of Local *Drosophila melanogaster* during Late Larval Stage." Nature **138**: 402.

ELTON, C. S. (1927). "Animal Ecology." London.

ELTON, C. S. (1930). "Animal Ecology and Evolution." Oxford.

ELTON, C. [S.] (1938). "Notes on the Ecological and Natural History of Pabbay, etc." J. Ecol. **26**: 275.

ELTRINGHAM, M. (1910). "African Mimetic Butterflies." Oxford.

EMERSON, A. E. (1934). Biology of Termites [Review]. Ecology **15**: 204.

EMERSON, A. E. (1935). "Termitophile Distribution and Quantitative Characters of Physiological Speciation, etc." Ann. ent. Soc. Amer. **28**: 369.

EMERSON, A. E. (1937). "Ecological Animal Geography." Ecology **18**: 541–2.

EMERSON, A. E. (1938). "Termite Nests: a Study of the Phylogeny of Behaviour." Ecol. Monogr. **8**: 247.

EMERSON, A. E. (1939). "Populations of Social Insects." Ecol. Monogr. **9**: 287.

ENDRÖDI, S. V. (1938). "Die paläarktischen Rassenkreise des Genus *Oryctes* (Ill.). Arch. Naturgesch. (N.F.) **7**: 53.

ENGELS, W. L. (1936). "An Insular Population of *Peromyscus maniculatus*, etc." Amer. Midl. Nat. Notre Dame **17**: 776.

ENGELS, W. L. (1940). "Structural Adaptations in Thrashers (Mimidae: Genus *Toxostoma*), etc." Univ. Calif. Publ. Zool. **42**: 341.

ESLICK, A. (1940). "An Ecological Study of *Patella* at Port St. Mary, Isle of Man." Proc. Linn. Soc. Lond. **152**: 45.

EVANG, K. (1925). "The Sex-Linked Mutants Vesiculated and Semi-Lethal in *Drosophila melanogaster*." Z. ind. Abst. Vererb.l. **39**: 165.

EVANS, F. C., and VEVERS, H. G. (1938). "Notes on the Biology of the Faeroe Mouse (*Mus musculus faeroensis*). J. Anim. Ecol. **7**: 290.

EVERETT, W. G. (1932). "The Uniqueness of Man." Univ. Calif. Publ. Zool. **16**: 1.

FABERGÉ, A. C. (1936). "The Physiological Consequences of Polyploidy." J. Genet. **33**: 365.

FANTHAM, H. B., PORTER, A., and RICHARDSON, L. R. (1939). "Some Myxosporidia Found in Certain Fresh-Water Fishes in Quebec Province, Canada." Parasitol. **31**: 1.

FEDERLEY, H. (1911). "Vererbungsstudien an der Lepidopteren-Gattung *Pygaera*." Arch. Rass. u. Ges. Biol. **8**: 281.

FEDERLEY, H. (1932). "Die Bedeutung der Kreuzung für die Evolution." Jena. Z. Naturw. **67**: 364.

FERNALD, N. V. L. (1933): "Recent Discoveries in the Newfoundland Flora.' Rhodora 35: 327.

FISCHER-PIETTE, E. (1935). "Systematique et Biogéographie: les Patelles d'Europe et d'Afrique du Nord." J. Conchyl. 69: 5.

FISHER, J. (1939a). "Birds as Animals." London.

FISHER, J. (1939b). "Distribution of the Colour Phases of the Fulmar (*Fulmarus glacialis*)." Nature 144: 941.

FISHER, J. (1940a). "The Status of the Fulmar in the British Isles." Bull. Brit. Orn. Cl. 60: 87.

FISHER, J. (1940b). [Fulmar: Distribution, British Isles.] in WITHERBY, H. F., and others. "The Handbook of British Birds." Vol. 4: 73. London.

FISHER, J. (1940c). "Watching Birds." Harmondsworth.

FISHER, J., and WATERSTON, G. (1941). "The Breeding Distribution, History and Population of the Fulmar (*Fulmarus glacialis*), etc." J. Anim. Ecol. 10:204.

FISHER, R. A. (1928). "The Possible Modification of the Response of the Wild Type to Recurrent Mutations" *and* "Two Further Notes on the Origin of Dominance." Amer. Nat. 62: 115 and 571.

FISHER, R. A. (1930a). "The Genetical Theory of Natural Selection." Oxford.

FISHER, R. A. (1930b). "The Evolution of Dominance in Certain Polymorphic Species." Amer. Nat. 64: 385.

FISHER, R. A. (1931). "The Evolution of Dominance." Biol. Rev. 6: 345.

FISHER, R. A. (1932). "The Bearing of Genetics on Theories of Evolution." Sci. Progr. 27: 273.

FISHER, R. A. (1933a). "On the Evidence Against the Chemical Induction of Melanism in the Lepidoptera." Proc. Roy. Soc. (B) 112: 407.

FISHER, R. A. (1933b). "Number of Mendelian Factors in Quantitative Inheritance." Nature 131: 400.

FISHER, R. A. (1934). "Professor Wright on the Theory of Dominance." Amer. Nat. 68: 370.

FISHER, R. A. (1935). "Dominance in Poultry." Philos. Trans. (B) 225: 195.

FISHER, R. A. (1937a). "The Relation between Variability and Abundance shown by the Measurements of the Eggs of British Nesting Birds." Proc. Roy. Soc. (B) 122: 1.

FISHER, R. A. (1937b). "The Wave of Advance of Advantageous Genes." Ann. Eugen. 7: 355.

FISHER, R. A. (1938). "Dominance in Poultry, etc." Proc. Roy. Soc. Lond. (B) 125: 25.

FISHER, R. A. (1939). "Selective Forces in Wild Populations of *Paratettix texanus*." Ann. Eugen. 9: 109.

FISHER, R. A., and FORD, E. B. (1928). "The Variability of Species in the Lepidoptera, etc." Trans. ent. Soc. Lond. 86: 367.

FISHER, R. A., FORD, E. B., and HUXLEY, J. S. (1939). "Taste-testing the Anthropoid Apes." Nature 144: 750.

FITCH, H. S. (1938). "A Systematic Account of the Alligator Lizards (*Gerrhonotus*) in the Western United States and Lower California." Amer. Midl. Nat. 20: 381.

FITCH, H. S. (1940). "A biogeographical Study of the *ordinoides* Artenkreis of Garter Snakes (genus *Thamnophis*)." Univ. Calif. Publ. Zool. 44: 1.

FLEMING, J. H., and SNYDER, L. L. (1939). "On *Melospiza melodia* in Ontario." Roy. Ontario Mus. Zool. Occas. Pap. No. 5.

FORBES, W. T. M. (1928). "Variation in *Junonia lavinia* (Lepidoptera, Nymphalidae)." J. N.Y. Ent. Soc. 36: 306.

FORBES, W. T. M. (1931). "Notes on the Dioptidae (Lepidoptera)." J. N.Y. Ent. Soc. **39**: 69.

FORD, E. B. (1924). "The Geographical Races of *Heodes phloeas* L." Trans. ent. Soc. Lond. **1923-4**: 692.

FORD, E. B. (1930). "The Theory of Dominance." Amer. Nat. **64**: 560.

FORD, E. B. (1936). "The Genetics of *Papilio dardanus*." Trans. Roy. ent. Soc. Lond. **85**: 435.

FORD, E. B. (1937). "Problems of Heredity in the Lepidoptera." Biol. Rev. **12**: 461.

FORD, E. B. (1940a). "Polymorphism and Taxonomy," in "The New Systematics," ed. J. S. Huxley. Oxford.

FORD, E. B. (1940b). "Genetic Research in the Lepidoptera." Ann. Eugen. **10**: 227.

FORD, E. B. (1940c). "Mendelism and Evolution" (3rd ed.). London.

FORD, E. B. (1941). "Studies on the Chemistry of Pigments in the Lepidoptera, with reference to their bearing on Systematics. I. The Anthoxanthins." Proc. Roy. ent. Soc. Lond. (A), **16**: 65.

FORD, H. D., and FORD, E. B. (1930). "Fluctuation in Numbers and its Influence on Variation in *Melitaea aurinia*." Trans. ent. Soc. Lond. **78**: 345.

FORD, E. B., and HUXLEY, J. S. (1929). "Genetic Rate-factors in *Gammarus*." Arch. Entw. Mech. **117**: 67.

FORMOSOV, A. N. (1933). "The Crop of Cedar Nuts, Invasions into Europe of the Siberian Nutcracker (*Nucifraga caryocatactes macrorhynchus* Brehm), etc." J. Anim. Ecol. **2**: 70.

FOX, D. L., and PANTIN, C. F. A. (1941). "The Colours of the Plumose Anemone *Metridium senile* (L.)." Philos. Trans. (B) **230**: 415.

FOX, H. MUNRO (1939). "The Activity and Metabolism of Poikilothermal Animals in Different Latitudes. V." Proc. Zool. Soc. Lond. (A) **109**: 141.

FOX, H. MUNRO, and WINGFIELD, C. A. (1937). "The Activity and Metabolism of Poikilothermal Animals in Different Latitudes. II." Proc. Zool. Soc. Lond. (A) **1937**: 275.

FRANKEL, O. (1941). "Cytology and Taxonomy of *Hebe*, *Veronica* and *Pygmaea*. Nature **147**: 117.

FRIES, R. E., and T. C. E. (1922). Ueber die Riesen-Senecionen der Afrikanischen Hochgebirge. Svensk Bot. Tidsk. **16**: 321.

GARNER, W. W., and ALLARD, H. A. (1920). "Effect of Relative Length of Day and Night and Other Factors of Environment on Growth and Reproduction in Plants." J. Agric. Res. **18**: 553.

GARSTANG, W. (1922). "The Theory of Recapitulation, etc." J. Linn. Soc. (Zool.) **35**: 81.

GATES, R. R. (1916). "On Pairs of Species." Bot. Gaz. **61**: 177.

GATES, R. R. (1930). "Heredity in Man." London and New York.

GAUSE, G. F. (1930). "Die Variabilität der Zeichnung bei den Blattkäfern der Gattung *Phytodecta*." Biol. Zentralbl. **50**: 235.

GAUSE, G. F. (1934). "The Struggle for Existence." Baltimore.

GAUSE, G. F., and SMARAGDOVA, N. P. (1939). "The Decrease in Weight and Mortality in Dextral and Sinistral Individuals of the Snail *Fruticicola lantzi*." Zool. J. (Moscow) **18**: 161.

GEROULD, J. H. (1921) "Blue-Green Caterpillars: the Origin and Ecology of a Mutation in Hemolymph Colour in *Colias* (*Eurymus*) *philodice*." J. exp. Zool. **34**: 385.

GEROULD, J. H. (1923). "Inheritance of White Wing Color, a Sex-limited (Sex-controlled) Variation in Yellow Pierid Butterflies." Genetica 8: 495.

GERSHENSON, S. (1928). "A New Sex-ratio Abnormality in *Drosophila obscura*." Genetics 13: 488.

GHIGI, A. (1909). "Ricerche di Sistematica Sperimentale sul Genere *Gennaeus* Wagler." Mem. R. Acc. Sci. Inst. Bologna 6: 133.

GILMOUR, J. S. L. (1932). "The Taxonomy of Plants intermediate between *Medicago sativa* L. and *M. falcata* L., etc." Rep. Bot. Exch. Cl. 1933: 393.

GILMOUR, J. S. L. (1937). "A Taxonomic Problem." Nature 139: 1040.

GILMOUR, J. S. L. (1940). "Taxonomy and Philosophy," in "The New Systematics," ed. J. S. Huxley. Oxford.

GILMOUR, J. S., L. and GREGOR, J. W. (1939). "Demes: a Suggested New Terminology." Nature 144: 333.

GLADKOV, N. A. (1941). "Taxonomy of Palearctic Goshawks." Auk 58: 80.

GLASS, H. B. (1933). "A New Allelomorphic Compound presenting the Phenotype of the Wild *Drosophila melanogaster*." J. Genet. 27: 233.

GOLDSCHMIDT, R. (1927). "Physiologische Theorie der Vererbung." Berlin.

GOLDSCHMIDT, R. (1928). "Einführung in die Vererbungswissenschaft." (5th ed.). Berlin.

GOLDSCHMIDT, R. (1932). "Genetik der geographischen Variation." Proc. VI. Int. Congr. Genet. (Ithaca) 1: 173.

GOLDSCHMIDT, R. (1934). "Lymantria." Bibliogr. Genet. 11: 1.

GOLDSCHMIDT, R. (1935). "Geographische Variation und Artbildung." Naturwiss. 23: 169.

GOLDSCHMIDT, R. (1938a). "Physiological Genetics." New York.

GOLDSCHMIDT, R. (1938b). "A Note Concerning the Adaptation of Geographic Races of *Lymantria dispar* L. to the Seasonal Cycle in Japan." Amer. Nat. 72: 385.

GOLDSCHMIDT, R. (1940). "The Material Basis of Evolution." New Haven, London and Oxford.

GOLDSCHMIDT, R., and FISCHER, E. (1922). "*Argynnis paphia-valesina*, ein Fall geschlechtskontrollierter Vererbung bei Schmetterlingen." Genetica 4: 247.

GONZALEZ, B. M. (1923). "Experimental Studies on the Duration of Life: VIII." Amer. Nat. 57: 289.

GOODSPEED, T. H. (1934). "*Nicotiana* Phylesis in the Light of Chromosome Number, Morphology and Behavior." Univ. Calif. Publ. Bot. 17: 369.

GORDON, C. (1935). "An Experiment on a Released Population of *D. melanogaster*." Amer. Nat. 69: 381.

GORDON, C. (1936). "The Frequency of Heterozygosis in Free-living Populations of *Drosophila*, etc." J. Genet. 33: 25.

GORDON, C., and GORDON, F. (1940). "The Genetical Analysis of a Sex-limited Character in *Drosophila melanogaster*, etc." Proc. Roy. Soc. (B) 127: 487.

GORDON, C., and SANG, J. H. (1941). Proc. Roy. Soc. (B), in press.

GORDON, M. (1931). "Hereditary Basis of Melanosis in Hybrid Fishes." Amer. J. Cancer 15: 1495.

GORDON, M. (1939). "Gene Frequencies and Parallel Variations in Natural Populations, etc." Rec..Genet. Soc. Amer. 8: 118.

GOWEN, J. W., and GAY, E. H. (1933). "On Ever-Sporting as a Function of the Y-chromosome in *Drosophila melanogaster*." Amer. Nat. 67: 68.

GRAVES, W. W. (1932). "A Note on Inherited Variations and Fitness Problems." Sci. Pap. III. Int. Eugen. Congr. (1932): 457.

GREGOR, J. W. (1938a). "Experimental Taxonomy, II. Initial Population Differentiation in *Plantago maritima* L. of Britain." New Phytol. 37: 15.

GREGOR, J. W. (1938b). "Reflections Concerning New Crop Varieties." Herbage Rev. 6: 234.

GREGOR, J. W. (1939). "Experimental Taxonomy, IV. Population Differentiation in North American and European Sea Plantains Allied to *Plantago maritima* L." New Phytol. 38: 293.

GREGORY, W. K. (1936). "On the Meaning and Limits of Irreversibility of Evolution." Amer. Nat. 70: 517.

GRINNELL, J. (1922). "A Geographical Study of the Kangaroo Rats of California." Univ. Calif. Publ. Zool. 24: 1.

GRINNELL, J. (1928). "Distributional Summation of the Ornithology of Lower California." Univ. Calif. Publ. Zool. 32: 1.

GROSS, A. O. (1928). "The Heath Hen." Mem. Boston Soc. Nat. Hist. 6: 487.

GRÜNEBERG, H. (1937). "The Position Effect Proved by a Spontaneous Reinversion, etc." J. Genet. 34: 169.

GRÜNEBERG, H. (1938). "An Analysis of the 'Pleiotropic' Effects of a New Lethal Mutation in the Rat (*Mus norvegicus*)." Proc. Roy. Soc. (B) 125: 123.

GULICK, A. (1932). "Biological Peculiarities of Oceanic Islands." Quart. Rev. Biol. 7: 405.

GULICK, A. (1938). "What Are the Genes? II." Quart. Rev. Biol. 13: 140.

GULICK, J. T. (1905). "Evolution, Racial and Habitudinal." Publ. Carneg. Instn. no. 25.

GUSTAFSSON, A. (1941). "Mutation Experiments in Barley, etc." Hereditas, Lund 27: 225, 337.

HACKETT, L. W. (1937). "Malaria in Europe." London.

HACKETT, L. W., and MISSIROLI, A. (1935). "The Varieties of *Anopheles maculipennis* and Their Relation to the Distribution of Malaria in Europe." Riv. Malariol. 14: 45.

HAECKER, V. (1925). "Aufgaben und Ergebnisse der Phänogenetik." Bibliogr. Genet. 1: 95.

HAECKER, V. (1927). "Phänogenetische Untersuchungen über die tierische Zeichnung." Naturwiss. 15: 710.

HAGEDOORN, A. C., and HAGEDOORN, A. L. (1917). "Rats and Evolution." Amer. Nat. 51: 385.

HAGERUP, O. (1932). "Über Polyploidie in Beziehung zu Klima, Ökologie und Phylogenie, etc." Hereditas, Lund 16: 19.

HALDANE, J. B. S. (1927a). "The Comparative Genetics of Colour in Rodents and Carnivora." Biol. Rev. 2: 199.

HALDANE, J. B. S. (1927b). "Possible Worlds." London.

HALDANE, J. B. S. (1930). "A Note on Fisher's Theory of the Origin of Dominance, etc." Amer. Nat. 64: 87.

HALDANE, J. B. S. (1932a). "The Causes of Evolution." London.

HALDANE, J. B. S. (1932b). "The Time of Action of Genes, etc." Amer. Nat. 66: 5.

HALDANE, J. B. S. (1932c). "Can Evolution be Explained in Terms of Known Genetical Facts?" Proc. VI. Int. Congr. Genet. (Ithaca) 1: 185.

HALDANE, J. B. S. (1933). "The Part Played by Recurrent Mutations in Evolution." Amer. Nat. 67: 5.

HALDANE, J. B. S. (1935a). "Darwinism under Revision." Rationalist Annual 1935: 19.

HALDANE, J. B. S. (1935b). "The Rate of Spontaneous Mutation of a Human Gene." J. Genet. 31: 317.

HALDANE, J. B. S. (1938). "The Marxist Philosophy and the Sciences." London.

HALDANE, J. B. S. (1939a). "The Theory of the Evolution of Dominance." J. Genet. 37: 365.

HALDANE, J. B. S. (1939b). "The Equilibrium between Mutation and Random Extinction." Ann. Eugen. 9: 400.

HALDANE, J. B. S. (1940). "The Blood-group Frequencies of European Peoples, and Racial Origins." Human Biol. 12: 457.

HALL, A. D. (1940). "The Genus Tulipa." London.

HALL, E. R. (1938). "Variation among Insular Mammals of Georgia Strait, British Columbia." Amer. Nat. 72: 453.

HALL, E. R. (1939). "Remarks on the Primitive Structure of 'Mustela stolzmanni,' etc." Physis, Buenos Aires, 16: 159.

HAMILTON, J. STEVENSON (1919). "Field Notes on Some Mammals in the Bahr-el-Gebel, Southern Sudan." Proc. Zool. Soc. Lond. 1919: 341.

HAMMOND, J. (1928a). "How Feeding Affects Conformation." Fmr. & Stk.-Breed. & Agric. Gaz. 1928: 10 Dec.: 4.

HAMMOND, J. (1928b). "Selection for Meat Production." Verh. V. Int. Kongr. Vererb. (Berlin, 1927) 2: 789.

HARDY, E. (1937). "Polluted Wild Life." Country Life 81: 676.

HARLAND, S. C. (1932). "The Genetics of Cotton. VI. The Inheritance of Chlorophyll Deficiency in New World Cottons." J. Genet. 25: 271.

HARLAND, S. C. (1933). "The Genetics of Cotton. IX. Further Experiments on the Inheritance of the Crinkled Dwarf Mutant, etc." J. Genet. 28: 315.

HARLAND, S. C. (1936). "The Genetical Conception of the Species." Biol. Rev. 11: 83.

HARLAND, S. C. (1940). "New Polyploids in Cotton by the Use of Colchicine." Trop. Agric. 17: 53.

HARLAND, S. C. (1941). "Genetical Studies in the Genus Gossypium and Their Relationship to Evolutionary and Taxonomic Problems." Proc. VII. Int. Genet. Congr. (Edinburgh, 1939): 138.

HARLAND, S. C., and ATTECK, O. M. (1941): "The Genetics of Cotton. XIX. Normal Alleles of the Crinkled Mutant of Gossypium barbadense L., etc." J. Genet. 42: 21.

HARMS, J. W. (1934). "Wandlungen des Artgefüges, etc." Tübingen.

HARRISON, H. S. (1936). "Concerning Human Progress." J. Roy. Anthr. Inst. 66: 1.

HARRISON, J. W. H. (1920a). "Genetical Studies in the Moths of the Geometrid Genus Oporabia (Oporinia) with a Special Consideration of Melanism in the Lepidoptera." J. Genet. 9: 195.

HARRISON, J. W. H. (1920b). "The Inheritance of Melanism in the Genus Tephrosia (Ectropis) with Some Consideration of the Inconstancy of Unit Characters under Crossing." J. Genet. 10: 61.

HARRISON, J. W. H. (1927). "Experiments on the Egg-Laying Habits of the Sawfly Pontania salicis Chr., etc." Proc. Roy. Soc. (B) 101: 115.

HARRISON, J. W. H. (1928). "A Further Induction of Melanism in the Lepidopterous Insect, Selenia bilunaria Esp., and its Inheritance." Proc. Roy. Soc. (B) 102: 338.

HARRISON, J. W. H. (1932). "The Recent Development of Melanism in the Larvae of Certain Species of Lepidoptera, etc." Proc. Roy. Soc. (B) 111: 188.

HARRISON, J. W. H. (1935). "The Experimental Induction of Melanism, and Other Effects, in the Geometrid Moth *Selenia bilunaria* Esp." Proc. Roy. Soc. (B) 117: 78.

HARRISON, J. W. H., and CARTER, W. (1924). "The British Races of *Aricia medon*, etc." Trans. Nat. Hist. Soc. Northumb. (N.S.) 6: 89.

HARTERT, E. (1903–1935). "Die Vögel der paläarktischen Fauna." Vols. 1–3 (1903–1922) and Supplement (1935). Berlin.

HASBROUCK, E. M. (1893). "Evolution and Dichromatism in the genus *Megascops*." Amer. Nat. 27: 521, 638.

HASEBROEK, K. (1934). "Industrie und Grossstadt als Ursache des neuzeitlichen vererblichen Melanismus der Schmetterlinge in England und Deutschland." Zool. Jahrb. (Abt. Zool. Phys.) 53: 411.

HAWKINS, H. L. (1936). "Palaeontology and Humanity." Rep. Brit. Ass. 1936: 59.

HAYS, F. A. (1940). "Breeding Small Flocks of Domestic Fowl for High Fecundity." Poultry Sci. 19: 380.

HEINROTH, O. (1924). "Lautäusserungen der Vögel." J. Orn. 72: 223.

HEINROTH, O. (1938). "Die Balz des Bulwersfasans, *Lobiophasis bulweri* Sharpe." J. Orn. 86: 1.

HEINROTH, O., and HEINROTH, M. (1924–26). "Die Vögel Mitteleuropas." Berlin.

HERBST, C. (1924). "Beiträge zur Entwicklungsphysiologie der Färbung und Zeichnung der Tiere. 2. etc. Arch. Mikr. Anat. 102: 130.

HERRICK, F. H. (1939). "The Individual Versus the Species in Behavior Studies." Auk 56: 244.

HERSH, A. H. (1934). "Evolutionary Relative Growth in the Titanotheres." Amer. Nat. 58: 537.

HERZBERG, F., and MASSLER, M. (1940). "The Phylogenetic Growth-pattern of the Conical Forms of Teeth." J. Dent. Res. 19: 511.

HESSE, R. (1924). "Tiergeographie." Jena.

HESSE, R. (1929). "Bericht über das 'Tierreich.'" S.B. Preuss. Akad. Wiss. 1929: xl.

HESSE, R., ALLEE, W. C., and SCHMIDT, K. P. (1937). "Ecological Animal Geography." New York and London.

HEWITSON, W. C. (1874). "Notes on the Capture of *Papilio antimachus*, etc." Ent. mon. Mag. 11: 113.

HILE, R. (1936). "Summary of Investigations on the Morphometry of the Cisco, *Leucichthys artedi*, etc." Pap. Mich. Acad. Sci. 21: 619.

HILL, A. W. (1930). "Present-day Problems in Taxonomic and Economic Botany." Nature 126: 476.

HILL, J. E. (1939). "In Black and White. Identical Animals on Adjacent Areas, etc." Nat. Hist. N.Y. 43: 172.

HILL, W. C. OSMAN (1940). "Observations on the Structure and Mechanism of the External Ear, etc." Ceylon J. Sci. (B) 22: 135.

HINTON, M. A. C. (1920). "Rats and Mice as Enemies of Mankind." Brit. Mus. (Nat. Hist.), Econ. Ser. 8.

HOGBEN, L. T. (1930). "The Nature of Living Matter." London.

HOGBEN, L. T. (1931). "Genetic Principles in Medicine and Social Science." London.

HOGBEN, L. T. (1933). "Nature and Nurture." London.

HOGBEN, L. T. (1940). "Problems of the Origin of Species," in "The New Systematics," ed. J. S. Huxley. Oxford.

HOLMES, W. (1940). "The Colour Changes and Colour Patterns of *Sepia officinalis* L." Proc. Zool. Soc. Lond. (A) **110**: 17.

HORNELL, J. (1916). "The Indian Varieties and Races of the Genus *Turbinella*." Mem. Ind. Mus. **6**: 109.

HORNELL, J. (1917). "A Revision of the Indian Species of *Meretrix*." Rec. Ind. Mus. **13**: 153.

HOUGH, W. S. (1934). "Colorado and Virginia Strains of Codling Moth, etc." J. Agric. Res. **48**: 533.

HOVANITZ, W. (1940). "Ecological Color Variation in a Butterfly and the Problem of 'Protective Coloration.'" Ecology **21**: 371.

HOVANITZ, W. (1941). "Parallel Ecogenotypical Color Variation in Butterflies." Ecology **22**: 259.

HOWARD, H. E. (1900). "Variation in the Notes and Songs of Birds in Different Districts." Zoologist **58**: 382.

HOWARD, H. E. (1902). "The Birds of Sark, etc." Zoologist **60**: 416.

HUBBS, C. L. (1930). "The Importance of the Race Investigations on Pacific Fishes." Proc. IV. Pacific Sci. Congr. Batavia-Bandoeng, **3**: 13.

HUBBS, C. L. (1934). "Racial and Individual Variation in Animals, especially Fishes." Amer. Nat. **68**: 115.

HUBBS, C. L. (1938). "Fishes from the Caves of Yucatan." Publ. Carneg. Instn. no. **491**: 261.

HUBBS, C. L. (1940a). "Speciation of Fishes." Amer. Nat. **74**: 198.

HUBBS, C. L. (1940b). "Fishes of the Desert." Biologist **22**: 61.

HUBBS, C. L. (1941). "Increased Number and Delayed Development of Scales in Abnormal Suckers." Pap. Michigan Acad. Sci. (1940), **26**: 229.

HUBBS, C. L., and COOPER, G. P. (1935). "Age and Growth of the Long-eared and the Green Sunfishes in Michigan." Pap. Mich. Acad. Sci. (1934) **20**: 669.

HUBBS, C. L., and HUBBS, L. C. (1932). "Apparent Parthenogenesis in Nature, in a Form of Fish of Hybrid Origin." Science **76**: 628.

HUBBS, C. L., and HUBBS, L. C. (1933). "The Increased Growth, Predominant Maleness, and Apparent Infertility of Hybrid Sunfishes." Pap. Mich. Acad. Sci. **17**: 613.

HUBBS, C. L., and TRAUTMAN, M. B. (1937). "A Revision of the Lamprey Genus *Ichthyomyzon*." Misc. Publ. Mus. Zool. Univ. Mich. no. **35**.

HUGHES, A. W. McK. (1932). "Induced Melanism in Lepidoptera." Proc. Roy. Soc. (B) **110**: 378.

HUSKINS, C. L. (1927). "On the Genetics and Cytology of Fatuoid or False Wild Oats." J. Genet. **18**: 315.

HUSKINS, C. L. (1928). "On the Cytology of Speltoid Wheats in Relation to Their Origin and Genetic Behaviour." J. Genet. **20**: 103.

HUSKINS, C. L. (1931). "The Origin of *Spartina Townsendii*." Genetica **12**: 531.

HUSKINS, C. L. (1934). "Inheritance of Egg-Colour in the 'Parasitic' Cuckoos." Nature **133**: 260.

HUTCHINSON, J. B. (1931). "A Possible Explanation of the Apparently Irregular Inheritance of Polydactyly in Poultry." Amer. Nat. **65**: 376.

HUTCHINSON, J. B., and GHOSE, R. L. M. (1937). "Occurrence of Crinkled Dwarf in *Gossypium hirsutum* L." J. Genet. **34**: 437.

HUTT, F. B. (1938). "Genetics of the Fowl. VII. Breed Differences in Susceptibility to Extreme Heat." Poultry Sci. **17**: 454.

HUXLEY, A. [L.] (1937). "Ends and Means." London.

HUXLEY, J. S. (1912). "The Individual in the Animal Kingdom." Cambridge.

HUXLEY, J. S. (1923a). "Progress," in "Essays of a Biologist." London.

HUXLEY, J. S. (1923b). "Courtship Activities in the Red-throated Diver, etc." J. Linn. Soc. (Zool.) 35: 253.

HUXLEY, J. S. (1924). "Constant Differential Growth-ratios and Their Significance." Nature 114: 895.

HUXLEY, J. S. (1932). "Problems of Relative Growth." London.

HUXLEY, J. S. (1935). "The Field Concept in Biology." Trans. Dynam. Development (Moscow) 10: 269.

HUXLEY, J. S. (1936). "Natural Selection and Evolutionary Progress." Rep. Brit. Ass. 106: 81.

HUXLEY, J. S. (1938a). "The Present Standing of the Theory of Sexual Selection," in "Evolution," ed. G. R. De Beer. Oxford.

HUXLEY, J. S. (1938b). "Darwin's Theory of Sexual Selection, etc." Amer. Nat. 72: 416.

HUXLEY, J. S. (1938c). "Threat and Warning Coloration in Birds, etc." Proc. VIII. Int. Orn. Congr. (Oxford, 1934): 430.

HUXLEY, J. S. (1938d). "Species Formation and Geographical Isolation." Proc. Linn. Soc. Lond. 150: 253.

HUXLEY, J. S. (1939a). "Clines: an Auxiliary Method in Taxonomy." Bijdr. Dierk. 27: 491.

HUXLEY, J. S. (1939b). "Subspecies and Varieties." Proc. Linn. Soc. Lond. 151: 105.

HUXLEY J. [S.] (1940). "The Uniqueness of Man." London.

HUXLEY, J. S. (1941a). "Evolutionary Genetics." Proc. VII. Int. Genet. Congr. (Edinburgh, 1939): 157.

HUXLEY, J. S., and CARR-SAUNDERS, A. M. (1924). "Absence of Prenatal Effects of Lens-Antibodies in Rabbits." Brit. J. Exper. Biol. 1: 215.

HUXLEY, J. S., and DE BEER, G. R. (1934). "The Elements of Experimental Embryology." Cambridge.

HUXLEY, J. S., and HADDON, A. C. (1935). "We Europeans." London and New York.

HUXLEY, J. S., and TEISSIER, G. (1936). "Terminology of Relative Growth." Nature 137: 780.

HUXLEY, T. H. (1853). "On the Morphology of the Cephalous Mollusca, etc." Philos. Trans. 143: 29.

HUXLEY, T. H. (1854). "On the Common Plan of Animal Forms." Proc. Roy. Inst. Lond. 1: 444.

ILJIN, N. A. (1929). "Analysis of Pigment Formation by Low Temperature." Trans. Lab. exp. Biol. Zoopark. Moscow 3: 183.

ILJIN, N. A. (1931). "Farbenveränderungen der Russenkaninchen, etc." Arch. EntwMech. 125: 306.

ILJIN, N. A. (1941). "Wolf-Dog Genetics." J. Genet. 42: 359.

ILJIN, N. A., and ILJIN, V. N. (1930). "Temperature Effects on the Color of the Siamese Cat." J. Hered. 21: 309.

ILJINA, E. D. (1935). "Osnovy genetiki i selekcii pušnyh zverei. [Principles of Genetics and Breeding of Fur-bearing Animals.]" Moscow.

INGOLDBY, C. M. (1927). "Notes on the African Squirrels of the Genus Helio-sciurus." Proc. Zool. Soc. Lond. 1927: 471.

JAMESON, H. L. (1898). "On a Probable Case of Protective Coloration in the Mouse (*Mus musculus*, Linn.)." J. Linn. Soc. (Zool.) **26**: 465.

JANAKI-AMMAL, E. K. (1940). "Chromosome Diminution in a Plant." Nature **146**: 839.

JENKINS, J. A. (1939). "The Cytogenic Relationships of Four Species of *Crepis*." Univ. Calif. Publ. Agric. Sci. **6**: 369.

JENNINGS, H. S. (1920). "Life and Death, Heredity and Evolution in Unicellular Organisms." Boston.

JENNINGS, H. S. (1929). "Genetics of the Protozoa." Bibliogr. Genet. **5**: 108.

JOHANNSEN, W. (1913). "Mutations dans les lignées pures, etc." Rep. IV. Int. Congr. Genet. (Paris, 1911): 160.

JOHANNSEN, W. (1926). "Elemente der exakten Erblichkeitslehre" (Jena).

JOHNSON, R. H. (1910). "Determinate Evolution in the Color-pattern of the Lady-Beetles." Publ. Carneg. Instn. no. **122**.

JOHNSON, T., and NEWTON, M. (1938). "The Origin of Abnormal Rust Characteristics through Inbreeding, etc." Canad. J. Res. **16**: 38.

JOLLOS, V. (1930). "Studien zum Evolutionsproblem. I." Biol. Zentralbl. **50**: 541.

JORDAN, D. S. (1909). "Isolation as a Factor in Organic Evolution," in "Fifty Years of Darwinism." New York.

JOUARD, H. (1929). "De la variabilité géographique d' *Aegithalos caudatus* dans l'Europe occidentale." Alauda **1**: 111.

JOURDAIN, F. C. R. (1925). "A Study of Parasitism in the Cuckoos." Proc. Zool. Soc. Lond. **1925**: 639.

KALABUCHOV, N. (1939). "On Ecological Characters of Closely Related Species of Rodents. 3. The Peculiarities of the Reaction of Wood Mice (*Apodemus sylvaticus* L. and *A. flavicollis* Melch.) and Ground Squirrels (*Citellus pygmaeus* Pall. and *C. suslica* Gueld.) to the Temperature Gradient." Zool. J. (Moscow) **18**: 915. [Russian, English Res.]

KALMUS, H. (1941a). "Resistance to Desiccation of Some Body-Color Mutants in *Drosophila*." Proc. Roy. Soc. London (B) **130**: 185, and Dros. Inf. Serv. **14**: 51.

KALMUS, H. (1941b). Physiology and Ecology of Cuticle Colour in Insects. Nature **148**: 428.

KAMMERER, P. (1926). "Der Artenwandel." Leipzig and Vienna.

KAPPERS, C. U. A. (1928). "The Influence of the Cephalization Coefficient and Body-size upon the Form of the Fore-brain in Mammals." Proc. Acad. Sci. Amsterdam **31**: 65.

KARPECHENKO, G. D. (1928). "Polyploid Hybrids of *Raphanus sativus* L. × *Brassica oleracea* L." Z. ind. Abst. Vererb.l. **48**: 1.

KEITH, A., and MCCOWN, T. D. (1937). "Mount Carmel Man: His Bearing upon Ancestry of Modern Races." Pan.-Amer. Geol. **67**: 321.

KENNEDY, J. N. (1913). "*Carduelis carduelis bermudiana* subsp. n. described." Bull. Brit. Orn. Cl. **33**. 33.

KERNER, A., and OLIVER, F. W. (1902). "The Natural History of Plants." London.

KIKKAWA, H. (1936). "Two Races of *Drosophila montium*." Jap. J. Genet. **12**: 137.

KINSEY, A. C. (1936). "Origin of Higher Categories in *Cynips*." Indiana Univ. Publ. (Sci. Ser.) no. **4**: 1.

KINSEY, A. C. (1937). "Supra-Specific Variation in Nature and in Classification from the Viewpoint of Zoology." Amer. Nat. **71**: 206.

KIRIKOV, S. V. (1934). "Sur la Distribution du Hamster Noir, etc." Zool. J. (Moscow) **13**: 361.

KLAUBER, L. M. (1938). "A Statistical Study of the Rattlesnakes." Occas. Pap. San Diego Soc. Nat. Hist. no. **4**: 1.

KLEINSCHMIDT, O. (1929). "Der Formenkreis *Parus acredula* (Kl.), etc." Berajah **1929**: 1.

KOROTNEFF, A. (1905–1912). "Wissenschaftliche Ergebnisse einer zoologischen Expedition nach dem Baikalsee, etc." Kiev and Berlin.

KOSSWIG, C. (1929). "Ueber die veränderten Wirkung von Farbgenen des *Platypoecilus*, etc." and "Zur Frage der Geschwulstbildung bei Gattungs-bastarden, etc." Z. ind. Abst. Vererb.l. **50**: 63 and **52**: 114.

KOSTOFF, D. (1938). "Studies on Polyploid Plants. XXI." J Genet. **37**: 129.

KRAMER, G., and MERTENS, R. (1938a). "Rassenbildung bei westistrianischen Inseleidechsen, etc." Arch. Naturgesch. (N.F.) **7**: 189.

KRAMER, G., and MERTENS, R. (1938b). "Zur Verbreitung und Systematik der festländischen Mauer-Eidechsen Istriens." Senckenbergiana **20**: 48.

KRUMBIEGEL, I. (1932). "Untersuchungen über physiologische Rassenbildung." Zool. Jahrb. (Syst.) **63**: 183.

KUNN, A. (1934). "Genetische und entwicklungsphysiologische Untersuchungen au *Ephestia kühniella* Z." Z. ind. Abst. Vererb.l. **67**: 197.

LACK, D. (1939). "The Behaviour of the Robin, etc." Proc. Zool. Soc. Lond. (A) **109**: 169.

LACK, D. (1940a). "Evolution of the Galapagos Finches." Nature **146**: 324.

LACK, D. (1940b). "Habitat Selection and Speciation in Birds." Brit. Birds **34**: 80.

LACK, D. (1940c). "Variation in the Introduced English Sparrow." Condor **42**: 239.

LACK, D., and VENABLES, L. S. V. (1939). "The Habitat Distribution of British Woodland Birds." J. Animal Ecol. **8**: 39.

LACK, D. (1941). "Some Aspects of Instinctive Behaviour and Display in Birds." Ibis (14) **5**: 407.

LAMMARTS, W. E. (1932). "An Experimentally Produced Secondary Polyploid in the Genus *Nicotiana*." Cytologia, Tokyo **4**: 38.

LAMOREUX, W. F., and HUTT, F. B. (1939). "Breed Differences in Resistance to a Deficiency of Vitamin B_1 in the Fowl." J. Agric. Res. Washington **58**: 307–16.

LAMPRECHT, H. (1941). "The Limit Between *Phaseolus vulgaris* and *Ph. multiflorus* from the Genetical Point of View. Proc. VII. Int. Genet. Congr. (Edinburgh, 1939): 179.

LANDAUER, W. (1937). "Disturbances in Temperature Regulation of Frizzle Fowl, a Consequence of Excessive Loss of Body Heat." Arch. Int. Pharmacodyn. Thérap. **56**: 121.

LANDAUER, W., and DUNN, L. C. (1930). "The Frizzle Character of Fowls." J. Hered. **21**: 291.

LANDAUER, W., and UPHAM, E. (1936). "Weight and Size of Organs in Frizzle Fowl, etc." Storrs Agric. Exper. Sta. Bull. no. **210**.

LANG, A. (1908). "Die Bastarde von *Helix hortensis* Müller and *Helix nemoralis* L." Jena.

LANG, W. D. (1938). "Some Further Considerations on Trends in Corals." Proc. Geol. Ass. **49**: 148.

LANGLET, O. (1937). "Study of the Physiological Variability of Pine and its Relation to the Climate." U.S. Forest Service Translation no. 293. Washington [tr. of Medd. Skogsförsöksanst. 29: 421 (1936)].

LARAMBERGUE, M. DE (1939). "Étude de l'Autofécondation chez les Gastéropodes pulmonés. Recherches sur l'Aphallie et la Fécondation chez Bulinus (Isidora) contortus Michaud." Bull. Biol. 123: 19.

LARAMBERGUE, M. DE (1941). "Races aphalliques et euphalliques de Bulinus contortus, etc." Proc. VII. Int. Genet. Congr. (Edinburgh, 1939): 185.

LAWRENCE, W. J. C., and PRICE, J. R. (1940). "The Genetics and Chemistry of Flower Colour Variation." Biol. Rev. 15: 35.

LEA, D. E. (1940). "Determination of the Sizes of Viruses and Genes by Radiation Methods." Nature 146: 137.

LEBEDEFF, G. A. (1933). "Studies on Factor Interaction in Drosophila virilis." Amer. Nat. 67: 69.

LEDINGHAM, G. F. (1940). "Cytological and Developmental Studies of Hybrids between Medicago sativa and a Diploid Form of M. falcata." Genetics 25: 1.

LEITCH, D. (1940). "A Statistical Investigation of the Anthracomyas of the Basal Similis-Pulchra Zone in Scotland." Quart. J. Geol. Soc. Lond. 96: 13.

LEVICK, G. M. (1914). "Antarctic Penguins." London.

LEWIS, D. (1941). "Male Sterility in Natural Populations of Hermaphrodite Plants, etc." New Phytol. 40: 56.

L'HÉRITIER, P., NEEFS, Y., and TEISSIER, G. (1937). "Aptérisme des Insectes et Sélection Naturelle." C. R. Acad. Sci. Paris 204: 907.

L'HÉRITIER, P., and TEISSIER, G. (1938). "Transmission Héréditaire de la Sensibilité au Gaz Carbonique chez la Drosophile." C. R. Acad. Sci. Paris 206: 1683.

LINSDALE, J. M. (1928). "Variations in the Fox Sparrow, etc." Univ. Calif. Publ. Zool. 30: 251.

LINSDALE, J. M. (1936). "Coloration of Downy Young Birds and Nest Linings." Condor 38: 111.

LINSDALE, J. M. (1938). "Environmental Responses of Vertebrates in the Great Basin." Amer. Midland Nat. 19: 1.

LLOYD, R. E. (1912). "The Growth of Groups in the Animal Kingdom." London.

LOCKLEY, R. M. (1940). "Some Experiments in Rabbit Control." Nature 145: 767.

LOEB, J. (1912). "The Mechanistic Conception of Life." New York.

LONGLEY, W. H. (1933). "Taxonomy and Evolution." Nature 131: 863.

LÖNNBERG, E. (1937). "Notes on Some South American Mammals." Ark. Zool. 29: (A) no. 19: 1.

LØPPENTHIN, B. (1932). "Die Farbenvariation der Europäischen Baumkleiber, etc." Vidensk. Medd. Naturh. Forening 94: 147.

LORENZ, K. (1935). "Der Kumpan in der Umwelt des Vogels." J. Orn. 83: 137, 289.

LOWE, P. R. (1912). "Observations on the Genus Coereba, etc." Ibis (9) 6: 489.

LOWE, P. R. (1936). "The Finches of the Galapagos Islands in Relation to Darwin's Conception of Species." Ibis (13) 6: 310.

LOWE, P. R., and MACKWORTH-PRAED, C. W. (1921). "The Last Phase of the Subspecies." Ibis (11) 3: 344.

LÜHRING, R. (1928). "Das Haarkleid von Sciurus vulgaris, etc." Z. Morph. Oekol. Tiere 11: 667.

LULL, R. C. (1917). "Organic Evolution." New York.

LUMER, H. (1940). "Evolutionary Allometry in the Skeleton of the Domesticated Dog." Amer. Nat. 74: 439.

LYNES, H. (1930). "Review of the Genus *Cisticola.*" Ibis (12) 6: suppl. 1–673.

McATEE, W. L. (1932). "Effectiveness in Nature of the So-called Protective Adaptations, etc." Smithson Instn. Misc. Coll. 85: no. 7: 1.

MACBRIDE, E. W. (1936). "Insect Coloration and Natural Selection." Nature 138: 365.

McCABE, T. T., and MILLER, A. H. (1933). "Geographic Variation in the Northern Water-Thrushes." Condor 35: 192.

McCONAILL, M. A., and RALPHS, F. L. (1937). "Post-natal Development of Hair and Eye-colour, etc." Ann. Eugen. 7: 218.

MACDOUGAL, D. T. (1912). "The Water-Balance of Desert Plants." Ann. Bot. 26: 71.

McEWEN, R. S. (1937). "The Reactions to Light and to Gravity in *Drosophila* and its Mutants." J. Exp. Zool. 25: 49.

MACFADYEAN, W. A. (1940). "Foraminifera from the Green Ammonite Beds, Lower Lias, of Dorset." Proc. Roy. Soc. Lond. (B) 129: abstr. S.43.

MACFADYEAN, W. A. (1941). "Foraminifera from the Green Ammonite Beds, Lower Lias, of Dorset." Philos. Trans. (B) 231: 1.

MACKENZIE, K., and MULLER, H. J. (1940). "Mutation Effects of Ultra-Violet Light in *Drosophila.*" Proc. Roy. Soc. Lond. (B) 129: 491.

McMEEKAN, C. P. (1940–1941). "Growth and Development in the Pig, etc." J. Agric. Sci. 30: 276, 387; 31: 1.

MALINOVSKY, A. A. (1941). "The Rôle played by Chromosome Inversions, etc." Drosoph. Inf. Serv. no. 15: 29.

MANWELL, R. D. (1936). "The Problem of Species, with Special Reference to the Malaria Parasites." Ann. Trop. Med. Parasit. 30: 435.

MANTON, I. (1934). "The Problems of *Biscutella laevigata* L." Z. ind. Abst. Vererb.l. 67: 41.

MARCHLEWSKI, T. (1941). "Change of Dominance in Canine Colour Genetics." Proc. VII. Int. Genet. Congr. (Edinburgh, 1939): 211.

MARETT, R. R. (1933). "Progress as a Sociological Category." Sociol. Rev. 1933: Jan.–Apr.: 3.

MARETT, R. R. (1939). "Charity and the Struggle for Existence." J. Roy. Anthr. Inst. 69: part 2.

MARSDEN-JONES, E. M., and TURRILL, W. B. (1930). "Species Studies in Plants." Rep. Bot. Exchange Cl. 1930: 416.

MARSDEN-JONES, E. M., and TURRILL, W. B. (1933). "Studies in Variation of *Anthyllis vulneraria.*" J. Genet. 27: 261.

MARSDEN-JONES, E. M., and TURRILL, W. B. (1938). "Transplant Experiments of the British Ecological Society, etc." J. Ecol. 16: 380.

MARSHALL, F. H. A. (1910). "The Physiology of Reproduction." London.

MARSHALL, W. W., and MULLER, H. J. (1917). "The Effect of Long-Continued Heterozygosis, etc." J. Exp. Zool. 22: 457.

MATHER, K. (1940). "Outbreeding and Separation of the Sexes." Nature 145: 484.

MATHER, K. (1941). "Variation and Selection of Polygenic Characters." J. Genet. 41: 159.

MATHER, K., and DOBZHANSKY, T. (1939). "Morphological Differences between the 'Races' of *Drosophila pseudoobscura.*" Amer. Nat. 73: 5.

MATHER, K., and NORTH, S. B. (1940). "Umbrous: A Case of Dominance Modification in Mice." J. Genet. 40: 229.

MATHER, K., and DE WINTON, D. (1941). "Adaptation and Counter-Adaptation of the Breeding System in *Primula*." Ann. Bot. (N.S.) **5**: 297.

MATTHEW, W. D. (1915). "Climate and Evolution." Ann. N.Y. Acad. Sci. **24**: 171.

MATTHEW, W. D. (1926). "The Evolution of the Horse, etc." Quart. Rev. Biol. **1**: 139.

MATTHEWS, L. H. (1939a). "The Subspecies and Variation of the Spotted Hyaena, *Crocuta crocuta* Erxl." Proc. Zool. Soc. Lond. (B) **109**: 237.

MATTHEWS, L. H. (1939b). "Reproduction in the Spotted Hyaena, *Crocuta crocuta* (Erxleben)." Philos. Trans. (B) **30**: 1.

MAYR, E. (1931–1940). "Birds Collected During the Whitney South Sea Expedition. XII–XLI." Amer. Mus. Novit., various numbers.

MAYR, E. (1940a). "Speciation Phenomena in Birds." Amer. Nat. **74**: 249.

MAYR, E. (1940b). "*Pericrocotus brevirostris* and its Double." Ibis (14) **4**: 712.

MAYR, E., and GREENWAY, J. C. (1938). "Forms of *Mesia argentauris*." Proc. New. Engl. Zool. Cl. **17**: 1.

MAYR, E., and RAND, A. L. (1937). "Results of the Archbold Expeditions. 14." Bull. Amer. Mus. Nat. Hist. **73**: 1.

MAYR, E., and SERVENTY, D. L. (1938). "A Review of the Genus *Acanthiza* Vigors and Horsfield." Emu **38**: 245.

MEINERTZHAGEN, R. (1919). "A Preliminary Study of the Relation Between Geographical Distribution and Migration, etc." Ibis (11) **1**: 379.

MEINERTZHAGEN, R. (1921). "Notes on Some Birds from the Near East and from Tropical East Africa." Ibis (11) **3**: 621.

MEINERTZHAGEN, R. (1934). "The Relation Between Plumage and Environment, etc." Ibis (13) **4**: 52.

MEISE, W. (1928). "Die Verbreitung der Aaskrähe (Formenkreis *Corvus corone* L.). J. Orn. **76**: 1.

MEISE, W. (1936). "Ueber Artentstehung durch Kreuzung in der Vogelwelt." Biol. Zbl. **56**: 590.

MEISE, W. (1938). "Fortschritte der ornithologischen Systematik seit 1920." Proc. VIII Int. Orn. Congr. (Oxford, 1934): 49.

MEISENHEIMER, J. (1921). "Geschlecht und Geschlechter." Jena.

MELLANBY, K. (1940). "Temperature Coefficients and Acclimatization." Nature **146**: 165.

MELVILLE, R. (1939). "The Application of Biometrical Methods to the Study of Elms." Proc. Linn. Soc. Lond. **151**: 152.

METALNIKOV, S. (1924). "Sur l'Hérédité de l'Immunité Acquise." C.R. Acad. Sci. Paris **179**: 514.

METCALF, M. M. (1929). "Parasites and the Aid They Give in Problems of Taxonomy, Geographical Distribution, and Paleogeography." Smithson. Misc. Coll. **81**: no. 8.

METZ, C. W. (1938). "Chromosome Behaviour, Inheritance and Sex Determination in *Sciara*." Amer. Nat. **72**: 485.

MEYER, H. (1938). "Investigations Concerning the Reproductive Behaviour of *Mollienisia 'formosa.'*" J. Genet. **36**: 329.

MILLER, A. H. (1931). "Systematic Revision and Natural History of the American Shrikes (*Lanius*)." Univ. Calif. Publ. Zool. **38**: 11.

MILLER, A. H. (1937). "Structural Modifications in the Hawaiian Goose (*Nesochen sandvicensis*), etc." Univ. Calif. Publ. Zool. **42**: 1.

MILLER, A. H. (1938). "Problems of Speciation in the Genus *Junco*." Proc. VIII. Int. Orn. Congr. (Oxford, 1934): 277.

MILLER, A. H. (1939). "Analysis of Some Hybrid Populations of Juncos." Condor 41: 211.

MILLER, A. H., and McCABE, T. T. (1935). "Racial Differentiation in *Passerella* (*Melospiza*) *lincolnii*." Condor 37: 144.

MILLER, G. S. (1909). "The Mouse-Deer of the Rhio-Linga Archipelago, etc." Proc. U.S. Nat. Mus. 37: 1.

MILLER, G. S. (1912). "Catalogue of the Mammals of Western Europe, etc." London.

MILLER, G. S. (1924). "List of North American Mammals." Bull. U.S. Nat. Mus. 128: 1.

MÖBIUS, K., and HEINCKE, F. (1883). "Die Fische der Ostsee." Ber. Comm. Wiss. Unters. deuts. Meere. Kiel 4: 1.

MOHR, C. L. (1929). "Exaggeration and Inhibition Phenomena Encountered in the Analysis of an Autosomal Dominant." Z. ind. Abst. Vererb.l. 50: 113.

MOHR, C. L. (1932). "On the Potency of Mutant Genes and Wild-type Allelomorphs." Proc. VI. Int. Congr. Genet. (Ithaca) 1: 190.

MOLONY, H. J. C. (1937). "Evolution Out of Doors." London.

MOORE, A. R. (1910). "A Biochemical Conception of Dominance." Univ. Calif. Publ. Physiol. 4: 9.

MOORE, A. R. (1912). "On Mendelian Dominance." Arch. Entw.-Mech. 34: 168.

MOORE, J. A. (1940). "Adaptative Differences in the Egg-membranes of Frogs." Amer. Nat. 74: 89.

MOORE, J. A. (1941). "Developmental Rate of Hybrid Frogs." J. Exp. Zool. 86: 405.

MORDVILKO, A. (1937). "Artbildung und Evolution. II. Teil." Biol. Gen. 12: 271.

MOREAU, R. E. (1930). "On the Age of Some Races of Birds." Ibis (12) 6: 229.

MORGAN, C. LLOYD (1900). "Animal Behaviour." London.

MORGAN, T. H. (1915). "The Role of the Environment, etc." Amer. Nat. 49: 385.

MORGAN, T. H. (1925). "Evolution and Genetics." Princeton.

MORGAN, T. H. (1926). "The Theory of the Gene." New Haven.

MORGAN, T. H. (1929). "Variability of *Eyeless*." Publ. Carneg. Instn. No. 399: 139.

MORGAN, T. H. (1932). "The Scientific Basis of Evolution." London.

MORGAN, T. H., BRIDGES, C. B., and STURTEVANT, A. H. (1925). "The Genetics of Drosophila." Bibliogr. Genet. 2: 1.

MORGAN, T. H., SCHULTZ, J., and CURRY, V. (1940). "Investigations on the Constitution of the Germinal Material in Relation to Heredity." Yearb. Carneg. Instn. 39: 251.

MOY-THOMAS, J. A. (1934). "The Structure and Affinities of *Tarrasius problematicus* Traquair." Proc. Zool. Soc. Lond. 1934: 367.

MOY-THOMAS, J. A. (1938). "The Problem of the Evolution of the Dermal Bones in Fishes," in "Evolution," ed. G. R. De Beer. Oxford.

MULLER, H. J. (1918). "Genetic Variability, Twin Hybrids and Constant Hybrids, in a Case of Balanced Lethal Factors." Genetics 3: 422.

MULLER, H. J. (1925). "Why Polyploidy is Rarer in Animals than in Plants." Amer. Nat. 59: 346.

MULLER, H. J. (1930). "Types of Visible Variations Induced by X-Rays in *Drosophila*." J. Genet. 22: 299.

MULLER, H. J. (1935). "On the Incomplete Dominance of the Normal Allelomorphs of White in *Drosophila*." J. Genet. 30: 407.

MULLER, H. J. (1936). "Out of the Night." London.
MULLER, H. J. (1939). "Reversibility in Evolution Considered from the Standpoint of Genetics." Biol. Rev. 14: 261.
MULLER, H. J. (1940). "The Bearing of the Drosophila Work on Systematics," in "The New Systematics," ed. J. S. Huxley. Oxford.
MULLER, H. J., and PONTECORVO, G. (1940). "Recombinants between Drosophila Species, the F₁ Hybrids of Which are Sterile." Nature 146: 199.
MULLER, H. J., PROKOFYEVA, A., and RAFFEL, D. (1935). "Minute Rearrangements as a Cause of Apparent 'Gene Mutation.'" Nature 135: 253.
MÜNTZING, A. (1931). "Notes on the Cytology of Some Apomictic Potentilla Species." Hereditas, Lund 15: 166.
MÜNTZING, A. (1932). "Cytogenetic Investigations on Synthetic Galeopsis tetrahit." Hereditas, Lund 16: 105.
MÜNTZING, A. (1936). "The Evolutionary Significance of Autopolyploidy." Hereditas, Lund 21: 263.
MÜNTZING, A. (1937). "Multiple Allels and Polymeric Factors in Galeopsis." Hereditas, Lund 23: 371.
MURPHY, R. C. (1936). "Oceanic Birds of South America, etc." New York.
MURPHY, R. C. (1938). "The Need of Insular Exploration as Illustrated by Birds." Science (N.S.) 88: 533.
MURPHY, R. C., and CHAPIN, J. P. (1929). "A Collection of Birds from the Azores." Amer. Mus. Novit. no. 384.

NABOURS, R. V. (1925). "Studies of Inheritance and Evolution in Orthoptera, V." Kansas Agric. Exper. Sta. Tech. Bull. 17: 1.
NASH, T. A. M. (1937). "Climate the Vital Factor in the Ecology of Glossina." Bull. ent. Res. 28: 75.
NASH, T. A. M. (1940). "The Effect upon Glossina of Changing the Climate in the True Habitat ,by Partial Clearing of Vegetation." Bull. ent. Res. 31: 69.
NEEDHAM, J. (1931). "Chemical Embryology." Cambridge.
NEEDHAM, J. (1937). "Integrative Levels: a Revaluation of the Idea of Progress. The Herbert Spencer Lecture." Oxford.
NEEDHAM, J. (1938). "Contributions of Chemical Physiology to the Problem of Reversibility in Evolution." Biol. Rev. 13: 225.
NEEDHAM, J., HUXLEY, J. S., and LERNER, I. M. (1941). "Terminology of Relative Growth-Rates." Nature 148: 225.
NEEDHAM, J., and LERNER, I. M. (1941). "Terminology of Relative Growth-Rates." Nature 146: 618.
NICHOLSON, A. J. (1933). "The Balance of Animal Populations." J. Anim. Ecol. 2: 132.
NICHOLSON, E. M., and FISHER, J. (1940). "A Bird Census of St. Kilda, 1939." Brit. Birds 34: 29.
NILSSON, N. H. (1930). "Synthetische Bastardierungsversuche in der Gattung Salix." Lunds Univ. Arsskrift (N.F.) Avd. 2, 27: no. 4.
NILSSON, N. H. (1936). "Ein oktonärer, fertiler Salix-Bastard und seine Deszendenz." Hereditas, Lund 22: 361.
NOBLE, G. K. (1930). "What Produces Species?" Nat. Hist. N.Y. 30: 60.
NOBLE, G. K., and BRADLEY, H. T. (1933). "The Mating Behavior of Lizards, etc." Ann. N.Y. Acad. Sci. 35: 25.
NOBLE, G. K., and JAECKLE, M. E. (1928). "The Digital Pads of the Tree-Frogs, etc." J. Morph. 45: 259.

NOBLE, G. K., and VOGT, W. (1935). "An Experimental Study of Sex Recognition in Birds." Auk 52: 278.

NOPCSA, F. (1923). "Vorläufige Notiz über die Pachyostose und Osteosklerose einiger mariner Wirbeltiere." Anat. Anz. 56: 353.

NOPCSA, F. (1930). "Notes on Stegocephalia and Amphibia." Proc. Zool. Soc. Lond. 1930: 979.

NORMAN, J. R. (1931). "A History of Fishes." London.

NORMAN, J. R. (1936). "Zoological Classification." School Sci. Rev. 18: 236.

OLDHAM, C. (1932). "Altitudinal Range of the Lesser Whitethroat (Sylvia curruca)." Ibis (13) 2: 162.

OMER-COOPER, J. (1931). "Species-Pairs Among Insects." Nature 127: 237.

ORR, R. T. (1940). "The Rabbits of California." Occ. Pap. Calif. Acad. Sci. no. 19.

OSBORN, H. F. (1897). "The Limits of Organic Selection." Amer. Nat. 31: 944.

OSBORN, H. F. (1910). "The Age of Mammals." New York.

OSBORN, H. F. (1929). "The Titanotheres of Ancient Wyoming, Dakota and Nebraska." U.S. Dept. Interior Geol. Surv. Monogr. no. 55.

OSBORN, H. F. (1936). "Proboscidea." New York.

OSGOOD, W. H. (1909). "Revision of the Mice of the American Genus Peromyscus." U.S. Dept. Agric., N. Amer. Fauna no. 28.

PALMGREN, P. (1938). "Zur Kausalanalyse der ökologischer und geographischer Verbreitung der Vögel Nordeuropas." Arch. Naturgesch. (N.F.) 7: 235.

PANIKKAR, N. K. (1940). "Influence of Temperature on Osmotic Behaviour of Some Crustacea and its Bearing on Problems of Animal Distribution." Nature 146: 366.

PARKIN, E. A. (1941). "Symbiosis in Larval Siricidae (Hymenoptera)." Nature 147: 329.

PATTERSON, J. T., and CROW, J. F. (1940). "Hybridization in the mulleri Group of Drosophila." Studies in the Genetics of Drosophila. Univ. Texas. Publ. (Austin) no. 4032: 251.

PATTERSON, J. T., and MULLER, H. J. (1930). "Are 'Progressive' Mutations Produced by X-Rays?" Genetics 15: 495.

PATTERSON, J. T., STONE, W., and GRIFFIN, A. B. (1940). "Evolution of the virilis Group in Drosophila." Studies in the Genetics of Drosophila. Univ. Texas Publ. (Austin) no. 4032: 218.

PAULIAN, R. (1936). "Sur la Nature Génétique de certains cas de Polymorphisme chez les Mâles de Lucanides." Proc. Zool. Soc. Lond. 1936: 751.

PAYNE, F. (1911). "Drosophila ampelophila Loew Bred in the Dark for Sixty-Nine Generations." Biol. Bull. 21: 297.

PEARSON, J. (1938). "The Tasmanian Brush Opossum: its Distribution and Colour Variations." Pap. Proc. Roy. Soc. Tasm. for 1937: 21.

PERLOVA, R. L. (1939). "Production of an Autohexaploid Solanum vallis-mexici Juz. by Means of its Cultivation at the Pamir." C.R. Acad. Sci. U.R.S.S. 25: 419.

PFLÜGER, E., and SMITH, W. J. (1883). "Untersuchungen über Bastardierung der anuren Batrachier und die Principien der Zeugung. I. etc." Pflüg. Arch. ges. Physiol. 32: 519.

PHILLIPS, J. C. (1915). "Notes on American and Old-World English Sparrows." Auk 32: 51.

PHILLIPS, W. W. A. (1940). "Some Observations on the Nesting of *Hemipus picatus leggei*, the Ceylon Black-backed Pied Shrike." Ibis (14) **4**: 450.

PICTET, A. (1933). "Formation de la Polydactylie, etc." Z. ind. Abst. Vererb.l. **63**: 1.

PILSBRY, H. A. (1912–1914). "Achatinellidae." Manual of Conchology, Philadelphia. Ser. 2, **22**: 1.

PLATE, L. (1913). "Selektionsprinzip und Probleme der Artbildung." Leipzig and Berlin.

PLOUGH, H. H. (1917). "The Effect of Temperature on Crossing-Over." J. Exp. Zool. **24**: 147.

PLOUGH, H. H., and IVES, P. T. (1934). "Heat-induced Mutations in *Drosophila*." Proc. Nat. Acad. Sci. Wash. **20**: 268.

PLUNKETT, C. C. (1932). "Temperature as a Tool of Research in Phenogenetics: Methods and Results." Proc. VI. Int. Congr. Genet. (Ithaca) **2**: 158.

POPHAM, E. J. (1941). "The Variation in the Colour of Certain Species of *Arctocorisa* (*Hemiptera, Corixidae*), and its Significance." Proc. Zool. Soc. Lond. (A.) **111**: (in press).

PORTER, K. R. (1941). "Diploid and Androgenetic Haploid Hybridization between Two Forms of *Rana pipiens*, Schreber." Biol. Bull. **80**: 238.

POULTON, E. B. (1890). "The Colours of Animals, etc." London.

POULTON, E. B. (1931). "A Hundred Years of Evolution." Rep. Brit. Ass. **1931**: 71.

POULTON, E. B. (1925). "The Forms of *Papilio dardanus* Brown and its Models from Marsabit, S.E. of Lake Rudolph." Trans. ent. Soc. Lond. **1925**: (Proc.) viii.

POULTON, E. B. (1937). "The History of Evolutionary Thought, etc." Rep. Brit. Ass. **1937**: 1.

PRATT, A. (1937). "The Call of the Koala." Melbourne.

PROMPTOFF, A. (1930). "Die geographische Variabilität des Buchfinkschlages (*Fringilla coelebs* L.), etc." Biol. Zbl. **50**: 478.

PRYOR, M. G. M. (1940). "On the Hardening of the Cuticle of Insects." Proc. Roy. Soc. Lond. (B) **128**: 393.

PRZIBRAM, H. (1925). "Die Schwanzlänge der Nachkommen temperatur-modifizierter Ratten, etc." Arch. Entw.-mech. **104**: 548.

PUMPHREY, R. J., and RAWDON-SMITH, A. F. (1936). "Hearing in Insects: the Nature of the Response of Certain Receptors to Auditory Stimuli." Proc. Roy. Soc. Lond. (B) **121**: 18.

PUMPHREY, R J., and YOUNG, J. Z. (1938). "The Rates of Conduction of Nerve Fibres in Cephalopods." J. Exp. Biol. **15**: 453.

PUNNETT, R. C. (1915). "Mimicry in Butterflies." Cambridge.

PUNNETT, R. C., and BAILEY, P. G. (1914). "On Inheritance of Weight in Poultry." J. Genet. **4**: 23.

PUNNETT, R. C., and PEASE, M. S. (1929). "Genetic Studies on Poultry. VII. Notes on Polydactyly." J. Genet. **21**: 341.

QUAYLE, H. J. (1938). "The Development of Resistance to Hydrocyanic Acid in Certain Scale Insects." Hilgardia **11**: 183.

RADL, E. (1930). "The History of Biological Theories." tr. E. J. Hatfield, London.

RAFFEL, D., and MULLER, H. J. (1940). "Position Effect and Gene Divisibility, etc." Genetics **25**: 541.

RAMSBOTTOM, J. (1940). "Taxonomic Problems in Fungi," in "The New Systematics," ed. J. S. Huxley. Oxford.

RANGER, G. (1941). "Observations on Lophoceros melanoleucos melanoleucos (Lichtenstein) in South Africa." Ibis (14) 5: 402.

REEVE, E. C. R. (1940). "Relative Growth in the Snout of Anteaters." Proc. Zool. Soc. Lond. (A) 110: 47.

REEVE, E. C. R. (1942). "A Statistical Analysis of Taxonomic Differences within the Genus Tamandua Gray (Xenarthra)." Proc. Zool. Soc. Lond. (A) 111: 279.

REEVE, E. C. R., and MURRAY, P. D. F. (1942). Nature 150: (in press).

REGAN, C. TATE (1906–1908). "Pisces," in "Biologia Centrali-Americana." London.

REGAN, C. TATE (1911). "The Freshwater Fishes of the British Isles." London.

REGAN, C. TATE (1924). "Reversible Evolution, with Examples from Fishes." Proc. Zool. Soc. Lond. 1924: 175.

REGAN, C. TATE (1926). "Organic Evolution." Rep. Brit. Ass. 1925: 75.

REINIG, W. F. (1937). "Elimination und Selektion." Jena.

REINIG, W. F. (1938). "Die Holarktis." Jena.

REINIG, W. F. (1939). "Die genetisch-chorologischen Grundlagen der gerichteten geographischen Variabilität." Z. ind. Abst. Vererb. l. 76: 260.

RENNER, O. (1925). "Untersuchungen über die faktorielle Konstitution einiger komplex-heterozygotischer Oenotheren." Bibliogr. Genet. 9: 1.

RENSCH, B. (1928). "Grenzfälle von Rasse und Art." J. Orn. 78: 222.

RENSCH, B. (1929). "Das Prinzip geographischer Rassenkreise und das Problem der Artbildung." Berlin.

RENSCH, B. (1932). "Ueber die Abhängigkeit der Grösse, des relativen Gewichtes und der Oberflächenstruktur der Landschneckenschalen von den Umweltsfaktoren." Z. Morph. Ökol. Tiere 25: 757.

RENSCH, B. (1933a). "Zoologische Systematik und Artbildungsproblem." Verh. dtsch. zool. Ges. 1933: 19.

RENSCH, B. (1933b). "Revision und Ergänzung der Sarasinschen Rassenkreise Celebesischer Landschnecken." Mitt. Zool. Mus. Berlin 19: 99.

RENSCH, B. (1934). "Kurze Anweisung für zoologisch-systematische Studïen." Leipzig.

RENSCH, B. (1936). "Studien über Klimatische Parallelität der Merkmalsausprägung bei Vögeln und Säugern." ' Arch. Naturgesch. (N.F.) 5: 317.

RENSCH, B. (1938a). "Bestehen die Regeln klimatischer Parallelität . . . zu Recht?" Arch. Naturgesch. (N.F.) 7: 364.

RENSCH, B. (1938b). "Einwirkung des Klimas bei der Auspragung von Vogelrassen, etc." Proc. VIII. Int. Orn. Congr. (Oxford, 1934): 285.

RENSCH, B. (1939a). "Typen der Artbildung." Biol. Rev. 14: 186.

RENSCH, B. (1939b). "Klimatische Auslese der Grossenvarianten." Arch. Naturgesch. (N.F.) 8: 89.

RENSCH, B. (1939c). "Ueber die Anwendungsmöglichkeit zoologisch-systematischer Prinzipien in der Botanik." Chron. Bot. 5: 46.

RHINE, J. B. (1935). "Extra-Sensory Perception." London.

RICHARDS, O. W. (1934). "The American Species of the Genus Trypoxylon, etc." Trans. Roy. ent. Soc. 82: 173.

RICHARDS, O. W. (1938). "The Formation of Species," in "Evolution," ed. G. R. de Beer. Oxford.

RICHTER, R. (1938). "Beobachtungen an einer gemischten Kolonie, etc." J. Orn. 86: 366.

RIDDLE, O., BATES, R. W., and OTHERS (1938). "Endocrine Studies." Ann. Rep. Director Dept. Genet., Carneg. Instn. Wash. 1937–1938: 52.

RITCHIE, J. (1930). "Scotland's Testimony to the March of Evolution." Scot. Nat. 1930: 161.

ROBB, R. C. (1935, 1936). "A Study of Mutations in Evolution, I–III." J. Genet. 31: 39; 33: 267.

ROBERTS, A. (1935). "Scientific Results of the Vernay-Lang Kalahari Expedition, March to September, 1930. Birds." Ann. Transvaal Mus. 16: 1.

ROBERTS, A. (1938). "The Physical Conditions of South Africa and Their Bearing on Ornithology." Proc. VIII. Int. Orn. Congr. (Oxford, 1934): 634.

ROBERTS, J. A. F. (1932). "Colour Inheritance in Sheep, VI." J. Genet. 25: 1.

ROBERTS, J. A. F., and WHITE, R. G. (1930). "Colour Inheritance in Sheep, V." J. Genet. 22: 181.

ROBERTS, MORLEY (1920). "Warfare in the Human Body." London.

ROBERTS, MORLEY (1930). "The Serpent's Fang." London.

ROBSON, G. C. (1923). "Parthenogenesis in the Mollusc Paludestrina jenkinsi." Brit. J. Exp. Biol. 1: 65.

ROBSON, G. C. (1928). "The Species Problem." London.

ROBSON, G. C., and RICHARDS, O. W. (1936). "The Variation of Animals in Nature." London.

ROTHSCHILD, W., and HARTERT, E. (1911). "Ornithological Explorations in Algeria." Novit. Zool. 18: 456.

ROTHSCHILD, W., and JORDAN, K. (1903). "Lepidoptera Collected by Oscar Neumann in North-East Africa." Novit. Zool. 10: 491.

ROWAN, W. (1931). "The Riddle of Migration." Baltimore.

RUBTZOV, I. A. (1935). "Phase-Variation in Non-Swarming Grasshoppers." Bull. ent. Res. 26: 499.

RUSSELL, E. S. (1941). "Biological Adaptedness, etc." Nature 147: 729.

RUXTON, A. E., and SCHWARZ, E. (1929). "On Hybrid Hartebeests, etc." Proc. Zool. Soc. Lond. 1929: 567.

SALISBURY, E. J. (1929). "The Biological Equipment of Species in Relation to Competition." J. Ecol. 17: 197.

SALISBURY, E. J. (1939). "Ecological Aspects of Meteorology." Quart. J. R. met. Soc. 65: 337.

SALOMONSEN, F. (1933). "Troglodytes-Studien." J. Orn. 81: 100.

SALOMONSEN, F. (1935). "Aves", in "Zoology of the Faeroes," ed. S. Jensen, W. Lundbeck, T. Mortensen. Copenhagen.

SALOMONSEN, F. (1938). "Mutationen bei Lybius torquatus." Proc. VIII. Int. Orn. Congr. (Oxford, 1934): 190.

SANDER, F. (1931). "Orchid Hybrids." Sander's Complete List, etc. 2: 226.

SANDERSON, A. R. (1940). "Maturation in the Parthenogenetic Snail, Potamopyrgus jenkinsi Smith, etc." Proc. Zool. Soc. Lond. (A) 110: 11.

SAUNDERS, E. R. (1920). "Multiple Allelomorphs and Limiting Factors in Inheritance in the Stock (Matthiola incana)." J. Genet. 10: 149.

SCHAEFER, H. (1935). "Studien an mitteleuropäischen Kleinsäuger, etc." Arch. Naturgesch. (N.F.) 4: 535.

SCHILDER, F. A., and SCHILDER, M. (1938). "Prodrome of a Monograph on Living Cypraeidae." Proc. Malacol. Soc. 23: 119, 181.

SCHMIDT, J. R. (1918). "Racial Studies in Fishes, I." J. Genet. 7: 105.

SCHNAKENBECK, W. (1931). "Zum Rassenproblem bei den Fischen." Z. Morph. Ökol. Tiere 21: 409.

SCHULTZ, J. (1935). "Aspects of the Relation between Genes and Development in Drosophila." Amer. Nat. 69: 30.

SCHULTZ, J. (1941). "The Function of Heterochromatin." Proc. VII. Int. Genet. Congr. (Edinburgh, 1939): 257.

SCHULTZ, J., CASPERSSON, T., and AQUILONIUS, L. (1940). "The Genetic Control of Nucleolar Composition." Proc. Nat. Acad. Sci. Wash. 26: 515.

SCHWANWITSCH, B. N. (1924). "On the Ground-Plan of the Wing-Pattern in Nymphalids, etc." Proc. Zool. Soc. Lond. 1924: 509.

SCHWANWITSCH, B. N. (1926). "On the Modes of Evolution of the Wing-Pattern in Nymphalids, etc." Proc. Zool. Soc. Lond. 1926: 493.

SCHWARZ, E. (1928). "Stadien der Artbildung, etc." Verh. V. Int. Congr. Vererb. (Berlin, 1927) 2: 1299.

SCHWARZ, E. (1929). "On the Local Races and Distribution of the Black and White Colobus Monkeys." Proc. Zool. Soc. Lond. 1929: 585.

SCHWEPPENBURG, H. G. VON (1938). "Zur Systematik der fuscus-argentatus Möwen." J. Orn. 86: 345.

SCOTT, A. C. (1936). "Haploidy and Aberrant Spermatogenesis in a Coleopteran, Micromalthus debilis Leconte." J. Morph. 59: 485.

SCOTT, J. P. (1938). "The Embryology of the Guinea-Pig. II." J. Morph. 62: 299.

SCOTT, W. E. (1901-2). "Data on Song in Birds, etc." Science (N.S.) 14: 522; 15: 178.

SETH-SMITH, D. (1907). "The Yellow-Rumped Finch (Munia flaviprymna), etc." Avic. Mag. (N.S.) 5: 195.

SEXTON, E. W. (1939). "On a New Species of Gammarus (G. tigrinus) from Droitwich District." J. Mar. Biol. Ass. U.K. 23: 543.

SEXTON, E. W., and CLARK, A. R. (1936a). "Heterozygosis in a Wild Population of Gammarus chevreuxi Sexton." J. Mar. Biol. Ass. U.K. 21: 319.

SEXTON, E. W., and CLARK, A. R. (1936b). "A Summary of the Work on the Amphipod Gammarus chevreuxi, etc." J. Mar. Biol. Ass. U.K. 21: 357.

SEXTON, E. W., CLARK, A. R., and SPOONER, G. M. (1930). "Some New Eye-Colour Changes in Gammarus chevreuxi Sexton." J. Mar. Biol. Ass. U.K. 16: 189.

SHORTRIDGE, G. C. (1934). "The Mammals of South-West Africa, etc." London.

SHULL, A. F. (1936). "Evolution." New York and London.

SHULL, G. H. (1937). "The Geographical Distribution of the Diploid and Double-Diploid Species of Shepherd's-Purse," in Nelson Fithian Davis Birthday Volume, ed. H. K. Youngken. Boston, p. 1.

SICK, H. (1937). "Morphologischfunktionelle Untersuchungen über die Feinstruktur der Vogelfeder." J. Orn. 1937: 206.

SIKKA, S. M. (1940). "Cytogenetics of Brassica Hybrids and Species." J. Genet. 40: 441.

SILOW, B. A. (1941). "The Comparative Genetics of Gossypium anomalum, etc." J. Genet. 42: 259.

SINNOTT, E. W. (1935). "The Genetic Control of Developmental Relationships, etc." Science 81: 420.

SINNOTT, E. W., and DUNN, L. C. (1932). "Principles of Genetics." New York.

SINSKAIA, E. N. (1931). "The Study of Species, etc." Bull. appl. Bot. (Leningrad) 25: 1.

SLADDEN, D. E., and HEWER, H. R. (1938). "Transference of Induced Food-Habit from Parent to Offspring. III." Proc. Roy. Soc. (B) 126: 30.

SMART, J. (1940). "Entomological Systematics Examined as a Practical Problem," in "The New Systematics," ed. J. S. Huxley. Oxford.

SMITH, M. (1938). "Evolutionary Changes in the Middle Ear of Certain Agamid and Iguanid Lizards." Proc. Zool. Soc. Lond. (B) 108: 543.

SMITH, S. G. (1940). "A New Form of Spruce Sawfly, etc." Sci. Agric. 21: 245

SMITH, S. G. (1941). "Cytology and Parthenogenesis of *Diprion polytomum* Hartig." Proc. VII. Int. Genet. Congr. (Edinburgh, 1939): 267.

SNYDER, J. O. (1933). "California Trout." California Fish and Game **19**: 81.

SNYDER, L. L. (1935). "A Study of the Sharp-Tailed Grouse." Univ. Toronto Stud. Biol. no. **40**: 1.

SOKOLOV, N. N., and DUBININ, N. P. (1941). "Permanent Heterozygosity in *Drosophila*." Drosoph. Inf. Serv. no. **15**: 39.

SOUTH, R. (1939). "The Moths of the British Isles" (3rd ed.). London.

SOUTHERN, H. N. (1939). "The Status and Problems of the Bridled Guillemot." Proc. Zool. Soc. Lond. (B) **109**: 31.

SPATH, L. F. (1924). "The Ammonites of the Blue Lias." Proc. Geol. Ass. Lond. **35**: 186.

SPENCE, K. W., and YERKES, R. M. (1937). "Weight, Growth and Age in Chimpanzee." Amer. J. Phys. Anthrop. **22**: 229.

SPENCER, W. P. (1932). "The Vermilion Mutant of *Drosophila hydei* breeding in Nature." Amer. Nat. **66**: 474

SPENCER, W. P. (1940). "Levels of Divergence in *Drosophila* Speciation." Amer. Nat. **74**: 299.

SPENCER, W. P. (1941). "Ecological Factors and the Distribution of Genes, etc." Proc. VIII. Int. Genet. Congr. (Edinburgh, 1939): 268.

SPOONER, G. M. (1941). [*Gammarus zaddachi*]. J. Mar. Biol. Ass. U.K., in press; and **24**: 444.

STADLER, H. (1929). "Die Vogelstimmungsforschung als Wissenschaft." Verh. VI. Int. Orn. Kongr. (Copenhagen, 1926): 338.

STANFORD, J. K., and MAYR, E. (1940). "The Vernay-Cutting Expedition to Northern Burma." Ibis (14) **4**: 679.

STAPLEDON, R. G. (1928). "Cocksfoot Grass (*Dactylis glomerata* L.): Ecotypes in Relation to the Biotic Factor." J. Ecol. **15**: 71.

STEBBINS, G. L. (1940*a*). "The Significance of Polyploidy in Plant Evolution." Amer. Nat. **74**: 54.

STEBBINS, G. L. (1940*b*). "Studies in the Cichoreae, etc." Mem. Torrey Bot Cl. **19**: (pt. 3): 1.

STEGMANN, B. (1934). "Ueber die Formen der grossen Möwen (subgenus *Larus*) und ihre gegenseitigen Beziehungen." J. Orn. **82**: 340.

STEPHENSON, T. A. (1929). "On Methods of Reproduction as Specific Characters." J. Mar. Biol. Ass. U.K. **16**: 131.

STERN, C. (1936). "Interspecific Sterility." Amer. Nat. **70**: 123.

STIRTON, R. A. (1940). "Phylogeny of North American Equidae." Bull. Dep. Geol. Univ. Calif. **25**: 165.

STOCKARD, C. R. (1931). "The Physical Basis of Personality." New York.

STOCKARD, C. R. (1938). "Constitutional and Genetic Reactions Associated with the Pituitary Gland." Proc. Ass. Res. Nerv. and Ment. Disease **17**: 616.

STOCKARD, C. R., and collaborators (1941). "The Genetic and Endocrine Basis for Differences in Form and Behaviour, etc." Wistar Inst., Philadelphia.

STONE, W. S., and GRIFFEN, A. B. (1940). "Changing the Structure of the Genome in *D. melanogaster*." Univ. Texas Publ. (Austin) no. **4032**: 208.

STONOR, C. R. (1936). "The Evolution and Mutual Relationships of Some Members of the Paradiseidae." Proc. Zool. Soc. Lond. **1936**: 1177.

STONOR, C. R. (1938). "Some Features of the Variation of the Birds of Paradise." Proc. Zool. Soc. Lond. (B) **108**: 417.

STONOR, C. R. (1940). "Courtship and Display among Birds." London.

STOREY, H. H. (1932). "The Inheritance by an Insect Vector of the Ability to Transmit a Plant Virus." Proc. Roy. Soc. (B) **112**: 46.

STOVIN, G. H. T. (1937). "Great Wood, Belfairs, Hadleigh, Essex." Soc. Promot. Nat. Reserves Handb. **1937**: 14.

STRESEMANN, E. (1919). "Beiträge zur Zoogeographie der paläarktischen Region, I." Munich.

STRESEMANN, E. (1923–1926). "Mutationstudien, I–XXV," in Orn. Monatsb. **31–34**, and J. Orn. **71–74**.

STRESEMANN, E. (1927). "Die Entwicklung der Begriffe *Art, Varietät, Unterart* in der Ornithologie." Mitt. Verein. Sächs. Orn. **2**: 1.

STRESEMANN, E. (1931). "Die Zosteropiden der indo-australischen Subregion." Mitt. Zool. Mus. Berlin **17**: 201.

STROHL, J., and KÖHLER, W. (1934). "Experimentelle Untersuchungen über die Entwicklungsphysiologie der Flügelzeichnung bei der Mehlmotte." Verh. schweiz. naturf. Ges. **115**: 367.

STUBBE, A., and VOGT, M. (1940a). "Ueber die Homologie einiger Augenfarbgene bei *Drosophila*, etc." Z. ind. Abst. Vererb.l. **78**: 251.

STUBBE, A., and VOGT, M. (1940b). "Vergleichende Untersuchungen der Wildtypen verschiedener *Drosophila*-Arten an Hand von Transplantationen von Augenanlagen." Z. ind. Abst. Vererb.l. **78**: 255.

STULL, O. G. (1940). "Variations and Relationships in the Snakes of the Genus *Pituophis*." Bull. U.S. Nat. Mus. **175**.

STURTEVANT, A. H. (1912). "Federley's Breeding Experiments with the Moth *Pygaera*." Amer. Nat. **46**: 565.

STURTEVANT, A. H. (1921). "The North American Species of *Drosophila*." Publ. Carneg. Instn. no. **301**.

STURTEVANT, A. H. (1924). "An Interpretation of Orthogenesis." Science (N.S.) **59**: 579.

STURTEVANT, A. H. (1937). "Essays on Evolution. I." Quart. Rev. Biol. **12**: 464.

STURTEVANT, A. H. (1939). "On the Subdivision of the Genus *Drosophila*." Proc. Nat. Acad. Sci. Wash. **25**: 137.

STURTEVANT, A. H., and BEADLE, G. W. (1938). "The Relations of Inversions in the X-chromosome of *Drosophila melanogaster* to Crossing-over and Disjunction." Genetics **21**: 554.

STURTEVANT, A. H., and DOBZHANSKY, T. (1936). "Geographical Distribution and Cytology of 'Sex-Ratio,' etc." Genetics **21**: 473.

SÜFFERT, F. (1932). "Phänomene visueller Anpassung, I. bis III. Mitteilung." Z. Morph. Ökol. Tiere **26**: 147.

SÜFFERT, F. (1935). "Neue Arbeit an den Fragen der visuellen Aupassung." Verh. dtsch. zool. Ges. **1935**: 248.

SUKATSCHEW, W. (1928). "Einige experimentelle Untersuchungen über den Kampf ums Dasein, etc." Z. ind. Abst. Vererb.l. **47**: 54.

SUMNER, F. B. (1932). "Genetic, Distributional and Evolutional Studies of the Subspecies of Deer-Mice (*Peromyscus*)." Bibliogr. Genet. **9**: 1.

SUOMALAINEN, E. (1941). "Vererbungsstudien an der Schmetterlingsart *Leucodonta bicoloria*." Hereditas, Lund **27**: 313.

SVIRIDENKO, P. A. (1940). "The Nutrition of 'Mouse-Like Rodents, etc." Zool. J. (Moscow) **19**: 680.

SWARTH, H. S. (1920). "Revision of the Avian Genus *Passerella*, etc." Univ. Calif. Publ. Zool. **21**: 75.

SWARTH, H. S. (1931). "The Avifauna of the Galapagos Islands." Calif. Acad. Sci. Occas. Pap. no. **18**.

SWARTH, H. S. (1934). "The Bird Fauna of the Galapagos Islands in Relation to Species Formation." Biol. Rev. **9**: 213.

SWEADNER, W. R. (1937). "Hybridization and the Phylogeny of the Genus *Platysamia*." Ann. Carneg. Mus. **25**: 163.

SWELLENGREBEL, N. H., and DE BUCK, A. (1938). "Malaria in the Netherlands." Amsterdam.

SWINNERTON, H. H. (1921). "The Use of Graphs in Palaeontology." Geol. Mag. **58**: 357, 397.

SWINNERTON, H. H. (1932). "Unit Characters in Fossils." Biol. Rev. **7**: 321.

SWINNERTON, H. H. (1938). "Development and Evolution." Rep. Brit. Ass. **108**: 57.

SWINNERTON, H. H. (1940). "On the Study of Variation in Fossils." Quart. J. Geol. Soc. Lond. **96**: lxxvii.

TANSLEY, A. G. (1917). "On the Competition Between *Galium saxatile* L. and *G. silvestre* Poll. on Different Types of Soil." J. Ecol. **5**: 173.

TAVERNER, P. A. (1927). "A Study of *Buteo borealis*, the Red-tailed Hawk and its Varieties in Canada." Canad. Victoria Memorial Mus. Bull. No. **48**.

TAVERNER, P. A. (1934). "Flicker Hybrids." Condor **36**: 34.

TAVERNER, P. A. (1936). "Taxonomic Comments on Red-tailed Hawks." Condor **38**: 66.

TCHERNAVIN, V. (1939*a*). "Ripe Salmon Parr: A Summary of Research." Proc. Roy. Phys. Soc. Edin. **23**: 734.

TCHERNAVIN, V. (1939*b*). "The Origin of Salmon." Salm. Trout Mag. no. **95**: 1.

TEDIN, O. (1925). "Vererbung, Variation und Systematik in der Gattung *Camelina*." Hereditas, Lund **6**: 275.

THAYER, G. H. (1909). "Concealing Coloration in the Animal Kingdom." New York.

THOMAS, O., and WROUGHTON, R. C. (1916). "Scientific Results of the Mammal Survey, XII." J. Bombay Nat. Hist. Soc. **24**: 224.

THOMPSON, D. H. (1931). "Variation of Fishes as a Function of Distance." Trans. Illinois State Acad. Sci. **23**: 276.

THOMPSON, D'ARCY W. (1917). "Growth and Form." Cambridge.

THOMPSON, W. R. (1939). "Biological Control and the Theories of the Interaction of Populations." Parasitol. **31**: 299.

THOMSEN, M., and LEMCKE, H. (1933). "Experimente zur Erzielung eines erblichen Melanismus bei dem Spanner *Selenia bilunaria* Esp." Biol. Zbl. **53**: 541.

THOMSON, A. L. (1923). "The Migrations of Some British Ducks: Results of the Marking Method." Brit. Birds **16**: 262.

THOMSON, G. H. (1936). "Intelligence and Civilisation." Edinburgh.

THORPE, W. H. (1930). "Biological Races in Insects and Allied Groups." Biol. Rev. **5**: 177.

THORPE, W. H. (1936). "On a New Type of Respiratory Interrelation between an Insect (Chalcid) Parasite and its Host (Coccidae). Parasitol. **28**: 517.

THORPE, W. H. (1938). "Further Experiments on Olfactory Conditioning in a Parasitic Insect. The Nature of the Conditioning Process." Proc. Roy. Soc. Lond. (B) **126**: 370.

THORPE, W. H. (1939). "Further Studies on Pre-Imaginal Olfactory Conditioning in Insects." Proc. Roy. Soc. Lond. (B) **127**: 424.

THORPE, W. H. (1940). "Ecology and the Future of Systematics," in "The New Systematics," ed. J. S. Huxley. Oxford.

THORPE, W. H., and JONES, F. G. W. (1937). "Olfactory Conditioning in a Parasitic Insect, etc." Proc. Roy. Soc. Lond. (B) 124: 56.

TICEHURST, C. B. (1938). "A Systematic Review of the Genus *Phylloscopus*." British Museum. London.

TIMOFÉEFF-RESSOVSKY, N. W. (1932a). "Verschiedenheit der 'normalen' Allele der white-serie, etc." Biol. Zbl. 52: 468.

TIMOFÉEFF-RESSOVSKY, N. W. (1932b). "The Genogeographical Work with *Epilachna chrysomelina*, etc." Proc. VI. Int. Congr. Genet. (Ithaca) 2: 230.

TIMOFÉEFF-RESSOVSKY, N. W. (1933). "Ueber die relative Vitalität von *Drosophila melanogaster* und *D. funebris*, etc." Arch. Naturgesch (N.F.) 2: 285.

TIMOFÉEFF-RESSOVSKY, N. W. (1934a). "The Experimental Production of Mutations." Biol. Rev. 9: 411.

TIMOFÉEFF-RESSOVSKY, N. W. (1934b). "Ueber den Einfluss des genotypischen Milieus, etc." Nachr. Ges. Wiss. Göttingen (Biol.) (N.F.) 1: 53.

TIMOFÉEFF-RESSOVSKY, N. W. (1935). "Ueber geographische Temperaturrassen bei *Drosophila funebris* F." Arch. Naturgesch. (N.F.) 4: 245.

TIMOFÉEFF-RESSOVSKY, N. W. (1937). "Experimentelle Mutationsforschung in der Vererbungslehre." Dresden and Leipzig.

TIMOFÉEFF-RESSOVSKY, N. W. (1940). "Mutation and Geographical Variation," in "The New Systematics," ed. J. S. Huxley. Oxford.

TIMOFÉEFF-RESSOVSKY, N. W., and E. A. (1940). "Populationsgenetische Versuche an *Drosophila*, I–III." Z. ind. Abst. Vererb.l. 79: 28.

TINIAKOV, G. G. (1941). "A New Case of Spontaneous Mutability, etc." Drosoph. Inf. Serv. no. 15: 40.

TISCHLER, G. (1941). "Die Bedeutung chromosomaler Rassedifferenzen, etc." Proc. VII. Int. Genet. Congr. (Edinburgh, 1939): 295.

TRUEMAN, A. E. (1922). "The Use of *Gryphaea* in the Correlation of the Lower Lias." Geol. Mag. 59: 258.

TURESSON, G. (1922). "The Genotypical Response of the Plant Species to the Habitat." Hereditas, Lund 3: 211.

TURESSON, G. (1927). "Contributions to the Genecology of Glacial Relics." Hereditas, Lund 9: 81.

TURESSON, G. (1930). "The Selective Effect of Climate upon Plant Species." Hereditas, Lund 14: 99, 274, 300.

TURRILL, W. B. (1929). "The Plant Life of the Balkan Peninsula." Oxford.

TURRILL, W. B. (1934). "The Correlation of Morphological Variation with Distribution in Some Species of *Ajuga*." New Phytol. 33: 218.

TURRILL, W. B. (1936). "Contacts between Plant Classification and Experimental Botany." Nature 137: 563.

TURRILL, W. B. (1938a). "The Expansion of Taxonomy, with Special Reference to Spermatophyta." Biol. Rev. 13: 342.

TURRILL, W. B. (1938b). "Material for a Study of Taxonomic Problems in *Taraxacum*." Rep. Bot. Exch. Cl. 1937: 570.

TURRILL, W. B. (1938c). "Problems of British *Taraxaca*." Proc. Linn. Soc. Lond. 150: 120.

TURRILL, W. B. (1940). "Experimental and Synthetic Plant Taxonomy," in "The New Systematics," ed. J. S. Huxley. Oxford.

TYRRELL, G. N. M. (1935). "Some Experiments in Undifferentiated Extra-Sensory Perception." J. Soc. Psych. Res. 29: 52.

UBISCH, L. VON (1933). "Untersuchungen über Formbildung, III." Arch. EntwMech. 127: 216.

UBISCH, L. VON (1939). "Keimblattchimärenforschung an Seeigellarven." Biol. Rev. **14**: 88.

UPCOTT, M. (1939). "The Genetic Structure of *Tulipa*. III. Meiosis in Polyploids." J. Genet. **37**: 303.

UPHOF, J. C. T. (1938). "Cleistogamous Flowers." Bot. Rev. **4**: 21.

UVAROV, B. P. (1938). "Ecological and Biographical Relations of Eremian Acrididae." Mem. Soc. Biogéogr. Paris **6**: 231.

VANDEL, A. (1937). "Chromosome Number, Polyploidy and Sex in the Animal Kingdom." Proc. Zool. Soc. Lond. (A) **107**: 519.

VANDEL, A. (1939). "Polyploidy and Geographical Distribution." Advanc. Sci. (Rep. Brit. Ass.) **1**: 45.

VAN OORT, E. D. (1926). "Ornithologia Neerlandica. De Vogels van Nederland," Vol. II. Leiden.

VAVILOV, N. I. (1927). "Geographical Regularities in the Distribution of the Genes of Cultivated Plants." Bull. appl. Bot. (Leningrad) **17**: 411.

VAVILOV, N. I. (1940). "The New Systematics of Cultivated Plants," in "The New Systematics," ed. J. S. Huxley. Oxford.

VELIKOKHATKO, F. D. (1941). "Some Materials to the Knowledge of the Bream from the Dnieper River." Zool. J. (Moscow) **20**: 116.

VESEY-FITZGERALD, D. (1941). "Further Contributions to the Ornithology of the Seychelles." Ibis (14) **5**: 518.

VOGT, C., and VOGT, O. (1938). "Sitz und Wesen der Krankheiten, Pt. II (1)." Leipzig.

VOGT, O. (1909 and 1911). "Studien über das Artproblem, I and II." S.B. Ges. naturf. Fr. Berlin. **1909**: 28, and **1911**: 31.

VRIES, H. DE (1901). "Die Mutationstheorie, etc." Leipzig.

VRIES, H. DE (1905). "Species and Varieties; their Origin by Mutation, etc." Chicago.

WADDINGTON, C. H. (1939). "An Introduction to Modern Genetics." London.

WADDINGTON, C. H. (1941a). "The Pupal Contraction as an Epigenetic Crisis in *Drosophila*." Proc. Zool. Soc. Lond. (A) **111** : (in press).

WADDINGTON, C. H. (1941b). "Evolution of Developmental Systems." Nature **147**: 108.

WALLACE, A. R. (1889). "Darwinism, etc." London.

WALTHER, H. (1927). "Ueber Melanismus." Iris **41**: 32.

WARNKE, H. E., and BLAKESLEE, A. F. (1939). "Sex Mechanisms in Polyploids of *Melandrium*." Science **89**: 391.

WARREN, B. C. S. (1936). "Monograph of the Genus *Erebia*." London.

WARREN, B. C. S. (1937). "On the Evolution of Subspecies, etc." J. Linn. Soc. (Zool.) **40**: 305.

WATSON, D. M. S. (1926). "The Evolution and Origin of the Amphibia." Philos. Trans. (B) **214**: 189.

WATSON, D. M. S., and others (1936). "A Discussion on the Present State of the Theory of Natural Selection." Proc. Roy. Soc. Lond. (B) **121**: 43.

WEBBER, J. M. (1930). "Interspecific Hybridization in *Nicotiana*, XI, etc." Univ. Calif. Publ. Bot. **11**: 319.

WEIDENREICH, F. (1941). "The Brain and its Rôle in the Phylogenetic Transformation of the Human Skull." Trans. Amer. Phil. Soc. (N.S.) **31**: 321.

WEISMANN, A. (1894). "Aeussere Einflüsse als Entwicklungsreize." Jena.

WEISSMAN, A. (1904). "The Evolution Theory." trans. J. A. and M. R. Thomson. London.

WELCH, D'A. A. (1938). "Distribution and Variation of *Achatinella mustelina*, etc." Bernice P. Bishop Mus. Bull. Honolulu, **152**.

WELDON, W. F. R. (1901). "A First Study of Natural Selection in *Clausilia laminata*." Biometrika **1**: 109.

WELLINGTON, R. (1932). "The Value of the European Grape in Breeding Grapes for New York State." Proc. VI Int. Congr. Genet. (Ithaca) **2**: 208.

WELLS, H. G., HUXLEY, J. S., and WELLS, G. P. (1930). "The Science of Life." London.

WENT, F. W. (1940). "Local Reactions in Plants." Amer. Nat. **74**: 107.

WESTOLL, T. S. (1936). "On the Structure of the Dermal Ethmoid Shield of *Osteolepis*." Geol. Mag. **73**: 157.

WHEELER, W. M. (1910). "Ants." New York.

WHITE, M. J. D. (1937). "The Chromosomes." London.

WHITE, M. J. D. (1940). "Evidence for Polyploidy in the Hermaphrodite Groups of Animals." Nature **146**: 132.

WHITE, O. E. (1926). "Geographical Distribution and the Cold-Resisting Character of Certain Herbaceous Perennial and Woody Plant Groups." Brooklyn Bot. Gard. Rec. **15**: 1.

WHITNEY, R. J. (1939). "The Thermal Resistance of Mayfly Nymphs from Ponds and Streams." J. Exp. Biol. **16**: 374.

WILLIS, J. C. (1922). "Age and Area." Cambridge.

WILLIS, J. C. (1940). "The Course of Evolution." Cambridge.

WILMOTT, A. J. (1934). "Some Interesting British Sorbs." Proc. Linn. Soc. Lond. **146**: 73.

WILSON, E. B. (1925). "The Cell in Development and Inheritance" (3rd ed.). New York.

WINGE, O. (1927). "The Location of Eighteen Genes in *Lebistes reticulatus*." J. Genet. **18**: 1.

WINGE, O. (1938). "Inheritance of Species Characters in *Tragopogon*." G.R. Lab. Carlsberg, **22**: 155.

WINGFIELD, C. A. (1939*a*). "The Activity and Metabolism of Poikilothermal Animals in Different Latitudes." Proc. Zool. Soc. Lond. (A) **109**: 103.

WINGFIELD, C. A. (1939*b*). "The Function of the Gills of Mayfly Nymphs from Different Habitats." J. Exp. Biol. **16**: 363.

WINTER, F. L. (1929). "The Mean and Variability as Affected by Continuous Selection for Composition in Corn." J. Agric. Res. **39**: 451.

WINTERBOTTOM, J. M. (1929). "Studies in Sexual Phenomena. VII. Transference of Male Secondary Sexual Display Characters, etc." J. Genet. **21**: 367.

WINTERBOTTOM, J. M. (1932). "Studies in Sexual Phenomena. VIII. Transference and Eclipse Plumage in Birds." J. Genet. **25**: 395.

WITHERBY, H. F., and others (1938–41). "The Handbook of British Birds." London.

WITSCHI, E. (1930). "Studies on Sex Differentiation and Sex Determination in Amphibians. IV." J. Exp. Zool. **56**: 149.

WOLF, F. (1909). "Ueber Modifikationen und experimentell ausgelöste Mutationen von *Bacillus* prodigiosus und anderen Schizophyten." Z. ind. Abst. Vererb.l. **2**: 90.

WOOD, H. E. (1941). "Trends in Rhinoceros Evolution." Trans. N.Y. Acad. Sci. (2) **3**: 83.

WOOD, T. B. (1905). "Note on the Inheritance of Horns and Face-Colour in Sheep." J. Agric. Sci. **1**: 364.

WOOD-JONES, F. (1936). "The Breeding of the Sooty Shearwater (*Puffinus griseus*) on Tasman Island." S. Austral. Orn. **13**: 197.

WOOD-JONES, F. (1939a). "The Forearm and Manus of the Giant Panda, *Ailuropoda melanoleuca.*" Proc. Zool. Soc. Lond. (B) **109**: 113.
WOOD-JONES, F. (1939b). "Life and Living." London.
WORTHINGTON, E. B. (1937). "On the Evolution of Fish in the Great Lakes of Africa." Int. Rev. ges. Hydrobiol. Hydrogr. **35**: 304.
WORTHINGTON, E. B. (1940). "Geographical Differentiation in Fresh Waters, etc.," in "The New Systematics," ed. J. S. Huxley. Oxford.
WRIGHT, SEWALL (1929). "Fisher's Theory of Dominance." Amer. Nat. **63**: 274.
WRIGHT, SEWALL (1931). "Evolution in Mendelian Populations." Genetics **16**: 97.
WRIGHT, SEWALL (1932). "The Roles of Mutation, Inbreeding, Crossbreeding and Selection, etc." Proc. VI.; Int. Congr. Genet. (Ithaca) **1**: 356.
WRIGHT, SEWALL (1934a). "Physiological and Evolutionary Theories of Dominance." Amer. Nat. **68**: 24.
WRIGHT, SEWALL (1934b). "A Mutation of the Guinea Pig, Tending to Restore the Pentadactyl Foot, etc." Genetics **20**: 84.
WRIGHT, SEWALL (1939). "Genetic Principles Governing the Rate of Progress of Livestock Breeding." 32nd Ann. Proc. Amer. Soc. Anim. Production (1939): 18.
WRIGHT, SEWALL (1940a). "The Statistical Consequences of Mendelian Heredity, etc.," in "The New Systematics," ed. J. S. Huxley. Oxford.
WRIGHT, SEWALL (1940b). "Breeding Structure of Populations in Relation to Speciation." Amer. Nat. **74**: 232.

YOCOM, H. B., and HUESTIS, R. R. (1928). "Histological Differences in the Thyroid Glands from Two Subspecies of *Peromyscus.*" Anat. Rec. **39**: 57.
YONGE, C. M. (1936). "Mode of Life, Feeding, Digestion and Symbiosis in the Tridacnidae." Sci. Rep. Gt. Barrier Reef Exped. 1928–29 (London) **1**: 283.
YONGE, C. M. (1938a). "The Prosobranchs of Lake Tanganyika." Nature **142**: 464.
YONGE, C. M. (1938b). "Evolution of Ciliary Feeding in the Prosobranchia, etc." J. Mar. Biol. Assoc. U.K. **22**: 453.
YULE, G. U., and WILLIS, J. C. (1922). "Some Statistics of Evolution and Geographical Distribution in Plants and Animals, etc." Nature **109**: 177.

ZARAPKIN, S. R. (1930). "Ueber gerichtete Variabilität bei Coccinelliden. I." Z. Morph. Ökol. Tiere **17**: 719.
ZARAPKIN, S. R. (1934). "Zur Phänoanalyse von geographischen Rassen und Arten." Arch. Naturgesch. (N.F.) **3**: 161.
ZARAPKIN, S. R., and TIMOFÉEFF-RESSOVSKY, H. A. (1932). "Zur Analyse der Formvariationen. II." Naturwiss. **20**: 384.
ZIMMERMANN, K. (1935). "Zur Rassenanalyse der mitteleuropäischen Feldmäuse." Arch. Naturgesch. (N.F.) **4**: 258.
ZIMMERMANN, K. (1936). "Zur Kenntnis der Europäischen Waldmäuse, etc." Arch. Naturgesch. (N.F.) **5**: 116.
ZIMMERMANN, K. (1941). "Some Results of Genetical Analysis in Populations of Wild Rodents." Proc. VII. Int. Genet. Congr. (Edinburgh, 1939): 332.
ZUCKERMAN, S. (1940). "Human Genera and Species." Nature **145**: 510.
ZUITIN, A. I. (1941). "The Changes in the Environment as the Principal External Factor in Natural Mutations." Drosoph. Inf. Serv. no. **15**: 41.

SUPPLEMENTARY BIBLIOGRAPHY

ADAMSON, JOY. (1961). "Living Free." Collins, London.

ALLEE, W. C. et al. (1949). "Principles of Animal Ecology." W. B. Saunders, Philadelphia and London.

ANDREWARTHA, H. G. (1961). "Introduction to the Study of Animal Populations." Methuen, London.

BABERS, F. H. and PRATT, J. J. (1951). "Development of Insect Resistance to Insecticides. II." U.S. Dept. Agric. E818, May, 1951. Washington, D.C.

BALDWIN, E. (1949). "An Introduction to Comparative Biochemistry," 3rd ed., Cambridge.

BARNETT, A. (1950). "The Human Species." Macgibbon and Kee, London.

BARNETT, S. A. (ed.). (1958). "A Century of Darwin." Heinemann, London.

BEALE, G. H. (1954). "The Genetics of Paramecium aurelia." Cambridge.

BELL, P. R. (ed.). (1959). "Darwin's Biological Work." Cambridge Univ. Press.

BERRILL, N. J. (1961). "Growth, Development and Pattern." W. H. Freeman, San Francisco and London.

BLACKETT, P. M. S. (1960 and 1961). (paleomagnetism). Proc. Roy. Soc. (B). **256,** 291 and **263,** 1.

BLUM, H. F. (1955). "Time's Arrow and Evolution." Princeton Univ. Press.

BONNER, J. T. (1958). "The Evolution of Development." Cambridge Univ. Press.

BOYD, W. C. (1950). "Genetics and the Races of Man." Little Brown, Boston.

BRAUN, W. (1953). "Bacterial Genetics." Saunders, Philadelphia and London.

BROWN, A. W. A. (1958). "Insecticide Resistance in Arthropods." World Health Organ. Monog. Ser. **38.**

BURNET, F. M. (1959). "The Clonal Selection Theory of Acquired Immunity." Cambridge Univ. Press.

BURNET, F. M. (1960). "Principles of Animal Virology," 2nd ed. Academic Press, New York.

BURNET, F. M. and STANLEY, W. M., ed. (1960). "The Viruses." 3 vols. Academic Press, New York.

BURNET, F. M. (1962). "The Thymus Gland." Sci. American. **207,** 50.

CAIN, A. J. (1954). "Animal Species and their Evolution." Hutchinson, London.

CAIN, A. J. and CURRY, J. D. (1963). "Area Effects in Cepaea." Phil. Trans. Roy. Soc. (B.), 1963.

CALVIN, M. (1962). "The Origin of Life on Earth and Elsewhere." Persp. Biol. Med. **5**, 399.

CALVIN, M. (1962a). "Evolution of Photosynthetic Mechanisms." Persp. Biol. Med. **5**, 147.

CARSON, R. 196, 196. "The Silent Spring." Houghton Mifflin, Boston; Hamish Hamilton, London.

CARTER, G. S. (1951). "Animal Evolution." Sidgwick and Jackson, London.

CARTER, G. S. (1957). "A Hundred Years of Evolution." Sidgwick and Jackson, London.

CATCHESIDE, D. G. (1951). "The Genetics of Micro-organisms." London and New York.

CHARGAFF, E. and DAVIDSON, J. N., ed. (1955-60). "The Nucleic Acids." Academic Press, New York.

CLARK, W. E. LE GROS. (1955). "The Fossil Evidence of Human Evolution." Chicago.

CLARK, W. E. LE GROS. (1959). "The Antecedents of Man." Edinburgh.

CLARKE, C. A. (1961). in "Progress in Medical Genetics," **1**, ed. A. G. Steinberg. Grune, U.S.A.

CLARK, C. A. (1962). "Genetics for the Clinician." Blackwell, Oxford.

CLARKE, C. A. and SHEPPARD, F. N. (1960). "The Genetics of Papilio dardanus Brown", Genetics, **45**, 4.

CORNING, W. C. and JOHN, E. R. (1961). "Effect of ribonuclease on retention of conditioned response in regenerated Planarians." Science, **134**, 1363.

COON, C. S. (1962). "The Origin of Races." Knopf, New York.

COUNT, E. W. (1950). "This is Race." Schuman, New York.

CREED, DOWDESWELL, FORD and MCWHIRTER. (1960, 1962). (differentiation without isolation; selection-pressure). Heredity, **14**, 363 and **17**, 237.

DARLING, F. FRASER. (1960). "Wild life in an African territory." Oxford Univ. Press, London.

DARLINGTON, C. D. (1958). "The Evolution of Genetic Systems," 2nd ed. Edinburgh.

DARLINGTON, C. D. and MATHER, K. (1949). "The Elements of Genetics." Allen and Unwin, London.

DARLINGTON, P. J. (1957). "Zoogeography; The Geographical Distribution of Animals." John Wiley and Sons, New York; Chapman & Hall, London.

DAVIDSON, J. N. (1960). "The Biochemistry of the Nucleic Acids," 4th ed. Methuen, London.

DE BEER, G. R. (1954). "Archeopteryx and Evolution." Adv. Sci. **42**, 160.

DE BEER, G. R. (1958). "Embryos and Ancestors," 3rd ed. Clarendon Press, Oxford.

DOBZHANSKY, TH. (1951). "Genetics and the Origin of Species." New York.

DOBZHANSKY, TH. (1955). "A review of some fundamental concepts and problems of population genetics." Cold Spring Harbor Symp. Quant. Biol. **20,** 1.

DOBZHANSKY, TH. (1962). "Mankind Evolving." Yale Univ. Press, New Haven and London.

DUNN, L. C. (ed.). (1951). "Genetics in the 20th Century." MacMillan, New York.

ELTON, C. S. (1958). "The Ecology of Invasions by Animals and Plants." London, Methuen.

FENNER, F. J. (1962). "Interactions between Pox Viruses." Leeuwenhoek Lecture, Proc. Roy. Soc. (B) **156,** 388.

FLORKIN, E. and MORGULIS, S. (1949). "Biochemical Evolution." Academic Press, New York.

FORD, E. B. (1936). "The Genetics of Papilio dardanus Brown (Lep)." Trans. Roy. Ent. Soc. **85,** 435.

FORD, E. B. (1961). "Genetics for Medical Students," 5th ed. Methuen, London.

FORD, E. B. (1949). "Polymorphism." Biol. Rev. **20,** 73.

FORD, E. B. (1955). "A uniform notation for the Human Blood-groups." Heredity, **9,** 135.

FORD, E. B. (1963). "Ecological Genetics." London, Methuen.

FRISCH, J. E. (1959). "Research on primate behaviour in Japan." Amer. Anthropol. **61:** 584-96.

FRISCH, K. V. (1955). "The Dancing Bees." Harcourt Brace, New York.

GERARD, R. W. (1961). "The Fixation of Experience." In "Brain Mechanisms and Learning," ed. J. F. Delafresnaye. Oxford, Blackwell.

HALDANE, J. B. S. (1954). "The Biochemistry of Genetics." Allen and Unwin, London.

HALDANE, J. B. S. (1959). "Natural Selection," in Bell (ed.) "Darwin's Biological Work," Cambridge, chap. 3.

HAYES, W. and CLOWES, R. C. (ed.). (1960). "Microbial Genetics." Cambridge.

HEBERER, G. and SCHWANITZ, F. (1960). "Hundert Jahre Evolutionsforschung." Gustav Fischer, Stuttgart.

HOAGLAND, H. and BURHOE, R. W. (ed.). (1962). "Evolution and Man's Progress." Columbia Univ. Press, New York and London.

HORIZONS IN BIOCHEMISTRY. (1962). Albert Szent-Györgi dedicatory volume. Academic Press, New York and London.

HOVANITZ, W. (1953). "Polymorphism and Evolution." In Symp. Soc. Exp. Biol. VII, (Evolution). Cambridge, p. 238.

HUXLEY, J. S. (1947). "A re-definition of 'Progress'." Pilot Papers, **2** (3), 8-25; in "New, Bottles for New Wine" (1957; Harpers, New York; Chatto and Windus London) p. 93.

HUXLEY, J. S. (1949). "Soviet Genetics and World Science." Chatto and Windus, London; with title "Heredity East and West," Schuman, New York.

HUXLEY, J. S. (1955). "Morphism and Evolution." Heredity, **9,** 1.

HUXLEY, J. S. (1957). "The Three Types of Evolutionary Process." Nature, **180,** 454.

HUXLEY, J. S. (1958a). "Evolutionary Processes and Taxonomy with Special Reference to Grades." Uppsala Universitets Arsskrift, **6,** 21.

HUXLEY, J. S. (1958b). "Biological Aspects of Cancer." Allen and Unwin, London; Harcourt Brace, New York.

HUXLEY, J. S. (1961). Introduction to "The Humanist Frame." Allen and Unwin, London; Harpers, New York.

HUXLEY, J. S. (1962a). "Eugenics in Evolutionary Perspective." Eug. Rev. **54,** 123.

HUXLEY, J. S. (1962b). "Psychometabolism." J. Neuropsychiatry, **3,** suppl. 1. p.3.

HUXLEY, J. S. (1962c). "Higher and Lower Organisation in Evolution." J. Roy. Coll. Surg. Edinburgh, **7,** 163.

HYDEN, H. (1961). (learning and RNA). In "Control of the Mind," ed. Farber and Wilson, McGraw Hill, New York.

JACOB, F. and WOLLMAN, E. L. (1961). "Sexuality and the Genetics of Bacteria." Academic Press, New York and London.

KALMUS, H. (1957). "Variation and Heredity." Routledge and Kegan Paul, London.

KING, R. C. (1962). "Genetics." Oxford Univ. Press, New York.

KUMAR, H. D. (1962). (blue-green algae). Nature, **196,** 1121.

LEDERBERG, J. (1957). "Viruses, Genes and Cells." Bact. Rev. **21,** 133.

LEDERBERG, J. (1959). "Genes and Antibodies." Science, **129,** 1649.

LEHMANN, F. G. (1945). "Einführung in die physiologische Embryologie." Birkhäuser, Basel.

LEMCHE, H. (1957). "A new living deep-sea mollusc of the Cambro-Devonian class Monoplacophora." Nature, **179,** 413.

L'HÉRITIER, P. (1962). "Le Problème de l'hérédité non-chromosomique." Année Biol. (1962), 3.

LILLY, J. C. (1961). "Man and Dolphin." Doubleday, New York.

LISSMANN, H. W. (1961). "Zoology, Locomotory Adaptation and the Problem of Electric Fish." In "The Cell and the Organism," ed. J. A. Ramsay and V. B. Wigglesworth, Cambridge.

MANTON, E. M. (1961). "Experimental Zoology and Problems of Arthropod Evolution." In "The Cell and the Organism," ed. J. A. Ramsay and V. B. Wigglesworth, Cambridge.

MARLER, P. (1959). "Developments in the Study of Animal Communication." In "Darwin's Biological Work. ed. Bell, P. R. et al., Cambridge Univ. Press.

MATHER, K. (1953). "The Genetical Structure of Populations." In Symp. Soc. Exp. Biol. VII. Cambridge Univ. Press.

MATHER, K. et al. (1956). (discussion of heterosis). Proc. Roy. Soc., (B), **144**, 143.

MATHER, K. (1961). "Genetics," in MacLeod and Cobley, ed., "Contemporary Botanical Thought." Oliver and Boyd, Edinburgh.

MAYR, E. (1942). "Systematics and the Origin of Species." Columbia Univ. Press, New York.

MAYR, E. (1963). "Animal Species and Evolution." Harvard Univ. Press, Cambridge, Mass.

MCCONNELL, J. V. (1962). "Memory Transfer through Cannibalism." J. Neuropsych. **3**, 42.

MEDAWAR, P. B. (1958). "The Homograft Reaction." Croonian Lecture, Proc. Roy. Soc. (B), **149**, 145.

MEDAWAR, P. B. (1960). "The Future of Man." Methuen, London.

MOMENT, G. B. (1961). "Reflexive Selection: A Possible Answer to an Old Puzzle." Science, **136**, 262.

MOODY, P. A. (1953). "Introduction to Evolution." Harper and Bros., New York.

MORRIS, D. (1962). "The Biology of Art." Methuen, London.

MOURANT, A. E. (1954). "The distribution of the human blood-groups." Blackwell, Oxford.

MOURANT, A. E., et al. (1958). "The ABO blood-groups," etc. Blackwell, Oxford.

MOURANT, A. E. (1961). "Evolution, Genetics and Anthropology." (Huxley Memorial Lecture). J. Roy. Anthrop. Soc. **91**, Pt. II, 151.

MULLER, H. J. (1959). "The Guidance of Human Evolution." Persp. Biol. Med. **3**, 1.

MULLER, H. J. (1962). "Should we weaken or strengthen our genetic heritage?" In Hoagland and Burhoe, 1962. p. 22.

OPARIN, A. (1957). "The Origin of Life," 3rd ed. Oliver and Boyd, London; Academic Press, New York.

OUDIN, J. (1958). "La Variabilité de Certaines Protéines de Serum." In "Symposium on Protein Structure," p. 298. ed. A. Newberger. Methuen, London.

PISANI, V. (1962). "Storia della Lingua Latina." Turin.

PITTENDRIGH, C. S. (1958). "Adaptation, Natural Selection and Behaviour." In "Behaviour and Evolution," ed. A. Roe and G. G. Simpson, New Haven.

PONTECORVO, C. (1959). "Trends in Genetic Analysis." Columbia Univ. Press, New York; Clarendon Press, Oxford.

PONTECORVO, C. (1963). "Microbial Genetics: Achievements and Prospects." Leeuwenhoek Lecture, Proc. Roy. Soc. (B), **157**.

PRINGLE, J. W. S. (1953). (Origin of Life). In Symp. Soc. Exp. Biol. VII., Cambridge.

RAE, R. R. and SANGER, R. (1962). "Blood Groups in Man," 4th ed. Blackwell, Oxford.

REEVE, E. C. R. and HUXLEY, J. S. (1945). "Some Problems in the Study of Allometric Growth." In "Essays on Growth and Form." ed. Le Gros Clark and Medawar, Clarendon Press, Oxford.

RENSCH, B. (1954). "Neuere Probleme der Abstammungslehre." Ferdinand Enke, Stuttgart.

RENSCH, B. (1959a). "Evolution Above the Species Level." Methuen, London. Columbia Univ. Press, New York.

RENSCH, B. (1959b). "Homo Sapiens: Vom Tier zum Halbgott." Göttingen.

ROBERTS, J. FRASER. (1959). "An Introduction to Medical Genetics," (2nd ed.). Oxford Univ. Press, London.

ROE, A. and SIMPSON, G. G. (ed.). (1958). "Behaviour and Evolution." Yale Univ. Press, New Haven.

ROPP, R. S. DE. (1957). "Drugs and the Mind." St. Martin's Press, New York.

ROTHSCHILD, M. and CLAY, T. 1952. "Fleas, Flukes and Cuckoos." Collins, London.

SAHLINS, M. D. and SERVICE, E. R. (ed.). (1960). "Evolution and Culture." Univ. of Michigan Press, Ann Arbor.

SALISBURY, E. (1961). Weeds and Aliens." Collins, London.

SHEPPARD, P. M. (1958). "Natural Selection and Heredity." Hutchinson, London.

SHOLL, D. A. (1956). "The Organisation of the Cerebral Cortex." Methuen, London.

SIMPSON, G. G. (1944). "Tempo and Mode in Evolution." Columbia Univ. Press, New York.

SIMPSON, G. G. (1949). "The Meaning of Evolution." Yale Univ. Press, New Haven; Oxford Univ. Press, London.

SIMPSON, G. G. (1951). "Horses." Oxford Univ. Press, New York.

SIMPSON, G. G. (1953). "The Major Features of Evolution." Columbia Univ. Press, New York.

SIMPSON, G. G. (1961). "Principles of Animal Taxonomy." Columbia Univ. Press, New York.

SMITH, J. MAYNARD. (1958). "The Theory of Evolution." Penguin Books, London.

SMITH, K. M. (1962). "Viruses." Cambridge.

SMITHIES, O. et al. (1962). "Chromosomal Rearrangement and the Evolution of Haptoglobin Genes." Nature, 196, 232.

SOUTHERN, H. N. (1951). "Change in status of the bridled guillemot after ten years." Proc. Zool. Soc. 121, 657.

SOUTHERN, H. N. (1954). "Mimicry in Cuckoos' Eggs." In "Evolution as a Process," ed. J. S. Huxley et al. Methuen, London.

SOUTHERN, H. N. (1962). "Survey of bridled guillemots, 1959-60." Proc. Zool. Soc. **138,** 455.

SRB, A. M. and OWEN, R. D. (1952). "General Genetics." W. H. Freeman & Co., San Francisco.

STEBBINS, G. L. (1950). "Variation and Evolution in Plants." New York.

STERN, C. (1959). (genetic assimilation). Amer. Phil. Soc. **103,** 183.

STEWARD, J. H. and SHIMKIN, D. B. (1962). In "Evolution and Man's Progress." Columbia Univ. Press, New York and London.

SYLVESTER-BRADLEY, P. C. (ed.). (1956). "The Species Concept in Palaeontology." Systematics Assoc., Nat. Hist. Mus., London.

SOCIETY FOR EXPERIMENTAL BIOLOGY SYMPOSIA, VII, 1953: "Evolution." Cambridge Univ. Press.

TAYLOR, J. H. (1962). "Molecular Genetics." Vol. 4 of Molecular Biology. Academic Press, New York and London.

THODAY, J. M. (1953). "Components of Fitness." In Symp. Soc. Exp. Biol. VII, Evolution, p. 96.

THODAY, J. M. (1958). "Natural Selection and Biological Progress." In Barnett, S. A., "A Century of Darwin." Heinemann, London.

TEILHARD DE CHARDIN, P. (1959). "The Phenomenon of Man." Collins, London.

THORPE, W. H. (1956). "Learning and Instinct in Animals." Methuen and Co., London.

THORPE, W. H., 1961. "Progress and Prospects in Ethology." In Ramsay. J. A. and Wigglesworth, V.B., ed., "The Cell and the Organism," Cambridge.

THORPE, W. H. and ZANGWILL, O. L. (1961). "Current Problems in Animal Behaviour." Cambridge Univ. Press.

TINBERGEN, N. (1951). "The Study of Instinct." Clarendon Press, Oxford.

TINBERGEN, N. (1960). In "Evolution after Darwin"; Vol. II. "The Evolution of Man," ed. Sol Tax. Univ. of Chicago Press.

WADDINGTON, C. H. (1957). "The Strategy of the Genes." Allen and Unwin, London.

WADDINGTON, C. H. (1960). "The Ethical Animal." Allen and Unwin, London.

WADDINGTON, C. H. (1960). "Evolutionary Adaptation." In "Evolution after Darwin." Vol. I. "The Evolution of Life," ed. Sol Tax., Univ. of Chicago Press, p. 381.

WADDINGTON, C. H. (1961). "The Nature of Life." Allen and Unwin, London.

WADDINGTON, C. H. (1962). "New Patterns in Genetics and Development." Columbia Univ. Press, New York and London.

WHITE, M. J. D. (1951). In Dunn, L. C. ed. "Genetics in the 20th Century." Macmillan, New York

WHITE, M. J. D. (1954). "Animal Cytology and Evolution," (2nd ed.). Cambridge Univ. Press.

WHITE, M. J. D. (1961). "The Chromosomes," (5th ed.). Methuen, London; Chap. 11.

WILLIAMS, R. J. (1956). "Biochemical Individuality." John Wiley, New York.

WILLIAMS, R. J. (1960). "Chemical Anthropology—an Open Door," in Taylor, H. S. ed., "Science in Progress." New Haven.

WYNNE-EDWARDS, V. C. (1962). "Animal Dispersion in relation to Social Behaviour." Oliver and Boyd, Edinburgh and London.

YOUNG, J. Z. (1950). "The Life of Vertebrates." Clarendon Press, Oxford.

ZEUNER, F. E. (1963). "A History of Domesticated Animals." Hutchinson, London.

ZIRKLE, C. (1959). "Evolution, Marxian Biology, and the Social Scene." Univ. of Pennsylvania Press, Philadelphia.

BIBLIOGRAPHY TO THE INTRODUCTION TO
THE THIRD EDITION

ANDERSON, E. S. (1968). "The Ecology of Transferable Drug Resistance in the Enterobacteria." Ann. Rev. Microbiol. **22:** 131.

ANDREWS, S. M. and WESTOLL, T. S. (1970). "The Postcranial Skeleton of *Eusthenopteron foordi* Whiteaves." Trans. Roy. Soc. Edinb. **68:** 207.

ANTINOVICS, J. (1968). "Evolution of self-fertility". Heredity **23:** 219.

ARBER, W. (1968). "Host-controlled Restriction and Modification of Bacteriophages." Symp. Soc. Gen. Microbiol. **18:** 295.

ASKEW, R. R., COOK, L. M. and BISHOP, J. A. (1971). "Atmospheric Pollution and Melanic Moths in Manchester and its Environs." J. Appl. Ecol. **8:** 247.

AVERY, O. T., MACLEOD, C. M. and MCCARTY, M. (1944). "Studies on the Chemical Nature of the Substance Inducing Transformation of Pneumococcal Types. I. Induction of Transformation by a Desoxyribonucleic Acid Fraction Isolated from Pneumococcus Type III." J. Exptl. Med. **79:**137.

BAKER, J. R. (1974). "Race." London.

BALDWIN, J. M. (1896). "A New Factor in Evolution." Amer. Nat. **30:** 354 and 536.

BALDWIN, J. M. (1897). "Organic Selection." Nature **55:** 558.

BERGER, P. L. and LUCKMANN, T. (1967). "The Social Construction of Reality." Penguin.

BERGEY, D. H. (1957). "Bergey's Manual of Determinative Bacteriology." (7th ed.). London.

BERNHARD, W. (1966). "Über die Beziehung zwischen ABO-Blutgruppen und Pockensterblichkeit in Indien und Pakistan." Homo **17:** 111.

BERRY, R. J. and DAVIS, P. E. (1970). "Polymorphism and Behaviour in the Arctic Skba (*Stercorarius parasiticus* (L.))" Proc. Roy Soc. (B) **175:** 255.

BISHOP, W. W. and MILLER, J. A. (1972). "Calibration of Hominid Evolution. Recent Advances in Isotopic and other Dating Methods applicable to the Origin of Man." Edinburgh.

BLACKWELL, J. A. and DOWDESWELL, W. H. (1951). "Local Movement in the Blue Tit." Brit. Birds **44:** 397.

BLURTON-JONES, N. G. (1967). "An Ethological Study of Some Aspects of Social Behaviour of Children in Nursery Schools," in: "Primate Ethology," ed. D. Morris. London.

BLURTON-JONES, N. G. (ed.) (1972). "Ethological Studies of Child Behaviour." London

BOBROW, M., PEARSON, P. L. and COLLACOTT, H. E. A. C. (1971). "Paranucleolar Position of the Human Y Chromosome in Interphase Nuclei." Nature **232**: 556.

BOBROW, M., PEARSON, P. L., PIKE, M. C. and EL-ALFI, O. S. (1971). "Length Variation in the Quinacrine-banding Segment of Human Y Chromosomes of Different Sizes." Cytogenetics **10**: 190.

BOBROW, M., MADAN, K. and PEARSON, P. L. (1972). "Staining of Some Specific Regions of Human Chromosomes, Particularly the Secondary Constriction of No. 9." Nature New Biol. **238**: 122.

BOYER, H. B. (1971). "DNA Restriction and Modification Mechanisms in Bacteria." Ann. Rev. Microbiol. **25**: 153.

BRACE, C. L. (1967). "The Stages of Human Evolution: Human and Cultural Origins." Englewood Cliffe, N. J.

BRADSHAW, A. D. (1965). "Evolutionary Significance of Phenotypic Plasticity in Plants." Advanc. Genet. **13**: 115.

BRADSHAW, A. D. (1971). "Plant Evolution in Extreme Environments", in "Ecological Genetics and Evolution", ed. E. R. Creed. Oxford.

BRADSHAW, A. D., MCNEILLY, T. S. and GREGORY, R. P. G. (1965). "Industrialization, Evolution and the Development of Heavy Metal Tolerance in Plants." Brit. Ecol. Soc. Symp. **5**: 327.

BRANNIGAN, C. and HUMPHRIES, D. (1969). "I See What You Mean." New Sci. **42**: 406.

BRINTON, C. C. (1965). "The Structure, Function, Synthesis and Genetic Control of Bacterial Pili and a Molecular Model for DNA and RNA Transport in Gram-negative Bacteria." Trans. N.Y. Acad. Sci. **27**: 1003.

BULLINI, L. and COLUZZI, M. (1972). "Natural Selection and Genetic Drift in Protein Polymorphism." Nature **239**: 160.

BULMER, M. G. (1971). "Protein Polymorphism." Nature **234**: 410.

BURNS, J. M. (1966). "Expanding Distribution and Evolutionary Potential of *Thymelicus lineola*." Canadian Entom. **98**: 859.

BUTZER, K. W. (1969). "Geological Interpretation of two Pleistocene Hominid Sites in the Lower Omo Basin." Nature **222**: 1133.

CADBURY, C. J. (1969). "*Melanism in Moths with Special Reference to Selective Predation by Birds.*" D. Phil. Thesis, Oxford University.

CALDER, N. (1973). "The Life Game." London.

CAMPBELL, B. G. (1966). "Human Evolution: an Introduction to Man's Adaptations." Chicago.

CASPERSSON, T., LOMAKKA, G. and ZECH, L. (1971). "The 24 Fluorescent Patterns of the Human Metaphase Chromosomes—Distinguishing Characters and Variability." Hereditas, Genetiskt Arkiv **67**: 89.

CHIARELLI, B. (1962). "Comparative Morphometric Analysis of Primate Chromosomes. I. The Chromosomes of Anthropoid Apes and of Man." Caryologia **15**: 99.

CHIARELLI, B. (1972). "Comparative Chromosome Analysis Between Man and Chimpanzee." J. Hum. Evol. 1: 389.

CHU, E. H. Y. and BENDER, M. A. (1961). "Cytogenetics and Evolution of Primates." Ann. N.Y. Acad. Sci. 102: 253.

CLARK, A. H., WYON, S. M., and RICHARDS, M. P. M. (1969). "Free-play in Nursery School Children." J. Child Psychol. 10: 205.

CLARK, A. J. (1871). "Toward a Metabolic Interpretation of Genetic Recombination in Escherichia coli and Its Phages." Ann. Rev. Microbiol. 25: 437.

CLARKE, C. A. (1964). "Genetics for the Clinician." (2nd ed.). Oxford.

CLARKE, C. A. (1971). "Blood Group Interactions between Mother and Foetus, in "Ecological Genetics and Evolution," ed. E. R. Creed. Oxford, p. 324.

CLARKE, C. A. and SHEPPARD, P. M. (1963). "Frequencies of the Melanic Forms of the Moth Biston betularia L. on Deeside and in Adjacent Areas." Nature 198: 1219.

CLARKE, C. A. and SHEPPARD, P. M. (1964). "Genetic Control of the Melanic Form insularia of the Moth Biston betularia." Nature 202: 215.

CLARKE, C. A. and SHEPPARD, P. M. (1966). "A Local Survey of the Distribution of Industrial Melanic Forms in the Moth Biston betularia and Estimates of the Selective Values of these in an Industrial Environment." Proc. Roy Soc. (B) 165: 424.

CLARKE, C. A. and SHEPPARD, P. M. (1971). "Further Studies on the Genetics of the Mimetic Butterfly Papilio memnon L." Phil. Trans. Roy Soc. (B) 263: 35.

CLARKE, C. A., SHEPPARD, P. M. and THORNTON, I. B. W. (1968). "The Genetics of the Mimetic Butterfly Papilio Memnon." Phil. Trans. Roy. Soc. (B) 254: 37.

CLOWES, R. C. (1972). "Molecular Structure of Bacterial Plasmids." Bact. Rev. 32: 320.

CODY, M. C. (1966). "A General Theory of Clutch Size." Evolution, Pa. 20: 174.

CONNELL, J. H. (1961). "The Effects of Competition, Predation by Thais lapillus, and Other Factors on Natural Populations of the Barnacle, Balanus balanoides." Ecol. Monogr. 31: 61.

CORNEO, G. (1973). "Satellite and Repeated Sequences in Human DNA," in Pfeiffer (1973).

CROMPTON, A. W. (1972). "Postcanine Occlusion in Cynodonts and Tritylodonts." Bull. Brit. Mus. Nat. Hist. Geol. 21: No. 2.

CROMPTON, A. W. and JENKINS, F. A., Jr. (1968). "Molar Occlusion in Late Triassic Mammals." Biol. Rev. 43: 427.

CROOK, J. (1967). "Correspondence." Man 2: No. 1.

CROOK, J. (1968). "Gelada Baboon Herd Structure and Movement." Symp. Zool. Soc. Lond. 18: 237.

DARLINGTON, C. D. (1964). "Genetics and Man." London.

DART, R. (1949). "The Predatory Implemental Technique of *Australopithecus*." Amer. J. Phys. Anthrop. **7**: 1.

DART, R. (1957). "The Osteodontokeratic Culture of *Australopithecus prometheus*." Transvaal Museum Memoirs **10**: 1.

DARWIN, C. (1872). "The Expression of the Emotions in Man and Animals." London.

DAY, M. H. (1969). "Omo Human Skeletal Remains." Nature **222**: 1135.

DAY, M. H. (1971). "Postcranial Remains of *Homo erectus* from Bed IV, Olduvai Gorge, Tanzania." Nature **232**: 383.

DENISON, R. (1968a). "Early Devonian Lungfishes from Wyoming, Utah and Idaho." Fieldiana, Geol. **17**: 353.

DENISON, R. (1968b). "The Evolutionary Significance of the Earliest Known Lungfish *Uranolophus*." Nobel Symposium **4**: 247. (Stockholm.)

DOBZHANSKY, T. (1951). "Genetics and the Origin of Species." New York.

DOBZHANSKY, TH. and PAVLOVSKY, O. (1966). "Spontaneous Origin of an Incipient Species in the *Drosophila paulistorum* Complex." Proc. Nat. Acad. Sci. Wash. **55**: 727.

DOOLITTLE, R. F., WOODING, G. L., LIN, Y. and RILEY, M. (1971). "Hominoid Evolution as Judged by Fibrinopeptide Structures." J. Mol. Evol. **1**: 74.

DROZDA, A. (1970). "Studia i Materialy Entomologiczne." Bytom, Poland (Rocznik Museum Gornoslaskiego w Bytomui), p. 7.

DRUMMOND, D. C. (1970). "Variation in Rodent Populations in Response to Control Measures," in "Variation in Mammalian Populations," ed. R. J. Berry and H. N. Southern. London.

EASTERLING, S. B., JOHNSON, E. M., WOHLHEITER, J. A. and BARON, L. S. (1969). "Lactose Fermenting Salmonella Strains." J. Bact. **100**: 35.

EDMUND, A. G. (1960). "Tooth Replacement Phenomena in Lower Vertebrates." Contr. R. Ont. Mus., Life Sci. Div. **52**.

EIBL-EIBESFELDT, I. (1970). "Ethology, the Biology of Behaviour." New York.

EIBL-EIBESFELDT, I. (1971). "Love and Hate." London.

EKMAN, P. (1969). "Pan-cultural Elements in Facial Displays of Emotion." Science **164**: 86.

EWER, R. F. (1952). "Notes on Adaption." New Biology (Penguin), **13**: 117.

EWER, R. F. (1960). "Natural Selection and Neoteny." Acta Biotheoretica **13**: 161.

FEENY, P. (1970). "Seasonal Changes in Oak Leaf Tannins and Nutrients as a Cause of Spring Feeding by Winter Moth Caterpillars." Ecology **51**: 565.

FENNER, F., and RATCLIFFE, F. N. (1965). "Myxomatosis." Cambridge.

FISHER, R. A. (1930). "The Genetical Theory of Natural Selection." Oxford.

FITCH, F. J. and MILLER, J. A. (1970). "Radioisotopic Age Determinations of Lake Rudolf Artefact Site." Nature 226: 226.

FORD, E. B. (1971). "Ecological Genetics." (3rd ed.). London and Paris.

FORD, E. B. (1972). "Génétique écologique." Paris.

FORD, E. B. (1973). "Genetics for Medical Students." (7th ed.). London.

FOX, R. (1967). "In the Beginning: Aspects of Hominid Behavioural Evolution." J. R.A.I. (3) 2: 415.

FOX, R. (1970). "Comparative Family Patterns," in "The Family and its Future," ed. K. Elliott. London.

FOX, R. (1970). "The Cultural Animal." UNESCO (1) 9: 7.

FRETWELL, S. (1969). "Ecotypic Variation in the Non-breeding Season in Migratory Populations: a Study of Tarsal Length in some Fringillidae." Evolution, Pa. 23: 406.

FRYER, G., and ILES, T. D. (1969). "Alternative Routes to Evolutionary Success as Exhibited by African Cichlid Fishes of the Genus *Tilapia* and the Species Flocks of the Great Lakes." Evolution, Pa. 23: 359.

FRYER, G., and ILES, T. D. (1972). "The Cichlid Fishes of the Great Lakes of Africa." Edinburgh.

GLAESSNER, M. F. (1962). "Pre-Cambrian Fossils." Biol. Rev. 37: 467.

GOODALL, J. (1965). "Chimpanzees of the Gombe Stream Reserve" in "Primate Behaviour," ed. I. Devore. New York.

GOODMAN, M., BARNABAS, J., MATSUDA, G. and MOORE, G. W. (1971). "Molecular Evolution in the Descent of Man." Nature 233: 604.

GOULD, S. J. (1966). "Allometry and Size in Ontogeny and Phylogeny." Biol. Rev. 41: 587.

GRANT, E. C. (1969). "Human Facial Expression." Man 4 (n.s.): 525.

HALDANE, J. B. S. (1924). "A Mathematical Theory of Natural and Artificial Selection." Trans. Cam. Phil. Soc. 23: 26.

HAMERTON, J. L., KLINGER, H. P., MUTTON, D. E. and LANG, E. M. (1963). "The Somatic Chromosomes of the Hominoidea." Cytogenetics 2: 240.

HANDFORD, P. T. (1973). "Patterns of Variation in a Number of Genetic Systems in *Maniola jurtina*." Proc. Roy. Soc. (B) 183: 265 and 285.

HARDY, A. C. (1949). "Zoology Outside the Laboratory." Advancement of Science 6: 221.

HARDY, A. C. (1957). Discussion following H. G. Cannon's paper on "What Lamarck Really Said." Proc. Linn. Soc. Lond. 168: 85.

HARDY, A. C. (1965). "The Living Stream". London.

HARLAND, W. B. et al. (1964). "The Phanerozoic Time Scale." Q. J. Geol. Soc. Lond. 120S (and supplements in the Journal of the same Society).

HARLAND, W. B. et al. (1967). "The Fossil Record." London.

HARRIS, R., HARRISON, G. A. and RONDLE, C. J. M. (1963). "Vaccinia Virus and Human Blood-group A Substance." Acta genet. (Basel) 13: 44.

HAYES, W. (1968). "The Genetics of Bacteria and their Viruses." (2nd ed.). Edinburgh and Oxford.

HENDERSON, A. S., WARBURTON, D. and ATWOOD, K. C. (1972). "Location of Ribosomal DNA in the Human Chromosome Complement." Proc. Nat. Acad. Sci. U.S.A. **69**: 3394.

HIATT, L. R. (1968). "Ownership and Use of Land among the Australian Aborigines" in "Man the Hunter," ed. R. B. Lee and I. De Vore. Chicago.

HOWELL, F. C. (1972). Article on "Pliocene/Pleistocene Hominidae in Eastern Africa: Absolute and Relative Ages" in Bishop and Miller (1972), p. 331.

HUBBY, J. L. and THROCKMORTON, L. H. (1968). "Protein Differences in Drosophila. iv. A study of Sibling Species." Ama. Nat. **102**: 193.

HUTCHINSON, G. E. (1957). "Concluding Remarks." Cold Spring Harb. Symp. Quant. Biol. **22**: 415.

HUXLEY, J. S. (1914). "The Courtship-habits of the Great Crested Grebe (*Podiceps cristatus*); with an Addition to the Theory of Sexual Selection." Proc. Zool Soc. Lond. (vol. not numbered): 491.

HUXLEY, J. (1923). "Courtship Activities in the Red-throated Diver, etc." J. Linn. Soc. (Zool.) **35**: 253.

HUXLEY, J. (1962). "Evolution: The Modern Synthesis." (2nd ed.). London.

INSELBERG, J. (1970). "Segregation into and Replication of Plasmid DNA in Chromosome-less Segregants of *Escherichia coli.*" J. Bact. **102**: 642.

JACOBS, P. A., PRICE, W. H., RICHMOND, S. and RATCLIFFE, R. A. W. (1971). "Chromosome Surveys in Penal Institutions and Approved Schools." J. Med. Genet. **8**: 49.

JANZEN, D. H. (1969). "Seed-eaters versus Seed Size, Number, Toxicity and Dispersal." Evolution, Pa. **23**: 1.

JANZEN, D. H. (1973). "The Role of the Seed Predator Guild in a Tropical Deciduous Forest, with some Reflections on Tropical Biological Control," in "Biology in Pest and Disease Control," ed. D. Price Jones and M. E. Solomon. Oxford.

JARVIK, E. (1952). "On the Fish-like Tail in the Ichthyostegid Stegocephalians etc." Medd. Grønland **114**: 1.

JARVIK, E. (1960). "Théories de l'evolution des vertébrés." Paris.

JEWELL, P. A. and LOIZOS, C. (1966). "Play, Exploration and Territory in Mammals." Symp. Zool. Soc. Lond. **18**.

JOHNSTON, R. F. and SELANDER, R. K. (1964). "House Sparrows: Rapid Evolution of Races in North America." Science **144**: 548.

JOLLY, C. (1970). "The Seed-eaters: A New Model of Hominid Differentiation Based on a Baboon Analogy." Man (1) **5**: 5.

JONES, D. and SNEATH, P. H. A. (1970). "Genetic Transfer and Bacterial Taxonomy." Bact. Rev. **34**: 40.

JONES, K. W. (1973). "Structure of Constitutive Heterochromatin as Revealed by the In Situ Hybridization of Natural and Synthetic Polynucleotides," in Pfeiffer (1973).

JONES, K. W. and CORNEO, G. (1971). "Location of Satellite and Homogeneous DNA Sequences on Human Chromosomes." Nature New Biol. **233**: 268.

JOYSEY, K. A. (1959). "The Evolution of the Liassic Oysters *Ostrea-Gryphaea*." Biol. Rev. **34**: 297.

KERMACK, K. A. and HALDANE, J. B. S. (1950). "Organic Correlation and Allometry." Biometrika **37**: 30.

KETTLEWELL, H. B. D. (1955*a*). "Selection Experiments on Industrial Melanism in the Lepidoptera." Heredity (3) **9**: 323.

KETTLEWELL, H. B. D. (1955*b*). "Recognition of Appropriate Backgrounds by the Pale and Black Phases of Lepidoptera." Nature **175**: 943.

KETTLEWELL, H. B. D. (1956). "Further Selection Experiments on Industrial Melanism in the Lepidoptera." Heredity (3) **10**: 287.

KETTLEWELL, H. B. D. (1957). "Industrial Melanism in Moths and its Contribution to our Knowledge of Evolution." Proc. Roy. Instn. Gr. Br. (164) **36**: 1.

KETTLEWELL, H. B. D. (1958). "A Survey of the Frequencies of *Biston betularia* L. (Lep.) and its Melanic Forms in Britain." Heredity **12**: 51.

KETTLEWELL, H. B. D. (1959). "New Aspects of the Genetic Control of Industrial Melanism in the Lepidoptera." Nature **183**: 918.

KETTLEWELL, H. B. D. (1963). "Recent Advances in our Knowledge of Melanism in the Lepidoptra." Proc. 16th Int. Congr. Zool. **2**: 198.

KETTLEWELL, H. B. D. (1965). "Insect Survival and Selection for Pattern." Science **148**: 1290.

KETTLEWELL, H. B. D. (1973). "The Evolution of Melanism." Oxford.

KETTLEWELL, H. B. D., CADBURY, C. J. and LEES, D. R. (1971). "Recessive Melanism in the Moth *Lasiocampa quercus* L." in "Ecological Genetics and Evolution," ed. R. Creed, Oxford.

KIMURA, M. (1968). "Evolutionary Rate at the Molecular Level." Nature **217**: 624.

KIMURA, M. and OHTA, T. (1971). "Protein Polymorphism as a Phase of Molecular Evolution." Nature **229**: 467.

KING, J. L. and JUKES, T. H. (1969). "Non-Darwinian Evolution." Science **164**: 788.

KLINEBERG, O. (1951). "Race and Psychology." UNESCO.

KONNER, M. J. (1972). "Aspects of the Developmental Ethology of a Foraging People," in: "Ethological Studies of Child Behaviour," ed. N. Blurton Jones. Cambridge.

KUMMER, H. (1968). "Social Organisation of Hamadryas Baboons." Chicago.

LACK, D. (1947–48). "The Significance of Clutch-size." Ibis **89**: 302 and **90**: 25.

LACK, D. (1965). "Evolutionary Ecology." J. Anim. Ecol. **34**: 223.

LACK, D. (1966). "Population Studies of Birds." Oxford.

LACK, D. (1971). "Ecological Isolation in Birds." Oxford.

LEAKEY, L. S. B. (1960). "Recent Discoveries at Olduvai Gorge." Nature **188**: 1050.

LEAKEY, L. S. B. (1961a). "New Finds at Olduvai Gorge." Nature **189**: 649.

LEAKEY, L. S. B. (1961b). "The Juvenile Mandible from Olduvai." Nature **191**: 417.

LEAKEY, L. S. B. (1966). "*Homo habilis, Homo erectus,* and the Australopithecines." Nature **209**: 1279.

LEAKEY, L. S. B. and GOODALL, V. M. (1970). "Unveiling Man's Origins. Ten Decades of Thought about Human Evolution." London.

LEAKEY, L. S. B. and HOWELL, C. (1960). "The newest Link in Human Evolution. The Discovery by L. S. B. Leakey of *Zinjanthropus boisei.*" Current Anthropol. **1**(1): 76.

LEAKEY, L. S. B., TOBIAS, P. V. and NAPIER, J. R. (1964). "A New Species of the Genus *Homo* from Olduvai Gorge." Nature **202**: 7.

LEAKEY, M. D. (1970). Early Artefacts from the Koobi Fora Area." Nature **226**: 228.

LEAKEY, M. D., CLARKE, R. J. and LEAKEY, L. S. B. (1971). "New Hominid Skull from Bed I, Olduvai Gorge, Tanzania." Nature **232**: 308.

LEAKEY, R. E. F. (1970). "New Hominid Remains and Early Artefacts from Northern Kenya." Nature **226**: 223.

LEAKEY, R. E. F. (1971). "Further Evidence of Lower Pleistocene Hominids from East Rudolf, North Kenya." Nature **231**: 241.

LEAKEY, R. E. F. (1973a). "Further Evidence of Lower Pleistocene Hominids from East Rudolf, North Kenya, 1972." Nature **242**: 170.

LEAKEY, R. E. F. (1973b). "Evidence for an Advanced Plio-Pleistocene Hominid from East Rudolf, Kenya." Nature **242**: 447.

LEAKEY, R. E. F., MUNGAI, J. M. and WALKER, A. C. 1971). "New Australopithecines from East Rudolf, Kenya." Amer. J. Phys. Anthrop. **35**: 175.

LEE, R. and DEVORE, I. (eds.) (1968). "Man the Hunter." Chicago.

LEES, D. R. (1968). "Genetic Control of the Melanic Form *insularia* of the Peppered Moth *Biston betularia* L." Nature **220**: 1249.

LEES, D. R. (1971). "Distribution of Melanism in the Pale Brindled Beauty Moth, *Phigalia pedaria*, in Britain," in "Ecological Genetics and Evolution," ed. R. Creed. Oxford.

LEMPKE, B. J. (1960). "Catalogus der Nederlanse Macrolepidoptera." Tijdschr. Ent. **103**: 145.

LEVI-STRAUSS, C. (1970). "The Elementary Structures of Kinship." Oxford.

LOFFLER, L. G. (1968). Comment on K. Kortmulder: "An Ethological Theory of Incest Taboo and Exogamy." Current Anth. (5) **9**: 442.

LORENZ, K. (1966). "On Agression." London.

MACARTHUR, R. H., and WILSON, E. O. (1967). "The Theory of Island Biogeography." Princeton.

MAGLIO, V. J. (1972). "Vertebrate Faunas and Chronology of Hominid-bearing Sediments East of Lake Rudolf, Kenya." Nature 239: 379.

MCGREW, W. C. (1969). "An Ethological Study of Agonistic Behaviour in Pre-School Children." Proc. 2nd Int. Congr. Primat. 1: 149.

MCNEILLY, T. S. (1968). "Evolution in Closely Adjacent Plant Populations." Heredity 23: 99.

MCNEILLY, T. S. and ANTINOVICS, J. (1968). "Barriers to Gene-flow." Heredity 23: 205.

MACURDAY, D. B. (ed.) 1968. "Palaeobiological Aspects of Growth and Developments; a Symposium." Palaeont. Soc. Mem. 2.

MCWHIRTER, K. G. (1957). "A Further Analysis of Variability in Maniola jurtina L." Heredity 11: 359.

MCWHIRTER, K. G. (1969). "Heritability of Spot-number in Scillonian Strains of the Meadow Brown Butterfly (Maniola jurtina)." Heredity 24: 314.

MCWHIRTER, K. G. and CREED, E. R. (1971). "An Analysis of Spot Placing in the Meadow Brown Butterfly, Maniola jurtina." in "Ecological Genetics and Evolution," ed. E. R. Creed, p. 275. Oxford.

MAKARIUS, R. (1968). Comment on K. Kortmulder, "An Ethological Theory of the Incest Taboo and Exogamy." Current Anth. (5) 9: 443.

MALINOWSKI, B. (1922). "Argonauts of the Western Pacific." London.

MARTIN, R. D. (1972). "Adaptive Radiation and Behaviour of the Malagasy Lemurs." Phil. Trans. Roy. Soc. London. (B) 264: 295.

MAYR, E. (1960). "The Emergence of Evolutionary Novelties," in "Evolution after Darwin, I, The Evolution of Life," p. 371. Chicago.

MAYR, E. (1963). "Animal Species and Evolution." Oxford; and Cambridge, Mass.

MAYR, E. (1970). "Evolution und Verhalten." Verhandlungen der Deutschen Zoologischen Gesellschaft 64: 322.

MEAD, M. (1935). "Sex and Temperament in Three Primitive Societies." New York.

MEREDITH, M. (1974). "Ethiopian man." Sunday Times, 13 Jan., p. 9.

MEYNELL, G. G. (1973). "Bacterial Plasmids." London.

MILLER, R. S. (1967). "Pattern and Process in Competition." Adv. Ecol. Res. 4: 1.

MILNE, H., and ROBERTSON, F. W. (1965). "Polymorphisms in Egg Albumen Protein and Behaviour in the Eider Duck." Nature 205: 367.

MITCHISON, J. M. (1971). "The Biology of the Cell Cycle." Cambridge.

MOWOD, J. (1972). "Chance and Necessity." London.

MOORE, R. C. (ed.), (1953 et seq.). "Treatise on invertebrate Palaeontology." Geol. Soc. America.

MOREAU, R. E. (1930). "On the Age of Some Races of Birds." Ibis (12) 6: 229.

MOREAU, R. E. (1972). "The Palaearctic-African Bird Migration Systems." London.

MORGAN, C. LLOYD (1896a). "On Heredity and Variation." Science (N.S.) 4: 733.

MORGAN, C. LLOYD (1896*b*). "Habit and Instinct." London.

MORRIS, D. (1967). "The Naked Ape." London.

MOSELEY, B. E. B. (1968). "The Repair of Damaged DNA in Irradiated Bacteria." Advanc. Microb. Physiol. **3**: 173.

MOY-THOMAS, J. A. and MILES, R. S. (1971). "Palaeozoic Fishes." (2nd ed.). London.

NELSON, J. B. (1964). "Factors Influencing Clutch-size and Chick Growth in the North Atlantic Gannet *Sula bassana*." Ibis **106**: 63.

NEWELL, N. D. (1949). "Phyletic Size-increase—an Important Trend Illustrated by Fossil Invertebrates." Evolution **3**: 103.

NICHOLS, D. (1959). "Changes in the Chalk Heart-urchin *Micraster* Interpreted in Relation to Living Forms." Phil. Trans. Roy. Soc. Lond. (B) **242**: 347.

OHNO, S. (1969). "Evolution of Sex Chromosomes in Mammals." Ann. Rev. Genetics **3**: 495.

ORIANS, G. H. (1962). "Natural Selection and Ecological Theory." Amer. Nat. **96**: 257.

OSBORN, H. F. (1896). "A Mode of Evolution . . ." Trans. New York Acad. Sci. **15**: 141 and 148.

OSBORN, H. F. (1897). "The Limits of Organic Selection." Amer. Nat. **31**: 941.

OWEN, D. F. (1961). "Industrial Melanism in North American Moths." Amer. Nat. **95**: 227.

OWEN, D. F. (1962). "The Evolution of Melanism in Six Species of North American Geometrid Moths." Ann. Ent. Soc. Am. **55**: 695.

PARK, T. (1948). "Experimental Studies of Interspecies Competition. I. Competition between Populations of the Flour Beetles *Tribolium confusum* Duval and *Tribolium castaneum* Herbst." Ecol. Monogr. **18**: 265.

PARRINGTON, F. R. (1971). "On the Upper Triassic Mammals." Phil. Trans. Roy. Soc. (B) **261**: 231.

PARRINGTON, F. R. and WESTOLL, T. S. (1940). "On the Evolution of the Mammalian Palate." Phil. Trans. Roy. Soc. Lond. (B) **230**: 305.

PARTRIDGE, T. C. (1973). "Geomorphological Dating of Cave Openings at Makapansgat, Sterkfontein, Swartkrans and Taung." Nature **246**: 75.

PATTERSON, B., BEHRENSMEYER, A. K. and SILL, W. D. (1970). "Geology and Fauna of a New Pliocene Locality in North-western Kenya." Nature **226**: 918.

PATTERSON, C. (1964). "A Review of Mesozoic Acanthopterygian Fishes, with Special Reference to those of the English Chalk." Phil. Trans. Roy. Soc. (B) **247**: 739.

PEARSON, P. L. (1972). "The Use of New Staining Techniques for Human Chromosome Identification." J. Med. Genet. **9**: 264.

PEARSON, P. L. (1973). "Polymorphism of the Human Karyotype" in Pfeiffer (1973).

PEARSON, P. L., BOBROW, M., VOSA, C. G. and BARLOW, P. W. (1971). "Quinacrine Fluorescence in Mammalian Chromosomes." Nature 231: 326.

PERRINS, C. (1964). "Survival of Young Swifts in Relation to Brood-size." Nature 201: 1147.

PFEIFFER, R. A. (Chairman of Symposium) (1973). "Modern Aspects of Cytogenetics: Constitutive Heterochromatin in Man." (Symposia Medica Hoechst, No. 6). Stuttgart.

POLANYI, M. (1958). "Personal Knowledge." London.

POLANYI, M. (1959). "The Study of Man." London.

POWELL, J. R. (1971). "Genetic Polymorphisms in Varied Environments". Science 174: 1035.

PRAKASH, S., LEWONTIN, R. C. and HUBBY, J. L. (1969). "A Molecular Approach to the Study of Genic Heterozygosity in Natural Populations." Genetics 61: 841.

PRICE, P. M., CONOVER, J. H. and HIRSCHHORN, K. (1972). "Chromosomal Localisation of Human Haemoglobin Structural Genes." Nature 237: 340.

PUNNETT, R. C. (1915). "Mimicry in Butterflies." Cambridge.

RADCLIFFE-BROWN, A. R. (1931). "Social Organisation of Australian Tribes." Oceania Monographs 1.

RASMUSSEN, D. I. (1970). "Biochemical Polymorphisms and Genetic Structure in Populations of Peromyscus," in "Variation in Mammalian Populations," ed. R. J. Berry and H. N. Southern. London.

RAUP, D. M. and STANLEY, S. M. (1971). "Principles of Palaeontology." San Francisco.

RENSCH, B. (1960). "Evolution above the Species Level." New York.

REYNOLDS, V. and REYNOLDS, F. (1965). "Chimpanzees of the Budongo Forest," in "Primate Behaviour," ed. I. Devore. New York.

REYNOLDS, V. (1966). "Open Groups in Hominid Evolution." Man (4) 1: 441.

RICHARDS, M. P. M. and BERNAL, J. (1972). "An Observational Study of Mother-Infant Interaction," in "Ethological Studies of Child Behaviour," ed. N. Blurton Jones. Cambridge.

RICHMOND, M. H. (1970). "Plasmids and Chromosomes in Prokaryotic Cells." Symp. Soc. Gen. Microbiol. 20: 249.

RICHMOND, M. H. (1973). "Resistance Factors and their Ecological Importance to Bacteria and to Man." Progress in Nucleic Acid Research and Molecular Biology, 13: 191.

RICHMOND, M. H. and WIEDEMAN, B. (1974). "Plasmids and Bacterial Evolution." Symp. Soc. Gen. Microbiol. 24.

ROBINSON, J. T. (1965). "Homo habilis and the Australopithecines." Nature 205: 121.

ROBINSON, J. T. (1966). "The Distinctiveness of Homo habilis" (Reply to another communication). Nature 209: 957.

ROBINSON, R. (1971). "Lepidoptera Genetics." Oxford.

ROMER, A. S. (1941). "Notes on the Crossopterygian Hyomandibular and Braincase." J. Morphol. 69: 141.

ROMER, A. S. (1966). "Vertebrate Paleontology." (3rd ed.). Chicago.

ROMER, A. S. (1968). "Notes and Comments on Vertebrate Paleontology." Chicago.

ROMER, A. S. (1970). "The Chanares (Argentina) Triassic Reptile Fauna VI: A Chiniquodontid Cynodont with an Incipient Squamosaldentary Jaw Articulation." Breviora, Mus. Comp. Zool. 344.

SARGENT, T. D. (1966). "Background Selections of Geometrid and Noctuid Moths." Science 154: 1674.

SARGENT, T. D. (1968). "Cryptic Moths: Effects on Background Selections of Painting the Circumocular Scales." Science 159: 100.

SARGENT, T. D. (1969a). "Behavioural Adaptations of Cryptic Moths. II. Experimental Studies on Bark-like Species." J. N.Y. Ent. Soc. (2) 77: 77.

SARGENT, T. D. (1969b). "Behavioural Adaptations of Cryptic Moths. III. Resting Attitudes." Anim. Behav. 17: 670.

SARGENT, T. D. and KEIPER, R. R. (1969). "Behavioural Adaptations of Cryptic Moths. I. Preliminary Studies of bark-like species." J. Lepid. Soc. 23: 1.

SCALI, V. (1971). "Spot Distribution in Maniola jurtina (L.) (Lepidoptera Satyridae): Tuscan Mainland 1967–1969." Monitore Zool. Ital. (N.S.). 5: 147.

SELANDER, R. K., HUNT, W. G. and YANG, S. Y. (1969). "Protein Polymorphism and Genic Heterozygosity in Two European Subspecies of the House Mouse." Evolution 23: 379.

SETLOW, J. K. and DUGGAN, D. E. (1964). "The Resistance of Micrococcus radiodurans to Ultra-violet Irradiation." Biochim. biophys. Acta. 87: 664.

SIMPSON, G. G. (1944). "Tempo and Mode in Evolution." New York.

SIMPSON, G. G. (1951). "Horses." New York.

SIMPSON, G. G. (1953a). "The Major Features of Evolution." New York.

SIMPSON, G. G. (1953b). "The Baldwin Effect." Evolution 7: 110.

SKEHAL, J. and CARLILE, M. (eds.) (1974). "Evolution in the Microbial World." Symp. Soc. Gen. Microbiol. 24.

SMITH, P. K. (1970). "Social and Play Behaviour of Pre-School Children." (Ph.D. Thesis), Sheffield University.

SOKAL, R. R. and SNEATH, P. H. A. (1963). "Principles of Numerical Taxonomy." San Francisco.

SOUTHERN, H. N. (1962). "Survey of Bridled Guillemots, 1959–60." Proc. Zool. Soc. Lond. 138: 455.

SOUTHERN, H. N. (1970). "The Natural Control of a Population of Tawny Owls (Strix aluco)." J. Zool. Lond. 162: 197.

SOUTHERN, H. N., CARRICK, R., and POTTER, W. G. (1965). "The Natural History of a Population of Guillemots (*Uria aalge* Pont.)." J. Anim. Ecol. **34:** 649.

STENT, G. (1971). "Molecular Genetics." San Francisco.

SWINNERTON, H. H. (1940). "The Study of Variation in Fossils." Quart. J. Geol. Soc. Lond. **96**.

SYLVESTER-BRADLEY, P. C. (ed.). (1956). "The Species Concept in Palaeontology." Systematics Assoc. **2**.

TIGER, L. and FOX, R. (1971). "The Imperial Animal." London.

TOBIAS, P. V. (1967). "The Cranium and Maxillary Dentition of *Australopithecus* (*Zinjanthropus*) *boisei*." (Vol. 2 of "Olduvai Gorge", edited by L. S. B. Leakey.) Cambridge.

TOBIAS, P. V. (1973). "Implications of the New Age Estimates of the Early South African Hominids." Nature **246:** 79.

TRUEMAN, A. E. (1940). "The Meaning of Orthogenesis." Trans. Geol. Soc. Glasg. **20**.

TURLEAU, C. and DE GROUCHY, M. (1972). "Caryotypes de l'homme et du chimpanzé. Comparaison de la topographie des bandes. Mécanismes évolutifs possibles." C.R. Acad. Sci. Paris **274:** 2355.

VOGEL, F. and CHAKRAVARTTI, M. R. (1966). "ABO Blood Groups and Small-pox. . ." Humangenetik **3:** 166.

WADDINGTON, C. H. (1959). "Evolutionary Systems—Animal and Human." Nature **183:** 1634.

WARNECKE, G. (1913). "Einige Bemerkungen über die melanistischen Formen von *Cymatophora or* F. aus dem Niederelbgebiet." Ent. Mitt. (9) **2:** 282.

WASHBURN, S. L. and DEVORE, I. (1961). "The Social Life of Baboons." Sci. Am. **June**.

WATSON, A., and MOSS, R. (1970). "Dominance, Spacing Behaviour and Aggression in Relation to Population Limitation in Vertebrates," in "Animal Populations in Relation to their Food Resources," ed. A. Watson. Oxford.

WEISBLUM, B. and HASETH, P. L. DE (1972). "Quinacrine. A Chromosome Stain Specific for Deoxyadenylate-Deoxythymidylate rich Regions in DNA." Proc. Nat. Acad. Sci. U.S.A. **69:** 629.

WESTOLL, T. S. (1943). "The Origin of the Tetrapods." Biol. Rev. **18:** 78.

WESTOLL, T. S. (1949). "On the Evolution of the Dipnoi," in "Genetics, Palaeontology and Evolution," ed. Jepsen, Simpson and Mayr. Princeton.

WESTOLL, T. S. (1950). "Some Aspects of Growth Studies in Fossils." Proc. Roy. Soc. Lond.(B) **137:** 490.

WESTOLL, T. S. (1962). "Some Crucial Stages in the Transition from Devonian Fish to Man," in "The Evolution of Living Organisms." Melbourne.

WHITING, J. W. M. and CHILD, I. L. (1953). "Child Training and Personality: a Cross-cultural Study." New Haven.

WILSON, A. C. and SARICH, V. M. (1969). "A Molecular Time Scale for Human Evolution." Proc. Nat. Acad. Sci. U.S.A. **63**: 1088.

WITKIN, E. M. (1969). "Ultra-violet Light Induced Mutation and DNA Repair." Ann. Rev. Genet. **3**: 525.

WOLBERG, D. L. (1970). "The Hypothesized Osteodontokeratic Culture of the Australopithecinae: a Look at the Evidence and the Opinions." Current Anthrop. **11**: 23.

WOLFF, P. H. (1969). "The Natural History of Crying and Other Vocalisations in Early Infancy," in "Determinants of Infant Behaviour," ed. B. M. Foss. London.

WORMS, C. DE (1961). "A Review of the Lepidoptera of the London Area for 1960 and 1961." Nature **41**: 60.

WRIGHT, D. and SMITH, S. G. (1956). "Experiments with a Remarkable Melanic Strain of *Arctia caja* L." Entomologist's Gaz. **7**: 119.

WYNNE-EDWARDS, V.C. (1962). "Animal Dispersion in Relation to Social Behaviour." Edinburgh.

YUNIS, J. J. and YASMINEH, W. G. (1971). "Heterochromatin, Satellite DNA, and Cell Function." Science **174**: 1200.

ZECH, L. (1969). "Investigation of Metaphase Chromosomes with DNA Binding Fluorochromes." Exp. Cell Res. **58**: 463.

ZINDER, N. D. (1953). "Infective Heredity in Bacteria." Cold Spring Harbor Symp. Quant. Biol. **18**: 26.

ZUCKERMAN, S. (1970). Chapter on "African Cousins" in his book, "Beyond the Ivory Tower: the Frontiers of Public and Private Science." London.

INDEX

SUBJECTS

ORGANISMS

Callosciurus, 193
Calosciurus sladeni, 219, 227
Camarhynchus, 326
Camel, 236
Camelina sativa, 115
Camperiella bifasciata, 299
Campion, 142
Canary, 305
Canidae, 294, 502, 539
Caninae, 351
Canis familiaris, 539
Canis lupus, 540
Capsella, 346
Capsella bursapastoris, 347
Capsella occidentalis, 347
Carabus granulatus, 176
Carabus monilis, 180
Carabus nemoralis, 206, 235, 314
Carduelis cannabina, 266, 306
Carduelis carduelis, 187 n., 194, 281, 290
Carduelis flammea, 212, 290
Carduelis flavirostris, 266
Caribou, 273
Carnivores, 490
Caryophyllaceae, 205
Cassowary, 476
Casuarius, 476
Cat, 103
  Siamese, 64, 546
Catastomus, 540
Catfish, Nile, 415
Cattle, 541
Caucalis arvensis, 278
Cave-bears, 506
Cavia, 501
Cedar of Lebanon, 438
Cedrus libani, 438
Celandine, lesser, 110
Centaurea, 147, 258
Centaurea nemoralis, 441
Cepaea, 202, 520, 532, 516
Cepaea hortensis, 99, 161, 291, 516
Cepaea nemoralis, 99, 161, 291, 516
Cerambycidae, 298 ·
Cercopithecus mona, 247
Cercopithecus polykomas, 247
Certhia brachydactyla, 245, 306
Certhia familiaris, 245
Certhidea, 326
Corvidae, 541
Cervus elaphus, 121, 225, 537
Cetacea, 240
Chaffinch, 183, 306, 307, 309

Chalcotheres, 491
Char, 177, 180, 231
Chat, 191
Chelonia, 505
Chickadee, 180, 270
Chickweed, 517
Chiffchaff, 278, 289, 306, 307
Chimpanzee, 53
Chloeon dipterum, 435
Chloris chloris, 306
Chorthippus, 516
Chrysanthemum, 348
Chrysolophus amherstiae, 66
Chrysomphalus aurantii, 299
Chub, 348
Cicadulina mobile, 312
Cichlids, 324, 493
Cichorieae, 377
Ciliates, 84
Cinclus, 434
Cinnyris manoensis, 272
Cinnyris zonarius, 272
Cisco, 178
Cisticola, 176, 289
Clausilia, 448
Clausilia bidentata, 246
Clausilia dubia, 246
Cleithrionomys, 118
Cleithrionomys glareolus, 118
Clypeola jonthlaspi, 197
Cob-antelope, 234
Coccinellidae, 220, 550
Coccothraustes coccothraustes, 281
Coccus pseudomagnoliarum, 471
Cockchafer, 312
Coelenterates, number of species, 168
Coereba, 184, 203
  melanism, 104
Coereba flaveola, 94 n.
Colaptes, 161, 250
Colaptes auratus, 288
Coleoptera, sex-determination in, 149
Colias, 516
Colias philodice, 98, 117
Columba oenas, 310
Compositae, 205
Conepatus, 548
Coracias, 252
Coracias garrulus, 444
Corals, 536
Coregonus, 178
Corixidae, 468
Cormorant, 310
  flightless, 243

AUTHORITIES